Ecology and the Environment

Teacher's Edition and Resource

interactive
SCIENCE

PEARSON

Boston, Massachusetts
Chandler, Arizona
Glenview, Illinois
Upper Saddle River, New Jersey

AUTHORS

You're an author!

As you write in this science book, your answers and personal discoveries will be recorded for you to keep, making this book unique to you. That is why you are one of the primary authors of this book.

In the space below, print your name, school, town, and state. Then write a short autobiography that includes your interests and accomplishments.

YOUR NAME

SCHOOL

TOWN, STATE

AUTOBIOGRAPHY

Your Photo

Acknowledgments appear on pages 222–223, which constitute an extension of this copyright page.

ISBN-13:   978-0-13-369365-2
ISBN-10:   0-13-369365-1
2 3 4 5 6 7 8 9 10 V003 14 13 12 11 10

ON THE COVER
Colorful Communication
Did you know that the change in color of a chameleon's skin communicates its mood to other chameleons? Light, temperature, and emotions determine the color changes. The four-horned chameleon, pictured on the cover, is native to Cameroon, Africa. It catches flies with its sticky tongue, which extends twice the length of its body!

Program Authors

DON BUCKLEY, M.Sc.
Information and Communications Technology Director,
The School at Columbia University, New York, New York
Mr. Buckley has been at the forefront of K–12 educational technology for nearly two decades. A founder of New York City Independent School Technologists (NYCIST) and long-time chair of New York Association of Independent Schools' annual IT conference, he has taught students on two continents and created multimedia and Internet-based instructional systems for schools worldwide.

ZIPPORAH MILLER, M.A.Ed.
Associate Executive Director for Professional Programs and Conferences, National Science Teachers Association, Arlington, Virginia
Associate executive director for professional programs and conferences at NSTA, Ms. Zipporah Miller is a former K–12 science supervisor and STEM coordinator for the Prince George's County Public School District in Maryland. She is a science education consultant who has overseen curriculum development and staff training for more than 150 district science coordinators.

MICHAEL J. PADILLA, Ph.D.
Associate Dean and Director, Eugene P. Moore School of Education, Clemson University, Clemson, South Carolina
A former middle school teacher and a leader in middle school science education, Dr. Michael Padilla has served as president of the National Science Teachers Association and as a writer of the National Science Education Standards. He is professor of science education at Clemson University. As lead author of the *Science Explorer* series, Dr. Padilla has inspired the team in developing a program that promotes student inquiry and meets the needs of today's students.

KATHRYN THORNTON, Ph.D.
Professor and Associate Dean, School of Engineering and Applied Science, University of Virginia, Charlottesville, Virginia
Selected by NASA in May 1984, Dr. Kathryn Thornton is a veteran of four space flights. She has logged over 975 hours in space, including more than 21 hours of extravehicular activity. As an author on the *Scott Foresman Science* series, Dr. Thornton's enthusiasm for science has inspired teachers around the globe.

MICHAEL E. WYSESSION, Ph.D.
Associate Professor of Earth and Planetary Science, Washington University, St. Louis, Missouri
An author on more than 50 scientific publications, Dr. Wysession was awarded the prestigious Packard Foundation Fellowship and Presidential Faculty Fellowship for his research in geophysics. Dr. Wysession is an expert on Earth's inner structure and has mapped various regions of Earth using seismic tomography. He is known internationally for his work in geoscience education and outreach.

Understanding by Design Author

GRANT WIGGINS, Ed.D.
President, Authentic Education, Hopewell, New Jersey
Dr. Wiggins is coauthor of *Understanding by Design*® (UbD), a philosophy of instructional design. UbD is a disciplined way of thinking about curriculum design, assessment, and instruction that moves teaching from covering the content to ensuring understanding. Dr. Wiggins is one of today's most influential educational reformers, and consults with schools, districts, and state education departments.

Planet Diary Author

JACK HANKIN
Science/Mathematics Teacher, The Hilldale School, Daly City, California Founder, Planet Diary Web site
Mr. Hankin is the creator and writer of Planet Diary, a science current events Web site. Mr. Hankin is passionate about bringing science news and environmental awareness into classrooms. He's offered numerous Planet Diary workshops at NSTA and other events to train middle school and high school teachers.

ELL Consultant

JIM CUMMINS, Ph.D.
Professor and Canada Research Chair, Curriculum, Teaching and Learning department at the University of Toronto
Dr. Cummins's research focuses on literacy development in multilingual schools and the role of technology in promoting student learning across the curriculum. The *Interactive Science* program incorporates essential research-based principles for integrating language with the teaching of academic content based on Dr. Cummins's instructional framework.

Reading Consultant

HARVEY DANIELS, Ph.D.
Professor of Secondary Education, University of New Mexico, Albuquerque, New Mexico
Dr. Daniels serves as an international consultant to schools, districts, and educational agencies. Dr. Daniels has authored or coauthored 13 books on language, literacy, and education. His most recent works include *Comprehension and Collaboration: Inquiry Circles in Action* and *Subjects Matter: Every Teacher's Guide to Content-Area Reading.*

REVIEWERS

Contributing Writers

Edward Aguado, Ph.D.
Professor, Department of
Geography
San Diego State University
San Diego, California

Elizabeth Coolidge-Stolz, M.D.
Medical Writer
North Reading, Massachusetts

Donald L. Cronkite, Ph.D.
Professor of Biology
Hope College
Holland, Michigan

Jan Jenner, Ph.D.
Science Writer
Talladega, Alabama

Linda Cronin Jones, Ph.D.
Associate Professor of Science and
Environmental Education
University of Florida
Gainesville, Florida

T. Griffith Jones, Ph.D.
Clinical Associate Professor
of Science Education
College of Education
University of Florida
Gainesville, Florida

Andrew C. Kemp, Ph.D.
Teacher
Jefferson County Public Schools
Louisville, Kentucky

Matthew Stoneking, Ph.D.
Associate Professor of Physics
Lawrence University
Appleton, Wisconsin

R. Bruce Ward, Ed.D.
Senior Research Associate
Science Education Department
Harvard-Smithsonian Center for
Astrophysics
Cambridge, Massachusetts

Museum of Science.

Special thanks to the Museum of Science,
Boston, Massachusetts, and Ioannis Miaoulis,
the Museum's president and director, for
serving as content advisors for the technology
and design strand in this program.

Content Reviewers

Paul D. Beale, Ph.D.
Department of Physics
University of Colorado at Boulder
Boulder, Colorado

Jeff R. Bodart, Ph.D.
Professor of Physical Sciences
Chipola College
Marianna, Florida

Joy Branlund, Ph.D.
Department of Earth Science
Southwestern Illinois College
Granite City, Illinois

Marguerite Brickman, Ph.D.
Division of Biological Sciences
University of Georgia
Athens, Georgia

Bonnie J. Brunkhorst, Ph.D.
Science Education and Geological
Sciences
California State University
San Bernardino, California

Michael Castellani, Ph.D.
Department of Chemistry
Marshall University
Huntington, West Virginia

Charles C. Curtis, Ph.D.
Research Associate Professor
of Physics
University of Arizona
Tucson, Arizona

Diane I. Doser, Ph.D.
Department of Geological
Sciences
University of Texas
El Paso, Texas

Rick Duhrkopf, Ph.D.
Department of Biology
Baylor University
Waco, Texas

Alice K. Hankla, Ph.D.
The Galloway School
Atlanta, Georgia

Mark Henriksen, Ph.D.
Physics Department
University of Maryland
Baltimore, Maryland

Chad Hershock, Ph.D.
Center for Research on Learning
and Teaching
University of Michigan
Ann Arbor, Michigan

Jeremiah N. Jarrett, Ph.D.
Department of Biology
Central Connecticut State
University
New Britain, Connecticut

Scott L. Kight, Ph.D.
Department of Biology
Montclair State University
Montclair, New Jersey

Jennifer O. Liang, Ph.D.
Department of Biology
University of Minnesota–Duluth
Duluth, Minnesota

Candace Lutzow-Felling, Ph.D.
Director of Education
The State Arboretum of Virginia
University of Virginia
Boyce, Virginia

Cortney V. Martin, Ph.D.
Virginia Polytechnic Institute
Blacksburg, Virginia

Joseph F. McCullough, Ph.D.
Physics Program Chair
Cabrillo College
Aptos, California

Heather Mernitz, Ph.D.
Department of Physical Science
Alverno College
Milwaukee, Wisconsin

Sadredin C. Moosavi, Ph.D.
Department of Earth and
Environmental Sciences
Tulane University
New Orleans, Louisiana

David L. Reid, Ph.D.
Department of Biology
Blackburn College
Carlinville, Illinois

Scott M. Rochette, Ph.D.
Department of the Earth Sciences
SUNY College at Brockport
Brockport, New York

Karyn L. Rogers, Ph.D.
Department of Geological
Sciences
University of Missouri
Columbia, Missouri

Laurence Rosenhein, Ph.D.
Department of Chemistry
Indiana State University
Terre Haute, Indiana

Sara Seager, Ph.D.
Department of Planetary Sciences
and Physics
Massachusetts Institute of
Technology
Cambridge, Massachusetts

Tom Shoberg, Ph.D.
Missouri University of Science
and Technology
Rolla, Missouri

Patricia Simmons, Ph.D.
North Carolina State University
Raleigh, North Carolina

William H. Steinecker, Ph.D.
Research Scholar
Miami University
Oxford, Ohio

Paul R. Stoddard, Ph.D.
Department of Geology and
Environmental Geosciences
Northern Illinois University
DeKalb, Illinois

John R. Villarreal, Ph.D.
Department of Chemistry
The University of Texas–Pan
American
Edinburg, Texas

John R. Wagner, Ph.D.
Department of Geology
Clemson University
Clemson, South Carolina

Jerry Waldvogel, Ph.D.
Department of Biological Sciences
Clemson University
Clemson, South Carolina

Donna L. Witter, Ph.D.
Department of Geology
Kent State University
Kent, Ohio

Edward J. Zalisko, Ph.D.
Department of Biology
Blackburn College
Carlinville, Illinois

CONTENTS

 Enter the Lab zone for hands-on inquiry.

Chapter Lab Investigation:
• Directed Inquiry: World in a Bottle
• Open Inquiry: World in a Bottle

Inquiry Warm-Ups: • What's in the Scene?
• Populations • Can You Hide a Butterfly?
• How Communities Change

Quick Labs: • Organisms and Their Habitats
• Organizing an Ecosystem • Growing and
Shrinking • Elbow Room • Adaptations for
Survival • Competition and Predation • Type
of Symbiosis • Primary or Secondary

my science online.com

Go to MyScienceOnline.com to
interact with this chapter's content.
**Keyword: Populations and
Communities**

> **UNTAMED SCIENCE**
• Clown(fish)ing Around

> **PLANET DIARY**
• Populations and Communities

> **INTERACTIVE ART**
• Changes in Population • Animal Defense
Strategies

> **ART IN MOTION**
• Primary and Secondary Succession

> **REAL-WORLD INQUIRY**
• An Ecological Mystery

CHAPTER 2 — Ecosystems and Biomes

Lab® zone — Enter the Lab zone for hands-on inquiry.

Chapter Lab Investigation:
• Directed Inquiry: Ecosystem Food Chains
• Open Inquiry: Ecosystem Food Chains

Inquiry Warm-Ups: • Where Did Your
Dinner Come From? • Are You Part of a Cycle?
• How Much Rain Is That? • Where Does It
Live? • How Can You Move a Seed?

Quick Labs: • Observing Decomposition
• Following Water • Carbon and Oxygen Blues
• Playing Nitrogen Cycle Roles • Inferring
Forest Climates • Dissolved Oxygen • Relating
Continental Drift to Dispersal

my science online.com

**Go to MyScienceOnline.com to
interact with this chapter's content.
Keyword: Ecosystems and Biomes**

> **UNTAMED SCIENCE**
• Give Me That Carbon!

> **PLANET DIARY**
• Ecosystems and Biomes

> **INTERACTIVE ART**
• Ocean Food Web • Water Cycle • Cycles
of Matter • Earth's Biomes • Continental
Drift • Seed Dispersal

> **VIRTUAL LAB**
• Where's All the Food?

CONTENTS

 Enter the Lab zone for hands-on inquiry.

Chapter Lab Investigation:
• Directed Inquiry: Recycling Paper
• Open Inquiry: Recycling Paper

Inquiry Warm-Ups: • How Do You Decide?
• Using Resources • Doubling Time • What
Happened to the Tuna? • How Much Variety
Is There?

Quick Labs: • Environmental Issues
• Comparing Costs and Benefits • Natural
Resources • Human Population Growth
• Comparing Populations • Shelterwood
Cutting • Managing Fisheries • Modeling
Keystone Species • Grocery Gene Pool
• Humans and Biodiversity

my science online.com

Go to MyScienceOnline.com to
interact with this chapter's content.
Keyword: Resources and Living Things

> UNTAMED SCIENCE
• The Great Macaw Debate

> PLANET DIARY
• Resources and Living Things

> INTERACTIVE ART
• Logging Methods • Exploring
Environmental Impact

> ART IN MOTION
• Human Population Growth

> VIRTUAL LAB
• Is Variety the Spice of Life?

CHAPTER 4
Land, Air, and Water Resources

Enter the Lab zone for hands-on inquiry.

Chapter Lab Investigation:
• Directed Inquiry: Waste, Away!
• Open Inquiry: Waste, Away!

Inquiry Warm-Ups: • How Does Mining Affect the Land? • What's in the Trash? • How Does the Scent Spread? • How Does the Water Change? • Is It From the Ocean?

Quick Labs: • Land Use • Modeling Soil Conservation • It's in the Numbers • Half-Life • How Acid Is Your Rain? • Analyzing Ozone • It's in the Air • Where's the Water? • Cleaning Up Oil Spills • Getting Clean • Seaweed Candy • Ocean Trash

my science online

Go to MyScienceOnline.com to interact with this chapter's content. Keyword: Land, Air, and Water Resources

> **UNTAMED SCIENCE**
• Manatee Survival

> **PLANET DIARY**
• Land, Air, and Water Resources

> **INTERACTIVE ART**
• Air Pollution • Match the Material

> **ART IN MOTION**
• Ocean Resource Management

> **REAL-WORLD INQUIRY**
• Mutation M'ystery

CONTENTS

 Enter the Lab zone for hands-on inquiry.

Chapter Lab Investigation:
• Directed Inquiry: Design and Build a Solar Cooker
• Open Inquiry: Design and Build a Solar Cooker

Inquiry Warm-Ups: • What's in a Piece of Coal? • Can You Capture Solar Energy? • Which Bulb Is More Efficient?

Quick Labs: • Observing Oil's Consistency • Fossil Fuels • Producing Electricity • Human Energy Use • Future Energy Use

my science online.com

Go to MyScienceOnline.com to interact with this chapter's content.
Keyword: Energy Resources

> **UNTAMED SCIENCE**
• Farming the Wind

> **PLANET DIARY**
• Energy Resources

> **INTERACTIVE ART**
• Hydroelectric Power Plant • Nuclear Power Plant

> **ART IN MOTION**
• Oil: Long to Form, Quick to Use

> **REAL-WORLD INQUIRY**
• Energy Conservation

Untamed Science created this captivating series for interactive SCIENCE featuring a unique video for every chapter of the program.

Featuring videos such as

Clown(fish)ing Around
Chapter 1 Follow Jonas of the Untamed Science crew as he dives under water to explore the symbiotic relationship between clownfish and anemones.

Give Me That Carbon!
Chapter 2 The Untamed Science crew examines the journey of a carbon atom as it cycles through an ecosystem.

The Great Macaw Debate
Chapter 3 What happens when a treasured animal's habitat is also valuable land? The Untamed Science crew explores the controversy over the scarlet macaw.

Manatee Survival
Chapter 4 The Untamed Science crew looks at the negative effects people have had on manatees in the past and how they, as well as their environment, can be protected in the future.

Farming the Wind
Chapter 5 This video explores why it is important to have a small carbon footprint and just what can be done to shrink yours.

INQUIRY IN THE SCIENCE CLASSROOM

Program Author of
Interactive Science

Associate Dean and Director of
Eugena P. Moore School of Education
Clemson University
Clemson, South Carolina

Michael J. Padilla, Ph.D.

"If students are busy doing lots of hands-on-activities, are they using inquiry skills? What is inquiry, anyway? If you are confused, you're not alone. Inquiry is the heart and soul of science education, with most of us in continuous pursuit of achieving it with our students."

What Is Inquiry?

Simply put, inquiry is thinking like a scientist—being inquisitive, asking why, and searching for answers. It's the process of taking a close examination of something in the quest for information.

Minds-on Inquiry

Students are naturally inquisitive; they want to learn, and they are always asking "Why?" They need practice and support to find answers for themselves. That's why they need experiences that are carefully scaffolded to guide them. We built that scaffolding right into this program.

Scaffolded Learning

The framework below illustrates a series of skill levels developed by educational psychologist Benjamin Bloom in the 1950s, later modified in the 1990s to reflect relevance to 21st century work. Look for the skills questions and tasks throughout the student book, scaffolded just right to provide students with the guidance and intellectual challenge they need.

Bloom's Taxonomy (adapted)

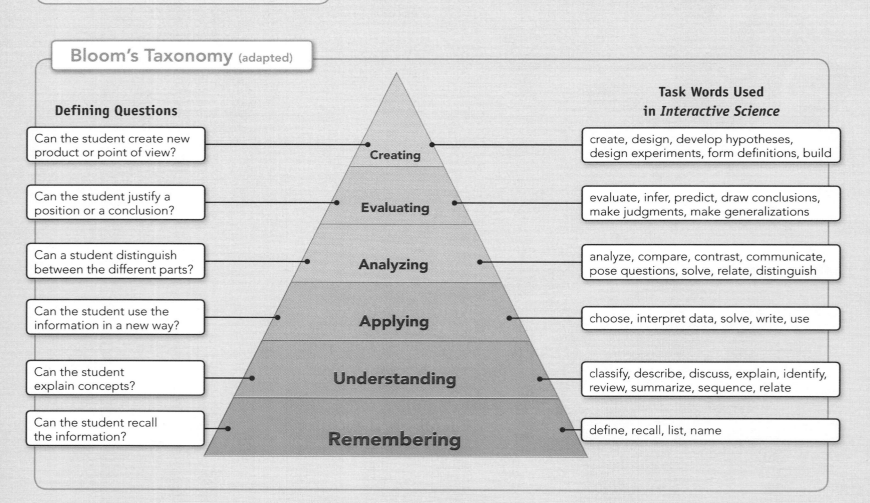

Defining Questions

Can the student create new product or point of view?

Can the student justify a position or a conclusion?

Can a student distinguish between the different parts?

Can the student use the information in a new way?

Can the student explain concepts?

Can the student recall the information?

Task Words Used in *Interactive Science*

Creating — create, design, develop hypotheses, design experiments, form definitions, build

Evaluating — evaluate, infer, predict, draw conclusions, make judgments, make generalizations

Analyzing — analyze, compare, contrast, communicate, pose questions, solve, relate, distinguish

Applying — choose, interpret data, solve, write, use

Understanding — classify, describe, discuss, explain, identify, review, summarize, sequence, relate

Remembering — define, recall, list, name

Student Interactivity

Science is the study of the world around us. Studies show that students learn science best through posing questions, investigating, and communicating and collaborating about what they've learned. That's why *Interactive Science* gets students involved in their learning each day, on every page. Because the student edition is consumable, it provides students with unique opportunities to become totally engaged in their learning. Students interact with every page, whether it's marking the text, completing an illustration or a chart, summarizing relationships through Venn diagrams and other graphic devices, or recording ideas and findings about scientific concepts.

Apply It! Students combine new content understandings with their knowledge of scientific process and experimentation.

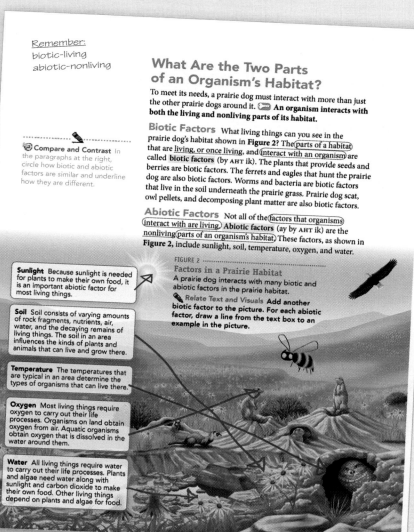

Remember:
biotic-living
abiotic-nonliving

What Are the Two Parts of an Organism's Habitat?

To meet its needs, a prairie dog must interact with more than just the other prairie dogs around it. **An organism interacts with both the living and nonliving parts of its habitat.**

Compare and Contrast In the paragraphs at the right, circle how biotic and abiotic factors are similar and underline how they are different.

Biotic Factors What living things can you see in the prairie dog's habitat shown in **Figure 2**? The (parts of a habitat) that are <u>living, or once living,</u> and (interact with an organism) are called **biotic factors** (by AHT ik). The plants that provide seeds and berries are biotic factors. The ferrets and eagles that hunt the prairie dog are also biotic factors. Worms and bacteria are biotic factors that live in the soil underneath the prairie grass. Prairie dog scat, owl pellets, and decomposing plant matter are also biotic factors.

Abiotic Factors Not all of the (factors that organisms interact with are living.) **Abiotic factors** (ay by AHT ik) are the <u>nonliving</u> (parts of an organism's habitat.) These factors, as shown in **Figure 2**, include sunlight, soil, temperature, oxygen, and water.

Sunlight Because sunlight is needed for plants to make their own food, it is an important abiotic factor for most living things.

Soil Soil consists of varying amounts of rock fragments, nutrients, air, water, and the decaying remains of living things. The soil in an area influences the kinds of plants and animals that can live and grow there.

Temperature The temperatures that are typical in an area determine the types of organisms that can live there.

Oxygen Most living things require oxygen to carry out their life processes. Organisms on land obtain oxygen from air. Aquatic organisms obtain oxygen that is dissolved in the water around them.

Water All living things require water to carry out their life processes. Plants and algae need water along with sunlight and carbon dioxide to make their own food. Other living things depend on plants and algae for food.

FIGURE 2
Factors in a Prairie Habitat
A prairie dog interacts with many biotic and abiotic factors in the prairie habitat.

Relate Text and Visuals Add another biotic factor to the picture. For each abiotic factor, draw a line from the text box to an example in the picture.

MY SCIENCE ONLINE | Biotic and Abiotic Factors | APPLY IT | MY SCIENCE COACH

apply it!

Salt is an abiotic factor found in some environments. To see how the amount of salt affects the hatching of brine shrimp eggs, varying amounts of salt were added to four different 500-mL beakers.

❶ Observe In which beaker(s) did the eggs, shown as purple circles, hatch? _B, C, D_

❷ Infer The manipulated variable was _the amount of salt._

❸ Infer The responding variable was _the number of hatching shrimp._

❹ **CHALLENGE** Beaker _A_ was the control.

❺ Draw Conclusions What can you conclude about the amount of salt in the shrimps' natural habitat? _It is similar to the amount in Beaker B, since that is where the most eggs hatched._

Beaker A
500 mL spring water

Beaker B
500 mL spring water + 2.5 g salt

Beaker C
500 mL spring water + 7.5 g salt

Beaker D
500 mL spring water + 15 g salt

Assess Your Understanding

1a. Interpret Diagrams List two biotic and two abiotic factors in **Figure 2**.
Biotic—grass and eagle
Abiotic—the rocky part of soil and sunlight

b. Draw Conclusions Name two abiotic factors in your habitat and explain how your life would be different without them.
Sunlight and oxygen. If there was no sunlight, I would not have enough food to eat. If there was no oxygen, I would not be able to breathe.

Lab Do the Lab Investigation
zone World in a Bottle.

got it?

○ I get it! Now I know that the two parts of an organism's habitat are _living, or biotic, factors and nonliving, or abiotic, factors._

○ I need extra help with _Biotic factors_
Go to MY SCIENCE COACH online for help with this subject.

Students demonstrate critical connections between text and illustration.

Hands-on Inquiry

We know that it is through student engagement and discovery that students really learn to think like scientists. Hands-on inquiry lab activities are built into the program; there are multiple activities per lesson.

Teacher's Lab Resource

Because there are so many labs, you will want to select which ones are best for your students and your class time. That is why the labs are organized in print as blackline masters in the *Teacher's Lab Resource*. Just photocopy the lab activities you want, when you want them. Or access them in your teacher center at MyScienceOnline.com. There you can download and even edit the labs to more closely align them with a student's needs.

Lab activities vary from both directed to open-ended, and quick and simple to more complex.

1. **Inquiry Warm-Ups.** One per lesson, as a lesson starter
2. **Quick Labs.** One per lesson objective
3. **Lab Investigations.** One full-blown lab per chapter, either as a directed lab or through an in-depth inquiry approach. You choose which approach is best for your students.

Using the Labs

The yellow LabZone symbols in the student edition indicate the lab activities that support your instruction. Look for the LabZone symbol. To find your lab, look for its name in the *Teacher's Lab Resource* books or online in the teacher center.

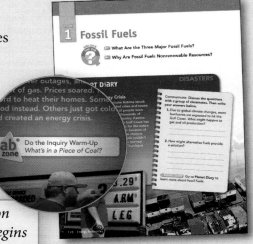

Inquiry Warm-Ups Hands-on experience before the lesson begins

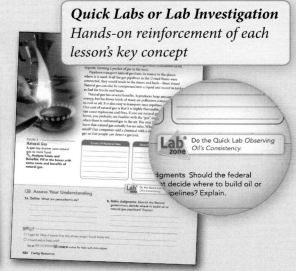

Quick Labs or Lab Investigation Hands-on reinforcement of each lesson's key concept

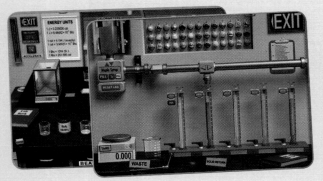

Online Labs and Simulations

Don't have time to dedicate to lab work today? For lab experiences without materials, you'll love the Online Virtual Labs. They're realistic, time efficient, and great when meeting in a laboratory is not possible. Have students use them individually, with a partner, or as a class activity to stimulate discussion or shared learning.

Inquiry Skill-Building Outside the Student Books

There are many forms of inquiry learning in *Interactive Science*, with lots of options to enrich your students' experiences. All components are in print or online for easy downloading.

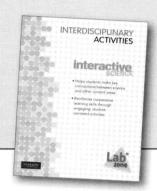

Allow students to demonstrate their understanding of chapter concepts in longer term projects.

Provide students with opportunities to apply the science they have learned to other subject areas.

Stretch students with real-life problem solving—perfect for challenging the advanced students.

Even more minds-on/hands-on activities, each targeting specific science process skills.

Interactive Science—Inquiry Learning at Its Best

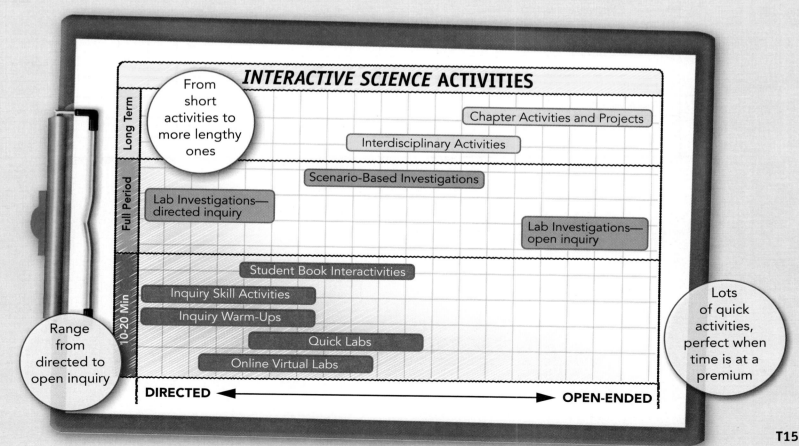

MODULE 6		Observe	Infer	Predict	Classify	Make Models	Calculate	Graph	Create Data Tables	Communicate	Develop Hypotheses	Interpret Data	Draw Conclusions	Analyze Costs and Benefits	Evaluate Impact on Society
	Lesson	*Inquiry Skills*									*Integrated Skills*				
Chapter 1 Populations and Communities	1. Living Things and the Environment	✔	✔		✔					✔			✔		
	2. Populations		✔				✔	✔		✔	✔	✔			
	3. Interactions Among Living Things		✔	✔	✔	✔		✔	✔	✔		✔	✔		
	4. Changes in Communities	✔							✔	✔					
Chapter 2 Ecosystems and Biomes	1. Energy Flow in Ecosystems				✔		✔			✔					
	2. Cycles of Matter	✔	✔	✔			✔				✔				
	3. Biomes		✔				✔			✔		✔	✔		
	4. Aquatic Ecosystems			✔		✔				✔					
	5. Biogeography	✔		✔						✔					
Chapter 3 Resources and Living Things	1. Introduction to Environmental Issues									✔			✔		
	2. Introduction to Natural Resources						✔		✔						✔
	3. Human Population Growth			✔			✔			✔		✔			
	4. Forests and Fisheries									✔				✔	
	5. Biodiversity		✔				✔			✔					
Chapter 4 Land, Air, and Water Resources	1. Conserving Land and Soil		✔							✔					
	2. Waste Disposal and Recycling						✔			✔					
	3. Air Pollution and Solutions		✔				✔			✔				✔	
	4. Water Pollution and Solutions									✔				✔	
	5. Ocean Resources						✔			✔			✔	✔	
Chapter 5 Energy Resources	1. Fossil Fuels						✔		✔	✔			✔	✔	
	2. Alternative Sources of Energy		✔				✔			✔				✔	
	3. Energy Use and Conservation	✔								✔					

CRITICAL THINKING SKILLS

Critical Thinking Skills

Define	Identify	Name	Review	List	Describe	Explain	Sequence	Interpret Diagrams, Photos, Maps, Tables	Read Graphs	Apply Concepts	Solve Problems	Make Generalizations	Make Judgments	Relate Text and Visuals	Summarize	Relate Cause and Effect	Compare and Contrast	Design Experiments	Design a Solution
				✔				✔		✔				✔					
	✔		✔	✔					✔	✔					✔	✔			
✔	✔		✔	✔	✔	✔		✔	✔	✔		✔					✔		
✔					✔		✔												
✔	✔				✔			✔		✔							✔	✔	
	✔				✔			✔											
	✔		✔	✔	✔	✔		✔	✔				✔	✔					
	✔			✔								✔							
						✔											✔		
✔				✔							✔	✔			✔				
✔			✔	✔	✔			✔							✔		✔		
								✔											
✔	✔												✔	✔					
✔	✔		✔		✔	✔		✔		✔				✔					
	✔	✔	✔		✔	✔		✔		✔									
✔		✔	✔		✔			✔			✔		✔		✔				✔
	✔	✔	✔			✔	✔	✔	✔		✔		✔		✔				
✔	✔					✔	✔	✔								✔		✔	
		✔	✔	✔	✔			✔			✔		✔				✔		
✔	✔							✔	✔				✔		✔	✔	✔		
	✔		✔		✔	✔		✔									✔		
✔					✔	✔					✔								

Writing in the book is helpful because I can take notes near where the information is being presented in the text, and my notes act like a study guide.

—Middle grades student
Winston-Salem, NC

The best part about Interactive Science is that we actually get to apply what we learned.

—Middle grades student
Federal Way, WA

READING, VOCABULARY, MATH SKILLS

MODULE 6	Lesson	Target Reading Skills								Vocabulary				Math Skills						
		Compare, Contrast	Relate Cause, Effect	Relate Text, Visuals	Sequence	Outline	Ask Questions	Identify the Main Idea	Summarize	Word Origins	Prefixes	Related Word Forms	Academic Vocabulary	Interpret Bar Graph	Interpret Line Graph	Calculate	Draw Bar Graph	Interpret Circle Graph	Interpret Data	Use Formulas / Solve
Chapter 1 — Populations and Communities	1. Living Things and the Environment	✔																		
	2. Populations		✔							✔				✔	✔	✔				✔
	3. Interactions Among Living Things			✔												✔				✔
	4. Changes in Communities	✔																		✔
Chapter 2 — Ecosystems and Biomes	1. Energy Flow in Ecosystems			✔							✔					✔				
	2. Cycles of Matter				✔															
	3. Biomes	✔														✔				
	4. Aquatic Ecosystems				✔														✔	✔
	5. Biogeography		✔													✔				
Chapter 3 — Resources and Living Things	1. Introduction to Environmental Issues		✔								✔									
	2. Introduction to Natural Resources		✔													✔				✔
	3. Forests and Fisheries							✔								✔				
	4. Human Population Growth								✔											
	5. Biodiversity	✔														✔				
Chapter 4 — Land, Air, and Water Resources	1. Conserving Land and Soil		✔																	
	2. Waste Disposal and Recycling	✔									✔							✔		✔
	3. Air Pollution and Solutions		✔													✔				
	4. Water Pollution and Solutions				✔															
	5. Ocean Resources							✔						✔						✔
Chapter 5 — Energy Resources	1. Fossil Fuels								✔							✔		✔		✔
	2. Alternative Sources of Energy		✔										✔			✔				
	3. Energy Use and Conservation					✔													✔	

PACING GUIDE

CHAPTER	Lesson	Periods (days)	Blocks
Chapter 1 **Populations and Communities**	1. Living Things and the Environment	2–3	1–1½
	2. Populations	2–3	1–1½
	3. Interactions Among Living Things	2–3	1–1½
	4. Changes in Communities	1–2	½–1
Chapter 2 **Ecosystems and Biomes**	1. Energy Flow in Ecosystems	1–2	½–1
	2. Cycles of Matter	2–3	1–½
	3. Biomes	2–3	1–½
	4. Aquatic Ecosystems	1–2	½–1
	5. Biogeography	1–2	½–1
Chapter 3 **Resources and Living Things**	1. Introduction to Environmental Issues	2–3	1–1½
	2. Introduction to Natural Resources	2–3	1–1½
	3. Forests and Fisheries	1–2	½–1
	4. Human Population Growth	2–3	1–1½
	5. Biodiversity	1–2	½–1
Chapter 4 **Land, Air, and Water Resources**	1. Conserving Land and Soil	2–3	1–1½
	2. Waste Disposal and Recycling	2–3	1–1½
	3. Air Pollution and Solutions	2–3	1–1½
	4. Water Pollution and Solutions	2–3	1–1½
	5. Ocean Resources	1–2	½–1
Chapter 5 **Energy Resources**	1. Fossil Fuels	1–2	½–1
	2. Alternative Sources of Energy	2–3	1–1½
	3. Energy Use and Conservation	1–2	½–1

Teacher Notes:

interactive SCIENCE

Dear Family Member,

As your child's science teacher, I am looking forward to helping your child learn about science. Because I know that you want your child to be successful, I offer these suggestions so that you can help your child gain proficiency in science.

- Your child's textbook is very different from most—it's meant for students to write in it. Therefore, it is a record of learning. Look through lessons your child has completed recently, and be sure to ask lots of questions. One of the best ways for students to check on their learning is to explain it to someone else.
- Ask your child about homework assignments and check that he or she has completed them.
- Help your child collect materials and information for school activities.
- Encourage computer literacy. Advise your child to use computers in school or at the library. If you have a home computer, help your child do research online.

In this unit of study, your child will be introduced to living things and how they interact in and are dependent on the environment. Students will also learn about the land, air, water, and energy resources that make up our Earth. In the following weeks of study, the unit will provide your child with a deepening of understanding behind the science of ecology and the environment.

I encourage you to stay involved in your child's learning. By all means, visit the classroom during open house or make an appointment with me if you have questions.

Cordially,

_____

Science Teacher

To learn more about *Interactive Science* and to see how your student is progressing through the program, go to **www.interactivescience.com**.

Estimados familiares:

Como maestro de ciencias de su hijo, me es un placer ayudarlo a descubrir las ciencias. Como sé que ustedes quieren que su hijo tenga un buen desempeño académico, les ofrezco estas sugerencias para que ayuden a su hijo a dominar las ciencias.

- El libro de texto de su hijo es muy diferente de los demás: tiene como objetivo que su hijo escriba en el libro. Por esa razón, es un registro de aprendizaje. Fíjense en las lecciones que su hijo ha terminado recientemente y asegúrense de hacerle muchas preguntas. Para los estudiantes, una de las mejores formas de repasar lo que han aprendido es explicándoselo a otras personas.
- Pregúntenle a su hijo sobre la tarea que se le asigna y asegúrense de que la complete.
- Ayúdenlo a reunir materiales e información relacionados con las actividades escolares.
- Anímenlo a adquirir destrezas con la computadora, y a usar computadoras en la escuela o en la biblioteca. Si tienen una computadora en casa, ayúdenlo a hacer investigaciones en Internet.

En esta unidad, su hijo comenzará a explorar el mundo de los seres vivos, cómo interactúan con su medio ambiente y cómo dependen de él. Los estudiantes también aprenderán sobre la tierra, el aire, el agua y los recursos energéticos que componen la Tierra. En las semanas que siguen, la unidad ayudará a su hijo a comprender mejor las ciencias ecológicas y el medio ambiente.

Los animo a que participen en el proceso de aprendizaje de su hijo. Los invito a visitar el salón de clases durante las horas de visita o a que hagan una cita para reunirse conmigo si tienen dudas.

Cordialmente,

_____

Maestro de Ciencias

Para más información sobre *Ciencias interactivas* y para ver cómo está progresando en el programa su estudiante, visite **www.interactivescience.com**.

Big Ideas of Science

According to Grant Wiggins' Understanding by Design framework, students reveal their understanding most effectively when provided with complex, authentic opportunities to explain, interpret, apply, shift perspective, empathize, and self-assess. Each chapter in the student edition uses a Big Question to focus students' attention on the content of the chapter. Related Big Questions are organized under one or more Big Ideas. A Big Idea is a concept, theory, principle, or theme that helps learners make sense of a subject.

Students will explore the Big Idea before they read a chapter, writing about what they already know and what they want to know about the topic. After completing the chapter, students will return to these pages in order to record what they have learned and how their thoughts have changed during that learning process.

BIG IDEAS OF SCIENCE

Have you ever worked on a jigsaw puzzle? Usually a puzzle has a theme that leads you to group the pieces by what they have in common. But until you put all the pieces together you can't solve the puzzle. Studying science is similar to solving a puzzle. The big ideas of science are like puzzle themes. To understand big ideas, scientists ask questions. The answers to those questions are like pieces of a puzzle. Each chapter in this book asks a big question to help you think about a big idea of science. By answering the big questions, you will get closer to understanding the big idea.

✎ **Before you read each chapter, write about what you know and what more you'd like to know.**

Grant Wiggins, coauthor of Understanding by Design

These prairie dogs live in grasslands and make their homes underground. To stay alive, prairie dogs search for food and water and hide from animals that eat them.

Living things interact with their environment.

What do you already know about how the animals and plants in your neighborhood live together? ✎ **What more would you like to know?**

_____

_____

_____

_____

Big Questions:

❓ How do living things affect one another? Chapter 1

❓ How do energy and matter move through ecosystems? Chapter 2

❓ How do people use Earth's resources? Chapter 3

❓ What can people do to use resources wisely? Chapter 4

❓ What are some of Earth's energy sources? Chapter 5

✎ **After reading the chapters, write what you have learned about the Big Idea.**

_____

_____

_____

_____

_____

Connect to the Big Idea ❓ UbD

Have the class discuss what they already know about the Big Idea. Ask individuals to write in their student editions what else they personally would like to know. Individuals can then share their items with the class as the teacher compiles responses on the board and eliminates any duplicates. Finally, have the class agree on one key item they all want to learn about. Make sure all students who want to share are heard.

EXTENSION Select one item about which students want to learn more and assign as an extra credit project.

Populations and Communities

Introduce the Big Q  UbD

Have students look at the image and read the Engaging Question and description. Ask them to write a hypothesis for how the sea anemone might benefit from having the clownfish nearby. Have volunteers read their hypotheses out loud. Point out that living things interact with one another in many ways. Tell students they will learn more about how living things affect one another in this chapter. Ask: **Which people in your community help others who live there?** (*Firefighters save people from fires, police keep everyone safe from criminals*) **Can anyone think of something or someone that may hurt the community?** (*A thief, the flu*) **Are there ways to protect yourself from these dangers?** (*Locking doors, getting a flu shot*)

Untamed Science Video

CLOWN(FISH)ING AROUND Before viewing, invite students to suggest some ways in which organisms interact. Then play the video. Lead a class discussion and make a list of questions that this video raises. You may wish to have students view the video again after they have completed the chapter to see if their questions have been answered.

> **To access the online resources for this chapter, search or navigate to *Populations and Communities*.**
>
> **Untamed Science Video** shows interactions between organisms.
>
> **The Big Question** allows students to answer the Engaging Question about how the sea anemone benefits from its interaction with the clownfish.

my science online.com ▶ **Populations and Communities**

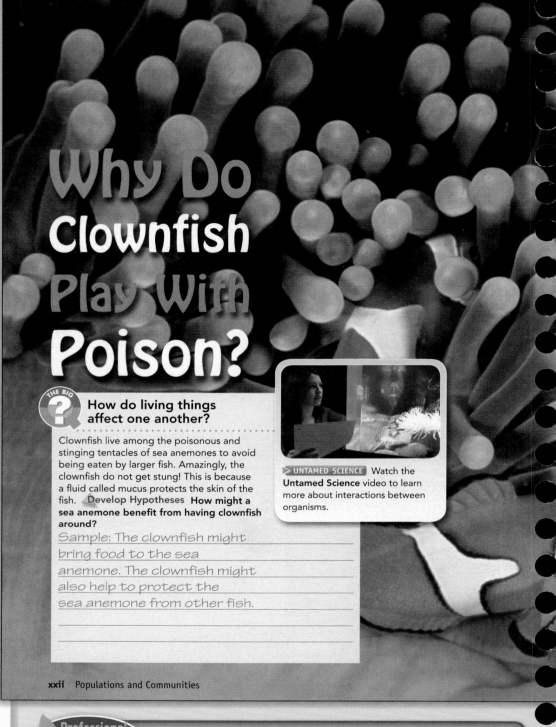

Why Do Clownfish Play With Poison?

? THE BIG

How do living things affect one another?

Clownfish live among the poisonous and stinging tentacles of sea anemones to avoid being eaten by larger fish. Amazingly, the clownfish do not get stung! This is because a fluid called mucus protects the skin of the fish. ◢ **Develop Hypotheses** How might a sea anemone benefit from having clownfish around?

Sample: The clownfish might bring food to the sea anemone. The clownfish might also help to protect the sea anemone from other fish.

▶ **UNTAMED SCIENCE** Watch the **Untamed Science** video to learn more about interactions between organisms.

Professional Development Note **From the Author**

I have a pecan tree in my backyard very near my porch. On a recent winter day I noticed a series of holes in the trunk that were evenly drilled around the entire trunk, from top to bottom. It looked like someone had measured and taken a drill to make them. When I looked this up on the Internet, I found I had a tree that was well appreciated by a Yellow-Bellied Sapsucker. You may think this is a fictitious bird created by a comedian for a joke, but it is really a type of woodpecker. This bird drills the hole to create a sap well and then returns to trees that produce large amounts to lick its meals. Learning this made me think about all the unique niches animals and plants fill in our world. What an amazing place!

✏ *Michael Padilla*

Populations and Communities

CHAPTER 1

Chapter at a Glance

CHAPTER PACING: 8–12 periods or 4–6 blocks

INTRODUCE THE CHAPTER: Engage students with the Engaging Question and the opening image. Activate prior knowledge and preteach vocabulary using the Getting Started pages.

Lesson 1: Living Things and the Environment

Lesson 2: Populations

Lesson 3: Interactions Among Living Things

Lesson 4: Changes in Communities

ASSESSMENT OPTIONS: Chapter Test, **EXAM**VIEW® Assessment Suite, Performance Assessment, Progress Monitoring Assessments, SuccessTracker™

Preference Navigator, in the online Planning tools, allows you to customize *Interactive Science* to your own teaching style. You can also edit lesson plans by selecting the Lesson Planner option.

Digital Teacher's Edition allows you to access your Teacher's Edition and Resource materials online.

my science online

Differentiated Instruction

L1 Sea Anemones Make sure that students understand that the sea anemone is an animal, not a plant. Students who have seen jellyfish may be surprised at the short tentacles of the anemone. Tell students that jellyfish and anemones are related, and that stinging tentacles are a characteristic of this group of animals. To give students some sense of the size of the organisms shown, point out that the photograph is enlarged. A clownfish is usually about 8 cm long.

L3 Clownfish Have students research the clownfish to find out more about its habitat, life cycle, and behavior, giving special attention to the relationship between the clownfish and the sea anemone. Students can present their findings to the class.

1

Getting Started

Check Your Understanding

This activity assesses students' understanding of what living things get from their environment. After students have shared their answers, point out that precipitation provides the water that all living things need to carry out their life processes. The atmosphere provides carbon dioxide required by plants. The composition of the soil in an area influences what kinds of plants can grow there.

Preteach Vocabulary Skills

Explain to students that many English words come from Latin, the language originally spoken in Ancient Rome. Learning the meaning of Latin roots can make it easier to learn new vocabulary words. Also point out the definition of *immigration*. Have students note that the prefix *im-* is similar in meaning to the word *in*. This may help them remember that immigration is movement into a population.

---

1 Getting Started

Check Your Understanding

1. **Background** Read the paragraph below and then answer the question.

> Raquel planted a garden in a sunny area near her home. First, she loosened the **soil**, so the plant roots could easily grow. If days passed with no **precipitation**, she watered the plants. That was all she had to do—the rest of what the plants needed came from the **atmosphere!**

Soil is made up of rock fragments, water, air, and decaying plant and animal matter.

Rain, hail, sleet, and snow are all types of **precipitation.**

Earth's **atmosphere** contains oxygen, carbon dioxide, nitrogen, and other gases.

• How do soil, precipitation, and the atmosphere help a plant grow?

   Sample: Plants get minerals from the soil, water from precipitation, and gases (carbon dioxide and oxygen) from the atmosphere.

> **MY READING WEB** If you had trouble completing the question above, visit **My Reading Web** and type in *Populations and Communities.*

Vocabulary Skill

Latin Word Origins Some key terms in this chapter contain word parts with Latin origins. The table below lists two of the Latin words that key terms come from.

Latin Word	Meaning of Latin Word	Example
aptare	to fit	adaptation, *n.* a characteristic that allows an organism to live successfully in its environment
migrare	(to move)	immigration, *n.* movement into a population

2. **Quick Check** The terms *immigration* and *emigration* both come from the Latin word *migrare*. Circle the meaning of *migrare* in the table above.

My Reading Web offers leveled readings related to chapter content.

Vocab Flash Cards offer extra practice with the chapter vocabulary words.

Digital Lesson

• Assign the *Check Your Understanding* activity online and have students submit their work to you.

• Assign the *Vocabulary Skill* activity online and have students submit their work to you.

my science online .com | **Populations and Communities**

organism

immigration

adaptation

predation

Chapter Preview

LESSON 1
- organism • habitat
- biotic factor • abiotic factor
- species • population
- community • ecosystem
- ecology

  Compare and Contrast
  Draw Conclusions

LESSON 2
- birth rate • death rate
- immigration • emigration
- population density
- limiting factor
- carrying capacity

  Relate Cause and Effect
  Infer

LESSON 3
- natural selection • adaptation
- niche • competition • predation
- predator • prey • symbiosis
- mutualism • commensalism
- parasitism • parasite • host

  Relate Text and Visuals
  Classify

LESSON 4
- succession • primary succession
- pioneer species
- secondary succession

  Compare and Contrast
  Observe

> VOCAB FLASH CARDS For extra help with vocabulary, visit **Vocab Flash Cards** and type in *Populations and Communities.*

3

Preview Vocabulary Terms

Have students work together to create a word wall to display the vocabulary terms for the chapter. Be sure to discuss and analyze each term before posting it on the wall. As the class progresses through the chapter, the words can be sorted and categorized in different ways. A list of Academic Vocabulary for each lesson can be found in the Support All Readers box at the start of the lesson.

L1 Have students look at the images on this page as you pronounce the vocabulary word. Have students repeat the word after you. Then read the definition. Use the sample sentence in italics to clarify the meaning of the term.

organism *(awr guh NIZ um)* A living thing. *The prairie dog in the image is an example of an organism.*

immigration *(im uh GRAY shun)* Moving into a population. *These white-tailed deer are on their way from one place to another in a process known as immigration.*

adaptation *(ad ap TAY shun)* The behaviors and physical characteristics that allow organisms to live successfully in their environments. *An adaptation helpful to the survival of this animal, the pangolin, is its ability to roll up into an armored ball when threatened.*

predation *(pree DAY shun)* An interaction in which one organism kills another for food or nutrients. *The predation method used by this plant, a sundew, is to snag its food with its sticky bulbs.*

CHAPTER 1

ELL Support

Have students work together to sort and categorize the words on the word wall. As the class progresses through the chapter and new words are introduced, be sure to say each word aloud and have students repeat it.

Beginning
LOW/HIGH Create a drawing or symbol to support the word.

Intermediate
LOW/HIGH Write the definition for each word and present it.

Advanced
LOW/HIGH Challenge students to come up with new categories to classify the words.

Living Things and the Environment

How do living things affect one another?

Lesson Pacing: 2–3 periods or 1–1½ blocks

🕐 **SHORT ON TIME?** To do this lesson in approximately half the time, do the Activate Prior Knowledge activity on page 4. A discussion of the key concepts on pages 5, 6, and 9 will familiarize students with the lesson content. Use the Explore the Big Q to help students understand how living things affect one another. Have students do the Quick Labs and the Real-World Inquiry online. The rest of the lesson can be completed by students independently.

Preference Navigator, in the online Planning tools, allows you to customize *Interactive Science* to your own teaching style. You can also edit lesson plans by selecting the Lesson Planner option.

Digital Teacher's Edition allows you to access your Teacher's Edition and Resource online.

my science online.com

Lesson Vocabulary

- organism
- habitat
- biotic factor
- abiotic factor
- species
- population
- community
- ecosystem
- ecology

 Content Refresher

Carbon Dioxide Carbon dioxide is an abiotic factor that all plants and some algae require to carry out photosynthesis. Chlorophyll, the green pigment in plants and some algae, absorbs energy from sunlight. The organism uses this energy to combine carbon dioxide and water in a chemical reaction that produces sugars, including glucose. Water and oxygen are produced as byproducts of the reaction. The sugars provide energy for sustaining the organism's life processes. Other organisms obtain this energy when they eat plants or algae. The energy is released during cellular respiration when glucose is broken down into carbon dioxide and water.

Biosphere All of Earth's communities are part of a higher level of organization, the biosphere. The levels of organization that make up the biosphere interact with each other. But they also interact in various ways with Earth's other "spheres." These include the atmosphere, the hydrosphere, and the lithosphere.

LESSON OBJECTIVES

🔑 Identify the needs that must be met by an organism's surroundings.

🔑 Identify biotic and abiotic parts of a habitat.

🔑 Describe the levels of organization within an ecosystem.

Blended Path
Active learning using Student Edition, Inquiry Path, and Digital Path

ENGAGE AND EXPLORE

To teach this lesson using a variety of resources, begin by reading **My Planet Diary** as a class. Have students share ideas about the mouse lemur population and identify what they know about habitats. Then do the **Inquiry Warm-Up activity.** Students will identify living and nonliving things in magazine pictures. Discuss the connections different students chose and how they decided to test the living thing's dependence. The **After the Inquiry Warm-Up worksheet** sets up a discussion about how living things also depend on other living things. Have volunteers share their answers to number 4 about the effect of different seasons.

EXPLAIN AND ELABORATE

Teach Key Concepts by explaining the term *habitat* and having students answer questions about what a habitat provides.

Continue to **Teach Key Concepts** by explaining the difference between biotic and abiotic factors. Ask students to compare and contrast living and nonliving things in their own environment. Use **Figure 2** to illustrate biotic and abiotic factors in the prairie dog's habitat. Then have students practice the lesson's inquiry skill in the **Apply It activity.** In the chapter **Lab Investigation activity,** students will build a terrarium and observe the interactions between the biotic and abiotic parts of the closed ecosystem.

Using a park ecosystem as an example, **Teach Key Concepts** by asking students to identify the levels of organization from smallest to largest. Use the **Explore the Big Question activity** to illustrate the levels of an ecosystem. Students can do the **Real-World Inquiry** online to experiment with the effects of changing certain factors of a population in a habitat. Discuss student responses to the **Answer the Big Question activity.** Hand out the **Key Concept Summaries** as a review of each part of the lesson. Students can also use the online **Vocab Flash Cards** to review key terms.

EVALUATE

Have students take the **Lesson Quiz.** For an alternate assessment, see the **EXAM**VIEW® Assessment Suite, Progress Monitoring Assessments, or SuccessTracker™.

ⒺⓁⓁ Support

1 Content and Language

Compare the words *organism/organize, abiotic/biotic,* and *ecosystem/ecology,* featured in the lesson vocabulary. Explain what the word parts signal: *organ-* to arrange into systems; *a-* not; *bio-* living; *eco-* relating to the environment.

Lab zone Inquiry Path
Hands-on learning in the Lab zone

Digital Path
Online learning at my science online.com

ENGAGE AND EXPLORE

To teach this lesson with an emphasis on inquiry, begin with the **Inquiry Warm-Up activity.** Students identify living and nonliving things in magazine pictures. Lead a discussion about the connections different students chose and how they decided to test the living thing's dependence. Have students do the **After the Inquiry Warm-Up worksheet.** Talk about how living things also depend on other living things. Have volunteers share their answers to number 4 about the effect of different seasons.

EXPLAIN AND ELABORATE

Focus on the **Inquiry Skill** for the lesson. Point out that when you draw a conclusion, you make a statement summing up what you have learned from an experiment. What conclusion can be drawn from the **Inquiry Warm-Up activity?** (*All living things depend on other living things and non-living things in their habitat to survive.*) Have students do the first **Quick Lab** and then share their results. How do their inferences differ? Have volunteers suggest why that may be.

Do the **Teacher Demo** and classify the various materials under the headings BIOTIC and ABIOTIC on the board. Review *control, manipulated variable,* and *responding variable* before beginning the **Apply It activity.** Ask volunteers to share their conclusions. Have students do the **Lab Investigation.** In this investigation, students build a terrarium and observe the interactions between the biotic and abiotic parts of the closed ecosystem. You may elect to have them do the Open Inquiry version.

Use the **Explore the Big Q activity** to illustrate the levels of an ecosystem. Students can do the **Real-World Inquiry** online to experiment with the effects of changing certain factors of a population in a habitat. Do the **Quick Lab** to reinforce understanding of ecosystems. Discuss student responses to the **Answer the Big Q activity** in the student edition. Students can use the online **Vocab Flash Cards** to review key terms.

EVALUATE

Have students take the **Lesson Quiz.** For an alternate assessment, see the **EXAM**VIEW® Assessment Suite, Progress Monitoring Assessments, or SuccessTracker™.

ENGAGE AND EXPLORE

To teach this lesson using digital resources, begin by having students explore the real-world connections to living things and their environment at **My Planet Diary** online. Have them access the Chapter Resources to find the **Unlock the Big Question activity.** There they can answer the questions and refine their responses as they continue through the lesson. You can re-assign the activity and have students submit their work so you can track their progress.

EXPLAIN AND ELABORATE

Students reading above, at, or below the lexile measure of this lesson can access basic content readings at their level at **My Reading Web.** Have students use the online **Vocab Flash Cards** to preview key terms. Do the **Quick Lab** and then ask students to share their results. How do their inferences differ? Have volunteers suggest why that may be.

Review *control, manipulated variable,* and *responding variable* before assigning the online **Apply It activity.** Ask volunteers to share their conclusions and have all students submit their work to you. Do the **Teacher Demo** and classify the various materials under the headings BIOTIC and ABIOTIC on the board.

Assign the online **Real-World Inquiry** ahead of time. In this activity, students have an opportunity to experiment with the effects of changing certain factors of a population in a habitat. Have them answer the questions and submit their work. Discuss student responses to the online **Answer the Big Q.** The **Key Concept Summary** online allows students to read a summary and see an image associated with each part of the lesson. Online remediation is available at **My Science Coach.**

EVALUATE

Have students take the **Lesson Quiz.** For an alternate assessment, see the **EXAM**VIEW® Assessment Suite, Progress Monitoring Assessments, or SuccessTracker™.

2 Frontload the Lesson
Preview the lesson visuals, labels, and captions. Ask students what they know about the words *population* and *community.* Explain the specific meanings these words have in science.

3 Comprehensible Input
Have students study the visuals and their captions on pages 6 and 8–9 to support the key concepts of the lesson.

4 Language Production
Pair or group students with varied language abilities to complete labs collaboratively for language practice. Have each student copy the completed written lab for personal reference.

5 Assess Understanding
Make true or false statements using lesson content and have students indicate if they agree or disagree with a thumbs up or thumbs down gesture to check whole-class comprehension.

LESSON 1.1

Living Things and the Environment

Establish Learning Objectives

After this lesson, students will be able to:

🔑 Identify the needs that must be met by an organism's surroundings.

🔑 Identify biotic and abiotic parts of a habitat.

🔑 Describe the levels of organization within an ecosystem.

Engage

Activate Prior Knowledge

MY PLANET DIARY Read *Love Song* with the class. Point out that mouse lemurs live only on the island of Madagascar, off the eastern coast of Africa. Ask: **Why do you think mouse lemurs live only on this island?** *(It has the food they like to eat.)* **Different organisms live in different places, or habitats. What is your habitat?** *(My home; my room)* **What about that place makes it uniquely yours?** *(It has my stuff in it. It is comfortable for me. My family is there.)*

BIG IDEAS OF SCIENCE REFERENCE LIBRARY 📖 Have students look up the following topics: Amazon River, Colorado Plateau, Deep Sea Vents, Supercooling Frogs.

Explore

Lab Resource: Inquiry Warm-Up 🔺

L1 WHAT'S IN THE SCENE Students will identify parts of a habitat.

LESSON 1

Living Things and the Environment

UNLOCK THE BIG ?

🔑 **What Does an Organism Get From Its Environment?**

🔑 **What Are the Two Parts of an Organism's Habitat?**

🔑 **How Is an Ecosystem Organized?**

my planet diary

DISCOVERY

Love Song

The gray, golden brown, and Goodman's mouse lemurs are some of the world's smallest primates. These three lemurs look similar. Looking so similar makes it difficult for the lemurs to find members of their own kind or species during mating season. However, it seems that the lemurs can identify their own species by song. Scientists recorded the mating calls of the three species of lemurs. They discovered that the lemurs reacted more to the calls from their own species. This allows the lemurs to pick the right mate, even at night.

Communicate Answer these questions. Discuss your answers with a partner.

1. If you were looking for your sneakers among several pairs that looked just like yours, what characteristics would make it easier for you to find them?
   Size, smell, scuff marks, wear pattern

2. What do you think would happen if a lemur mated with a different kind of lemur?
   They would not be able to have offspring.

> PLANET DIARY Go to **Planet Diary** to learn more about habitats.

Golden brown mouse lemur

Goodman's mouse lemur

Gray mouse lemur

🔺 Lab zone ® Do the Inquiry Warm-Up *What's in the Scene?*

4 Populations and Communities

SUPPORT ALL READERS

Prior Exposure to Content: Most students have encountered this topic in earlier grades

Academic Vocabulary: *compare, contrast, describe*

Science Vocabulary: *abiotic factor, biotic factor*

Concept Level: Generally appropriate for most students in this grade

Preteach With: My Planet Diary "Love Song" and Figure 1 activity

Go to **My Reading Web** to access leveled readings that provide a foundation for the content.

my science online.com

Vocabulary

- organism • habitat • biotic factor • abiotic factor
- species • population • community • ecosystem
- ecology

Skills

↪ Reading: Compare and Contrast
△ Inquiry: Draw Conclusions

What Does an Organism Get From Its Environment?

If you were to visit Alaska, you might see a bald eagle fly by. A bald eagle is one type of **organism,** or living thing. Different types of organisms live in different types of surroundings, or environments. 🔑 **An organism gets food, water, shelter, and other things it needs to live, grow, and reproduce from its environment.** An environment that provides the things a specific organism needs to live, grow, and reproduce is called its **habitat.**

In a forest habitat, mushrooms grow in the damp soil and woodpeckers build nests in tree trunks. Organisms live in different habitats because they have different requirements for survival and reproduction. Some organisms live on a prairie, with its flat terrain, tall grasses, and low rainfall amounts. A prairie dog, like the one shown in **Figure 1,** obtains the food and shelter it needs from a prairie habitat. It could not survive on this rocky ocean shore. Likewise, the prairie would not meet the needs of a sea star.

FIGURE 1 ....

What's Wrong With This Picture?
Most people would never expect to see a prairie dog at the beach.
✎ **List** Give three reasons why this prairie dog would not survive in this habitat.

Sample: There is no grass to
eat; it is too wet; there is no
grass to hide from predators.

 Do the Quick Lab
Organisms and Their Habitats.

🔑 Assess Your Understanding

got it? ....

○ I get it! Now I know that an organism's environment provides food, water, and
shelter for the organism to live, grow, and reproduce.

○ I need extra help with See TE note.

Go to my science ⦿ coach *online for help with this subject.*

5

1 Content and Language
Ask students to restate the objectives in their own words. Have pairs complete and use flash cards with key vocabulary terms on one side, and a definition, visual, and sentence with the word on the other. Allow students with limited English to use their native languages for support.

2 Frontload the Lesson
Have students name an organism they

see often (a specific plant or animal) and list the things found in that organism's environment. Explain how some are living and others not.

3 Comprehensible Input
Explain the Explore the Big Q image and caption, restating information as needed. Have students complete the Apply Concepts activity, allowing them to draw or write according to their language proficiency level.

Explain

Introduce Vocabulary
To help students understand the term *habitat,* tell them that in Latin the word means "it inhabits." *Inhabit* means "lives in, resides, occupies."

Teach Key Concepts 🔑
Explain to students that organisms get the vital things they need to survive from their habitat. A habitat is an environment that is home to a particular organism. Ask: **Are all parts of the forest where organisms live the same?** *(No)* **How do they differ?** *(Some parts get more sunlight than other; some organisms live on the ground, others in the treetops.)* **Why do you find different kinds of organisms in different habitats?** *(Each kind of organism has specific needs. Different habitats provide different things.)*

Elaborate

21st Century Learning

CRITICAL THINKING Have students read *Deep Sea Vents* in the **Big Ideas of Science Reference Library.** Deep sea vents, also known as smokers, can be black, grey, white, or clear. Have students research one or more of these types and create a short multimedia presentation in which they answer these questions: What minerals cause the difference in color? What organisms live in this habitat?

Lab Resource: Quick Lab

L1 **ORGANISMS AND THEIR HABITATS** Students will infer what an animal's habitat is like.

Evaluate

Assess Your Understanding
Have students evaluate their understanding by completing the appropriate sentence.

RTI Response to Intervention
If students have trouble identifying what a habitat provides, **then** remind them that the basic needs of food, water, and shelter are the same for human beings.

my science ⦿ coach Have students go online for help in understanding habitats.

My Planet Diary provides an opportunity for students to explore real-world connections to living things and their environments.

my science online .com | Habitat

Explain

Teach Key Concepts 🔑

Explain to students that there are living and nonliving parts to their surroundings. They need both parts in order to survive. Ask: **What are some living things in or near your home?** (*Family, dog, cat, some foods, squirrels, birds, plants*) **What are some nonliving things in or near your home?** (*Furniture, clothing, toys, car, roads*) Point out to students that biotic factors include things that were once living or came from living things. Dead plants and animals are biotic factors, as are waste products. If students do not know the word *scat*, tell them that it is a term for animal droppings. Owl pellets are another waste product. Most of the indigestible parts of animals that an owl eats are regurgitated as pellets.

Compare and Contrast Explain that comparing and contrasting shows how ideas, facts and events are similar and different. The results of the comparison can be important.

Teach With Visuals

Tell students to look at **Figure 2.** Make sure students understand the meaning of decaying remains and aquatic. Help students identify the ferret, eagle, and owl in the prairie dog's habitat. (Ferret, eagle, owl) Point out that the prairie dog's habitat is also the ferret's habitat. Ask: **How do the prairie dog and ferret interact?** (*The ferret hunts the prairie dog.*) **What kind of factor in the ferret's habitat is the prairie dog?** (*Biotic*)

21st Century Learning

INFORMATION LITERACY Help students classify factors in an organism's environment. Ask: **What are the two kinds of factors in an organism's environment?** (*Biotic and abiotic*) **What factors in Figure 2 are biotic?** (*Prairie dogs, ferrets, eagle, owl, grass, flowers*) **What factors are abiotic?** (*Abiotic factors that can be seen are water and soil.*) **What factors cannot be seen?** (*Sunlight, temperature, oxygen*)

What Are the Two Parts of an Organism's Habitat?

To meet its needs, a prairie dog must interact with more than just the other prairie dogs around it. 🔑 **An organism interacts with both the living and nonliving parts of its habitat.**

Biotic Factors What living things can you see in the prairie dog's habitat shown in **Figure 2**? The parts of a habitat that are living, or once living, and interact with an organism are called **biotic factors** (by AHT ik). The plants that provide seeds and berries are biotic factors. The ferrets and eagles that hunt the prairie dog are also biotic factors. Worms and bacteria are biotic factors that live in the soil underneath the prairie grass. Prairie dog scat, owl pellets, and decomposing plant matter are also biotic factors.

Abiotic Factors Not all of the factors that organisms interact with are living. **Abiotic factors** (ay by AHT ik) are the nonliving parts of an organism's habitat. These factors, as shown in **Figure 2,** include sunlight, soil, temperature, oxygen, and water.

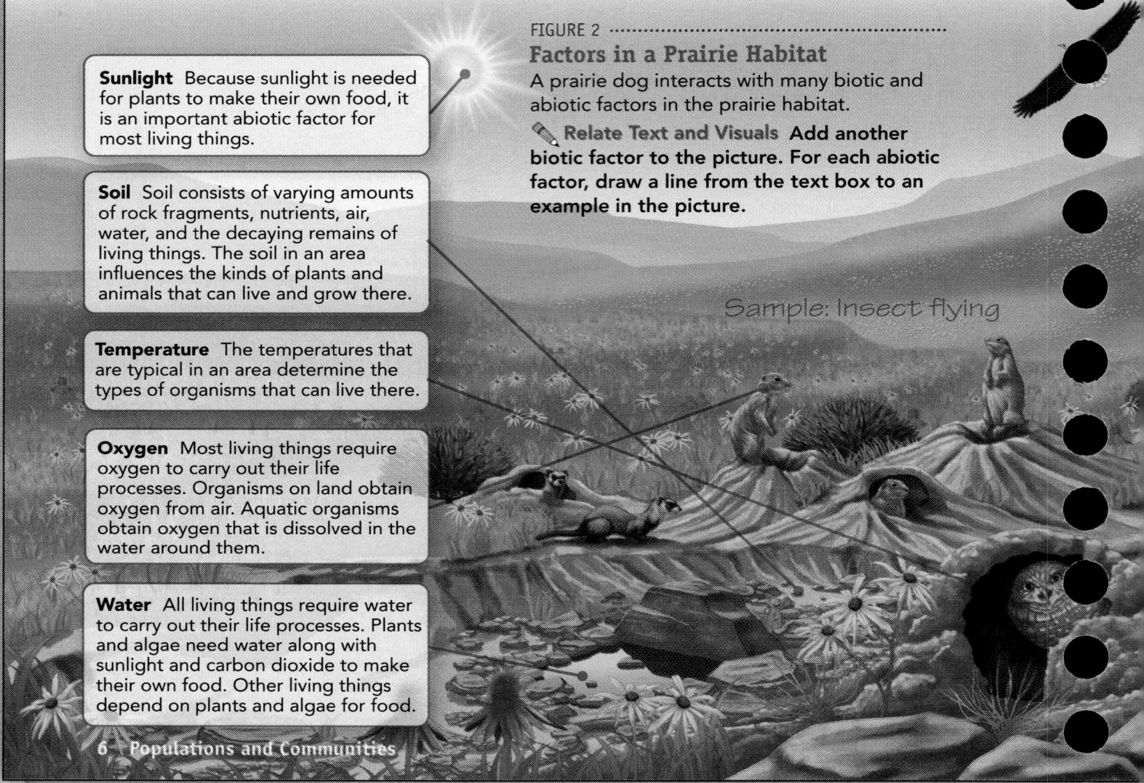

✏️ **Compare and Contrast** In the paragraphs at the right, circle how biotic and abiotic factors are similar and underline how they are different.

FIGURE 2

Factors in a Prairie Habitat
A prairie dog interacts with many biotic and abiotic factors in the prairie habitat.

✎ **Relate Text and Visuals** Add another biotic factor to the picture. For each abiotic factor, draw a line from the text box to an example in the picture.

Sample: Insect flying

Sunlight Because sunlight is needed for plants to make their own food, it is an important abiotic factor for most living things.

Soil Soil consists of varying amounts of rock fragments, nutrients, air, water, and the decaying remains of living things. The soil in an area influences the kinds of plants and animals that can live and grow there.

Temperature The temperatures that are typical in an area determine the types of organisms that can live there.

Oxygen Most living things require oxygen to carry out their life processes. Organisms on land obtain oxygen from air. Aquatic organisms obtain oxygen that is dissolved in the water around them.

Water All living things require water to carry out their life processes. Plants and algae need water along with sunlight and carbon dioxide to make their own food. Other living things depend on plants and algae for food.

Digital Lesson: Assign the *Apply It* activity online and have student submit their work to you.

my science online.com **Biotic and Abiotic Factors**

apply it!

Salt is an abiotic factor found in some environments. To see how the amount of salt affects the hatching of brine shrimp eggs, varying amounts of salt were added to four different 500-mL beakers.

1 **Observe** In which beaker(s) did the eggs, shown as purple circles, hatch? <u>B, C, D</u>

2 **Infer** The manipulated variable was <u>the amount of salt.</u>

3 **Infer** The responding variable was <u>the number of hatching shrimp.</u>

4 [CHALLENGE] Beaker <u>A</u> was the control.

5 ▲ **Draw Conclusions** What can you conclude about the amount of salt in the shrimps' natural habitat? <u>It is similar to the amount in Beaker B, since that is where the most eggs hatched.</u>

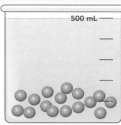
Beaker A
500 mL spring water

Beaker B
500 mL spring water + 2.5 g salt

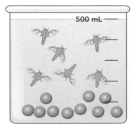
Beaker C
500 mL spring water + 7.5 g salt

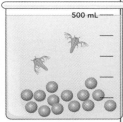
Beaker D
500 mL spring water + 15 g salt

Lab zone Do the Lab Investigation *World in a Bottle.*

⊂▭ Assess Your Understanding

1a. Interpret Diagrams List two biotic and two abiotic factors in **Figure 2**.
<u>Sample: Biotic—grass and eagle</u>
<u>Sample: Abiotic—the rocky part of soil and sunlight</u>

b. Draw Conclusions Name two abiotic factors in your habitat and explain how your life would be different without them.
<u>Sample: Sunlight and oxygen. If there was no sunlight, I would not have enough food to eat. If there was no oxygen, I would not be able to breathe.</u>

got it?

○ **I get it!** Now I know that the two parts of an organism's habitat are <u>living, or biotic, factors and nonliving, or abiotic, factors.</u>

○ **I need extra help with** <u>See TE note.</u>

Go to **my science coach** online for help with this subject.

7

Differentiated Instruction

[L1] Identify Biotic and Abiotic Factors Have students describe the environment where they live. Encourage them to make a list of features, including the climate, physical features, and organisms native to the area. Have students review their lists with the class.

[L3] Life Without Oxygen Most organisms need oxygen to carry out their life processes. Some organisms are able to live without oxygen, and some must live without oxygen. Have students research anaerobic bacteria to find examples of bacteria that live without oxygen and learn what happens to these bacteria when oxygen is present.

[L1] Words in Context Explain that the meaning of an unfamiliar word can often be determined by examining the words and phrases surrounding it. Have students examine the text surrounding the word *aquatic*. Point out the word *water* in the sentence. They can get the meaning of *aquatic* from the context.

Elaborate

Teacher Demo [Lab]

[L1] OBSERVING SOIL COMPONENTS

Materials soil sample, jar with screw-in lid, water

Time 10 minutes

Place about 200 mL of soil in a jar. Add water up to about 3 cm from the top. Screw on the lid tightly and shake the jar. Allow the contents to settle for a few minutes. Then allow students to observe the contents without shaking or opening the jar.

Ask: **What materials can you identify in the soil?** *(Small particles of rock, bits of plants, small invertebrates)* **Which materials are abiotic factors?** *(Particles of rock)* **Which materials are biotic factors?** *(Plant materials, invertebrates)*

Apply It!

[L2] Review *control, manipulated variable*, and *responding variable* before beginning the activity.

▲ **Draw Conclusions** If students have trouble coming up with a conclusion, point out that the best environment for brine shrimp is the one in which the greatest number of them was produced. Help students understand that a conclusion is not necessarily the end of a scientific investigation: A conclusion may lead right into another experiment.

Lab Resource: Lab Investigation [Lab]

[L2] WORLD IN A BOTTLE Students will explore the interactions of biotic and abiotic factors in a closed system.

Evaluate

Assess Your Understanding

After students answer the questions, have them evaluate their understanding by completing the appropriate sentence.

[RTI] Response to Intervention

1a. If students need help biotic and abiotic factors, **then** have them review the definitions of each type of factor.

b. If students have trouble explaining the importance of biotic and abiotic factors, **then** remind them that human beings need water for all vital body functions.

my science coach Have students go online for help in understanding biotic and abiotic factors.

Explain

Teach Key Concepts 🔑

Explain to students the progression from smallest to largest levels of organization of an ecosystem. Ask: **Using a park as an ecosystem, what is one squirrel considered to be?** *(An individual)* **What is the name given to a group of squirrels living in the park?** *(A population)* **If you add the birds, chipmunks, ants, and butterflies that live in the park, what is the group of organisms called?** *(A community)* **Now add the nonliving parts, such as water in a pond and oxygen in the air. What do you call this area now?** *(An ecosystem)* If possible, this exercise could be done outside or looking out a window. Have a volunteer select an animal or plant that is visible and build the ecosystem from there.

Lead a Discussion

DEFINE A POPULATION Review with students the definition of *population*. *(All the members of a species living in a particular area)* Ask: **If a grassland community includes grass, grasshoppers, field mice, and red-tailed hawks, what level of an ecosystem to the red-tailed hawks represent?** *(Population)* **Do all members of this species live in the same grassland?** *(No)* **If a forest contains birch, maple, and pine trees, do these trees make up a population? Explain.** *(No. They are a community because they are different species.)*

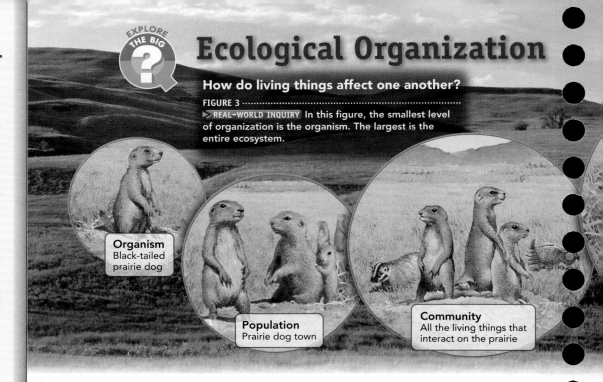

Ecological Organization

How do living things affect one another?

FIGURE 3 ··················

▶ **REAL-WORLD INQUIRY** In this figure, the smallest level of organization is the organism. The largest is the entire ecosystem.

Organism
Black-tailed prairie dog

Population
Prairie dog town

Community
All the living things that interact on the prairie

How Is an Ecosystem Organized?

Most organisms do not live all alone in their habitat. Instead, organisms live together in populations and communities that interact with abiotic factors in their ecosystems.

Organisms Black-tailed prairie dogs that live in prairie dog towns on the Nebraska plains are all members of one species. A **species** (SPEE sheez) is a group of organisms that can mate with each other and produce offspring that can also mate and reproduce.

Populations All the members of one species living in a particular area are referred to as a **population.** The prairie dogs in the Nebraska town are one example of a population.

Communities A particular area contains more than one species of organism. The prairie, for instance, includes prairie dogs, hawks, snakes, and grasses. All the different populations that live together in an area make up a **community.**

Real-World Inquiry allows students to determine what factors may be affecting a population within its habitat.

my science online .com ▷ | Ecosystems |

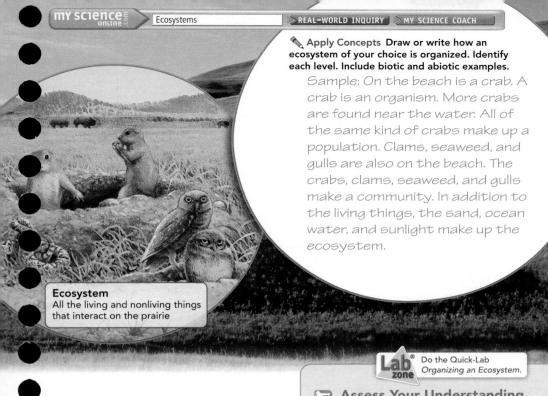

Ecosystem
All the living and nonliving things that interact on the prairie

✎ **Apply Concepts** Draw or write how an ecosystem of your choice is organized. Identify each level. Include biotic and abiotic examples.

Sample: On the beach is a crab. A crab is an organism. More crabs are found near the water. All of the same kind of crabs make up a population. Clams, seaweed, and gulls are also on the beach. The crabs, clams, seaweed, and gulls make a community. In addition to the living things, the sand, ocean water, and sunlight make up the ecosystem.

Ecosystems The community of organisms that live in a particular area, along with their non-living environment, make up an **ecosystem.** A prairie is just one of the many different ecosystems found on Earth. Other ecosystems are deserts, oceans, ponds, and forests.

Figure 3 shows the levels of organization in a prairie ecosystem. 🔑 **The smallest level of organization is a single organism, which belongs to a population that includes other members of its species. The population belongs to a community of different species. The community and abiotic factors together form an ecosystem.**

Because the populations in an ecosystem interact with one another, any change affects all the different populations that live there. The study of how organisms interact with each other and with their environment is called **ecology.**

Lab zone Do the Quick-Lab
Organizing an Ecosystem.

🦴 **Assess Your Understanding**

2a. Classify All of the different kinds of organisms in a forest are a ((community)/ population).

b. 🅰 How do living things affect one another?
Sample: Living things live together and interact with one another.

got it? ....

○ **I get it!** Now I know that ecosystems are organized into *organisms, populations, and communities.*

○ **I need extra help with** *See TE note.*

Go to **my science** ⑤ **coach** *online for help with this subject.*

9

Differentiated Instruction

L3 Compare Habitats Have students describe their own habitat and make a list of its biotic and abiotic factors. Then tell the students to explain how these factors differ from those of organisms living in natural habitats.

L1 Multiple Meanings Students likely have seen the word *population* used to mean the number of people living in a particular state or country. In science, *population* means a group of individuals

of the same species, not necessarily humans. In common use, *community* also refers to a group of people. In sciences, *community* includes more than one species.

L3 Other Ecosystems Ask students who have lived in, or traveled to, other ecosystems to share their experiences with the class.

LESSON 1.1

Elaborate

Explore the Big Q ❓ **UbD**

Direct students' attention to the images of the prairie ecosystem. Help students identify the badger, prairie chicken, owls, snake, and bison in the images. Ask: **What is the smallest level of organization?** *(Organism)* **With what other animals is the prairie dog interacting in the second circle?** *(Other prairie dogs)* **What other animals are part of the community shown in the third circle?** *(A badger and a prairie chicken)* **What other living things are part of the community shown in the third circle?** *(Grasses)* **What abiotic factor is visible in the fourth circle?** *(Soil)*

Lab Resource: Quick Lab

L1 ORGANIZING AN ECOSYSTEM Students will explore the four levels of an ecosystem: organism, population, community, and ecosystem.

Evaluate

Assess Your Understanding

After students answer the questions, have them evaluate their understanding by completing the appropriate sentence.

Answer the Big Q ❓ **UbD**

To help students focus on the Big Question, lead a class discussion about the ways living things interact with each other.

R T I Response to Intervention

2a. If students have trouble distinguishing between population and community, **then** have them review the definitions and give another example of each using a different animal.

b. If students need help how living things affect one another, **then** have them list examples of interactions at each level of organization: member of a species mates with another member; pair lives in the population; members of the population are eaten by other animals in the community.

my science ⑤ **coach** Have students go online for help in understanding the organization of an ecosystem.

Lab zone **After the Inquiry Warm-Up**

Living Things and the Environment

Inquiry Warm-Up, *What's in the Scene*?

In the Inquiry Warm-Up, you investigated living things and nonliving things in an environment. Using what you learned from that activity, answer the questions below.

1. **OBSERVE** What nonliving things could you observe in the picture?

   _____

   _____

2. **INFER** What nonliving things do you know of that are found in most environments but could not be observed in the picture?

   _____

   _____

3. **OBSERVE** Give an example of a living thing in the picture that is needed by another living thing in the picture. Explain why it is needed.

   _____

   _____

4. **PREDICT** How would the scene look different in another season? How might this affect the living things in this environment?

   _____

   _____

   _____

   _____

Living Things and the Environment

What Does an Organism Get From Its Environment?

got_it? ....

○ **I get it!** Now I know that an organism's environment provides _____
_____
_____
_____

○ **I need extra help with** _____
_____

What Are the Two Parts of an Organism's Habitat?

1a. INTERPRET DIAGRAMS List two biotic and two abiotic factors in Figure 2.

BIOTIC	ABIOTIC
_____	_____
_____	_____

b. DRAW CONCLUSIONS Name two biotic factors in your habitat and explain you your life would be different without them.

FACTOR	AFFECT
_____	_____
_____	_____

got_it? ....

○ **I get it!** Now I know that the two parts of an organism's habitat are _____
_____

○ **I need extra help with** _____
_____

Assess Your Understanding

Living Things and the Environment

How Is an Ecosystem Organized?

2a. CLASSIFY All of the different kinds of organisms in a forest are a (community/population).

b. ANSWER ❓ How do living things affect one another?

got_{it}?

○ **I get it!** Now I know that ecosystems are organized into _____

_____

_____

○ **I need extra help with** _____

_____

Name _____ Date _____ Class _____

Living Things and the Environment

What Does an Organism Get From Its Environment?

A living thing, or **organism**, needs certain things to live, grow, and reproduce. An organism gets food, water, shelter, and other things that it needs from its environment.

An environment that provides the things a specific organism needs to live, grow, and reproduce is called its **habitat**. A prairie dog gets food, shelter, and other things from a prairie habitat that has flat land, tall grasses, and little rainfall. A rocky ocean shore habitat would not provide what a prairie dog needs to survive.

What Are the Two Parts of an Organism's Habitat?

Biotic factors are the living, or once living, parts of a habitat. In the prairie dog's habitat, plants that provide food and decomposing plants are biotic factors. Ferrets and eagles that hunt the prairie dog are also biotic factors. Worms and bacteria that live in the soil are biotic factors too.

Abiotic factors are the nonliving parts of a habitat. Water, sunlight, oxygen, temperature, and soil are all abiotic factors in a prairie dog's habitat.

How Is an Ecosystem Organized?

A **species** is a group of organisms that can mate with each other and produce offspring that can also mate and reproduce. The black-tailed prairie dogs of the Nebraska plains are all members of one species. A **population** refers to all the members of one species living in a particular area. All of the prairie dogs in a prairie dog town are a population.

All of the different populations that live together in an environment are a **community**. For example, a prairie includes prairie dogs, hawks, grasses, snakes, and many other organisms. An **ecosystem** is made up of the community of organisms that live in a particular area, as well the nonliving surroundings.

On a separate sheet of paper, list the four levels of an ecosystem from smallest to largest and give an example of each.

Name _____ Date _____ Class _____

Living Things and the Environment

Understanding Main Ideas
Answer the following questions in the spaces provided.

1. What is ecology?

_____

_____

2. Name four abiotic factors found in a prairie ecosystem.

_____

_____

3. Name three populations found in a prairie ecosystem.

_____

Complete the table to show the levels of organization in an ecosystem. Start with the smallest unit.

4.

5.

6.

7.

Building Vocabulary
Fill in the blank to complete each statement.

8. An environment that provides the things a specific organism needs to live, grow, and reproduce is its _____.

9. All the living and nonliving things that interact in a particular area make up a(n) _____.

10. The parts of an organism's environment that are living or once living, and interact with the organism are _____.

11. All the different populations that live together in an area make up a(n) _____.

Enrich

Living Things and the Environment

The drawing below shows an ecosystem. Study the drawing and then answer the questions that follow.

1. Name the biotic factors in this ecosystem.

   _____

   _____

2. Name the abiotic factors in the ecosystem.

   _____

   _____

3. Identify the specific habitat of each animal shown.

   bear _____

   blue jay _____

   squirrel _____

   fish _____

   lizard _____

   dragonfly _____

   frog _____

Name _____ Date _____ Class _____

Living Things and the Environment

Write the letter of the correct answer on the line at the left.

1. ___ Which of the following lives in a prairie ecosystem?

A grass

B mushroom

C oak tree

D woodpecker

2. ___ Which of the following is a biotic factor?

A temperature

B sunlight

C bacteria

D water

3. ___ Which of the following lists the levels of an ecosystem in order from largest to smallest?

A population, organism, community, ecosystem

B ecosystem, community, organism, population

C organism, community, population, ecosystem

D ecosystem, community, population, organism

4. ___ An organism gets food, water, shelter, and other things it needs to live, grow, and reproduce from its

A population

B habitat

C abiotic factors

D species

If the statement is true, write _true_. If the statement is false, change the underlined word or words to make the statement true.

5. _____ The nonliving things that interact with an organism are called biotic factors.

6. _____ The study of how living things interact with each other and their environment is called ecology.

7. _____ A group of organisms that can mate with each other and produce offspring that can also mate and reproduce is called a species.

8. _____ Oxygen is an abiotic factor in the environment that is important for plants to make their own food.

9. _____ All the organisms that live in a particular area and their nonliving surroundings make up an ecosystem.

10. _____ All the members of one community living in a particular area make up a population.

Living Things and the Environment

Answer Key

After the Inquiry Warm-Up

1. Sample: water, soil, buildings or roads; students may list light if the sun is visible in the picture.

2. Sample: air, light

3. Students will likely identify one animal that eats another or an animal that eats a plant shown in the picture.

4. Accept all reasonable predictions. Sample: In the winter the water would be frozen and there would be fewer plants to eat. Animals might move to warmer areas to survive.

Key Concept Summaries

Sample:

Organism: one white pine tree

Population: all the white pine trees in a particular forest

Community: all the trees and animals in that forest

Ecosystem: the community in the forest and the nonliving factors, such as soil, water, and air

Review and Reinforce

1. Ecology is the study of how living things interact with each other and with their environment.

2. Accept four of the following: sunlight, soil, temperature, oxygen, water.

3. Accept three of the following: prairie dog, grass, owl, snake, eagle, ferret.

4. organism
5. population
6. community
7. ecosystem
8. habitat
9. ecosystem
10. biotic factors
11. community

Enrich

1. trees, bushes, bear, blue jay, squirrel, fish, lizard, dragonfly, flowering plant, grass, frog, water lilies, cattails (also bacteria and fungi, which are not visible)

2. soil, rocks, water, sunlight, air oxygen, temperature

3. Bear: the forest and grassy land

   Blue jay: trees, air, and ground

   Squirrel: trees and the ground around them

   Fish: the deeper water in the stream

   Lizard: dry land and rocks

   Dragonfly: the plants around the stream and the air

   Frog: the stream and the land close to the edge of the stream

Lesson Quiz

1. A
2. C
3. D
4. B
5. abiotic factors
6. true
7. true
8. sunlight
9. true
10. species

How do living things affect one another?

Lesson Pacing: 2–3 periods or 1–1½ blocks

🕐 **SHORT ON TIME?** To do this lesson in approximately half the time, do the Activate Prior Knowledge activity on page 10. A discussion of the key concepts on pages 10 and 15 will familiarize students with the lesson content. Have students do the Quick Labs. The rest of the lesson can be completed by students independently.

Preference Navigator, in the online Planning tools, allows you to customize *Interactive Science* to your own teaching style. You can also edit lesson plans by selecting the Lesson Planner option.

Digital Teacher's Edition allows you to access your Teacher's Edition and Resource materials online.

my science online.com

Lesson Vocabulary

* birth rate   * death rate   * immigration   * emigration
* population density   * limiting factor   * carrying capacity

 Content Refresher

Competitive Exclusion The Gause principle, also known as the principle of competitive exclusion, was named for G. F. Gause, a Soviet biologist. Gause was the first to suggest that species cannot coexist for long if they occupy the same niche. Gause developed his ideas by studying two similar species of *Paramecium*. When he grew populations of the two species separately, both grew rapidly and then leveled off at a population size that could be supported by available resources in the growing medium. However, when Gause grew the two species together, one species (*P. aurelia*) survived and the other species (*P. caudatum*) died out. Gause concluded that the surviving species had a competitive advantage in obtaining food and other resources. His work was later confirmed by other studies.

LESSON OBJECTIVES

🔑 Explain the causes of changes in population size.
🔑 Identify factors that limit population growth.

Blended Path
Active learning using Student Edition, Inquiry Path, and Digital Path

ENGAGE AND EXPLORE

To teach this lesson using a variety of resources, begin by reading **My Planet Diary** as a class. Have students share ideas and thoughts about this method of prairie dog population control. Then have students do the **Inquiry Warm-Up activity.** Students will use the process of estimation. Discuss the methods of estimation that different students chose and the accuracy of those methods. The **After the Inquiry Warm-Up worksheet** sets up a discussion about estimation of a population. Have volunteers share their answers to number 4 about the estimation of a tree population.

EXPLAIN AND ELABORATE

Teach Key Concepts by explaining the terms *birth rate, death rate, immigration, emigration,* and *population density* and having students answer questions about how these affect population size. **Lead a Discussion** explaining to students the processes of *immigration* and *emigration.* Use **Figure 2** to graphically demonstrate changes in a rabbit population. Then have students practice the inquiry skill in the **Apply It activity.**

Continue to **Teach Key Concepts** by explaining that environmental factors can limit population size. Ask students to name four limiting factors that affect population growth by relating cause and effect. Use the **Support the Big Q** to review *biotic* and *abiotic factors* and how they relate to population size. Then have students complete the **Apply It activity.**

Hand out the **Key Concept Summaries** as a review of each part of the lesson. Students can also use the online **Vocab Flash Cards** to review key terms.

EVALUATE

Have students take the **Lesson Quiz.** For an alternate assessment, see the **EXAM**VIEW® Assessment Suite, Progress Monitoring Assessments, or SuccessTracker™.

E L L Support

1 Content and Language

Compare the words *immigration* and *emigration* in the vocabulary. Students will learn in their textbook the root *migrate* "to move" and the prefixes *im-*in and *e-*out. Explain that the *-ation* means a process. *Immigration* is the process of moving into and *emigration* is the process of moving out of.

Lab zone Inquiry Path
Hands-on learning in the Lab zone

Digital Path
Online learning at my science online.com

ENGAGE AND EXPLORE

To teach this lesson with an emphasis on inquiry, begin with the **Inquiry Warm-Up activity.** Students will use the process of estimation. Lead a discussion about the methods of estimation different students chose and the accuracy of those methods. Have students do the **After the Inquiry Warm-Up worksheet.** Talk about estimation of a population. Have volunteers share their answers to number 4 about estimation of a tree population.

EXPLAIN AND ELABORATE

Focus on the inquiry skill for the lesson. Point out that when you infer, you draw a conclusion by reasoning. What conclusion can be drawn about estimation in the **Inquiry Warm-Up activity?** *(Accurate estimation of a sample can give a close calculation of population size.)*

Build Inquiry so students understand *birth rate* and *death rate.* Have students do the first **Quick Lab** to reinforce changes in population size and then share their results. Review *population density* and *carrying capacity* before beginning the **Apply It activity.** Ask volunteers to share what they know about limiting factors.

Use the **Support the Big Q** to review *biotic* and *abiotic factors* and how they relate to population size. Then have students complete the **Apply It activity.** Have students do the remaining **Quick Lab** to reinforce understanding of space as a limiting factor. Students can use the online **Vocab Flash Cards** to review key terms.

EVALUATE

Have students take the **Lesson Quiz.** For an alternate assessment, see the **EXAM**VIEW® Assessment Suite, Progress Monitoring Assessments, or SuccessTracker™.

ENGAGE AND EXPLORE

To teach this lesson using digital resources, begin by having students explore prairie dog population control at **My Planet Diary** online. Have them access the Chapter Resources to find the **Unlock the Big Question activity.** There they can answer the questions and refine their responses as they continue through the lesson. You can re-assign the activity and have students submit their work so you can track their progress.

EXPLAIN AND ELABORATE

Students reading above, at, or below the lexile measure of this lesson can access basic content readings at their level at **My Reading Web.** Have students use the online **Vocab Flash Cards** to preview key terms. Do the **Quick Labs** and then ask students to share their results.

Assign the **Do the Math activity** online and have students submit their work to you. Review *population density* and *limiting factors* before assigning the **Apply It activity.** Ask volunteers to share what they know about limiting factors.

Use the **Support the Big Q** to review *biotic* and *abiotic factors* and how they relate to population size. Then have students complete the **Apply It activity.**

The **Key Concept Summaries** online allow students to read a summary and see an image associated with each part of the lesson. Online remediation is available at **My Science Coach.**

EVALUATE

Have students take the **Lesson Quiz.** For an alternate assessment, see the **EXAM**VIEW® Assessment Suite, Progress Monitoring Assessments, or SuccessTracker™.

2 Frontload the Lesson
Preview the lesson visuals, labels, and captions. Ask students what they know about the words *population density* and *limiting factors.* Explain the specific meanings these words have in science.

3 Comprehensible Input
Have students study the visuals and their captions on pages 10 and 15 to support the key concepts of the lesson.

4 Language Production
Pair or group students with varied language abilities to complete labs collaboratively for language practice. Have each student copy the completed written lab for personal reference.

5 Assess Understanding
Make true or false statements using lesson content and have students indicate if they agree or disagree with a thumbs up or thumbs down gesture to check whole-class comprehension.

Populations

Establish Learning Objectives

After this lesson, students will be able to:

- Describe how populations change in size.
- Identify the factors that limit population growth.

Engage

Activate Prior Knowledge

MY PLANET DIARY Read *Prairie Dog Picker-Upper* with the class. Point out that prairie dog populations can be very large, with some colonies including millions of individuals and covering hundreds of acres. Students may find this passage upsetting. In fact, this program is controversial, in part because prairie dogs are threatened in some areas. Farmers see prairie dogs as threats, but they are an important biotic factor in the prairie ecosystem.

BIG IDEAS OF SCIENCE REFERENCE LIBRARY Have students look up the following topics: Bats, GPS Tracking.

Explore

Lab Resource: Inquiry Warm-Up

L1 POPULATIONS Students will explore ways to estimate the size of a population.

Populations

- How Do Populations Change in Size?
- What Factors Limit Population Growth?

MY PLANET DIARY

TECHNOLOGY

Prairie Dog Picker-Upper

Did you know that vacuum cleaners do more than just clean carpets? Across the Great Plains, farmers are using specially designed vacuum cleaners to help them remove black-tailed prairie dogs from the farm land. Prairie dogs can eat crops, cause soil erosion, and endanger cattle and farm machinery. The prairie dog vacuum uses a 4-in. plastic hose to suck prairie dogs out of the ground at 483 km/h! The prairie dogs end up in a padded tank, usually unharmed. They are then relocated or donated to the U.S. Fish and Wildlife Service to be fed to endangered eagles, hawks, and black-footed ferrets.

Prairie dogs

Communicate Discuss these questions with a group of classmates. Write your answers below.

1. If all of the prairie dogs were removed, how do you think the prairie ecosystem would be affected?
   Sample: The organisms that depend on the prairie dogs for food could starve.

2. Should prairie dogs be used as food for endangered species? Explain.
   Sample: No, one type of organism is not more important than another type of organism.

> **PLANET DIARY** Go to **Planet Diary** to learn more about populations.

 Do the Inquiry Warm-Up *Populations*.

How Do Populations Change in Size?

Ecologists are scientists who study biotic and abiotic factors of an ecosystem and the interactions between them. Some ecologists study populations and monitor the sizes of populations over time. **Populations can change in size when new members join the population or when members leave the population.**

10 Populations and Communities

SUPPORT ALL READERS

Lexile Measure = 960L   Lexile Word Count = 1485

Prior Exposure to Content: May be the first time students have encountered this topic

Academic Vocabulary: *cause, effect, infer*

Science Vocabulary: *carrying capacity, limiting factor*

Concept Level: May be difficult for students who struggle with math

Preteach With: My Planet Diary "Prairie Dog Picker-Upper" and the *Do the Math* activity

Go to **My Reading Web** to access leveled readings that provide a foundation for the content.

 MY SCIENCE online.com

Vocabulary
- birth rate • death rate • immigration
- emigration • population density
- limiting factor • carrying capacity

Skills
- Reading: Relate Cause and Effect
- Inquiry: Infer

Births and Deaths The most common way in which new individuals join a population is by being born into it. If more individuals are born into a population than die in any period of time, a population can grow. So when the **birth rate,** the number of births per 1,000 individuals for a given time period, is greater than its **death rate,** the number of deaths per 1,000 individuals for a given time period, the population may increase. The main way that individuals leave a population is by dying. If the birth rate is the same as the death rate, then the population may stay the same. In situations where the death rate is higher than the birth rate, then the population may decrease.

do the math!

Depending on the size and age of the female, an American Alligator can lay between 10 and 50 eggs per year.

1. **Graph** Using the data table and colored pencils, create a double bar graph showing alligator births and deaths for four years.
2. Label the x-axis and y-axis.
3. Write a title for the graph.
4. Fill in the graph using the colors shown.
5. **Develop Hypotheses** What factors might explain the number of births and deaths in Year 3?

   <u>Sample: Food may have</u>
   <u>been more abundant and</u>
   <u>there may have been</u>
   <u>construction near the</u>
   <u>alligators' habitat.</u>

Data Table

Year	Births	Deaths
1	32	8
2	28	13
3	47	21
4	33	16

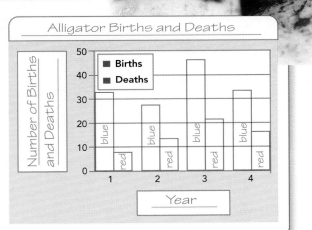

Alligator Births and Deaths

11

Explain

Introduce Vocabulary
To help students understand the terms *immigration* and *emigration*, point out the root word *migrate*, meaning "to move to a new place."

Teach Key Concepts 🔑
Explain to students that populations change in size when new members join the population or when members leave the population. Tell students that populations increase or decrease all the time. In some cases, the changes are small. In other cases, the changes are large. Ask: **What kinds of events can cause a population to increase?** *(Birth of new individuals or individuals moving into the population)* **What could cause a population to decrease?** *(More individuals die than are born; more individuals move out of the population than move into it.)* **What might cause a population to decrease rapidly?** *(A natural disaster or a disease epidemic)*

Elaborate

Do the Math!
L1 Point out that a graph makes it possible to see trends in data. If students have trouble drawing a double-bar graph, suggest that they graph all the birth data first, then draw the bars for death data next to each blue (birth) bar. Ask: **Look at the bars for Year 1. How is the number of deaths compared to the number of births different from other years?** *(Year 1 has the fewest deaths compared to number of births.)*
See *Math Skill and Problem-Solving Activities* for support.

My Planet Diary provides an opportunity for students to explore real-world connections to populations.

Digital Lesson: Assign the *Do the Math* activity online and have students submit their work to you.

ELL Support

1 Content and Language
Write the words *immigration* and *emigration* on the board and circle *migration* in each. Explain that migration means "traveling from one place to another." Have volunteers demonstrate these terms by walking in and out of the room.

2 Frontload the Lesson
Help students understand the ideas of birth rate and death rate. Explain that a rate tells how often something happens in a period of time.

3 Comprehensible Input
Before students read the Apply It passage on pandas, review the meaning of *endangered*. Ask students what *danger* means, and what it means to be *in danger*. Point out that endangered species are in danger of completely dying out.

Explain

Lead a Discussion

EMIGRATION AND IMMIGRATION Explain to students that *immigration* occurs when an individual moves into a population. *Emigration* occurs when an individual leaves a population. Ask: **What might cause individuals to immigrate?** *(Possible answers might include an abundant food supply.)* **Why might individuals emigrate?** *(Students might suggest decrease in food supply, drought, or habitat loss.)* **Why might scientists want to monitor the size of a population?** *(If the population gets too large, it could lead to starvation of some individuals or damage to the environment. If the population gets too small, it could be endangered.)*

21st Century Learning

CRITICAL THINKING Have students read the caption for **Figure 1.** Point out the words *due to* in the first sentence. Explain to students that this indicates a cause. Over-hunting is the cause. Ask: **What is the effect of over-hunting?** *(Population decreased so much that the deer were almost extinct in Iowa.)* **What is the cause and the effect described in the second sentence?** *(Immigration from other states is the cause. Reestablishment of the population is the effect.)*

Vocabulary Latin Word Origins
Both the terms *immigration* ("moving into a population") and *emigration* ("moving out of a population") come from the Latin word *migrare* ("to move"). What do you think the prefixes *im–* and *e–* mean?
Sample: im– means "in" and e– means "out."

The Population Statement When the birth rate in a population is greater than the death rate, the population will generally increase. This can be written as a mathematical statement using the "is greater than" sign:

If birth rate > death rate, population size increases.

However, if the death rate in a population is greater than the birth rate, the population size will generally decrease. This can also be written as a mathematical statement:

If death rate > birth rate, population size decreases.

Immigration and Emigration The size of a population also can change when individuals move into or out of the population. **Immigration** (im ih GRAY shun) means moving into a population. **Emigration** (em ih GRAY shun) means leaving a population. For instance, if food is scarce, some members of an antelope herd may wander off in search of better grassland. If they become permanently separated from the original herd, they will no longer be part of that population.

FIGURE 1

Immigration

In 1898, white-tailed deer were almost extinct in Iowa due to over-hunting. The deer population was reestablished as animals from Minnesota, Wisconsin, and Missouri immigrated into Iowa.

✎ **Apply Concepts** Using your classroom, describe an example of each of the following.
Immigration: _Sample: A new student, Sally, was added to my English class. She had moved from Denver when her dad was transferred for work._
Emigration: _Sample: Jordan had his schedule changed the first week of school and was moved into a different science class._

12 Populations and Communities

Interactive Art demonstrates how populations change over time.

my science online.com ▸ **Population Size**

Graphing Changes in Population Changes in a population's size can be displayed on a line graph. Figure 2 shows a graph of the changes in a rabbit population. The vertical axis identifies the number of rabbits in the population, while the horizontal axis shows time. The graph represents the size of the rabbit population over a ten-year period.

Changes in a Rabbit Population

From Year 4 to Year 8, more rabbits left the population than joined it, so the population decreased.

From Year 0 to Year 4, more rabbits joined the population than left it, so the population increased.

FIGURE 2 ···

▶ INTERACTIVE ART **Changes in a Rabbit Population**

✎ This graph shows how the size of a rabbit population changed over ten years.

1. **Interpret Data** In Year __4__, the rabbit population reached its highest point.

2. **Read Graphs** What was the size of the rabbit population in that year? About 850,000

3. CHALLENGE How do you think the rabbit population affected the fox population over the same ten-year period? Explain your reasoning.
Sample: The fox population changed in relation to its food (rabbits). As the number of rabbits increased, so did the number of foxes. When the number of rabbits decreased, so did the number of foxes.

13

Elaborate

Build Inquiry

L3 **CALCULATING GROWTH RATE**

Materials none

Time 5 minutes

Review with students the definitions of *birth rate* and *death rate*. Tell students that growth rate is the difference between birth rate and death rate.

$$growth\ rate = birth\ rate - death\ rate$$
$$g = b - d$$

Ask: **Suppose 1,600 snow geese were born the same year that 1,200 died. What would be the growth rate for that year?** *(1,600 − 1,200 = 400, so the growth rate is 400.)* **What does a negative growth rate mean?** *(There were more deaths than births.)* Look back at the *Do the Math* activity. **What are the growth rates for each year?** *(Year 1, 24; Year 2, 15; Year 3, 25; Year 4, 17)*

21st Century Learning

INTERPERSONAL SKILLS Have students read *GPS Tracking* in the **Big Ideas of Science Reference Library** and share ideas with a partner about the pros and cons of placing tracking devices on animals.

Differentiated Instruction

L1 **Inequalities** Help students review the use of the "is greater than" sign (>) in mathematical statements. Point out that the smaller value appears on the side of the symbol that forms the point. The larger value is on the side of the symbol with the wider, open end. If students still have difficulty with the concept, tell them to think of the sign as an alligator that always wants to eat the larger amount.

L3 **Growth Rate of a Population** Challenge advanced students to figure out how to use the data in **Figure 2** to find growth rates of the rabbit population. Make sure students can explain their reasoning. *(The increase or decrease in population from one year to the next is the growth rate for that year.)*

Elaborate

Apply It!

L1 Review the concept of population density before beginning the activity.

▲ **Infer** Make sure students understand that one piece of information, the total number of flamingos, is changing, while the other piece of information, the size of the pond, is not.

Lab Resource: Quick Lab

L2 **GROWING AND SHRINKING** Students will explore the use of graphs to show changes in a population.

Evaluate

Assess Your Understanding

After students answer the questions, have them evaluate their understanding by completing the appropriate sentence.

RTI Response to Intervention

1a. If students have trouble identifying the ways populations change, **then** have them review information on births, deaths, immigration, and emigration.

b. If students need help with calculating changes in populations, **then** suggest that they write the problem as two equations, one for the births and a second one for the deaths.

MY SCIENCE S COACH Have students go online for help in understanding how populations change.

Population Density Sometimes an ecologist needs to know more than just the total size of a population. In many situations, it is helpful to know the **population density**—the number of individuals in an area of a specific size. Population density can be written as an equation:

$$\text{Population density} = \frac{\text{Number of individuals}}{\text{Unit area}}$$

For example, suppose you counted 20 butterflies in a garden measuring 10 square meters. The population density would be 20 butterflies per 10 square meters, or 2 butterflies per square meter.

apply it!

In the pond on the top, there are 10 flamingos in 8 square meters. The population density is 1.25 flamingos per square meter.

❶ **Calculate** What is the population density of the flamingos in the pond on the bottom?
About 2.5 flamingos/m²

❷ **Infer** If 14 more flamingos landed in the pond on the bottom, what would the population density be then?
4.25 flamingos/m²

❸ **CHALLENGE** What do you think would happen if the population density of flamingos in the pond on the bottom became too great?
Sample: There would not be enough
food or space for all of the flamingos
to survive.

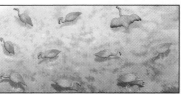
2 meters — 4 meters

2 meters

Lab zone Do the Quick Lab *Growing and Shrinking.*

🔑 Assess Your Understanding

1a. Review Two ways to join a population are _birth_ and _immigration_.
Two ways to leave a population are _death_ and _emigration_.

b. Calculate Suppose a population of 8 wolves has produced 20 young in a year. If 7 wolves have died, how many wolves are in the population now? (Assume no wolves have moved into or out of the population for other reasons.)
_21_

got it?

○ **I get it!** Now I know that population size changes due to _birth and immigration and_ _death and emigration._

○ **I need extra help with** _See TE note._

Go to MY SCIENCE S COACH online for help with this subject.

14 Populations and Communities

Digital Lesson: Assign the *Apply It* activity online and have students submit their work to you.

MY SCIENCE ONLINE.com | Population Size

What Factors Limit Population Growth?

When the living conditions in an area are good, a population will generally grow. But eventually some environmental factor will cause the population to stop growing. A **limiting factor** is an environmental factor that causes a population to stop growing or decrease in size. 🔑 **Some limiting factors for populations are weather conditions, space, food, and water.**

Climate Changes in climate conditions, such as temperature and the amount of rainfall, can limit population growth. A cold spring season can kill the young of many species of organisms, including birds and mammals. Unusual events like floods, hurricanes, and the tornado shown in **Figure 3**, can also have long-lasting effects on population size.

FIGURE 3 ·····
Weather as a Limiting Factor
A tornado or flood can destroy nests and burrows.
✏️ Identify **Name two types of natural disasters that you think can also limit population growth.**

<u>Sample: Volcanic eruptions</u>
<u>and droughts</u>

Tornado funnel
touching ground

·············· ✏️
🔄 **Relate Cause and Effect** As you read about the four factors that can limit populations, fill in the graphic organizer below.

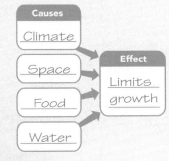

Causes

Climate

Space → **Effect**

Food → Limits growth

Water

15

15

Explain

Teach Key Concepts 🔑

Explain to students that limiting factors are factors that influence a population and affect its size. Ask: **What are some limiting factors for populations?** *(Weather conditions, space, food, and water.)* Explain to students that frost occurs when solid surfaces cool to below a point at which water vapor in the surrounding air will condense. Ask students if they have ever seen dew. Point out to them that frost can be considered frozen dew. Ask: **How might an unusually severe frost affect populations?** *(It might be too cold for some animals to stay warm enough to survive. The frost might kill some plants.)* Point out that limiting factors are different for different species. For example, a rain-forest plant requires much more water than a cactus does. A trout requires higher oxygen levels in a stream than a catfish does. For some microorganisms, oxygen is not a limiting factor at all because the organisms do not need oxygen to survive.

🔄 **Relate Cause and Effect** Explain that cause-and-effect relationships shows how ideas, facts, and events are related to one another.

Support the Big Q ❓ UbD

LIMITING FACTORS OF POPULATIONS Review with students the biotic and abiotic factors that might be found in an organism's habitat. Ask: **If all the needs of a population are met, what is likely to happen to the population?** *(It will increase.)* **Can a population continue to increase indefinitely? Explain.** *(No. Eventually it will run out of something it needs.)* **Is food a limiting factor for plants? Explain.** *(No. Plants make their own food.)* **What factors do limit the size of a plant population?** *(The amount of sunlight, the amount of carbon dioxide in the air, the amount of water available, the amounts of nutrients in the soil)*

LESSON 1.2

Differentiated Instruction

L1 Practice Calculations For students who need extra help with the *Apply It* activity, help them understand that the calculations involve two steps. First, they need to calculate the area of the pond. Then they can calculate the population density. Use this example: a lawn has 144 dandelions in an area that is 12 m long and 6 m wide. The area of the lawn is 72 m². Dividing 144 by 72 produces an answer of 2 dandelions/m². You may wish to allow students to use calculators.

L1 Population Density Before students go on to read about factors that limit population growth, make sure that they understand the concept of population density. Draw two circles of the same size on the board. Draw a few small triangles in one circle and about twice as many in the other circle. Ask students to identify the circle that has the greater population density of triangles and to explain their thinking.

15

Elaborate

21st Century Learning

CRITICAL THINKING Explain to students that being able to compete successfully for space is important to plants because they cannot move to a new place if their habitat becomes crowded. The roots of the sorghum plant produce a chemical that suppresses the growth of other species of plants. This chemical is called sorgolene. Ask: **How might sorgolene be useful for gardeners?** *(It might be used as a weed killer.)*

Make Analogies

L1 **CARRYING CAPACITY** To help students understand the concept of carrying capacity, compare an ecosystem to a container, such as a storage case for CDs. Ask: **What limits the number of CDs that you can keep in a storage case?** *(The size of the case)* **What would happen if you tried to put extra CDs into the storage case?** *(Some of the CDs might break.)* **How is this like a limiting factor that determines the carrying capacity of an ecosystem?** *(Space is a limiting factor that determines how many individuals can survive in an ecosystem. If there are too many individuals in an ecosystem, some of them will not survive.)*

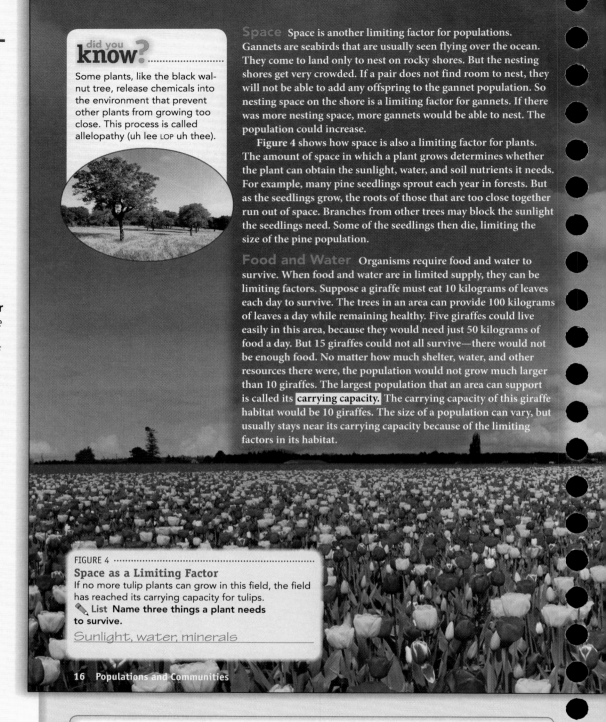

did you know?

Some plants, like the black walnut tree, release chemicals into the environment that prevent other plants from growing too close. This process is called allelopathy (uh lee LOP uh thee).

Space Space is another limiting factor for populations. Gannets are seabirds that are usually seen flying over the ocean. They come to land only to nest on rocky shores. But the nesting shores get very crowded. If a pair does not find room to nest, they will not be able to add any offspring to the gannet population. So nesting space on the shore is a limiting factor for gannets. If there was more nesting space, more gannets would be able to nest. The population could increase.

Figure 4 shows how space is also a limiting factor for plants. The amount of space in which a plant grows determines whether the plant can obtain the sunlight, water, and soil nutrients it needs. For example, many pine seedlings sprout each year in forests. But as the seedlings grow, the roots of those that are too close together run out of space. Branches from other trees may block the sunlight the seedlings need. Some of the seedlings then die, limiting the size of the pine population.

Food and Water Organisms require food and water to survive. When food and water are in limited supply, they can be limiting factors. Suppose a giraffe must eat 10 kilograms of leaves each day to survive. The trees in an area can provide 100 kilograms of leaves a day while remaining healthy. Five giraffes could live easily in this area, because they would need just 50 kilograms of food a day. But 15 giraffes could not all survive—there would not be enough food. No matter how much shelter, water, and other resources there were, the population would not grow much larger than 10 giraffes. The largest population that an area can support is called its **carrying capacity.** The carrying capacity of this giraffe habitat would be 10 giraffes. The size of a population can vary, but usually stays near its carrying capacity because of the limiting factors in its habitat.

FIGURE 4 ·····················

Space as a Limiting Factor
If no more tulip plants can grow in this field, the field has reached its carrying capacity for tulips.
✎ List **Name three things a plant needs to survive.**

Sunlight, water, minerals

Digital Lesson: Assign the *Apply It* activity online and have students submit their work to you.

my science online.com ▸ | Limiting Factors |

apply it!

Giant pandas live in the mountains of south central China. Most (99 percent) of the pandas' diet is made up of the bamboo plant. Bamboo is not nutrient rich. Pandas spend 55 percent of their day eating between 9 and 38 kilograms of bamboo. Getting enough bamboo to eat can be a challenge. Farming and the timber industry have destroyed the pandas' habitat and bamboo forests. In addition, when a bamboo plant flowers, the plant dies and does not regrow for several years. It is difficult for scientists to know exactly how many giant pandas exist in the wild. The best estimate is that there are about 1,600 of them. Due to the small population size, this species is classified as endangered.

✎ **Communicate** Write a letter to the editor that describes how food and space may be limiting factors for the giant panda species. Add a headline to your letter.

Sample headline: Pandas in Peril!
Sample: Dear Editor, I am concerned that pandas are endangered due to a lack of space and food. Pandas depend on bamboo to survive. When the bamboo plants die off or are destroyed, there may not be enough food to feed many pandas. Habitat destruction has also limited the space the pandas have to reproduce. If the pandas cannot reproduce, then there is no hope of increasing the panda population.

 Do the Quick Lab
Elbow Room.

🔑 Assess Your Understanding

2a. Summarize When the climate changes or there is not enough _space_ or _food_ or _water_, a population can (begin/(stop)) growing in size.

b. Relate Cause and Effect Choose a limiting factor and describe the factor's effect on population growth.
Sample: When there is not enough food, some organisms may die.

got it? ⋯⋯⋯⋯⋯⋯⋯⋯⋯⋯⋯⋯⋯⋯⋯

○ **I get it!** Now I know that populations can be limited when _there is climate change, not enough space, or not enough food and water._

○ **I need extra help with** _See TE note._

Go to **my science ⬤ COACH** online for help with this subject.

17

Elaborate ───────────

Apply It!

L1 Remind students that an effective letter begins with a topic statement that indicates the writer's main concern before beginning the activity.

Lab Resource: Quick Lab

L1 ELBOW ROOM Students will explore space as a limiting factor.

Evaluate ───────────

Assess Your Understanding

After students answer the questions, have them evaluate their understanding by completing the appropriate sentence.

🅁🅃🅘 Response to Intervention

2a. If students have trouble identifying limiting factors, **then** have them think about the things an organism needs to survive.

b. If students need help with relating limiting factors to population growth, **then** have them choose a factor and ask themselves what would happen to the population if there were too little of that factor.

my science ⬤ COACH Have students go online for help in understanding the factors that limit population growth.

Differentiated Instruction

L3 Space for Plants Have interested students look at garden catalogs or gardening books to find instructions for spacing plants in a garden. Explain to students that each plant must have adequate room to grow. Provide students with graph paper to plan the proper spacing of plants in a garden.

L1 Classroom Density If your classroom has movable desks and chairs, seat one student alone at a desk or table. Then seat a second student at the same desk or table. Seat a third, then a fourth, then a fifth. Each time you add a student, ask the seated students to try to write in their notebooks. Students should see that, as more people sit at a table, the workspace becomes more crowded until nobody has enough space to work. Based on their experience, students should estimate the carrying capacity of a desk or table.

Lab zone **After the Inquiry Warm-Up**

Populations

> **Inquiry Warm-Up, *Populations***
>
> In the Inquiry Warm-Up, you investigated the process of estimation. Using what you learned from that activity, answer the questions below.

1. **ESTIMATE** What method did you use to estimate the size of the population?

   _____

   _____

2. **EVALUATE** What are possible sources of inaccuracy or error in your method?

   _____

   _____

3. **INTERPRET DATA** What must be true of the beans if an estimate is to give reasonable results?

   _____

   _____

4. **PREDICT** How do you think a scientist might estimate the size of a population of trees?

   _____

   _____

   _____

   _____

Populations

How Do Populations Change in Size?

1a. REVIEW Two ways to join a population are _____
and _____. Two ways to leave a population are
_____ and _____.

b. CALCULATE Suppose a population of 8 wolves has produced 20 young
in a year. If 7 wolves have died, how many wolves are in the population now? (Assume no wolves have moved into or out of the population for other reasons.)

_____

got it?

○ **I get it!** Now I know that population size changes due to _____
_____

○ **I need extra help with** _____

What Factors Limit Population Growth?

2a. SUMMARIZE When the climate changes or there is not
enough _____ or _____ or
_____, a population can (begin/stop) growing in size.

b. RELATE CAUSE AND EFFECT Choose a limiting factor and describe the
factor's effect on population growth.

got it?

○ **I get it!** Now I know that populations can be limited when _____
_____
_____

○ **I need extra help with** _____
_____
_____

Name _____ Date _____ Class _____

Populations

How do Populations Change in Size?

Populations change in size when new members are born into it or when members die. The **birth rate** counts number of births in a population over a certain amount of time. The **death rate** counts the number of deaths over a certain amount of time.

When the birth rate is greater than the death rate, the population will generally increase. The population will generally decrease when the death rate is greater than the birth rate. For example, the white-tailed deer population in Iowa decreased due to over-hunting.

The population can also change when individuals move into or out of the population. **Immigration** means moving into a population and **emigration** means leaving a population. Ecologists can graph how a population changes over time. The **population density** is a measure of all of the individuals in one area at one time.

What Factors Limit Population Growth?

A **limiting factor** is something in the environment that keeps a population from growing or makes a population smaller. Some limiting factors are weather conditions, space, food, and water.

Climate changes and unusual weather events, such as tornados, can limit population growth. The amount of available space can limit population growth.

For example, a plant needs to grow in a large enough space to obtain the things it needs to survive. Food and water are also often limiting factors because they are in limited supply.

Limiting factors determine an area's carrying capacity. **Carrying capacity** is the largest population that an area can support.

On a separate sheet of paper, explain two ways a population increases and two ways it decreases.

Name _____ Date _____ Class _____

Populations

Understanding Main Ideas

Answer the following questions on a separate sheet of paper.

1. A vegetable garden is 12 meters long by 7 meters wide. It is home to 168 mice. What is the population density of the mice?

2. What are two ways that the size of a population can increase? What are two ways that the size of a population can decrease?

3. Identify three limiting factors that can prevent a population from increasing. Explain how each factor limits a population's size.

The line graph below shows how the size of the squirrel population in a city park changed over time. Use the line graph to answer questions 4–6.

4. Over which time period(s) did the squirrel population increase?

5. Over which time period(s) did the squirrel population decrease?

6. In which year did the population reach its lowest point? What was the size of the population that year?

Squirrel Population in a City Park, 1992-1999

Building Vocabulary

Fill in the blank to complete each statement.

7. Moving into a population is called _____.

8. Moving out of a population is called _____.

9. The largest _____ an area can support is called the carrying capacity.

10. The number of individuals that die in a population in a certain time period is the _____.

Enrich

Populations

> Read the passage below. Then complete the table and answer the questions that follow the passage.

Population Growth

Suppose that the organisms in a population have unlimited food, water, space, and other resources. Also suppose that the organisms are not killed by other organisms or by disease. With no limits on its growth, the population would increase at its highest possible rate.

Bacteria are microscopic, single-celled organisms that are often used to study population growth. Most bacteria reproduce by splitting in half. Under ideal conditions, bacteria can divide about every 30 minutes. In the first half hour, one bacterium produces two bacteria. In the second half hour, the two bacteria split to produce four bacteria. In the third half hour, the four bacteria split to produce eight bacteria. Every 30 minutes, the population doubles!

Time (hours)	Number of Bacteria
0	1
0.5	2
1.0	4
1.5	8
2.0	
2.5	
3.0	
3.5	
4.0	
4.5	
5.0	
5.5	
6.0	
7.5	
8.0	
8.5	
9.0	
9.5	
10.0	

1. On a sheet of graph paper, graph the data in your completed table.

2. Describe the shape of the graph, and explain what it shows about the bacteria population.

   _____

   _____

3. Does the graph show what usually happens in real life? Why or why not?

   _____

   _____

   _____

Lesson Quiz

Populations

If the statement is true, write *true*. If the statement is false, change the underlined word or words to make the statement true.

1. _____ The size of a population increases if the number of individuals added to the population is <u>equal to</u> the number of individuals leaving the population.

2. _____ Immigration means moving <u>out of</u> a population.

3. _____ Three coyotes per square kilometer is an example of <u>population density</u>.

4. _____ If foxes arrive in an area and catch and eat a large number of rabbits, the foxes are causing an increase in the <u>birth rate</u> of the rabbit population.

5. _____ Sunlight can be a limiting factor for populations of <u>plants</u>.

Fill in the blank to complete each statement.

6. Water and food are examples of _____ for populations.

7. If an area has all the wolves that it can support, the wolf population has reached its

   _____.

8. A population can decrease due to deaths or _____.

9. If animals cannot find enough places to build nests, it is because

   _____ is a limiting factor for the population.

10. A flood that covers and meadow and drowns animals and a late frost that kills young

    plants are examples of how _____ can affect the size of a population.

Populations

Answer Key

After the Inquiry Warm-Up

1. Answers may vary. Sample: I filled a small beaker with beans and counted the beans. Then I transferred the beans from one jar to the other, one beaker at a time. I kept track of the number of beakers of beans and multiplied that by the number of beans in one beaker.

2. Answers may vary. Sample: I may not have filled the beaker to the same height each time. I may have jostled the beaker, causing the beans to settle, giving an inaccurate measure on the transfers.

3. The beans must all be the same size.

4. Answers may vary. Sample: The scientist could count all the trees in a small measured area, such as 100 square meters, then measure the entire area. Multiple the entire area by the number of trees/100 square meters.

Key Concept Summaries

A population increases when new organisms are born. Immigration, the moving of organisms into a population, also increases the population. Deaths decrease population. Emigration, the moving of organisms away from a population, decreases the population.

Review and Reinforce

1. 168 mice/(12 m × 7 m) = 2 mice per square meter

2. A population can increase due to births or immigration. A population can decrease due to deaths or emigration.

3. Food: If food is limited, the population will not increase beyond the number that the food supply can support. Space: Without enough space, organisms may not be able to reproduce or ay not get enough of the

things that they need to survive, such as water, sunlight, and nutrients. Weather: Both normal seasonal changes in temperature or rainfall and severe weather conditions can kill many members of a population.

4. 1994–1997

5. 1992–1994 and 1997–1999

6. 1994; about 225 squirrels

7. immigration

8. population

9. emigration

10. death rate

Enrich

After 10 hours, there will be 262,144 bacteria.

1. The graph should show time (0 to 10 hours) on the x-axis and number of bacteria (in thousands, from 0 to 1,000) on the y-axis. The curve is nearly flat until 7 hours, when it begins to climb. Steepest slope is between 9 and 10 hours.

2. The curve goes up at a steep angle at the end, showing that the population is increasing rapidly.

3. The graph does not show what usually happens because limiting factors, such as lack of space or food, usually prevent such rapid growth of a population.

Lesson Quiz

1. greater than
2. into
3. true
4. death rate
5. true
6. limiting factors
7. carrying capacity
8. emigration
9. space
10. weather

Place the outside corner, the corner away from the dotted line, in the corner of your copy machine to copy onto letter-size paper.

Interactions Among Living Things

How do living things affect each other?

Lesson Pacing: 2–3 periods or 1–1½ blocks

🕐 **SHORT ON TIME?** To do this lesson in approximately half the time, do the Activate Prior Knowledge activity on page 18. A discussion of the key concepts on pages 20, 21, and 25 will familiarize students with the lesson content. Have students do the Quick Labs. The rest of the lesson can be completed by students independently.

Preference Navigator, in the online Planning tools, allows you to customize *Interactive Science* to your own teaching style. You can also edit lesson plans by selecting the Lesson Planner option.

Digital Teacher's Edition allows you to access your *Teacher's Edition and Resource* materials online.

my science online.com

Lesson Vocabulary

- natural selection
- adaptation
- niche
- competition
- predation
- predator
- prey
- symbiosis
- mutalism
- commensalism
- parasitism
- parasite
- host

Content Refresher

Wolf and Moose Populations When a population grows beyond the carrying capacity of its habitat, a population crash may occur. One such crash occured with the moose population on Isle Royale. Moose came to Isle Royale around 1900, by swimming from the mainland. Over the next 35 years, the moose thrived on the island due to a lack of predators. Eventually, the moose population increased to about 3,000. As a result, the supply of food became exhausted, and 90 percent of the moose starved. After this crash, the moose population increased again until 1948 and then declined sharply once more because of lack of food. Wolves arrived around 1950, probably crossing on an ice bridge from Canada. The moose and wolf populations have cycled up and down since then. Sometimes factors other than carrying capacity cause a population to decrease. In the early 1980s, the Isle Royale wolf population declined sharply. Biologists hypothesize that the extreme genetic uniformity of the population is one reason for the decline. Populations that lack genetic variability often have low reproductive success. Genetic uniformity also makes a population susceptible to disease.

LESSON OBJECTIVES

- 🔑 Explain how adaptations help an organism survive.
- 🔑 Describe competition and predation.
- 🔑 Identify the three types of symbiosis.

Blended Path
Active learning using Student Edition, Inquiry Path, and Digital Path

ENGAGE AND EXPLORE

To teach this lesson using a variety of resources, begin by reading **My Planet Diary** as a class. Have students share ideas about predators such as trap-jaw ants. Then have students do the **Inquiry Warm-Up activity.** Students will learn how coloring can help camouflage an animal. The **After the Inquiry Warm-Up worksheet** sets up a discussion about successful and unsuccessful camouflaging. Have volunteers share their answers to number 4 about how the results of the lab might differ with real butterflies.

EXPLAIN AND ELABORATE

Teach Key Concepts by explaining that are the behaviors and physical characteristics that allow organisms to live successfully in their environments. **Lead a Discussion** about natural selection based on **Figure 1.** Then have students do the **Apply It activity.**

Continue to **Teach Key Concepts** by explaining the two major types of interaction among organisms. Ask students to name them and tell how they differ. Use the **Support the Big Q** to illustrate how limited resources affect competition. Use **Figure 2** to illustrate how three bird species have adaptations that allow them to feed from different parts of the same tree. Use **Figures 3** and **4** to help students visualize predators and prey and predator adaptations in animals and plants.

Hand out the **Key Concept Summaries** as a review of each part of the lesson. Students can also use the online **Vocab Flash Cards** to review key terms.

EVALUATE

Have students take the **Lesson Quiz.** For an alternate assessment, see the **EXAM**VIEW® Assessment Suite, Progress Monitoring Assessments, or SuccessTracker™.

E L L Support

1 Content and Language
Introduce the term camouflage. Students may be familiar with the term because of clothing or family in the military. Explain that this is also an adaptation that helps an organism survive in a habitat.

Lab zone Inquiry Path
Hands-on learning in the Lab zone

ENGAGE AND EXPLORE

To teach this lesson with an emphasis on inquiry, begin with the **Inquiry Warm-Up activity.** Students will learn how coloring can help camouflage an animal. Discuss the coloring different students have observed and how the coloring helped hide an organism. Have students do the **After the Inquiry Warm-Up worksheet.** Talk about camouflaging efforts. Have volunteers share their answers to number 4 about how real butterflies differ from the lab results.

EXPLAIN AND ELABORATE

Focus on the **Inquiry Skill** for the lesson. Point out that when you classify, you assign something to a category. How could you classify the butterflies in the **Inquiry Warm-Up activity?** *(Those that were hidden, those that were not)* Have students do the **Quick Lab.** Review the meanings of *niche* and *adaptations* before assigning the **Apply It activity.** Ask volunteers to share their answers.

Continue to **Teach Key Concepts.** Use the **Support the Big Q** to illustrate how limited resources affect competition. Use **Build Inquiry** to introduce students to a plant that is a predator to an animal, a fairly unusual occurrence and **Figure 5 Interactive Art** to rate prey adaptation.

Do the **Quick Lab** to reinforce understanding of competition and predation. Continue to **Teach Key Concepts** by explaining the three types of symbiosis. Use **Figure 6** to explore mutalism with students and **Figure 7** to explore parasitism. **Lead a Discussion** about parasites students may be familiar with. Review the inquiry skill before assigning the **Apply It activity.** Have students complete the **Quick Lab** to identify types of symbiosis. Students can use the online **Vocab Flash Cards** to review key terms.

EVALUATE

Have students take the **Lesson Quiz.** For an alternate assessment, see the **EXAM**VIEW® Assessment Suite, Progress Monitoring Assessments, or SuccessTracker™.

Digital Path
Online learning at my science online.com

ENGAGE AND EXPLORE

To teach this lesson using digital resources, begin by having students explore predators, such as trap-jaw ants, at **My Planet Diary** online. Have them access the Chapter Resources to find the **Unlock the Big Question activity.** There they can answer the questions and refine their responses as they continue through the lesson. You can re-assign the activity and have students submit their work so you can track their progress.

EXPLAIN AND ELABORATE

Students reading above, at, or below the lexile measure of this lesson can access basic content readings at their level at **My Reading Web.** Encourage students to use the online **Vocab Flash Cards** to preview key terms. Review *niche* and *adaptation* before assigning the online **Apply It activity.** Ask volunteers to share their sample answers and have them submit their work to you.

Continue to **Teach Key Concepts** by discussing the two interactions: competition and predation. Have students **Support the Big Q** by noting that there are limited resources in an ecosystem.

The **Key Concept Summaries** online allow students to read a summary and see an image associated with each part of the lesson. Online remediation is available at **My Science Coach.**

EVALUATE

Have students take the **Lesson Quiz.** For an alternate assessment, see the **EXAM**VIEW® Assessment Suite, Progress Monitoring Assessments, or SuccessTracker™.

2 Frontload the Lesson
Preview the lesson questions that appear in blue heads. Ask students if there are any words they do not understand. Explain the specific meanings these words have in science.

3 Comprehensible Input
Have students help make a chart that briefly shows the differences in the three types of symbiosis.

4 Language Production
Pair or group students with varied language abilities to complete oral summaries collaboratively for language practice. Have each group share its summary with the class.

5 Assess Understanding
Have students keep a content area log for this lesson using a two-column format with the headings "What I Understand" and "What I Don't Understand." Follow up so that students can move items from the "Don't Understand" to the "Understand" column.

Interactions Among Living Things

Establish Learning Objectives

After this lesson, students will be able to:

🔑 Explain how adaptations help an organism survive.

🔑 Describe competition and predation.

🔑 Identify the three types of symbiosis.

Engage

Activate Prior Knowledge

MY PLANET DIARY Read *Predator Power* with the class. Point out that the ants use their jaws either to capture prey or propel themselves. Tell students that large numbers of trap-jaw ants have been observed jumping up and down when the nest is threatened. Ask: **How might this action help them protect the nest?** (*The sudden action might confuse an animal that was going to attack the nest.*)

BIG IDEAS OF SCIENCE REFERENCE LIBRARY 📖 Have students look up the following topics: Bush Baby, Butterflies, Camouflage, Patterns in Nature, Sharks, Vultures.

Explore

Lab Resource: Inquiry Warm-Up

🔲 **CAN YOU HIDE A BUTTERFLY?** Students will explore how an organism's coloring can help it survive.

Interactions Among Living Things

🔑 How Do Adaptations Help an Organism Survive?

🔑 What Are Competition and Predation?

🔑 What Are the Three Types of Symbiosis?

MY PLANET DIARY

Predator Power

What predator can close its jaws the fastest? You might think it is a lion or a shark, but you would be wrong. It is the trap-jaw ant that has the fastest strike in the animal kingdom. The trap-jaw ant closes its mouth around its prey in 0.13 milliseconds at speeds of 35 to 64 meters per second!

The force created when its jaw snaps shut also helps the ant escape danger by either jumping up to 8.3 centimeters high or 39.6 centimeters sideways.

A trap-jaw ant stalks its prey.

FUN FACT

Communicate Answer the questions below. Discuss your answers with a partner.

1. How does the trap-jaw ant's adaptation help it avoid becoming the prey of another organism?

The ant can jump away from predators if they try to attack.

2. What are some adaptations that other predators have to capture prey?

Sample: speed, sharp teeth and claws, good eyesight

▶ PLANET DIARY Go to **Planet Diary** to learn more about predators.

 Do the Inquiry Warm-Up *Can You Hide a Butterfly?*

How Do Adaptations Help an Organism Survive?

As day breaks, a sound comes from a nest tucked in the branch of a saguaro cactus. Two young red-tailed hawks are preparing to fly. Farther down the stem, a tiny elf owl peeks out of its nest in a small hole. A rattlesnake slithers around the base of the saguaro, looking for breakfast. Spying a shrew, the snake strikes it with needle-like fangs. The shrew dies instantly.

18 Populations and Communities

SUPPORT ALL READERS

Lexile Measure = 950L   Lexile Word Count = 1982

Prior Exposure to Content: Many students may have misconceptions on this topic

Academic Vocabulary: *classify, interpret, resources*

Science Vocabulary: *natural selection, adaptation, competition*

Concept Level: May be difficult for students who struggle with abstract ideas

Preteach With: My Planet Diary "Predator Power" and Figure 1 activity

Go to **My Reading Web** to access leveled readings that provide a foundation for the content.

My science online.com

Vocabulary
• natural selection • adaptation • niche • competition
• predation • predator • prey • symbiosis • mutualism
• commensalism • parasitism • parasite • host

Skills
⊙ Reading: Relate Text and Visuals
△ Inquiry: Classify

Figure 1 shows some organisms that live in, on, and around the saguaro cactus. Each organism has unique characteristics. These characteristics affect the individual's ability to survive and reproduce in its environment.

Natural Selection A characteristic that makes an individual better suited to a specific environment may eventually become common in that species through a process called **natural selection.** Natural selection works like this: Individuals whose unique characteristics are well-suited for an environment tend to survive and produce more offspring. Offspring that inherit these characteristics also live to reproduce. In this way, natural selection results in **adaptations,** the behaviors and physical characteristics that allow organisms to live successfully in their environments. For example, the arctic hare has fur that turns from gray to white in the winter which helps camouflage the hare against the snow.

Individuals with characteristics poorly suited to a particular environment are less likely to survive and reproduce. Over time, poorly suited characteristics may disappear from the species. If a species cannot adapt to changes in its environment, the entire species can disappear from Earth and become extinct.

FIGURE 1 ·······························
Saguaro Community
✎ Describe Circle two examples of how organisms interact in this scene. Describe each one.

Sample: The wasps have built a hive under a branch of the cactus. The red-tailed hawk has built a nest between branches of the cactus.

Purple martin

Red-tailed hawk

Flycatcher

Woodpecker

Elf owl

Saguaro cactus

Wasps

Gila monster

Rattlesnake

Scorpion

Roadrunner

19

E L L Support

1 Content and Language
Have students read the caption for **Figure 6.** If students are confused by the use of the word *cruise*, explain to them that the use of *cruise* is that the bird gets a ride on the impala. The word *snack* in the caption means that the bird gets its food.

2 Frontload the Lesson
Use **Figure 1** to help students understand adaptations. Point to an

organism and ask how that organism lives. Ask what body parts it has that enable it to do these tasks, and how they help the organism survive.

3 Comprehensible Input
Have each student make a two-column chart. Tell them to choose an organism from **Figure 1.** In the first column of the chart they should list the organism's adaptations. In the second column they should tell how each adaptation helps the organism survive.

Explain ──────────
Introduce Vocabulary
Students may be surprised to see the word *host* as a vocabulary term. Point out that in common use, a host welcomes guests. In parasitism, the "guest" is not welcome.

Lead a Discussion
NATURAL SELECTION Review the process of natural selection. Make sure that students understand that individuals in a population may vary in many ways. Have students locate the roadrunner shown in **Figure 1.** Tell them that this bird eats other animals, such as scorpions, snakes, lizards, rodents, and birds. Ask: **What makes these animals difficult to catch?** *(They can move quickly.)* **How do the long legs of a roadrunner help it get food?** *(They help it run fast after other animals.)* **If a population of roadrunners had some birds that could run faster than others, which birds would be more likely to survive?** *(The ones that run faster)* **What would you expect the next generation of roadrunners to be like?** *(They would be fast runners.)*

Address Misconceptions
L1 CHANGES WITHIN SPECIES Remind students that an organism does not change its traits to fit the environment. Describe a population of mice that have either gray or brown fur. Brown mice are more common because they escape predators more successfully. Then new predators that hunt by sound move in. Ask: **What traits might now determine how easily a mouse is caught?** *(How quietly or how quickly a mouse moves)* **Will any mice develop these traits because of the predators?** *(No.)* **How might the population of mice change?** *(The mice that make the most noise will likely be caught and eaten. The mice that are quiet will likely survive and produce offspring that are quiet.)*

My Planet Diary provides an opportunity for students to explore real-world connections to adaptations.

my science online.com ▶ | Adaptation and Niche

LESSON 1.3

Explain

Teach Key Concepts

Explain to students that each organism has adaptations that help it occupy a particular niche. Ask: **What are adaptations?** *(Behaviors and physical characteristics that allow organisms to live successfully in their environments)* **How does natural selection result in adaptations being common in a population?** *(Individuals that have an adaptation are more likely to survive and reproduce. They pass the adaptation on to their offspring. Individuals that lack the adaptation are less likely to survive and reproduce, so the next generation will have fewer individuals that lack the adaptation.)*

Elaborate

Apply It!

L1 Review *biotic* and *abiotic* factors with students before beginning the activity.

Lab Resource: Quick Lab

L2 **ADAPTATIONS FOR SURVIVAL** Students will model a variety of adaptations for feeding.

Evaluate

Assess Your Understanding

After students answer the questions, have them evaluate their understanding by completing the appropriate sentence.

RTI Response to Intervention

1a. If students cannot define *adaptation,* **then** have them look back through the section for the highlighted term and reread the definition.

b. If students have trouble listing examples of adaptations, **then** have them look back at **Figure 1** and think about how a snake uses its fangs.

my science coach Have students go online for help in understanding adaptations.

Niche The organisms in the saguaro community have adaptations that result in specific roles. The role of an organism in its habitat is called its **niche.** A niche includes what type of food the organism eats, how it obtains this food, and what other organisms eat it. A niche also includes when and how the organism reproduces and the physical conditions it requires to survive. Some organisms, like the birds in **Figure 2,** share the same habitat but have very specific niches that allow them to live together. **Every organism has a variety of adaptations that are suited to its specific living conditions and help it survive.**

apply it!

Organisms occupy many niches in an environment like the one in this picture.

❶ **Identify** List two abiotic factors in the picture.
Sample: Sunlight and water

❷ **Interpret Diagrams** Describe the niche of the squirrel in the picture.
Sample: The squirrel eats nuts
and seeds in the daytime.

❸ **Make Generalizations** What adaptations might the squirrel have that make it able to live in this environment?
Sample: A squirrel has sharp
teeth to open seeds and nuts.

Lab zone Do the Quick Lab *Adaptations for Survival.*

Assess Your Understanding

1a. Define Adaptations are the _behaviors_ and _physical_ characteristics that allow organisms to live successfully in their environments.

b. Explain How are a snake's sharp fangs an adaptation that help it survive in the saguaro community?
The sharp fangs help the snake
bite and poison its prey.

got it?

○ I get it! Now I know that adaptations are _characteristics that suit an organism_ _for specific environments and help it survive._

○ I need extra help with _See TE note._

Go to **my science coach** online for help with this subject.

20 Populations and Communities

Digital Lesson: Assign the *Apply It* activity online and have students submit their work to you.

my science online.com | **Adaptation and Niche**

What Are Competition and Predation?

During a typical day in the saguaro community, a range of inter-actions takes place among organisms. **Two major types of interactions among organisms are competition and predation.**

Competition Different species can share the same habitat and food requirements. For example, the flycatcher and the elf owl both live on the saguaro and eat insects. However, these two species do not occupy exactly the same niche. The flycatcher is active during the day, while the owl is active mostly at night. If two species occupy the same niche, one of the species might eventually die off. The reason for this is **competition.** The struggle between organisms to survive as they attempt to use the same limited resources is called competition. For example, weeds in a garden compete with vegetable crops for soil nutrients, water, and sunlight.

In any ecosystem, there are limited amounts of food, water, and shelter. Organisms that share the same habitat often have adaptations that enable them to reduce competition. For example, the three species of warblers in **Figure 2** specialize in feeding only in a certain part of the spruce tree.

Cape May Warbler
This species feeds at the tips of branches near the top of the tree.

Bay-Breasted Warbler
This species feeds in the middle part of the tree.

Yellow-Rumped Warbler
This species feeds in the lower part of the tree and at the bases of the middle branches.

FIGURE 2 ....
Niche and Competition
Each of these warbler species occupies a very specific location in its habitat. By feeding on insects in different areas of the tree, the birds avoid compet-ing for food and are able to live together.

1. **Predict** What could happen if these warbler species fed in the same location on the tree?

   One warbler would get more food and the other species might not survive.

2. **List** For what resources do the tree and the grass compete?

   Sunlight, water, minerals, space

21

Explain

Teach Key Concepts 🔑

Explain to students that organisms interact in one of two ways, competition or predation. Ask: **Why might two individuals compete with each other?** *(Possible answer: They might compete for food, shelter, or water.)* **Why might two organisms interact through predation?** *(One of the organisms is food for the other.)*

Support the Big Q ❓ UbD

LIMITED RESOURCES Remind students that in any ecosystem, there is a limited amount of some resources. Ask: **What happens when more than one species requires the same limited resources?** *(Competition)* **How does avoiding competition benefit species like the birds shown in Figure 2?** *(They don't waste energy chasing each other away from food as they would if they were competing for food.)*

Make Analogies

L1 **NOT IN COMPETITION** Point out to students that a niche is very specific. Although all three birds eat insects, the fact that they hunt in different places keeps them out of competition with each other. Ask: **How are people who work shifts at different times of day avoiding competition?** *(The person who wants to work at night is not competing for a job with the person who wants to work during the day.)* **How might organisms avoid competition by working different "shifts"?** *(Some organisms are active at night and sleep during the day, while other organisms are active during the day, and sleep at night. They do not feed at the same time.)*

Differentiated Instruction

L1 **Niche vs. Habitat** Organisms are often said to "occupy a niche." This may lead students to think a niche is a place to live. Remind them that an organism's place to live is its habitat. The organism's niche is *how* it lives, not *where* it lives. It may help students remember the difference if they think of a niche as the organism's occupation, or job.

L1 **Competition** To help students better understand the concept of competition, use a Venn diagram to compare and contrast the scientific meaning of competition with the more general sports-related meaning. Help students understand that the winner of a competition is the person (or team) with the best skills and abilities.

LESSON 1.3

Explain

Teach With Visuals

Tell students to look at **Figure 4.** Point out that with the touch of their toxic tentacles, some jellyfish can catch and kill fish. Ask: **How is the jellyfish like the sundew?** *(They both are predators.)* **How is predation by a jellyfish different from predation by a sundew?** *(The jellyfish can swim, so it can interact with prey more easily. The sundew cannot move, so it has to wait for an insect to come to it.)*

Address Misconceptions

L1 **TO PREY OR NOT TO PREY?** Some students may think predation is only bad for the prey. Point out to them that predation can be used to control overgrown populations, as a method of pest reduction, or to keep the prey species healthy. Ask: **How can predation keep the prey species healthy?** *(By preferentially killing the weak/sick members, leaving stronger and healthier members alive to reproduce)*

FIGURE 3 ....
Predation
This tiger shark and this albatross are involved in a predator-prey interaction.

✎ **Interpret Photos**
Label the predator and the prey in the photo.

Prey

Predator

Predation In **Figure 3,** a tiger shark bursts through the water to seize an albatross in its powerful jaws. An interaction in which one organism kills another for food or nutrients is called **predation.** The organism that does the killing is the **predator.** The organism that is killed is the **prey.** Even though they do not kill their prey, organisms like cows and giraffes are also considered predators because they eat plants.

Predation can have a major effect on a prey population size. Recall that when the death rate exceeds the birth rate in a population, the population size can decrease. So, if there are too many predators in an area, the result is often a decrease in the size of the prey population. But a decrease in the number of prey results in less food for their predators. Without adequate food, the predator population can decline. Generally, populations of predators and their prey rise and fall in related cycles.

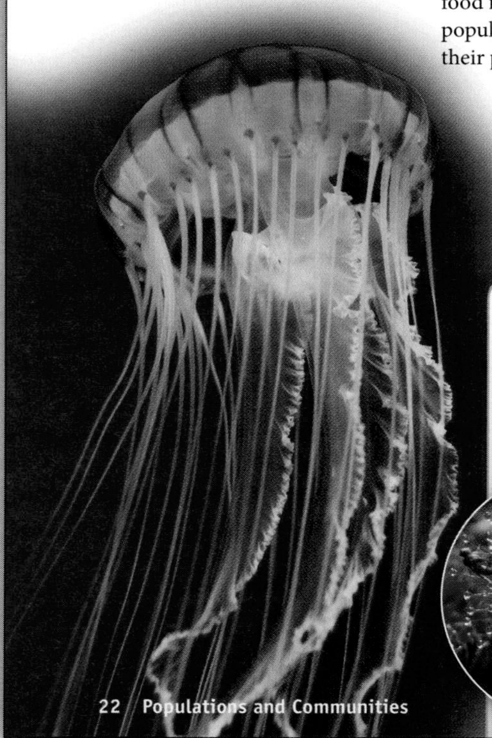

FIGURE 4 ....
Predator Adaptations
A jellyfish's tentacles contain a poisonous substance that paralyzes tiny water animals. The sundew is a plant that is covered with sticky bulbs on stalks. When a fly lands on a bulb, it remains snared in the sticky goo while the plant digests it.

✎ **Make Models** Imagine an ideal predator to prey upon a porcupine. Draw or describe your predator below and label its adaptations.

Sample: The predator would have long, sharp claws and thick fur to protect itself from the sharp porcupine quills.

22 | **Populations and Communities**

Professional Development Note **Teacher to Teacher**

Adaptations A common misconception students have when discussing adaptations is the belief that an individual organism *deliberately* chooses to change if its surrounding environment changes. To address this misconception I choose activities in which organisms become extinct. Placing black, white, and newspaper cutouts of moths on newspaper gives students a visual of how camouflage can affect an organism's ability to evade predators. Moving the cutouts to solid black or white paper shows students that, when a habitat changes, individual organisms are not able to choose at will to change their behaviors and structures.

✆ *Emily Compton*
Park Forest Middle School
Baton Rouge, LA

Predator Adaptations Predators, such as those in **Figure 4**, have adaptations that help them catch and kill their prey. A cheetah can run very fast for a short time, enabling it to catch its prey. Some predators, such as owls and bats, have adaptations that enable them to hunt at night when their prey, small mammals and insects, are active.

Prey Adaptations How do organisms avoid being killed by effective predators? The smelly spray of a skunk and the sharp quills of a porcupine help keep predators at a distance. As you can see in **Figure 5**, organisms have many kinds of adaptations that help them avoid becoming prey.

Warning Coloring Like many brightly colored animals, this frog is poisonous. Its bright blue and yellow colors warn predators not to eat it.

False Coloring Predators may be confused by a false eyespot and attack the wrong end of the fish. This allows the fish to swim safely away in the opposite direction.

Mimicry The mimic octopus (top) imitates the coloring, shape, and swimming style of the venomous sole fish (bottom) to discourage predators.

Protective Covering Have you ever seen a pinecone with a face? This is a pangolin, a small African mammal. When threatened, the pangolin protects itself by rolling up into a scaly ball.

Camouflage Is it a leaf? Actually, it's a walking leaf insect. But if you were a predator, you might be fooled into looking elsewhere for a meal.

FIGURE 5 ·······················
> INTERACTIVE ART Defense Strategies
Organisms display a wide range of adaptations that help them avoid becoming prey. ✎ **Communicate** In a group, rate each prey adaptation from 1 (best) to 5 (worst) in the circles. Explain your best choice.

Accept all ratings. Sample: Protective
covering is the best defense; it makes it
difficult for a predator to find its prey.

23

Elaborate

Build Inquiry

L2 OBSERVE AN INSECT-EATING PLANT

Materials sundew or Venus's fly-trap, cooked ground beef, tweezers

Time 5 minutes a day for several days

Have students take turns feeding the plant small pieces of the ground beef from time to time. Students should use the tweezers to place a small piece of meat on a trap. (**CAUTION:** _Remind students to wash their hands afterward._)

Ask: **What did you observe after you fed meat to the plant?** (_The leaves closed, trapping the meat inside._) **What did you notice when the leaves opened again?** (_The meat was gone._) **How does this adaptation enable carnivorous plants to live in areas of poor soil?** (_The plants get nutrients from the insects they consume._) Make sure that students understand that the plant is not getting energy from the food, as an animal would. It is only getting nutrients to help the plant make its own food.

Teach With Visuals

Tell students to look at **Figure 5**. Ask: **Which end of the brightly colored fish is the front?** (_Students may say it is the yellow end, but that is the false coloring. The pointed blue end is the front._) **What other animal do you know of that can roll up into a ball to protect itself?** (_Students may mention the armadillo or an isopod, also called a sow bug_) **What are some other kinds of defensive adaptations of plants and animals?** (_Accept all reasonable answers. Possible answers: thorns on a rose bush, spines on a porcupine, the foul-smelling liquid a skunk sprays._)

Interactive Art allows students to categorize images of different defense strategies.

my science online.com | **Competition and Predation**

Differentiated Instruction

L1 Classify Roles Give students examples of predator-prey pairs, such as lion-zebra, snake-mouse, and fox-rabbit. Ask students to identify the predator and prey in each pair and encourage them to use a graphic organizer of their choice to record the information.

L3 Radar in Animals Some predators have unusual adaptations that help them hunt. For example, bats use a form of radar called _echolocation_ to find flying insects. Invite students to research how bats are adapted for hunting as they fly in the dark.

Elaborate

Do the Math!

L1 Tell students that a line graph is a good way to show changes over time. Plotting two sets of data on one grid makes it easy to compare the data and identify trends. Have students look at high and low points of the wolf population. Ask: **What happens to the moose population in the few years following these points?** *(A spike in wolf population is followed by a decrease in moose population. A dip in wolf population is followed by an increase in moose population.)* **What is the lowest moose population recorded? What is the highest moose population recorded?** *(Lowest is about 400. Highest is about 2,400)* **What is the lowest wolf population recorded? What is the highest wolf population recorded?** *(Lowest is about 14. Highest is about 50.)* See *Math Skills and Problem-Solving Activities* for support.

Lab Resource: Quick Lab

L2 **COMPETITION AND PREDATION** Students will simulate competition for available food.

Evaluate

Assess Your Understanding

After students answer the questions, have them evaluate their understanding by completing the appropriate sentence.

RTI Response to Intervention

2a. If students have trouble with classifying interactions, **then** have them reread the Key Concept statement on the first page of this section.

b. If students cannot define *competition,* **then** have them scan for the highlighted term in the text and reread the definition.

c. If students need help with identifying adaptations, **then** have them look back at **Figure 5** and summarize the information.

MY SCIENCE COACH Have students go online for help in understanding competition and predation.

 do the math!

Predator-Prey Interactions

On Isle Royale, an island in Lake Superior, the populations of wolves (the predator) and moose (the prey) rise and fall in cycles. Use the graph to answer the questions.

1 Read Graphs What variable is plotted on the horizontal axis? What two variables are plotted on the vertical axis?
Year; number of wolves and moose

2 Interpret Data How did the moose population change between 2002 and 2007? What happened to the wolf population from 2003 through 2006?
The moose population decreased;
the wolf population increased.

3 Draw Conclusions How might the change in moose population have led to the change in the wolf population?
As the moose increased, more
food was available to the wolf
population, and it increased.

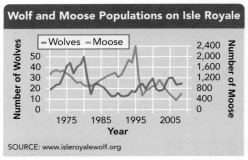

Wolf and Moose Populations on Isle Royale

SOURCE: www.isleroyalewolf.org

4 Explain What adaptations does a wolf have that make it a successful predator?
Sharp claws and teeth, good
sense of smell and eyesight, speed

5 Predict How might disease in the wolf population one year affect the moose population the next year?
Disease would cause a decrease
in the wolf population, so fewer
moose would be eaten and the
population would increase.

 Lab zone Do the Quick Lab
Competition and Predation.

🔑 Assess Your Understanding

2a. Review Two main ways in which organisms interact are ___competition___ and ___predation___.

b. Describe Give an example of competition. Explain your answer.
Sample: Weeds and crops com-
pete for resources such as water.

c. Apply Concepts Owls often prey on mice. What adaptations do you think the mice have that help them avoid becoming prey?
Sample: The color of the mice
provides camouflage, and their
small size helps them hide.

got it?

○ **I get it!** Now I know that competition and predation _are two major types of_
interactions between organisms.

○ **I need extra help with** _See TE note._

Go to **MY SCIENCE COACH** *online for help with this subject.*

Digital Lesson: Assign the *Do the Math* activity online and have students submit their work to you.

MY SCIENCE online .com | **Competition and Predation**

What Are the Three Types of Symbiosis?

In addition to competition and predation, symbiosis is a third type of interaction among organisms. **Symbiosis** (sim bee OH sis) is any relationship in which two species live closely together and at least one of the species benefits. 🗝 **The three main types of symbiotic relationships are mutualism, commensalism, and parasitism.**

Mutualism In some relationships, two species may depend on one another. This is true for some species of acacia trees and stinging ants in South America. The stinging ants nest only in the acacia tree, whose thorns discourage the ants' predators. The tree also provides the ants' only food. The ants, in turn, attack other animals that approach the tree and clear competing plants away from the base of the tree. This relationship is an example of **mutualism** (MYOO choo uh liz um). A relationship in which both species benefit is called mutualism. Other examples of mutualism can be seen in **Figure 6.**

FIGURE 6 ···
Mutualism
✎ An oxpecker rides and snacks aboard an impala. The oxpecker eat ticks living on the impala's ears. This interaction is an example of mutualism because both organisms benefit.

1. Infer How does the oxpecker benefit?

The oxpecker gets food.

2. Infer How does the impala benefit?

The impala gets rid of ticks.

3. [CHALLENGE] Explain how the relationship between the hummingbird and the flower is an example of mutualism.

The hummingbird benefits by getting food, and the flower benefits by getting pollinated.

25

Explain ──────────────

Teach Key Concepts 🗝

Explain to students that symbiosis is a general term for relationships in which two species live closely together. There are three types of symbiosis, defined by which species benefits and which, if any, is harmed. Ask: **Which of the species in mutualism benefit?** *(Both)* **How many species benefit in commensalism?** *(One)* **What happens to the other species?** *(It is neither harmed nor helped.)* **Which of the species benefits in parasitism?** *(Parasite)* **Which of the species is harmed?** *(Host)*

Teach With Visuals

Tell students to look at **Figure 6.** Ask: **What kind of food does the hummingbird get from the flower?** *(Nectar)* Students are probably most aware of the role of bees as pollinators. Point out that some birds and bats are also important pollinators

---

Differentiated Instruction

L3 Predator-Prey Interactions
Another factor in the fluctuations of the moose population on Isle Royale is available food, especially in the winter. Have students research this limiting factor and how it affects the moose population. Students can report their findings to the rest of the class in a presentation.

L1 Types of Symbiosis To help students distinguish among the three different types of symbiosis, have them create a chart for each type that lists pairs of species as examples. Students should identify how each species either benefits or is harmed in the relationship. Encourage students to illustrate their charts with photographs or other images of the species used as examples.

Explain

Lead a Discussion

PARASITES Ask students to name some examples of parasites. *(Students may mention ticks, tapeworms, or leeches.)* Ask: **How does a tick harm its host?** *(The tick takes blood from the host. The host may get an infection at the site of the bite. Some ticks carry diseases, such as Lyme disease.)* **How does a tapeworm harm its host?** *(The tapeworm consumes some of the host's food, which can cause the host to become weak.)*

Teach With Visuals

Tell students to look at **Figure 7**. Ask: **How is the cowbird different from the other parasites shown in Figure 7?** *(The cowbird does not live in direct contact with the host.)* Point out to students that this kind of parasitism, called brood parasitism or nest parasitism, is unusual. Most parasites live in direct contact with the host.

Relate Text and Visuals Explain that the text and visuals each provide important information that the student must synthesize.

21st Century Learning

COMMUNICATION Help students infer the effect of ticks on a moose population. Tell students that the moose tick is a parasite that lives on the blood of the moose. A tick does not consume much blood, but a moose may have as many as 80,000 ticks feeding on it. Too many ticks can weaken the moose, making it vulnerable to wolves and also to diseases. Unusually warm summers in the years 2001 though 2005 favored large tick populations. Have students look back at the graph of wolf and moose populations in the *Do the Math* activity. Ask: **What, if any, effect did the large number of parasites have on the moose population?** *(They did affect the moose population. The moose population dropped steadily over those years, even though the wolf population was not unusually large.)*

Relate Text and Visuals List the names of the parasites and the hosts in **Figure 7**.

Parasites	Hosts
Cowbird	Yellow warblers
Fish lice	Fish
Dwarf mistletoe	Tree

Commensalism Have you ever seen a bird build a nest in a tree? The bird gets a place to live while the tree is unharmed. This relationship is an example of commensalism. **Commensalism** (kuh MEN suh liz um) is a relationship in which one species benefits and the other species is neither helped nor harmed. In nature, commensalism is not very common because two species are usually either helped or harmed a little by any interaction.

Parasitism Many family pets get treated with medication to prevent tick and flea bites. Without treatment, pets can suffer from severe health problems as a result of these bites. A relationship that involves one organism living with, on, or inside another organism and harming it is called **parasitism** (PA ruh sit iz um). The organism that benefits is called a **parasite.** The organism it lives on or in is called a **host.** The parasite is usually smaller than the host. In a parasitic relationship, the parasite benefits while the host is harmed. Unlike a predator, a parasite does not usually kill the organism it feeds on. If the host dies, the parasite could lose its source of food or shelter.

Some parasites, like fleas and ticks, have adaptations that enable them to attach to their host and feed on its blood. Other examples of parasitism are shown in **Figure 7**.

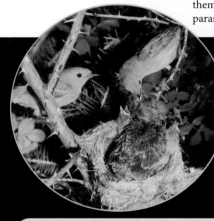

A parasitic cowbird laid its eggs in a yellow warbler's nest. The cowbird chick is outcompeting the warbler chicks for space and food.

Fish lice feed on the blood and other internal fluids of fish.

Dwarf mistletoe is a small parasitic flowering plant that grows into the bark of trees to obtain water and nutrients.

FIGURE 7 ·······························

Parasitism

There are many examples of parasitic relationships. Besides fleas, ticks, and tapeworms, some plants and birds are parasites. ✎ **Explain** Why doesn't a parasite usually kill its host?

If a parasite kills its host, the parasite will no longer have a source of food and may die.

26 **Populations and Communities**

Digital Lesson: Assign the *Apply It* activity online and have students submit their work to you.

my science ONLINE.com

Symbiosis

apply it!

Classify Each photograph on the right represents a different type of symbiosis. Classify each interaction as mutualism, commensalism, or parasitism. Explain your answers.

Interaction 1: A remora fish attaches itself to the underside of a shark without harming the shark, and eats leftover bits of food from the shark's meals.

Interaction 2: A vampire bat drinks the blood of horses.

Interaction 3: A bee pollinates a flower.

1 Interaction 1
Commensalism; the remora benefits and the shark is unaffected.

2 Interaction 2
Parasitism; the bat benefits and the horse is harmed.

3 Interaction 3
Mutualism; the bee gets food and the flower is able to reproduce.

Interaction 1

Interaction 2

Interaction 3

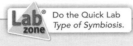
Lab zone Do the Quick Lab Type of Symbiosis.

🔑 Assess Your Understanding

3a. Identify The three types of symbiosis are _mutualism_, _commensalism_, and _parasitism_.

b. Classify Microscopic mites live at the base of human eyelashes, where they feed on tiny bits of dead skin. What type of symbiosis could this be? Explain your answer.
Commensalism, because the mites benefit by getting food and humans are unaffected

c. Compare and Contrast Name each type of symbiosis and explain how the two species are affected.
Mutualism—both species benefit; commensalism—one species benefits the other is unaffected; parasitism—one species benefits and the other is harmed.

got it? ⋯⋯⋯⋯⋯⋯⋯⋯⋯⋯⋯⋯⋯⋯⋯⋯⋯⋯⋯⋯⋯⋯⋯⋯⋯

○ **I get it!** Now I know that the three types of symbiosis differ in _how each organism in the relationship is affected._

○ **I need extra help with** _See TE note._

Go to **my science 🄢 coach** online for help with this subject.

27

Elaborate ————————
Apply It!
L1 Review the kinds of symbiosis and decide which one is a win-win situation (*Mutualism*), which is a win-lose situation (*Parasitism*), and which is a win-neutral situation (*Commensalism*) before beginning the activity.

Classify Have students review the three kinds of symbiosis, and think of them as categories into which the descriptions should fit. Ask: **Which animal shown is a parasite?** (*The vampire bat*)

Lab Resource: Quick Lab 🄛
L1 **TYPES OF SYMBIOSIS** Students will identify and compare symbiotic relationships.

Evaluate ————————
Assess Your Understanding
After students answer the questions, have them evaluate their understanding by completing the appropriate sentence.

🆁🆃🅸 Response to Intervention
3. If students have trouble identifying the different kinds of symbiosis, **then** have them review the section, locate the highlighted terms, and reread the definitions.

my science 🄢 coach Have students go online for help in understanding symbiosis.

Differentiated Instruction

L3 **Cowbirds** The cowbird is a nest parasite, laying its eggs in the nest of another species of bird, such as a warbler or a sparrow. Have students research the cowbird to learn more about this behavior.

L1 **Symbiosis** Help struggling students use mathematical symbols to summarize the three kinds of symbiosis. Use a plus sign for an organism that is helped, a minus sign for an organism that is harmed, and a zero for an organism that is neither helped nor harmed. Mutualism is +/+. Parasitism is +/−. Commensalism is +/0.

Name ______________________ Date ____________ Class ____________

Lab zone® After the Inquiry Warm-Up

Interactions Among Living Things

Inquiry Warm-Up, *Can You Hide a Butterfly?*
In the Inquiry Warm-Up, you investigated how coloring can help an animal hide from an enemy. Using what you learned from that activity, answer the questions below.

1. **OBSERVE** Was your butterfly found or missed? If there were other butterflies that looked like yours, were they found or missed? Suggest a reason for any difference.

2. **EVALUATE** Was any particular surface a better place for butterflies to hide than others? If so, explain why.

3. **OBSERVE** Was there anything about the way the person who looked for the butterflies that made some butterflies more likely to remain hidden?

4. **PREDICT** If these were real butterflies, what might cause some of the butterflies to be found, even if their colors matched the environment?

Place the outside corner, the corner away from the dotted line, in the corner of your copy machine to copy onto letter-size paper.

Assess Your Understanding

Interactions Among Living Things

How Do Adaptations Help an Organism Survive?

1a. **DEFINE** Adaptations are the _____ and

_____ characteristics that allow organisms to live successfully in their environments.

b. **EXPLAIN** How are a snake's sharp fangs an adaptation that help it survive in the saguaro community?

gotit? ....

○ **I get it!** Now I know that adaptations are _____

_____

_____

○ **I need extra help with** _____

_____

What Are Competition and Predation?

2a. **REVIEW** Two main ways in which organisms interact are

_____ and _____.

b. **DESCRIBE** Give an example of competition. Explain your answer.

_____

_____

c. **APPLY CONCEPTS** Owls often prey on mice. What adaptations do you
think the mice have that help them avoid becoming prey?

_____

_____

gotit? ....

○ **I get it!** Now I know that competition and predation _____

_____

○ **I need extra help with** _____

_____

Assess Your Understanding

Interactions Among Living Things

What Are the Three Types of Symbiosis?

3a. IDENTIFY The three types of symbiosis are _____,

_____, and _____.

b. CLASSIFY Microscopic mites lie at the base of human eyelashes, where
they feed on tiny bits of dead skin. What type of symbiosis could this
be? Explain your answer.

_____

_____

c. COMPARE AND CONTRAST Name each type of symbiosis and explain
how the two species are affected.

_____

_____

_____

gotit?···

○ **I get it!** Now I know that the three types of symbiosis differ in _____

_____

_____

○ **I need extra help with** _____

_____

Key Concept Summaries

Interactions Among Living Things

How Do Adaptations Help an Organism Survive?

Individuals with characteristics that are best suited for their environment tend to survive and pass on these characteristics to their offspring through a process called **natural selection**. The behaviors and characteristics that allow organisms to live successfully in their environments are called **adaptations**. Individuals with characteristics that are poorly suited for their environment are less likely to survive and reproduce.

An organism has a role, or **niche**, in its habitat. A niche includes the type of food the organism eats and how it gets this food. A niche also includes when and how the organism reproduces and the physical conditions that it needs to survive. Each organism has unique characteristics that affect the organism's ability to survive and reproduce in its environment. For example, many organisms live in and around the saguaro cactus.

What Are Competition and Predation?

Two major types of interactions among organisms are competition and predation. **Competition** is the struggle between organisms to survive as they attempt to occupy the same niche and use the same limited resources. Organisms that share the same habitat often have adaptations that reduce competition. For example, three types of birds can each get food from different parts of the same tree.

An interaction is which one organism kills another for food or nutrients is called **predation**. The **predator**

species kills the **prey** species. Predators have adaptations that help them catch prey. Organisms have adaptations that help them avoid becoming prey.

Predators can affect population size. If there are too many predators in an area, the number of prey will decrease. As a result, there is less food for predators and the predator population will go down too.

What Are the Three Types of Symbiosis?

The three main types of symbiotic relationships are mutualism, commensalisms, and parasitism. **Mutualism** is a relationship in which both species benefit. When an oxpecker eats ticks living on the impala's ear, both organisms benefit. **Commensalism** is a relationship in which one species benefits and

the other species is not affected, such as a bird's nest in a tree. **Parasitism** is a relationship in which one organism benefits and the other organism is harmed. The organism that benefits is called a **parasite**. The organism that is harmed is called the **host**. Fish lice are parasites that feed on the blood of a host fish.

On a separate sheet of paper, compare and contrast parasitism and mutualism.

Review and Reinforce

Interactions Among Living Things

Understanding Main Ideas
Answer the following questions on a separate sheet of paper.

1. How does natural selection result in adaptations in a species?
2. What is an organism's niche?
3. How do adaptations help an organism to reduce competition for food and other resources?

The line graph below shows how the populations of lynx and snowshoe hares has changed over time. Use the line graph to answer questions 4–6.

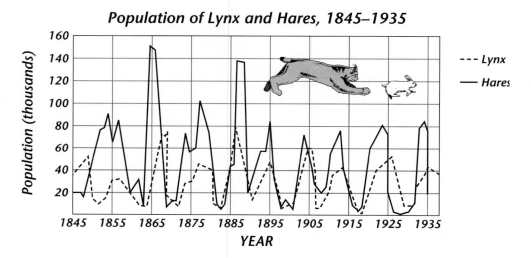

Population of Lynx and Hares, 1845–1935

4. When the hare population increased, what happened to the lynx population. Why?
5. How do you think an increase in the lynx population affected the hare population? Why?
6. What other factors could have caused a decrease in the hare population?

Building Vocabulary
On a separate sheet of paper, write a definition for each of these terms.

7. predator
8. competition
9. symbiosis

Enrich

Interactions Among Living Things

Read the passage and look at the graph below it. Then use a separate sheet of paper to answer the questions that follow the graph.

Analyzing Interactions Among Organisms

In 1997, a community decided to get rid of the population of rattlesnakes in the area. The graph below shows what happened to the populations of rattlesnakes, birds, and rodents. The rodents included animals such as mice, rats, and prairie dogs.

Populations of Rodents, Birds, and Rattlesnakes

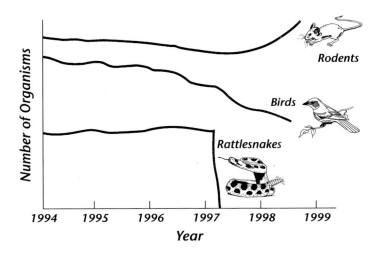

1. Did the bird populations appear to benefit from the elimination of the rattlesnakes? How do you know?
2. Did the rodent populations appear to benefit from the elimination of the rattlesnakes? How do you know?
3. What was the main source of food for the rattlesnakes? How can you tell?
4. Why do you think the bird populations decreased sharply after the rattlesnakes were eliminated?
5. Do you think it was a good idea for the community to eliminate the rattlesnake population? Explain your answer.

Interactions Among Living Things

If the statement is true, write *true*. If the statement is false, change the underlined word or words to make the statement true.

1. _____ In <u>natural selection</u>, individuals whose unique characteristics are well-suited for an environment tend to survive and produce more offspring.

2. _____ Adaptations are behaviors and <u>social</u> characteristics that allow organisms to live successfully in their environments.

3. _____ A grackle and a sparrow try to eat from the same ear of corn in a field. This is an example of <u>mutualism</u>.

4. _____ The two main kinds of interactions among organisms are competition and <u>adaptation</u>.

5. _____ An increase in a predator population will likely result in a <u>decrease</u> in the prey population.

6. _____ Dwarf mistletoe is a plant that grows into the bark of a tree to obtain water and nutrients. The mistletoe is a <u>parasite</u>.

Write the letter of the correct answer on the line at the left.

7. ___ When a snake kills a shrew, the shrew is the
   A host
   B prey
   C predator
   D parasite

8. ___ The role of an organism in its habitat is its
   A host
   B prey
   C niche
   D adaptation

9. ___ An example of an adaptation that helps a prey species avoid being caught is
   A claws
   B mimicry
   C sharp teeth
   D poisonous stingers

10. ___ A relationship in which two species live closely together and both benefit is
   A mutualism
   B predation
   C parasitism
   D commensalism

Interactions Among Living Things

Answer Key

After the Inquiry Warm-Up

1. Certain colors or patterns were better for keeping butterflies hidden.

2. Differences between horizontal and vertical surfaces may be affected by the angle of sunlight or the overhead lights.

3. Students may note that the searcher didn't look up at high places or down at low ones.

4. Sample: Their motion might give then away, or they might be found by an animal that searched by smell rather than sight.

Key Concept Summaries

Both are kinds of symbiosis. In mutualism, both organisms benefit from the relationship. In parasitism, only one organism benefits. The other is harmed.

Review and Reinforce

1. Organisms with characteristics that are well suited to their environment survive to reproduce and pass those characteristics along to their offspring. The offspring also survive and reproduce.

2. An organism's niche is its role in its habitat, what it eats and how it obtains its food.

3. Organisms' adaptations enable them to specialize in obtaining food, shelter, and other ecosystems resources so that they do not compete directly with other species.

4. The lynx increase, too, because they had more food.

5. The hares decreased because there were more lynx to prey on them.

6. lack of food or shelter; disease; predation by other predators

7. A predator is an organism that kills another organism for food.

8. Competition is the struggle between organisms to survive as they attempt to use the same resources.

9. Symbiosis is a relationship in which two species live closely together and at least one of the species benefits.

Enrich

1. No; their numbers decreased.

2. Yes; their numbers increased.

3. Rodents; when the rattlesnake population was killed off, the rodents increased.

4. Rodents may have been eating the birds' eggs and young or some of the same foods the birds were eating. When the rattlesnakes were killed, the rodents increased and the birds suffered more predation and/or competition.

5. The increasing numbers of rodents will present a problem for the community—perhaps even more of a problem than the population of rattlesnakes did.

Lesson Quiz

1. true	2. physical	3. competition
4. predation	5. true	6. true
7. B	8. C	9. B
10. A		

Changes in Communities

 How do living things affect one another?

Lesson Pacing: 1–2 periods or ½–1 block

🕐 **SHORT ON TIME?** To do this lesson in approximately half the time, do the Activate Prior Knowledge activity on page 28. A discussion of the key concept on page 30 will familiarize students with the lesson content. Have students do the Quick Lab. The rest of the lesson can be completed by students independently.

Preference Navigator, in the online Planning tools, allows you to customize *Interactive Science* to your own teaching style. You can also edit lesson plans by selecting the Lesson Planner option.

Digital Teacher's Edition allows you to access your *Teacher's Edition and Resource* materials online.

my science online.com

Lesson Vocabulary

- succession
- primary succession
- pioneer species
- secondary succession

Content Refresher

Professional Development Note

Lichens Lichens are an example of one type of symbiotic relationship—mutualism. In this type of association, both organisms depend on each other and cannot live independently. In the lichen, one organism, the alga, carries out photosynthesis and produces the food that the other organisgm, the fungus, requires. The fungus absorbs vital nutrients and water for the process. Lichens can grow in most habitats, especially those unsuitable for plant growth. Because of this, they are pioneer species in succession. Their activities prepare the soil for the mosses and other small plants that follow in succession. Lichens are very sensitive to sulfur dioxide, which makes them good indicators of pollution and acid rain. Because they can tolerate and accumulate metals, they can be an indicator of industrial pollution. Lichens are also used in traditional dyes, in herbal medicines, and as human and animal food.

LESSON OBJECTIVE

 Explain the difference between primary and secondary succession.

Blended Path
Active learning using Student Edition, Inquiry Path, and Digital Path

ENGAGE AND EXPLORE

To teach this lesson using a variety of resources, begin by reading **My Planet Diary** as a class. Have students share ideas any experience they may have had or knowledge of prescribed fires. Then have students do the **Inquiry Warm-Up activity.** Students will investigate the order in which organisms move into a community. The **After the Inquiry Warm-Up worksheet** sets up a discussion about kinds of plants and animals living in the area. Have volunteers share their answers to number 4 about abiotic factors that will determine which species will survive.

EXPLAIN AND ELABORATE

Teach Key Concepts by explaining the terms *primary* and *secondary succession*. Relate *pioneer species* to *primary succession*. Continue to **Teach Key Concepts** by explaining that secondary succession takes place after an area with an established ecosystem has been disturbed. Use the **Support the Big Q** to help students understand the stages of secondary succession. Ask students to use **Figures 1** and **2** to explain the difference between primary and secondary succession. Students can then practice the target skill in the **Apply It activity.**

Hand out the **Key Concept Summaries** as a review of each part of the lesson. Students can also use the online **Vocab Flash Cards** to review key terms.

EVALUATE

Have students take the **Lesson Quiz.** For an alternate assessment, see the **EXAM**VIEW® Assessment Suite, Progress Monitoring Assessments, or SuccessTracker™.

E L L Support

1 Content and Language

Compare the words *primary succession* and *secondary succession* in the vocabulary. Students may recognize the words *primary* and *secondary* from terms as *primary school* and *secondary school*. Point out that students in *primary school* may have little knowledge to build on much like an area undergoing *primary succession* with respect to organisms. Students in *secondary school* should have an established background of knowledge much like an established ecosystem in *secondary succession*.

DIFFERENTIATED INSTRUCTION KEY
L1 Struggling Students or Special Needs
L2 On-Level Students **L3** Advanced Students

LESSON PLANNER 1.4

Lab zone Inquiry Path
Hands-on learning in the Lab zone

Digital Path
Online learning at my science online.com

ENGAGE AND EXPLORE

To teach this lesson with an emphasis on inquiry, begin with the **Inquiry Warm-Up activity.** Students will investigate organisms moving into an ecosystem and the order in which they move in. Discuss pioneers in primary succession. Have students do the **After the Inquiry Warm-Up worksheet.** Have volunteers share their answers to number 4 about abiotic factors that determine which species are likely to survive.

EXPLAIN AND ELABORATE

Focus on the **Inquiry Skill** for the lesson. Point out that when you observe, you watch carefully or inspect. Review primary and secondary succession before assigning the **Apply It activity.** Ask students to share answers that are not reflected in the annotations. Have students do the **Quick Lab** and then share their observations of evidence of succession on or near their school grounds. Students can use the online **Vocab Flash Cards** to review key terms.

EVALUATE

Have students take the **Lesson Quiz.** For an alternate assessment, see the **EXAM**VIEW® Assessment Suite, Progress Monitoring Assessments, or SuccessTracker™.

ENGAGE AND EXPLORE

To teach this lesson using digital resources, begin by having students explore succession at **My Planet Diary** online. Have them access the Chapter Resources to find the **Unlock the Big Question activity.** There they can answer the questions and refine their responses as they continue through the lesson. You can re-assign the activity and have students submit their work so you can track their progress.

EXPLAIN AND ELABORATE

Students reading above, at, or below the lexile measure of this lesson can access basic content readings at their level at **My Reading Web.** Have students do the online **Art in Motion** activities associated with **Figures 1** and **2.** Encourage students to use the online **Vocab Flash Cards** to preview key terms.

Review *primary* and *secondary succession* before assigning the online **Apply It activity.** Ask volunteers for additional possible causes.

The **Key Concept Summaries** online allow students to read a summary and see an image associated with each part of the lesson. Online remediation is available at **My Science Coach.**

EVALUATE

Have students take the **Lesson Quiz.** For an alternate assessment, see the **EXAM**VIEW® Assessment Suite, Progress Monitoring Assessments, or SuccessTracker™.

2 Frontload the Lesson
Preview the lesson visuals, labels, and captions. In **Figure 1** be sure students understand that they must order or sequence the stages of primary succession and in **Figure 2** write titles for the stages of secondary succession.

3 Comprehensible Input
Have students study the visuals and their captions on pages 29–31 to support the key concepts of the lesson. Have students role-play pioneers in a primary succession.

4 Language Production
Pair or group students with varied language abilities to complete the sequencing and titling in **Figures 1** and **2.** Have each pair or group write a paragraph on primary or secondary succession.

5 Assess Understanding
Make statements about succession. Have students indicate if the statement applies to primary or secondary succession by holding up one hand for primary and two for secondary to check whole-class comprehension.

LESSON 1.4

Changes in Communities

Establish Learning Objective

After this lesson, students will be able to:

🔑 Explain the difference between primary and secondary succession.

Engage

Activate Prior Knowledge

MY PLANET DIARY Read *Fighting Fire With Fire* with the class. Explain that a fire is one of several ways that a community can be changed. Point out that a prescribed fire is set on a day with little wind and when conditions will help the firefighters control the burn. A prescribed fire would never be set during a very dry season. Ask: **How is a wildfire different from a prescribed fire?** *(A prescribed fire is carefully planned and controlled, and a wildfire is not.)*

BIG IDEAS OF SCIENCE REFERENCE LIBRARY 📖
Have students look up the following topic: Renewal.

Explore

Lab Resource: Inquiry Warm-Up

L1 **HOW COMMUNITIES CHANGE** Students will observe examples of succession.

LESSON 4

Changes in Communities

🔑 **How Do Primary and Secondary Succession Differ?**

my pLaNeT DiaRY

Fighting Fire With Fire

Wildfires are often reported in the national news. The images associated with these reports show how damaging these fires can be to property and to some ecosystems. What you may not know is that fire can actually help fight wildfires! Controlled burns, or prescribed burns, are fires that are purposely and carefully set by professional foresters. Prescribed burns are used to remove materials such as dead, dry branches and leaves that can fuel wildfires. A wildfire that occurs in an area that has previously been burned would cause less damage and be easier for firefighters to control.

This forester is carefully igniting a controlled burn.

MISCONCEPTION

Communicate Discuss these questions with a classmate. Write your answers below.

1. Why should only professional foresters set prescribed fires?
   <u>Sample: Professional foresters know how to set fires and keep them controlled.</u>

2. What do you think could be some other benefits to using prescribed burns in an ecosystem?
   <u>Sample: They help to control insects, increase nutrients in the soil, and improve habitats.</u>

▶ **PLANET DIARY** Go to **Planet Diary** to learn more about succession.

 Do the Inquiry Warm-Up *How Communities Change.*

How Do Primary and Secondary Succession Differ?

Fires, floods, volcanoes, hurricanes, and other natural disasters can change communities very quickly. But even without disasters, communities change. The series of predictable changes that occur in a community over time is called **succession.**

28 Populations and Communities

SUPPORT ALL READERS

Lexile Measure = 1020L   **Lexile Word Count = 686**

Prior Exposure to Content: May be the first time students have encountered this topic

Academic Vocabulary: *compare, contrast, observe*

Science Vocabulary: *primary succession, secondary succession*

Concept Level: Generally appropriate for most students in this grade

Preteach With: My Planet Diary "Fighting Fire With Fire" and Figure 1 activity

Go to **My Reading Web** to access leveled readings that provide a foundation for the content.

my scIence online.com

Vocabulary
- succession • primary succession
- pioneer species • secondary succession

Skills
- 🌀 Reading: Compare and Contrast
- △ Inquiry: Observe

Primary Succession When a new island is formed by the eruption of an undersea volcano or an area of rock is uncovered by a melting sheet of ice, no living things are present. Over time, living things will inhabit these areas. **Primary succession** is the series of changes that occur in an area where no soil or organisms exist.

Figure 1 shows how an area might change following a volcanic eruption. Just like the pioneers that first settled new frontiers, the first species to populate an area are called **pioneer species.** They are often carried to the area by wind or water. Typical pioneer species are mosses and lichens. Lichens are fungi and algae growing in a symbiotic relationship. As pioneer species grow, they help break up the rocks. When the organisms die, they provide nutrients that enrich the thin layer of soil that is forming on the rocks.

As plant seeds land in the new soil, they begin to grow. The specific plants that grow depend on the climate of the area. For example, in a cool, northern area, early seedlings might include alder and cottonwood trees. Eventually, succession may lead to a community of organisms that does not change unless the ecosystem is disturbed. Reaching this mature community can take centuries.

FIGURE 1 ···

> ART IN MOTION **Primary Succession**
Primary succession occurs in an area where no soil and no organisms exist.

✎ **Sequence** In the circles, number the stage of primary succession to show the correct order of events.

③ **Soil Creation**
As pioneer species grow and die, soil forms. Some plants grow in this new soil.

② **Pioneer Species**
The first species to grow are pioneer species such as mosses and lichens.

① **Volcanic Eruption**
Shortly after a volcanic eruption, there is no soil, only ash and rock.

④ **Fertile Soil and Maturing Plants**
As more plants die, they decompose and make the soil more fertile. New plants grow and existing plants mature in the fertile soil.

29

Explain ——————————

Introduce Vocabulary
To help students understand the term *pioneer species*, explain that these are the first organisms to live in a new area. Remind them that pioneers were the first settlers to move to the western prairies.

Teach Key Concepts 🗝
Explain to students that the changes occurring in an area without any soil or organisms are called *primary succession*. *Pioneer species* are the first organisms to populate such an area. Ask: **What are the pioneer species in succession in Figure 1?** *(Lichens and mosses)* **How might these species arrive at the area?** *(They might be carried by wind or water)* **What pattern is there in the kinds of plants that move in as succession continues?** *(Larger and larger plants move into the area over time.)*

My Planet Diary provides an opportunity for students to explore real-world connections to changes in communities.

Art in Motion shows primary succession in motion and animates the block diagrams.

my science online .com | Succession

E L L Support

1 Content and Language
Explain that *primary* means first. Then point out that primary succession is the *first* life to enter a new place.

2 Frontload the Lesson
Have students scan the section heads and visuals and then predict what this lesson will be about. Have students confirm their predictions after reading the lesson.

3 Comprehensible Input
Help students compare and contrast the information in the lesson by having them complete a Venn diagram. One circle should contain information about primary succession and the other circle should contain information about secondary succession. The overlapping section should contain information on how the processes are similar.

Explain

Teach Key Concepts 🔑

Explain to students that secondary succession, in contrast to primary succession, is a disturbance that occurs in a place with an established ecosystem. Ask: **How does secondary succession differ from primary succession?** *(Secondary succession occurs in an area where an ecosystem has been disturbed but soil and some organisms still exist. Primary succession occurs where there is no soil and there are no organisms present.)* **What kind of succession would occur in an area that has been damaged by floods? Explain.** *(It would be secondary succession because it is likely that soil and some organisms would be left behind after the flood.)*

Support the Big Q ❓ UbD

SECONDARY SUCCESSION Help students understand that secondary succession takes place after an area has been disturbed, and tends to return the area to the kind of ecosystem that was present before the disturbance. Tell students to look at **Figure 2.** Ask: **What is the first stage in this example of succession?** *(An abandoned field)* **What do you think the area looked like before the field was abandoned?** *(It was probably plowed for farming.)* **Before the field was cleared for farming, what did the area probably look like?** *(It was likely covered with trees.)* **What was the source of the trees seen in the later stage?** *(Remaining trees near the farm were the source of seeds of the trees.)*

FIGURE 2 ···

▶ ART IN MOTION **Secondary Succession**
Secondary succession occurs following a disturbance to an ecosystem, such as clearing a forest for farmland.
✏️ **Describe** Write a brief title that describes what happens at each of the four stages of secondary succession.

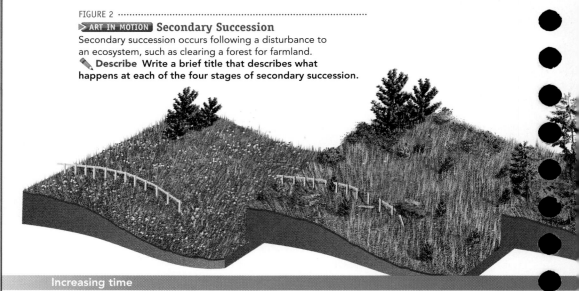

Increasing time

Title: Sample: Abandoned Field
Grasses and wildflowers have taken over this abandoned field.

Title: Sample: Tree Growth Begins
After a few years, pine seedlings and other trees replace some of the grasses and wildflowers.

apply it!

💡 **Compare and Contrast** Based on your reading, complete the table below.

Factors in Succession	Primary Succession	Secondary Succession
Possible Cause	Volcanic eruption	Fire
Type of Area	No soil or organisms exist.	Soil and organisms exist, but have been disturbed.
Existing Ecosystem?	No	Yes

Secondary Succession In October 2007, huge wildfires raged across Southern California. The changes following the California fires are an example of secondary succession. **Secondary succession** is the series of changes that occur in an area where the ecosystem has been disturbed, but where soil and organisms still exist. Natural disturbances that have this effect include fires, hurricanes, and tornadoes. Human activities, such as farming, logging, or mining, may also disturb an ecosystem and cause secondary succession to begin.

🔑 **Unlike primary succession, secondary succession occurs in a place where an ecosystem currently exists.** Secondary succession usually occurs more rapidly than primary succession because soil already exists and seeds from some plants remain in the soil. You can follow the process of succession in an abandoned field in **Figure 2.** After a century, a hardwood forest is developing. This forest community may remain for a long time.

30 Populations and Communities

Art in Motion shows secondary succession in motion and animates the block diagrams.

Digital Lesson: Assign the *Apply It* activity online and have students submit their work to you.

MY SCIENCE online.com ▶ **Succession**

Title: _Sample: A Forest Develops_

As tree growth continues, the trees begin to crowd out the grasses and wildflowers.

Title: _Sample: Mature Community_

Eventually, a forest of mostly oak, hickory, and some pine dominates the landscape.

 Do the Quick Lab
Primary or Secondary.

Assess Your Understanding

1a. Define Pioneer species are the _first_ species to populate an area.

b. Observe Is grass poking through a sidewalk crack primary or secondary succession? Why?
Secondary; before the sidewalk, soil was present and an ecosystem existed there.

c. [CHALLENGE] Why are the changes during succession predictable?
Plants and animals that will grow in an area are determined by climate conditions that are not affected by disasters.

got it?

O I get it! Now I know that primary and secondary succession differ in _whether an ecosystem exists, and the rate at which succession occurs._

O I need extra help with _See TE note._

Go to **MY SCIENCE COACH** online for help with this subject.

31

Differentiated Instruction

L3 Local Succession Encourage students to talk to friends or relatives who have lived in your area for a long time. Students should ask about natural areas and how they have changed. Students can take notes from the conversation and then tell the class what they learned. If students cannot find friends or relatives who know such information, suggest they visit the local library to learn more about the area's history.

L1 Interpret Diagrams Ask students to compare the pictures of the first stage in **Figures 1** and **2.** Help them see that **Figure 1** begins with an area that has no soil and no organisms, but in **Figure 2** the first picture has plants already living there. Help students relate these differences to those between primary succession and secondary succession. Have students create their own diagrams to show primary and secondary succession based on the lesson.

Elaborate

Apply It!

L1 Review the differences between primary succession and secondary succession before beginning the activity.

Compare and Contrast Point out that this table contrasts the two kinds of succession. To contrast is to show differences between two things. To compare is to show how two things are similar.

Lab Resource: Quick Lab

L1 PRIMARY OR SECONDARY Students will observe evidence of succession on or near their school grounds.

Evaluate

Assess Your Understanding

After students answer the questions, have them evaluate their understanding by completing the appropriate sentence.

RTI Response to Intervention

1a. If students cannot describe what a pioneer species is, **then** have them review **Figure 1** and reread the labels.

b. If students have trouble distinguishing between primary and secondary succession, **then** have them locate and reread the Key Concept statement for the lesson.

c. If students need help with explaining why succession is predictable, **then** discuss the climate conditions that can be inferred from **Figure 2** and help them see that the climate has not changed.

MY SCIENCE COACH Have students go online for help in understanding succession.

Lab zone **After the Inquiry Warm-Up**

Changes in Communities

Inquiry Warm-Up, *How Communities Change*

In the Inquiry Warm-Up, you investigated the order in which organisms move into an area. Using what you learned from that activity, answer the questions below.

1. **OBSERVE** What trend do you see in the kinds of plants that you can see in the drawings?

   _____

   _____

2. **PREDICT** When do you think animals will be found living in the area?

   _____

   _____

3. **EXPLAIN** How does soil form after a volcanic eruption that leaves only ash and rock?

   _____

   _____

4. **INFER** What are some abiotic factors that will determine which of the species that arrive in the area will survive?

   _____

   _____

   _____

Name _____ Date _____ Class _____

Changes in Communities

How Do Primary and Secondary Succession Differ?

1a. **DEFINE** During succession, pioneer species are the

_____ species to populate an area. They are carried to

an area by _____ and _____.

b. **OBSERVE** Grass poking through a crack in a sidewalk is an example of succession. Is it primary or secondary succession?

_____

_____

c. **CHALLENGE** Why are the changes during succession predictable?

_____

_____

got it? ··

○ **I get it!** Now I know that primary and secondary succession differ in _____

_____

_____

○ **I need extra help with** _____

_____

_____

Name _____ Date _____ Class _____

Changes in Communities

How Do Primary and Secondary Succession Differ?

The series of predictable changes that occur in a community over time is called succession. **Primary succession** happens where there is no soil or organisms in the environment. For example, primary succession may occur following a volcanic eruption.

Pioneer species, such as lichen, are the first organisms to populate the environment. Other plants can grow in the soil that pioneers help make. Eventually, a community of organisms develops.

Secondary succession occurs in an area where the ecosystem has been disturbed but soil and organisms remain, such as after forest is cleared. Secondary succession usually happens faster than primary succession because some soil and plant seeds remain after the disturbance.

On a separate sheet of paper, compare and contrast primary succession and secondary succession.

Changes in Communities

Understanding Main Ideas
Answer the following questions on a separate sheet of paper.

1. What organisms are usually the pioneer species in anew area? How do these organisms prepare the area for other species?

2. The illustration below shows succession in an abandoned field. How did the plant populations in the community change over time?

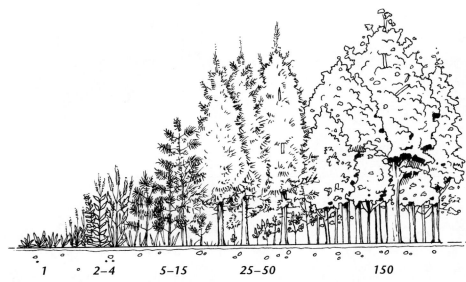

Years After Field Was Abandoned

1   2-4   5-15   25-50   150

Building Vocabulary
Identify each of the following as an example of primary succession or secondary succession. Write your answers in the spaces provided.

3. An old house was torn down. Small weeds and grasses grew in the vacant lot. Over the next few years, bushes and tree seedlings began to grow.

_____

4. An undersea volcano erupted and formed a small island. Mosses and lichens began to grow on the bare volcanic rock.

_____

Name _____ Date _____ Class _____

Changes in Communities

You have learned that over many years, the process of succession can transform an abandoned field into a forest. Succession can also transform a pond into a forest. How can an aquatic ecosystem change into a land ecosystem? Examine the sequence of changes shown in the figures below. Then answer the questions on a separate sheet of paper.

From Pond to Forest

1. What type of succession is shown in this example? Explain your answer.
2. Name two pond populations that could not survive in a forest ecosystem.
3. Name two forest populations that could not survive in a pond ecosystem.
4. Describe how the ecosystem changed from Figure 1 to Figure 4.

Changes in Communities

Fill in the blank to complete each statement.

1. Pioneer species break down rocks, forming the beginning of _____.

2. Two examples of pioneer species are _____ and lichens.

3. A lichen is a symbiotic combination of _____ and algae.

4. A forest fire is followed by _____ succession.

5. The series of changes that occur in an area where no soil or organisms exist is called _____ succession.

If the statement is true, write _true_. If the statement is false, change the underlined word or words to make the statement true.

6. _____ After a long time, a mature community is established and this community does not change unless it is <u>disturbed</u>.

7. _____ The first species to populate an area are called <u>primary</u> species.

8. _____ Unlike primary succession, secondary succession occurs in a place where an <u>ecosystem</u> currently exists.

9. _____ Secondary succession is usually <u>slower</u> than primary succession.

10. _____ Natural disturbances that lead to succession include fires, hurricanes, and <u>tornadoes</u>.

Changes in Communities

Answer Key

After the Inquiry Warm-Up

1. As time goes by, larger and larger plants are seen in the area.

2. Animals will be able to live in the area when there is available food and enough plant growth or soil development to provide shelter.

3. Soil forms from the mosses and lichens that grow and die on the ash and rock. Some plants can grow in the soil as the soil becomes fertile.

4. temperature, available water, amount of sunlight (length of day)

Key Concept Summaries

In both primary succession and secondary succession, new organisms move into an area and replace organisms that lived there before. In primary succession, the land is bare before new organisms move in. In secondary succession, the area has been disturbed, but some organisms are already there when new ones move in.

Review and Reinforce

1. Mosses and lichens are usually the pioneer species. As they grow on bare rock, they help break up the rocks to start forming soil. When they die, they provide nutrients that enrich the thin layer of soil that is forming, allowing plant seeds to grow.

2. First small weeds few, then larger weeds and pine seedlings. As the pines grew, a pine forest developed. Then seedlings of deciduous trees began to grow. Finally, a forest of mature deciduous trees replaced the pine trees.

3. secondary succession

4. primary succession

Enrich

1. secondary succession, because it occurs in a place where there already is an ecosystem

2. Sample: turtles, fish, water lilies

3. Sample: pal trees, rabbits, deer

4. In Figure 1, the pond was fairly deep. Water plants grew in the shallow water close to shore, and marsh plants grew at the edge of the pond. Fish and other aquatic organisms lived in and around the pond. In Figure 2, the pond and become shallower, but fish could still live in it. Aquatic plants grew farther out from the shore, and a wider band of marsh plants grew at the pond's edge. In Figure 3, the pond has filled in to the point where only small marshy areas are left. Some of the plants are the same, but no fish live there. In Figure 4, the marshy areas have completely filled in, and there's a meadow where the pond was. The forest has grown into the meadow.

Lesson Quiz

1. soil
2. mosses
3. fungi
4. secondary
5. primary
6. true
7. pioneer
8. true
9. faster
10. true

Place the outside corner, the corner away from the dotted line, in the corner of your copy machine to copy onto letter-size paper.

Study Guide

Review the Big Q ? UbD

Have students complete the statement at the top of the page. These Key Concepts support their understanding of the chapter's Big Question. Have students return to the chapter opener question. What is different about how students view the image of the clownfish and sea anemone now that they have completed the chapter? Thinking about this will help them prepare for the *Apply the Big Q* activity in the Review and Assessment.

Partner Review

Have partners review definitions of vocabulary terms by using the Study Guide to quiz each other. Students could read the Key Concept statements and leave out words for their partner to fill in, or change a statement so that it is false and then ask their partner to correct it.

Class Activity: Concept Map

Have students develop a concept map to show how the information in this chapter is related. Have students brainstorm to identify the key concepts, vocabulary, details, and examples, then write each one on a self-sticking note and attach it at random on chart paper or on the board. Explain that the concept map will begin at the top with Key Concepts. Ask students to use the following questions to help them organize the information on the notes:
- What does an organism get from its habitat?
- What is the difference between a population and a community?
- What are some ways in which populations can be changed?
- Why are adaptations important?
- What is a symbiotic relationship?

My Science Coach allows students to complete the *Practice Test* online.

The Big Question allows students to complete the *Apply the Big Q* activity about how living things affect one another.

Vocab Flash Cards offer a way to review the chapter vocabulary words.

my science online.com **Populations and Communities**

---

1 Study Guide

Living things interact in many ways, including competition and _predation_ , as well as through symbiotic relationships such as mutualism, commensalism, and _parasitism_ .

LESSON 1 Living Things and the Environment

🔑 An organism gets the things it needs to live, grow, and reproduce from its environment.

🔑 Biotic and abiotic factors make up a habitat.

🔑 The levels of organization in an ecosystem are organism, population, and community.

Vocabulary
- organism • habitat • biotic factor
- abiotic factor • species • population
- community • ecosystem • ecology

LESSON 2 Populations

🔑 Populations can change in size when new members join the population or when members leave the population.

🔑 Some limiting factors for populations are weather conditions, space, food, and water.

Vocabulary
- birth rate • death rate • immigration
- emigration • population density
- limiting factor • carrying capacity

LESSON 3 Interactions Among Living Things

🔑 Every organism has a variety of adaptations that are suited to its specific living conditions to help it survive.

🔑 Two major types of interactions among organisms are competition and predation.

🔑 The three main types of symbiotic relationships are mutualism, commensalism, and parasitism.

Vocabulary
- natural selection • adaptation • niche • competition
- predation • predator • prey • symbiosis • mutualism
- commensalism • parasitism • parasite • host

LESSON 4 Changes in Communities

🔑 Unlike primary succession, secondary succession occurs in a place where an ecosystem currently exists.

Vocabulary
- succession
- primary succession
- pioneer species
- secondary succession

E L L Support

4 Language Production

Divide the class into four groups and do a Gallery Walk to review each lesson. Post four large sheets of paper or poster board with the essential questions from each lesson at the top of each sheet. Position each group at one poster. Have them write down all they have learned that responds to the questions. Then have them rotate to the next poster to add information until all groups have worked with all posters.

Beginning
LOW/HIGH Allow students to answer with drawings, single words, or short phrases.

Intermediate
LOW/HIGH Have students draft sentences to answer the questions.

Advanced
LOW/HIGH Have students assist and/or edit the work of classmates with lower language proficiency.

Review and Assessment

LESSON 1 Living Things and the Environment

1. A prairie dog, a hawk, and a snake are all members of the same

a. niche.   **b.** community.

c. species.   d. population.

2. Grass is an example of a(n) <u>biotic factor</u> in a habitat.

3. Sequence Put these levels in order from the smallest to the largest: population, organism, ecosystem, community.

<u>organism, population,</u>
<u>community, ecosystem</u>

4. Apply Concepts Name two biotic and two abiotic factors you might find in a forest ecosystem.

<u>Sample: Biotic—trees, birds;</u>
<u>abiotic—sunlight, water</u>

5. Draw Conclusions In 1815, Mount Tambora, a volcano in Indonesia, erupted. So much volcanic ash and dust filled the atmosphere that 1816 is referred to as the "Year Without a Summer." How might a volcanic eruption affect the abiotic factors in an organism's habitat?

<u>Sample: The ash and dust</u>
<u>from a volcanic eruption could</u>
<u>block out sunlight. As a result,</u>
<u>temperatures would drop. The</u>
<u>air, water, and soil in a habitat</u>
<u>could also be polluted.</u>

6. **Write About It** Write at least one paragraph describing your habitat. Describe how you get the food, water, and shelter you need from your habitat. How does this habitat meet your needs in ways that another would not?
<u>See TE rubric.</u>

LESSON 2 Populations

7. All of the following are limiting factors for populations except

a. space.   **b.** food.

c. time.   d. weather.

8. <u>Emigration</u> occurs when individuals leave a population.

Use the data table to answer the questions below. Ecologists monitoring a deer population collect data during a 30-year study.

Year	0	5	10	15	20	25	30
Population (thousands)	15	30	65	100	40	25	10

9. Graph Use the data to make a line graph.

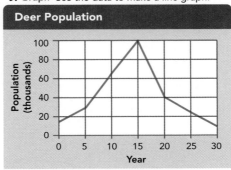

Deer Population

10. Interpret Data In which year was the deer population the highest? The lowest?
<u>Year 15; Year 30</u>

11. Develop Hypotheses In Year 16 of the study, this region experienced a severe winter. How might this have affected the deer population?
<u>The severe winter may have</u>
<u>killed weak or injured deer. A</u>
<u>food shortage may have also</u>
<u>weakened or killed the deer.</u>

33

Review and Assessment

Assess Understanding

Have students complete the answers to the Review and Assessment questions. Have a class discussion about what students find confusing. Write Key Concepts on the board to reinforce knowledge.

RTI Response to Intervention

3. If students have trouble describing the organization of an ecosystem, **then** have them use the mnemonic *Only People Can Eat* to remember the progression from Organism to Population to Community to Ecosystem.

8. If students need help contrasting immigration and emigration, **then** point out that, like *emigrate*, the word exit begins with the letter e. Individuals that are emigrating are exiting, or leaving, the population.

Alternate Assessment

L3 **DESIGN A GAME** Have students design and produce a game that uses the chapter content. Students should be sure to use all the Key Concepts and vocabulary in the game and to address the Big Question. For example, an ecosystem board game could include game pieces that represent the populations in a community. Spaces on the board and cards drawn from a pile would instruct players to adapt or interact, or impose a condition (such as a drought) on a population. The class can then use the game as a way to review the chapter material.

Write About It Assess student's writing using this rubric.

SCORING RUBRIC	SCORE 4	SCORE 3	SCORE 2	SCORE 1
Getting food, water, and shelter from habitat	Student describes sources of all items in detail.	Student describes sources of all items.	Student describes some sources of items.	Student does not describe sources of items.
How habitat is different from others	Student clearly identifies ways in which the habitat differs from others.	Student identifies ways in which the habitat differs from others.	Student incompletely identifies ways in which the habitat differs from others.	Student does not identify ways in which the habitat differs from others.

Review and Assessment, Cont.

RTI Response to Intervention

12. If students need help classifying interactions between species, **then** review with them the definitions of parasitism, mutualism, and commensalism. Invite students to give examples of each.

19. If students have trouble distinguishing primary and secondary succession, **then** review with them the definitions for both types of succession and have them provide examples of each.

Apply the Big Q ? UbD

TRANSFER Students should be able to demonstrate understanding of the relationships between living things by answering this question. See the scoring rubric below.

Connect to the Big Idea

BIG IDEA Living things interact with the environment.

Send students back to the Big Ideas of Science pages at the beginning of their student edition. Have them read what they wrote about how living things interact before they started the chapter. Lead a class discussion about how their thoughts have changed. If all chapters have been completed, have them fill in the bottom section for the Big Idea.

L3 WRITING IN SCIENCE Ask students to write a blog entry about the ways in which living things affect one another and how this demonstrates that living things interact with their environment.

LESSON 3 Interactions Among Living Things

12. In which type of interaction do both species benefit?

  a. predation   **(b.)** mutualism

  c. commensalism   **d.** parasitism

13. A parasite lives on or inside its <u>host</u>.

14. Relate Cause and Effect Name two prey adaptations. How does each adaptation protect the organism?

<u>Sample: Camouflage—An</u>
<u>organism blends in with its</u>
<u>surroundings, making it difficult</u>
<u>to see. Warning coloration—</u>
<u>Bright colors warn predators</u>
<u>not to eat the organism.</u>

15. Make Generalizations Competition for resources in an area is usually more intense within a single species than between two different species. Suggest an explanation for this observation. (*Hint:* Consider how niches help organisms avoid competition.)

<u>Organisms within a species share</u>
<u>the same niche, which intensifies</u>
<u>competition for limited resources.</u>
<u>Different species may share</u>
<u>parts of a habitat but may not</u>
<u>compete for all of the resources.</u>

16. **Write About It** Some scientists think that the relationship between clownfish and sea anemones is an example of commensalism. Other scientists think that the relationship is mutualism. If this relationship is actually mutualism, how might both the clownfish and sea anemone benefit?

<u>See TE rubric.</u>

LESSON 4 Changes in Communities

17. The series of predictable changes that occur in a community over time is called

  a. natural selection   **b.** ecology

  c. commensalism   **(d.)** succession

18. <u>Pioneer species</u> are the first species to populate an area.

19. Classify Lichens and mosses have just begun to grow on the rocky area shown below. What type of succession is occurring? Explain.

<u>Primary succession; there is no</u>
<u>soil present and only pioneer</u>
<u>organisms are shown.</u>

APPLY How do living things affect one another?

20. Humans interact with their environment on a daily basis. These interactions can have both positive and negative effects. Using at least four vocabulary terms from this chapter, describe a human interaction and the effect it has on the environment.

<u>Sample: When humans clear</u>
<u>land for construction, they</u>
<u>may destroy habitats. Oil and</u>
<u>gasoline from vehicles may get</u>
<u>into the ecosystem as abiotic</u>
<u>factors. Organisms may have</u>
<u>to emigrate to new habitats to</u>
<u>survive.</u>
<u>See TE rubric.</u>

Write About It Assess student's writing using this rubric.

SCORING RUBRIC	SCORE 4	SCORE 3	SCORE 2	SCORE 1
Ways in which clownfish benefits	Student identifies benefits to clownfish in detail.	Student identifies benefits to clownfish.	Student identifies some benefits to clownfish.	Student does not identify benefits to clownfish.
Ways in which sea anemone benefits	Student identifies benefits to sea anemone in detail.	Student identifies benefits to sea anemone.	Student identifies some benefits to sea anemone.	Student does not identify benefits to sea anemone.

? How do living things affect one another?
Assess student's response using this rubric.

SCORING RUBRIC	SCORE 4	SCORE 3	SCORE 2	SCORE 1
Interaction of humans and the environment	Student chooses an appropriate example.	Student chooses an appropriate example.	Student chooses an unlikely or inappropriate example.	Student does not identify an example.
Impact of the interaction on the environment	Student describes the impact accurately and in detail.	Student describes the impact accurately.	Student describes the impact incompletely.	Student does not describe the impact.

Standardized Test Prep

Multiple Choice

Circle the letter of the best answer.

1. Symbiotic relationships include mutualism, commensalism, and parasitism. Which of the images below shows mutualism?

Ⓐ Image 1   B Image 2
C Image 3   D Image 4

2. In general, which of the following is a true statement about population size?

A If birth rate < death rate, population size increases.

B If death rate < birth rate, population size decreases.

Ⓒ If birth rate > death rate, population size increases.

D If death rate > birth rate, population size increases.

3. Ecosystems have different levels of organization. A group of similar organisms makes up a _population_ , which, along with other types of organisms, makes up a(n) _community_ .

A species, population

B habitat, ecosystem

Ⓒ population, community

D population, habitat

4. Three different bird species all live in the same trees in an area, but competition between the birds rarely occurs. Which of the following is a likely explanation for this lack of competition?

Ⓐ The three species occupy different niches.

B The three species eat the same food.

C The three species have a limited supply of food.

D The three species live in the same part of the trees.

5. Which of the following is a typical pioneer species?

A grass

Ⓑ lichen

C pine trees

D soil

Constructed Response

Use the diagram below and your knowledge of science to help you answer Question 6. Write your answer on a separate piece of paper.

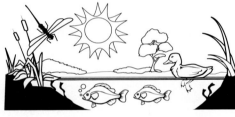

6. An organism interacts with both the biotic and abiotic factors in its habitat. List three biotic factors and three abiotic factors shown in the drawing above.

See TE note.

35

Test-Taking Skills

INTERPRETING IMAGES Tell students that when they answer questions like Question 1, where the choices are images, they should make sure they know what concept the image should represent. Students should keep that concept in mind as they look over the choices. In Question 1, choices **B** and **C** can be eliminated because an organism is being harmed. Choice **D** can be eliminated because it shows a parent and its offspring, not an example of symbiosis. Choice **A** shows mutualism, a symbiotic relationship in which both organisms benefit.

Constructed Response

6. Sample: Biotic—duck, plants, soil organisms (e.g. worm); Abiotic—sunlight, water, rock particles

Additional Assessment Resources

Chapter Test
EXAMVIEW® Assessment Suite
Performance Assessment
Progress Monitoring Assessments
SuccessTracker™

ⒺⓁⓁ Support

5 Assess Understanding

Have ELLs complete the Alternate Assessment. Provide guidelines on the information that it must cover, and a rubric for assessment.

Beginning

LOW Create the visual parts of the game, such as the game pieces and playing board.

HIGH Provide simple labels as needed.

Intermediate

LOW/HIGH Provide more extended language for parts of the game that require it, such as cards that are to be drawn by players that give simple instructions.

Advanced

LOW/HIGH Write the instructions for the game.

Remediate If students have trouble with...

QUESTION	SEE LESSON	STANDARDS
1	1	
2	2	
3	1	
4	3	
5	4	
6	1	

Science Matters

Careers

Have students read *Succession Ecologist*. Point out that ecology is a large field of study, and that ecologists specialize in smaller fields, such as succession ecology. Because some field work had been done in the forest that was destroyed, ecologists had data from before the eruption. This gave the ecologists a good idea of the community that existed before the eruption and helped them in their studies of the recovery.

Mount St. Helens is located in southwestern Washington. Help students locate the volcano on a map of the United States. To help students visualize the area of forest that was destroyed, find out the area of your community and tell students how many times that area would fit into 500 square kilometers. The area of forest that was destroyed is now Mount St. Helens National Volcanic Monument. You may wish to go to the website of the United States Forest Service to find images and information about the eruption and recovery.

Ask: **What are some other examples of natural and human-caused damage that a succession ecologist might study?** *(Sample: forest fires, landslides, floods, abandoned mines).* **How might information learned on Mount St. Helens be useful to ecologists helping areas recover from human-caused changes?** *(Sample: Ecologists might learn which plants grow best in a disturbed area.)*

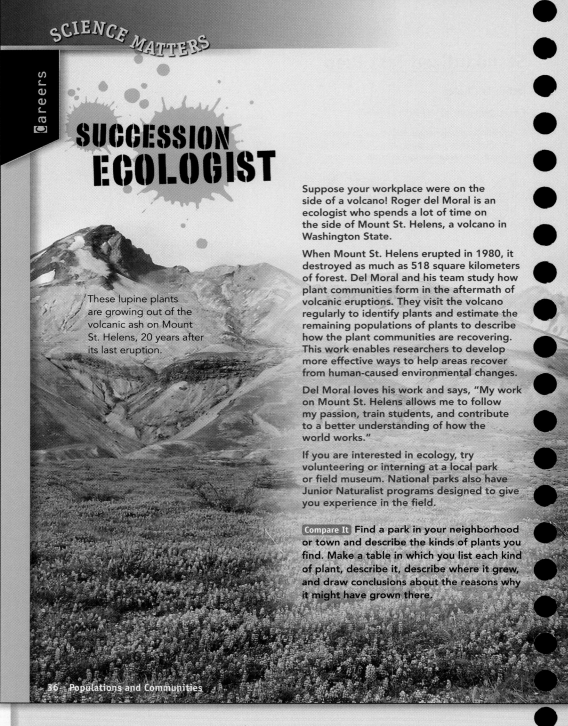

SCIENCE MATTERS

Careers

SUCCESSION ECOLOGIST

These lupine plants are growing out of the volcanic ash on Mount St. Helens, 20 years after its last eruption.

Suppose your workplace were on the side of a volcano! Roger del Moral is an ecologist who spends a lot of time on the side of Mount St. Helens, a volcano in Washington State.

When Mount St. Helens erupted in 1980, it destroyed as much as 518 square kilometers of forest. Del Moral and his team study how plant communities form in the aftermath of volcanic eruptions. They visit the volcano regularly to identify plants and estimate the remaining populations of plants to describe how the plant communities are recovering. This work enables researchers to develop more effective ways to help areas recover from human-caused environmental changes.

Del Moral loves his work and says, "My work on Mount St. Helens allows me to follow my passion, train students, and contribute to a better understanding of how the world works."

If you are interested in ecology, try volunteering or interning at a local park or field museum. National parks also have Junior Naturalist programs designed to give you experience in the field.

Compare It Find a park in your neighborhood or town and describe the kinds of plants you find. Make a table in which you list each kind of plant, describe it, describe where it grew, and draw conclusions about the reasons why it might have grown there.

36 Populations and Communities

Quick Facts

When the volcano erupted, the north side of the mountain exploded. Hot gases and pieces of rock blowing sideways moved at speeds varying from 360 to 1080 kilometers per hour. The force of this moving material blew trees over or broke them into pieces. The damage was not restricted to the side of Mount St. Helens. The blast was strong enough to damage trees on the sides of other mountains several kilometers away.

Have students find images of the damages to Mount St. Helen from the volcano eruption and current images of its recovery. Have students create a before-and-after recovery poster of Mount St. Helen.

BINOCULAR BOOT CAMP

▼ Populations of common and rare birds can be estimated based on input from students like you!

Kids Doing Science

Scientists need all the help they can get estimating large populations! Binocular Boot Camp, a program for kids in Sonoma Valley, California, trains kids to identify the songs, calls, and flight patterns of birds. Participants form teams and identify and count as many birds as they can in one afternoon. The information they gather gets entered into a huge database of bird observations.

You don't have to go to Binocular Boot Camp to help, though. For four days in February, schools, clubs, and individuals in the United States and Canada take part in the Great Backyard Bird Count (GBBC). All you need to do is count birds for 15 minutes, then fill out a form to help scientists learn how climate change, habitat change, and other factors affect bird populations.

Research It Find out more about the GBBC. Design a poster or use presentation software to create a presentation to convince your school to participate.

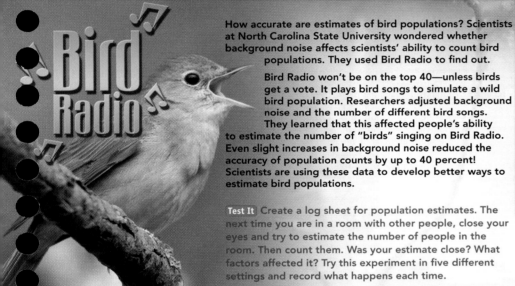

Bird Radio

Think Like a Scientist

How accurate are estimates of bird populations? Scientists at North Carolina State University wondered whether background noise affects scientists' ability to count bird populations. They used Bird Radio to find out.

Bird Radio won't be on the top 40—unless birds get a vote. It plays bird songs to simulate a wild bird population. Researchers adjusted background noise and the number of different bird songs. They learned that this affected people's ability to estimate the number of "birds" singing on Bird Radio. Even slight increases in background noise reduced the accuracy of population counts by up to 40 percent! Scientists are using these data to develop better ways to estimate bird populations.

Test It Create a log sheet for population estimates. The next time you are in a room with other people, close your eyes and try to estimate the number of people in the room. Then count them. Was your estimate close? What factors affected it? Try this experiment in five different settings and record what happens each time.

37

Kids Doing Science

Have students read *Binocular Boot Camp*. Ask students if they know anyone who has a birdfeeder. Invite students with some knowledge of birds and bird watching to share experiences with the class. If someone you know is a "birder," invite him or her to the class to talk about the Great Backyard Bird Count. If nature guides are available, show students some birds that are common in your area and point out the details that are used to identify birds.

Students may be able to get information about the bird count from local nature clubs or nature centers. If students do research on the Internet, suggest that they use *great backyard bird count* rather than *GBBC* as their search term.

Ask: **What could students' backyard bird count tell scientists?** *(Students will likely say that their bird counts could tell scientists what kind of birds and how many birds live in their area at a certain time of year.)* **Why might it be useful for scientists to do another Great Backyard Bird Count at another time of year?** *(Sample: Birds migrate and different kinds or different numbers of birds may be living in their area at different times of the year.)*

Think Like a Scientist

Have students read *Bird Radio*. Point out that each species of bird makes distinctive sounds. Birds that are closely related often have similar calls, or sounds, which make it difficult to distinguish between them. Some birds, such as crows and blue jays, have calls that are easy to identify. If recordings of bird calls are available at your library, you may wish to play some for the class. Some bird identification books include recorded bird calls.

Ask: **How well can you tell your friends apart by their voices?** *(Students will likely say that they can identify good friends by voice right away.)* **How well can you identify a voice when you are outdoors and there are noises from traffic and other sources? How well can you identify a voice when you are in a room where many people are talking, such as the lunchroom at school?** *(Students will likely say that background noise makes it more difficult to identify a voice.)*

Ecosystems and Biomes

Introduce the Big Q

Have students look at the image and read the Engaging Question and description. Ask them to write a hypothesis about where living things get their food. Point out that all living things require food for energy to carry out life processes. Some living things produce their own food, such as plants, while others must feed on other living things. Ask: **Where do you get energy to work or play?** *(Sample: Food)* **Where does a cow or chicken or fish get energy?** *(Grass, grain, plants, other fish)* **Where does an apple tree get energy?** *(The sun)*

Untamed Science Video

GIVE ME THAT CARBON! Before viewing, invite students to suggest ways in which matter might move from one organism to another in an ecosystem. Then play the video. Lead a class discussion and make a list of questions that this video raises. You may wish to have students view the video again after they have completed the chapter to see if their questions have been answered.

> To access the online resources for this chapter, search on or navigate to *Ecosystems and Biomes.*
>
> **Untamed Science Video** shows how carbon moves through an ecosystem.
>
> **The Big Question** allows students to answer the Engaging Question about the different ways organisms get their food.

my science online.com ▷ **Ecosystems and Biomes**

WHERE DOES FOOD COME FROM?

THE BIG ?

How do energy and matter move through ecosystems?

Flying around hunting for food, this barn owl spots a mouse for dinner. But what did the mouse eat? Perhaps it nibbled on seeds or a caterpillar. Then you might ask, where did the seeds and caterpillar get their food?

Develop Hypotheses **Where do living things get their food?**

Sample: Some living things can make their own food using sunlight. Other living things get their food from eating other plants and animals.

▷ UNTAMED SCIENCE Watch the **Untamed Science** video to learn more about ecosystems and biomes.

Professional Development Note **From the Author**

I have lived in several countries: Kenya, Italy, Nigeria and the United States. Each country has different organisms that are adapted to the climate and other conditions in the area. For example, there is a dry and a rainy season in Kenya where zebras, gazelles, lions, and flat-topped acacia trees live. The annual rainfall is 50 to 100 centimeters and the area is mostly a grassland biome called a savanna. In contrast, Maryland has a deciduous forest biome. The trees, such as flowering dogwood, sweet gum, and white oak—the Maryland state tree—are adapted to the changes in seasons. The leaves that grow in spring and summer are shed before the cold winter begins.

✒ *Zipporah Miller*

Ecosystems and Biomes

CHAPTER 2

Chapter at a Glance

CHAPTER PACING: 8–13 periods or 4–6$\frac{1}{2}$ blocks

INTRODUCE THE CHAPTER: Use the Engaging Question and the opening image to get students thinking. Activate prior knowledge and preteach vocabulary using the Getting Started pages.

Lesson 1: Energy Flow in Ecosystems

Lesson 2: Cycles of Matter

Lesson 3: Biomes

Lesson 4: Aquatic Ecosystems

Lesson 5: Biogeography

ASSESSMENT OPTIONS: Chapter Test, **EXAM**VIEW® Assessment Suite, Performance Assessment, Progress Monitoring Assessments, SuccessTracker™

Preference Navigator, in the online Planning tools, allows you to customize *Interactive Science* to your own teaching style. You can also edit lesson plans by selecting the Lesson Planner option.

Digital Teacher's Edition allows you to access your Teacher's Edition and Resource online.

my science online.com

my science online.com | Ecosystems and Biomes | UNTAMED SCIENCE | THE BIG QUESTION | 39

Differentiated Instruction

L1 Use Visuals Help students understand that the photograph is an extreme close-up action shot taken at night. Ask them to infer what happened moments before this image was taken, as well as to predict what will happen next. *(Moments before, the owl seized the rodent and took flight. Shortly the owl will kill and eat the rodent.)*

L3 Report on Owls Invite students to share facts they know about owls. Encourage interested students to research and report to the class about what owls eat. *(Students may mention that owls are nocturnal birds of prey that live in various places around the world. Owls feed on rodents, frogs, insects, and small birds.)*

Getting Started

Check Your Understanding

This activity assesses students' understanding of living and nonliving things in an ecosystem. After students have shared their answers, point out that things that once were living, such as leaves that have fallen off a tree, are considered biotic factors, even though they are no longer living.

Preteach Vocabulary Skills

Explain to students that many words can be modified by the addition of a prefix. Learning the meaning of prefixes can make it easier to learn new vocabulary words. Point out that students probably already know some of these prefixes, especially *inter-*, which makes up part of the words *internet*, *international*, and *interact*.

---

2 Getting Started

Check Your Understanding

1. **Background** Read the paragraph below and then answer the question.

> One morning, Han walks to the park and sits by the pond. He has just studied **ecosystems** in class, and now, looking at the pond, he realizes he sees things in a new way. He notices a turtle sunning itself on a rock, and knows that the sun and rock are **abiotic factors**, while the turtle, and other living things, are **biotic factors.**

> The community of organisms that live in a particular area, along with their nonliving environment, make up an **ecosystem.**
>
> **Abiotic factors** are the nonliving parts of an organism's habitat.
>
> **Biotic factors** are the living parts of an organism's habitat.

• Name one more biotic factor and one more abiotic factor that Han might see at the pond.

Sample: biotic, plants; abiotic, water

> **MY READING WEB** If you had trouble answering the question above, visit **My Reading Web** and type in *Ecosystems and Biomes.*

Vocabulary Skill

Prefixes Some words can be divided into parts. A root is the part of the word that carries the basic meaning. A prefix is a word part that is placed in front of the root to change the word's meaning. The prefixes below will help you understand some vocabulary in this chapter.

Prefix	Meaning	Example
bio-	life	biogeography, *n.* the study of where organisms live
inter-	between	intertidal, *adj.* ocean zone between the highest high-tide line and the lowest low-tide line

2. **Quick Check** Circle the prefix in each boldface word below.
• There was an **inter**mission between the acts of the play.
• The **bio**sphere is the area where life exists.

My Reading Web offers leveled readings related to chapter content.

Vocab Flash Cards offer extra practice with the chapter vocabulary words.

Digital Lesson
• Assign the *Check Your Understanding* activity online and have students submit their work to you.
• Assign the *Vocabulary Skill* activity online and have students submit their work to you.

MY SCIENCE online.com | **Ecosystems and Biomes**

consumer

precipitation

desert

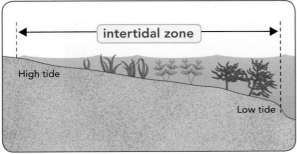
intertidal zone

High tide

Low tide

Chapter Preview

LESSON 1
- producer • consumer
- herbivore • carnivore • omnivore
- scavenger • decomposer
- food chain • food web
- energy pyramid
- 🔄 Relate Text and Visuals
- △ Classify

LESSON 2
- evaporation • condensation
- precipitation • nitrogen fixation
- 🔄 Sequence
- △ Infer

LESSON 3
- biome • climate • desert
- rain forest • emergent layer
- canopy • understory • grassland
- savanna • deciduous tree
- boreal forest • coniferous tree
- tundra • permafrost
- 🔄 Compare and Contrast
- △ Draw Conclusions

LESSON 4
- estuary
- intertidal zone
- neritic zone
- 🔄 Outline
- △ Communicate

LESSON 5
- biogeography
- continental drift • dispersal
- exotic species
- 🔄 Relate Cause and Effect
- △ Predict

> **VOCAB FLASH CARDS** For extra help with vocabulary, visit **Vocab Flash Cards** and type in *Ecosystems and Biomes.*

41

Preview Vocabulary Terms

Have students create a three-column chart to rate their knowledge of the vocabulary terms before they read the chapter. In the first column of the chart, students should list the terms for the chapter. In the second column, students should identify whether they can define and use the word, whether they have heard or seen the word before, or whether they do not know the word. As the class progresses through the chapter, have students write definitions for each term in the last column of the chart.

L1 Have students look at the images on this page as you pronounce each vocabulary word. Have students repeat the word after you. Then read the definition. Use the sample sentence in italics to clarify the meaning of the term.

consumer *(kun SOO mur)* An organism that obtains energy by feeding on other organisms. *A fox is a consumer of organisms such as berries, birds, mice, and insects.*

precipitation *(prih sip ih TAY shun)* Rain, snow, sleet, or hail that falls to Earth from clouds. *The precipitation took the form of rain and drenched the foothills.*

desert *(DEZ urt)* An area that receives less than 25 centimeters of rain per year. *The desert is home to plants such as cactus and various grasses.*

intertidal zone *(in tur TYD ul zohn)* The area on shore between the highest high-tide line and the lowest low-tide line. *An intertidal zone can stretch hundreds of meters and contains a variety of plant growth.*

CHAPTER 2

(E)(L)(L) Support

Have students work in small groups to complete their individual charts cooperatively for the **Preview Vocabulary Terms** activity. Be sure to use multiple-meaning words such as *competition* and *host* in their proper science contexts with students.

Beginning
LOW Complete the chart using the vocabulary terms in the native language.

HIGH Write a definition for each known vocabulary term in the native language.

Intermediate
LOW/HIGH Discuss the definitions for known vocabulary terms in cooperative groups.

Advanced
LOW/HIGH Write a sentence using each of the vocabulary terms.

Energy Flow and Ecosystems

How do energy and matter move through ecosystems?

Lesson Pacing: 1–2 periods or $\frac{1}{2}$–1 block

🕐 **SHORT ON TIME?** To do this lesson in approximately half the time, do the Activate Prior Knowledge activity on page 42. A discussion of the key concepts on pages 43, 46, and 48 will familiarize students with the lesson content. Have students do the Quick Lab. The rest of the lesson can be completed by students independently.

Preference Navigator, in the online Planning tools, allows you to customize Interactive Science to your own teaching style. You can also edit lesson plans by selecting the Lesson Planner option.

Digital Teacher's Edition allows you to access your Teacher's Edition and Resource materials online.

my science online.com

Lesson Vocabulary

- producer • consumer • herbivore • carnivore • omnivore
- scavenger • decomposer • food chain • food web
- energy pyramid

Content Refresher

Moving Through Energy Pyramids Energy in an ecosystem moves in only one direction, from the bottom (producers) to the top (top-level consumers) of an energy pyramid. Only about 10 percent of the energy in an energy pyramid is transferred from one level to the next. In a food web, energy may not be transferred to the next level for two reasons. First, some energy is given off as heat. Second, not all organisms in one level are eaten by those in the next level. As a result, some energy is not transferred at all. And even those organisms that are consumed might contain parts that cannot be digested—bones, beaks, shells, and so on—which further reduces the total amount of energy that can be transferred.

LESSON OBJECTIVES

Name and describe energy roles that organisms play in an ecosystem.

Explain how energy moves through an ecosystem.

Blended Path
Active learning using Student Edition, Inquiry Path, and Digital Path

ENGAGE AND EXPLORE

Teach this lesson using a variety of resources. Begin by reading **My Planet Diary** as a class. Have students share ideas about wild animals that live in their region and what they eat. Then have students do the **Inquiry Warm-Up activity.** Students will classify their own food and food sources. Discuss the categories different students chose and how they classified their food sources. The **After the Inquiry Warm-Up worksheet** sets up a discussion about common food sources. Have volunteers share their answers to number 4 about which foods come from multiple sources.

EXPLAIN AND ELABORATE

Discuss the terms *producer, composer, and decomposer.* **Teach Key Concepts** by explaining that ecosystem roles are based primarily on the way organisms obtain their energy. Ask students to name three energy roles in an ecosystem and tell how an organism fills one of these roles. Use the **Support the Big Q** to illustrate how decomposers get energy and the role of decomposers in an ecosystem. Use **Figure 2** to illustrate the roles of the different animals listed in the chart.

Using food chains and food webs, **Teach Key Concepts** by asking students how energy can be obtained and how it changes as it moves within a pyramid. Then have students practice the inquiry skill in the **Apply It activity.** In the chapter **Lab Investigation activity,** students will observe food chains in a local ecosystem. Hand out the **Key Concept Summaries** as a review of each part of the lesson. Students can also use the online **Vocab Flash Cards** to review key terms.

EVALUATE

Have students take the **Lesson Quiz.** For an alternate assessment, see the **EXAM**VIEW® Assessment Suite, Progress Monitoring Assessments, or SuccessTracker™.

E L L Support

1 Content and Language

Compare the words *herbivore, carnivore,* and *omnivore* in the vocabulary. Explain what the word parts signal. The root *-vore* means to devour. The word parts *herbi-, carni-,* and *omni-* tells what the organism devours: *herbi*—vegetable matter, *carni*—meat, and *omni*—all.

DIFFERENTIATED INSTRUCTION KEY
L1 Struggling Students or Special Needs
L2 On-Level Students **L3** Advanced Students

LESSON PLANNER 2.1

Lab zone Inquiry Path
Hands-on learning in the Lab zone

ENGAGE AND EXPLORE

To teach this lesson with an emphasis on inquiry, begin with the **Inquiry Warm-Up activity.** Students will classify food sources. Discuss the categories different students chose and how they classified food sources. Have students do the **After the Inquiry Warm-Up worksheet.** Talk about common food sources. Have volunteers share their answers to number 4 about which foods come from multiple sources.

EXPLAIN AND ELABORATE

Focus on the **Inquiry Skill** for the lesson. Point out that when you classify, you assign something to a category. What conclusion can be drawn from the categories in the **Inquiry Warm-Up activity?** *(Food sources can be grouped into categories based on the type of organism they come from.)* Have students do the **Quick Lab** to reinforce understanding of decomposition and then share their results.

Review *producer, consumer,* and *decomposer* before beginning the **Apply It activity.** Ask volunteers to share their categories. Have students do the **Lab Investigation activity.** In this investigation, students will observe food chains in a local ecosystem. Students can use the online **Vocab Flash Cards** to review key terms.

EVALUATE

Have students take the **Lesson Quiz.** For an alternate assessment, see the **EXAM**VIEW® Assessment Suite, Progress Monitoring Assessments, or SuccessTracker™.

Digital Path
Online learning at **my science online**.com

ENGAGE AND EXPLORE

Teach this lesson using digital resources. Begin by having students explore wild animals and what they eat at **My Planet Diary** online. Have them access the Chapter Resources to find the **Unlock the Big Question activity.** There they can answer the questions and refine their responses as they continue through the lesson. You can re-assign the activity and have students submit their work so you can track their progress.

EXPLAIN AND ELABORATE

Students reading above, at, or below the lexile measure of this lesson can access basic content readings at their level at **My Reading Web.** Encourage students to use the online **Vocab Flash Cards** to preview key terms. Have students do the **Quick Lab** and then share their results. What are their observations of decomposition?

Review *producer, consumer,* and *decomposer* before assigning the online **Apply It activity.** Ask volunteers to share their categories. Have students submit their work to you. Have students do the online **Interactive Art activity** to interpret food chains in a food web. Students can then do the online **Virtual Lab** to see how energy moves within a food pyramid. Assign the **Do the Math activity** online and have students submit their work to you. The **Key Concept Summaries** online allow students to read a summary and see an image associated with each part of the lesson. Online remediation is available at **My Science Coach.**

EVALUATE

Have students take the **Lesson Quiz.** For an alternate assessment, see the **EXAM**VIEW® Assessment Suite, Progress Monitoring Assessments, or SuccessTracker™.

2 Frontload the Lesson
Preview the lesson visuals, labels, and captions. Ask students what they know about the words *producer, consumer,* and *decomposer.* Explain the specific meanings these words have in science.

3 Comprehensible Input
Have students study the visuals and their captions on pages 44–45, and 47 to support the key concepts of the lesson.

4 Language Production
Pair or group students with varied language abilities to complete labs collaboratively for language practice. Have each copy the completed written lab for personal reference.

5 Assess Understanding
Have students create and illustrate their own food pyramids and cut each level as strips. Pair students to share and reassemble their food pyramids to demonstrate comprehension.

LESSON 2.1

Energy Flow in Ecosystems

Establish Learning Objectives

After this lesson, students will be able to:

🔑 Name and describe energy roles that organisms play in an ecosystem.

🔑 Explain how energy moves through an ecosystem.

Engage

Activate Prior Knowledge

MY PLANET DIARY Read *I'll Have the Fish* with the class. Invite students to name wild animals that live in their region. Urge students to think about how each animal may fit into an ecosystem. Ask: **What birds live in the area?** *(Students may indicate one or many bird species.)* **What do you think any of these birds eats?** *(Students may indicate small mammals, insects, or worms.)*

BIG IDEAS OF SCIENCE REFERENCE LIBRARY 📖 Have students look up the following topics: Sushi, Upwelling.

Explore

Lab Resource: Inquiry Warm-Up 🔬

L1 **WHERE DID YOUR DINNER COME FROM?**
Students will classify food sources.

LESSON

1 Energy Flow in Ecosystems

UNLOCK THE BIG ?

🔑 **What Are the Energy Roles in an Ecosystem?**

🔑 **How Does Energy Move Through an Ecosystem?**

MY PLANET DIARY   DISCOVERY

I'll Have the Fish

Scientists have noticed something fishy going on with the wolves in British Columbia, Canada. During autumn, the wolves ignore their typical food of deer and moose and feast on salmon instead. Salmon are very nutritious and lack the big horns and hoofs that can injure or kill wolves. Plus, there are plenty of fish in a small area, making them easier to find and catch.

Many animals, including the wolves, depend upon the salmon's annual mating trip upstream. Losing this important food source to overfishing would hurt the populations of bears, wolves, birds, and many other animals.

Communicate Discuss these questions with a classmate. Write your answers below.

1. What are two reasons the wolves may eat fish in autumn instead of deer or moose?
   <u>Sample: Fish are easier to find and don't hurt the wolves.</u>

2. What effect could overfishing salmon have on an ecosystem?
   <u>Sample: A lack of salmon could decrease the number of predators. With fewer predators, the number of salmon could increase.</u>

▶ **PLANET DIARY** Go to **Planet Diary** to learn more about food webs.

🔬 **Lab zone** Do the Inquiry Warm-Up *Where Did Your Dinner Come From?*

42 Ecosystems and Biomes

SUPPORT ALL READERS

Prior Exposure to Content: May be the first time students have encountered this topic

Academic Vocabulary: *apply, classify, describe, identify*

Science Vocabulary: *producer, consumer, decomposer*

Concept Level: Many students may have misconceptions on this topic

Preteach With: My Planet Diary "I'll Have the Fish" and Figure 2 activity

Go to **My Reading Web** to access leveled readings that provide a foundation for the content.

My science online.com

Vocabulary
- producer • consumer • herbivore • carnivore
- omnivore • scavenger • decomposer • food chain
- food web • energy pyramid

Skills
🔄 Reading: Relate Text and Visuals
△ Inquiry: Classify

What Are the Energy Roles in an Ecosystem?

Do you play an instrument in your school band? If so, you know that each instrument has a role in a piece of music. Similar to instruments in a band, each organism has a role in the movement of energy through its ecosystem.

An organism's energy role is determined by how it obtains food and how it interacts with other organisms. 🗝 **Each of the organisms in an ecosystem fills the energy role of producer, consumer, or decomposer.**

Producers Energy enters most ecosystems as sunlight. Some organisms, like the plants and algae shown in **Figure 1,** and some types of bacteria, capture the energy of sunlight and store it as food energy. These organisms use the sun's energy to turn water and carbon dioxide into food molecules in a process called photosynthesis.

An organism that can make its own food is a **producer.** Producers are the source of all the food in an ecosystem. In a few ecosystems, producers obtain energy from a source other than sunlight. One such ecosystem is found in rocks deep beneath the ground. Certain bacteria in this ecosystem produce their own food using the energy in hydrogen sulfide, a gas that is present in their environment.

FIGURE 1 ·····························
Producers
Producers are organisms that can make their own food.

✏️ **Identify** Complete the shopping list below to identify the producers that are part of your diet.
- ○ wheat
- ○ corn
- ○ banana
- ○ Sample: lettuce
- ○ Sample: orange
- ○ Sample: rice
- ○ Sample: apple
- ○
- ○

Tape grass and water milfoil

43

Explain ————

Introduce Vocabulary

To help students understand the terms *herbivore, carnivore,* and *omnivore,* point out that the root *-vore-* is related to the Latin word *vorare,* meaning "to devour or eat."

Teach Key Concepts 🗝

Explain to students that ecosystem roles are based primarily on the way organisms obtain energy. Remind students that every organism must obtain energy from some source and that organisms interact with other organisms within an ecosystem. Ask: **What are the names of the three energy roles in an ecosystem?** *(Producer, consumer, decomposer)* **What is a producer?** *(An organism that makes its own food)* **How do most producers make their own food?** *(Through photosynthesis)* **What is the source of energy for photosynthesis?** *(The sun)*

My Planet Diary provides an opportunity for students to explore real-world connections to energy roles in an ecosystem.

my science online .com | **Energy Roles in Ecosystems**

Ⓔ Ⓛ Ⓛ Support

1 Content and Language
Students will be introduced to a number of terms that look similar but can be differentiated by the prefixes (*eco-, bio-, herbi-, carni-, omni-*) and suffixes (*-ation, -er*) that are used.

2 Frontload the Lesson
Write the words *food* and *energy* on the board, and then have students complete a picture walk of the lesson. As they scan the pictures, ask them to identify the ways in which food is shown, and how this relates to energy.

3 Comprehensible Input
Ask students what is the name of the section in a local grocery store where one finds fruits and vegetables? (*Produce section*) Ask students to reason why this is the name of this area of the store.

Explain

Teach With Visuals

Have students do the detective work. As they study **Figure 2,** they should keep their eyes open for clues. Ask: **Which animal or animals might have eaten the chicken?** *(Wolf, bear)* **Which animal or animals might have eaten the vegetables on the ground?** *(Bear, rabbit)* **Which animals might have eaten food from inside the tent?** *(The wolf might have eaten the beef jerky, and the rabbit might have eaten the apples.)* **What animal might have eaten the strawberries?** *(Bear)* **How did you figure out these answers?** *(Sample: In most cases, I used the chart, looked at the illustration, and used the process of elimination.)*

Support the Big Q ⓆUbD

DECOMPOSERS Remind students that each organism in an ecosystem fills a specific energy role. Producers, such as oak trees, make their own food. Consumers, such as caterpillars and bluebirds, feed on other organisms. Ask: **Where do decomposers get energy?** *(From the materials they break down.)* **What role do decomposers play in the movement of matter through an ecosystem?** *(Decomposers break down wastes and dead organisms and recycle these materials.)*

21st Century Learning

INTERPERSONAL SKILLS Have students read the text about producers, consumers, and decomposers with a partner. One partner reads a paragraph aloud, and then the other partner summarizes the paragraph's main idea. Have partners switch roles until they have finished the section.

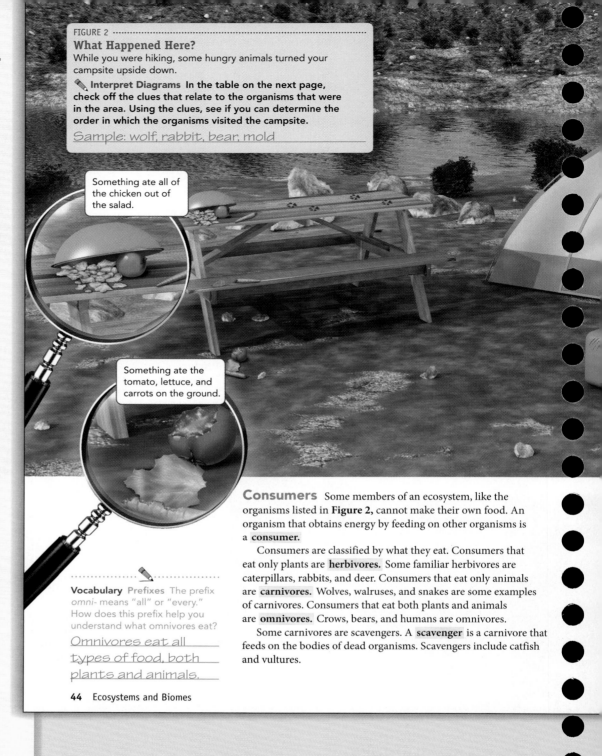

FIGURE 2

What Happened Here?

While you were hiking, some hungry animals turned your campsite upside down.

✎ **Interpret Diagrams** In the table on the next page, check off the clues that relate to the organisms that were in the area. Using the clues, see if you can determine the order in which the organisms visited the campsite.

Sample: wolf, rabbit, bear, mold

Something ate all of the chicken out of the salad.

Something ate the tomato, lettuce, and carrots on the ground.

Vocabulary Prefixes The prefix *omni-* means "all" or "every." How does this prefix help you understand what omnivores eat?

Omnivores eat all types of food, both plants and animals.

Consumers Some members of an ecosystem, like the organisms listed in **Figure 2,** cannot make their own food. An organism that obtains energy by feeding on other organisms is a **consumer.**

Consumers are classified by what they eat. Consumers that eat only plants are **herbivores.** Some familiar herbivores are caterpillars, rabbits, and deer. Consumers that eat only animals are **carnivores.** Wolves, walruses, and snakes are some examples of carnivores. Consumers that eat both plants and animals are **omnivores.** Crows, bears, and humans are omnivores.

Some carnivores are scavengers. A **scavenger** is a carnivore that feeds on the bodies of dead organisms. Scavengers include catfish and vultures.

44 Ecosystems and Biomes

Clues	Bear	Mold	Rabbit	Wolf
Can easily reach the table top	✓			✓
Grows on food and breaks it down		✓		
Small enough to enter and exit tent			✓	✓
Gets energy from meat	✓	✓		✓
Strong enough to open cooler	✓			
Not a picky eater	✓			
Gets energy from plants	✓	✓	✓	

Something ate the apples and beef jerky from inside the tent.

Something ate strawberries, even some of the moldy ones.

Decomposers If an ecosystem had only producers and consumers, the raw materials of life, such as carbon and nitrogen, would stay locked up in wastes and the bodies of dead organisms. However, there are organisms in ecosystems that prevent this from happening. **Decomposers** break down biotic wastes and dead organisms and return the raw materials to the ecosystem.

You can think of decomposers as nature's recyclers. While obtaining energy for their own needs, decomposers return simple molecules to the environment. These molecules can be used again by other organisms. Mushrooms, bacteria, and mold are common decomposers.

Lab zone Do the Quick Lab *Observing Decomposition.*

Assess Your Understanding

1a. Describe An organism's energy role is determined by how it obtains ___food___ and how it ___interacts___ with other organisms.

b. Apply Concepts What is the main source of energy for all three energy roles? Why?
___Sunlight; producers use___
___the energy to make food.___
___Consumers eat producers___
___directly or indirectly for___
___energy. Decomposers break___
___down dead producers and___
___consumers to get energy.___

got it? ....

○ **I get it!** Now I know that the energy roles in an ecosystem are ___producers,___ ___consumers, and___ ___decomposers.___

○ **I need extra help with** ___See TE note.___

Go to **my science COACH** *online for help with this subject.*

45

Elaborate

Make Analogies

L1 CONSUMERS AND PRODUCERS To help students understand the scientific definitions of the terms *consumer* and *producer*, compare energy roles to the manufacturing process. Ask: **What does a shoe manufacturer produce?** *(Shoes)* **How does a shoe manufacturer resemble a producer in an ecosystem?** *(Sample: Both produce something using raw materials.)* **What does a shopper purchase, or "consume," in a shoe store?** *(The item produced by the manufacturer, shoes)* **How does this interaction resemble the actions of a consumer in an ecosystem?** *(Sample: Both consume something that was produced elsewhere or outside itself.)*

Lab Resource: Quick Lab

L1 OBSERVING DECOMPOSITION Students will observe how materials decay in a compost pile.

Evaluate

Assess Your Understanding

After students answer the questions, have them evaluate their understanding by completing the appropriate sentence.

RTI Response to Intervention

1a. If students have trouble describing an energy role, **then** review with them the two characteristics that determine an organism's energy role.

b. If students need help identifying the energy source, **then** call on volunteers to give examples of organisms and their energy sources. Help students trace the energy source back to the sun.

my science COACH Have students go online for help in understanding energy roles in ecosystems.

Differentiated Instruction

L1 Concept Map Have students make a concept map of the three energy roles that organisms can fill in an ecosystem. Their maps should include an explanation of how producers, consumers, and decomposers get energy. Have students compare their concept maps when they have finished. Then ask them to make statements that describe the relationship between the roles.

L3 Observe a Local Habitat Invite students to observe a local habitat, such as their yard or the school grounds. Students should try to identify and describe at least one producer *(for example, grass or trees)*, one consumer *(worms, birds)*, and one decomposer *(mushrooms)* that they observe in this habitat. Have students present their findings orally supported with photographs, drawings, or other visual aids.

 LESSON 2.1

45

Explain

Teach Key Concepts 🗝

Explain to students that energy can be transferred from one organism to another in an ecosystem. Ask: **What happens to energy as one organism eats another in an ecosystem?** (Energy moves through the ecosystem.) **What is a food chain?** (A series of events in which one organism eats another and obtains energy) **How are food chains and a food web related?** (A food web is made up of many overlapping food chains in the same environment.)

Address Misconceptions

ENERGY FOR DARK ECOSYSTEMS Point out to students that producers can make their own food through photosynthesis or through chemosynthesis. Explain that not all ecosystems require light as an energy source. Help students understand that ecosystems surrounding deep-sea vents are too far below the water's surface to receive sunlight. In this ecosystem, bacteria living near the vents make food by using energy from chemicals in the water. Ask: **How is this ecosystem similar to the one based on photosynthesis?** (Like plants, bacteria are producers in the food web.) You may want to explain to students that deep-sea vents are just one ecosystem in which bacteria obtain energy from chemicals. Encourage interested students to research chemosynthesis to find out more about these bacteria.

How Does Energy Move Through an Ecosystem?

As you have read, energy enters most ecosystems as sunlight and is converted into food by producers. This energy is transferred to the organisms that eat the producers, and then to other organisms that feed on the consumers. 🗝 **Energy moves through an ecosystem when one organism eats another.** This movement of energy can be shown as food chains, food webs, and energy pyramids.

Food Chains One way to show how energy moves in an ecosystem is with a food chain. A **food chain** is a series of events in which one organism eats another and obtains energy. You can follow one example of a food chain in **Figure 3.**

Food Webs A food chain shows only one possible path along which energy can move through an ecosystem. Most producers and consumers are part of many food chains. A more realistic way to show the flow of energy through an ecosystem is with a food web. As shown in **Figure 4,** a **food web** consists of many overlapping food chains in an ecosystem.

Organisms may play more than one role in an ecosystem. Look at the crayfish in **Figure 4.** A crayfish is an omnivore that is a first-level consumer when it eats plants. But when a crayfish eats a snail, it is a second-level consumer.

Just as food chains overlap and connect, food webs interconnect as well. A gull might eat a fish at the ocean, but it might also eat a mouse at a landfill. The gull, then, is part of two food webs—an ocean food web and a land food web. All the world's food webs interconnect in what can be thought of as a global food web.

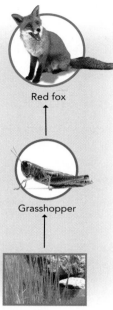

Red fox

Grasshopper

Plants

FIGURE 3 ⋯⋯⋯⋯⋯⋯⋯⋯⋯⋯
Food Chain
In this food chain, you can see how energy moves from plants, to a grasshopper, to the fox. The arrows show how energy moves up the food chain, from one organism to the next.

 **apply** it!

Classify Using what you have learned about food chains, draw or describe a food chain from your local ecosystem. Show at least three organisms in your food chain. Name each organism and label it as a producer, consumer, or decomposer.

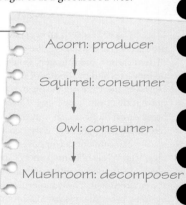

Acorn: producer

↓

Squirrel: consumer

↓

Owl: consumer

↓

Mushroom: decomposer

Interactive Art allows students to see the connections between organisms in a food web.

Digital Lesson: Assign the *Apply It* activity online and have students submit their work to you.

my science online.com ▶ **Energy Flow in Ecosystems**

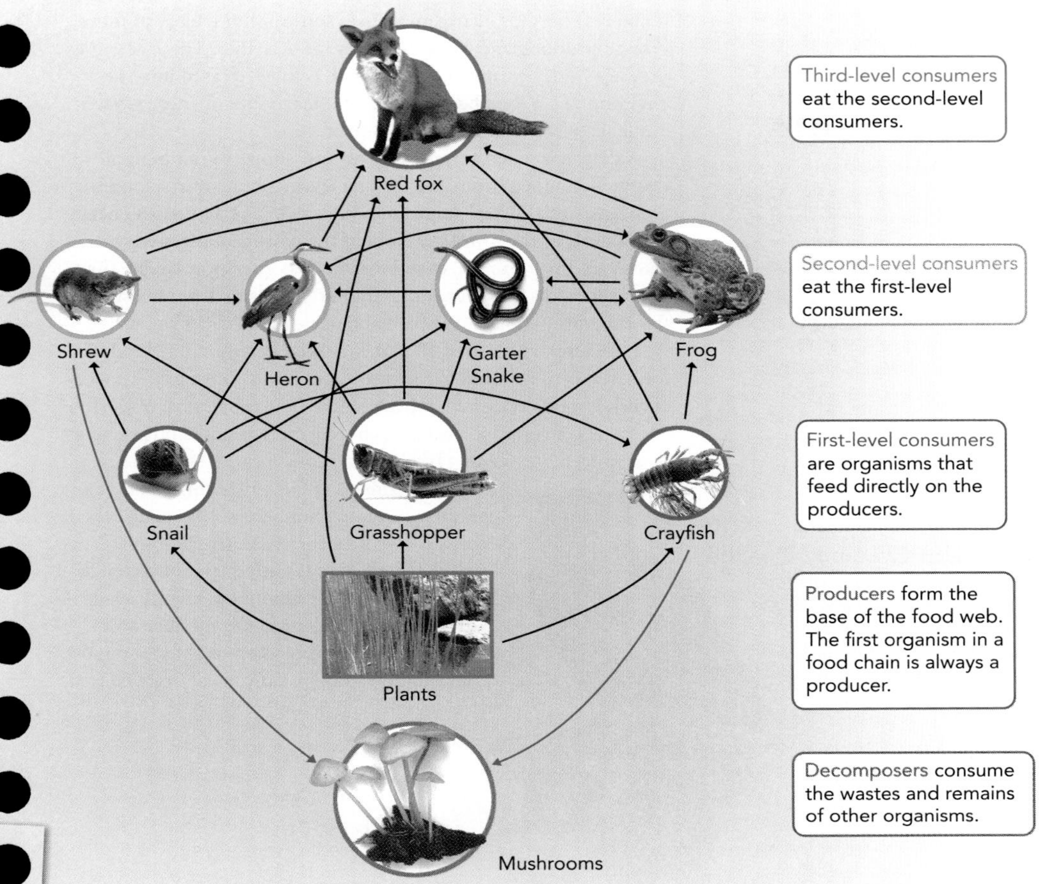

Third-level consumers eat the second-level consumers.

Second-level consumers eat the first-level consumers.

First-level consumers are organisms that feed directly on the producers.

Producers form the base of the food web. The first organism in a food chain is always a producer.

Decomposers consume the wastes and remains of other organisms.

FIGURE 4 ....
> INTERACTIVE ART **Food Web**
A food web consists of many interconnected food chains.

✎ **Complete the tasks.**

1. **Interpret Diagrams** Pick two organisms from the food web. Draw arrows connecting them to the decomposers.

2. 🔄 **Relate Text and Visuals** How can the fox be both a second-level and third-level consumer?

If the fox eats a first-level consumer, then the fox is a second-level consumer. If the fox eats a second-level consumer, then the fox is a third-level consumer.

47

Teach With Visuals

Tell students to look at **Figure 4.** Remind students that a food web includes several food chains. Ask: **What are the producers in this food web?** (Plants such as grasses) **What are the first-level consumers?** (Snail, grasshopper, crayfish) **What are the second-level consumers?** (Shrew, heron, garter snake, frog, red fox) **What is the third-level consumer?** (Red fox) **What is the decomposer?** (Mushrooms)

🔄 **Relate Text and Visuals** Explain to students that they should pay attention to how the text and visuals work together to communicate information. In **Figure 4,** the text and the visuals each provide information that the other does not: The text explains what first-level, second-level, and third-level consumers are, while the visuals show that the fox eats both first-level and second-level consumers.

Elaborate ——————————

Apply It!

L1 Review how energy moves through an ecosystem and review the terms producer, consumer, and decomposer before beginning the activity.

△ **Classify** Remind students that classifying involves organizing information based on a set of chosen characteristics. If students have difficulty classifying each organism as a producer, consumer, or decomposer, have them study the relationships among organisms in the food chain shown in **Figure 3.**

Differentiated Instruction

L1 **Demonstrate Omnivores' Relationships in a Food Web** Have pairs of students take turns tracing two arrows on the food web in **Figure 4** to show how a red fox and a crayfish can be both a first-level consumer and a second-level consumer. Have students show how a shrew can be both a second-level consumer and a third-level consumer. Remind students that the arrows show the direction of energy flow, from food to the organism that eats it.

L3 **Identify the Food Chains** Challenge students to analyze **Figure 4** in order to identify all of the distinct food chains that make up the food web in the illustration. Students can create a series of drawings to show each food chain in isolation from the others in the web.

Explain

Teach Key Concepts 🔑

Explain to students that an organism obtains energy when it eats or produces its own food. When it moves, grows, reproduces, and does other activities, it produces heat and releases that heat into the environment. This release of heat causes less energy to be available to the next consumer. Ask: **In an energy pyramid, where is the most energy available?** *(At the producer level)* **How does the amount of energy change as energy moves up the pyramid?** *(Each level on the pyramid has less energy available than the level below it.)* **How do producers obtain energy?** *(From sunlight)*

🔄 **Relate Text and Visuals** Remind students that relating the text and visuals involves understanding how the text pertains to the visuals in the diagram.

21st Century Learning

CRITICAL THINKING Solidify students' understanding of the calculations shown in the energy pyramid in **Figure 5** by explaining the steps they would take to find the products. They should enter into the calculator the number shown in parentheses next to the label *Producers*. Then they can press the multiply sign and enter the number 0.1 (one-tenth) to find the product 100 kcal. This number represents the amount of energy available to the next consumer in the energy pyramid. Have them repeat this process for each level in the diagram.

Elaborate

Build Inquiry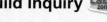

L2 IDENTIFY AVAILABLE ENERGY

Materials index cards

Time 10 minutes

Relate the shape of an energy pyramid to the diminishing amount of energy available, moving from bottom to top. Have one student draw an empty pyramid on the board. Have another student divide it into four horizontal sections. Provide index cards with these labels: *Most Energy Available, Least Energy Available, Producers, Consumers, Top Consumer*, and the like. Have students attach their labels to the pyramid on the board.

Ask: **Which section will include the producers?** *(Level 1)* **Which section includes the top consumer?** *(Level 4)* **Which sections include the consumers?** *(Levels 2, 3, and 4)* Have students consider which section represents the most available energy, as well as the least available energy.

Ask: **Which section supports the fewest organisms?** *(Level 4)*

✏️

🔄 **Relate Text and Visuals**
Look at the energy pyramid. Why is a pyramid the best shape to show how energy moves through an ecosystem?

A pyramid decreases in size from the bottom to the top, in the same way that the available food energy decreases from one level to the next.

FIGURE 5 ·····

VIRTUAL LAB Energy Pyramid
This energy pyramid diagram shows the energy available at each level of a food web and how it is calculated. Energy is measured in kilocalories, or kcal.

Energy Pyramids When an organism in an ecosystem eats, it obtains energy. The organism uses some of this energy to move, grow, reproduce, and carry out other life activities. These activities produce heat, a form of energy, which is then released into the environment. When heat is released, the amount of energy that is available to the next consumer is reduced.

A diagram called an **energy pyramid** shows the amount of energy that moves from one feeding level to another in a food web. You can see an energy pyramid in **Figure 5.** 🔑 **The most energy is available at the producer level of the pyramid. As energy moves up the pyramid, each level has less energy available than the level below.** An energy pyramid gets its name from the shape of the diagram—wider at the base and narrower at the top.

In general, only about 10 percent of the energy at one level of a food web is transferred to the next higher level. Most of the energy at each level is converted to heat. Since about 90 percent of the food energy is converted to heat at each step, there is not enough energy to support many feeding levels in an ecosystem.

The organisms at higher feeding levels of an energy pyramid do not necessarily require less energy to live than the organisms at lower levels. Because so much energy is converted to heat at each level, the amount of energy available at the producer level limits the number of consumers that the ecosystem is able to support. As a result, there are usually fewer organisms at the highest level in a food web.

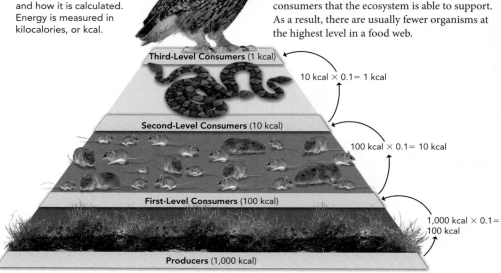

Third-Level Consumers (1 kcal)

$10 \text{ kcal} \times 0.1 = 1 \text{ kcal}$

Second-Level Consumers (10 kcal)

$100 \text{ kcal} \times 0.1 = 10 \text{ kcal}$

First-Level Consumers (100 kcal)

$1,000 \text{ kcal} \times 0.1 = 100 \text{ kcal}$

Producers (1,000 kcal)

48 Ecosystems and Biomes

Virtual Lab allows students to track the energy and biomass of a biome.

Digital Lesson: Assign the *Do the Math* activity online and have students submit their work to you.

MY SCIENCE online.com ▸ **Energy Flow in Ecosystems**

do the math!

Energy Pyramids

Suppose that the producers at the base of an energy pyramid contain 330,000 kilocalories.

Calculate Using **Figure 5** as a guide, label how much energy would be available at each level of the pyramid based on the questions below.

❶ If mice ate all of the plants, how much energy would be available to them as first-level consumers?

❷ If all of the mice were eaten by snakes, how much energy would the snakes receive?

❸ If all of the snakes were eaten by the owl, how much energy would the owl receive?

❹ [CHALLENGE] About how much energy would the owl use for its life processes or lose as heat? _297 kcal_

❺ [CHALLENGE] How much energy would be stored in the owl's body? _33 kcal_

330 kcal
Third-Level Consumers

3,300 kcal
Second-Level Consumers

33,000 kcal
First-Level Consumers

330,000 kcal
Producers

Do the Lab Investigation
Ecosystem Food Chains.

Assess Your Understanding

2a. Define A food (web/**chain**) is a series of events in which one organism eats another and obtains energy. A food (**web**/chain) consists of many overlapping food (webs/**chains**).

b. Compare and Contrast Why is a food web a more realistic way of portraying an ecosystem than a food chain?

Because most organisms are
part of many overlapping food
chains

c. Relate Cause and Effect Why are there usually fewer organisms at the top of an energy pyramid?

Since so much energy is lost
from one level to the next level
up, the energy available at the
top level can only support a few
organisms.

got it?

○ I get it! Now I know that energy moves through an ecosystem when _organisms eat_
other organisms.

○ I need extra help with _See TE note._

Go to **my science COACH** *online for help with this subject.*

49

Do the Math!

L1 Review with students the way energy moves through the levels of the energy pyramid. Some students may have difficulty with the last two questions. Point out that 10% of 330 is 33 and $330 - 33 = 297$.

See *Math Skill and Problem-Solving Activities* for support.

Lab Resource: Lab Investigation

L2 **ECOSYSTEM FOOD CHAINS** Students will observe food chains in a local ecosystem.

Evaluate

Assess Your Understanding

After students answer the questions, have them evaluate their understanding by completing the appropriate sentence.

RTI Response to Intervention

2a, b. If students need help distinguishing between food webs and food chains, **then** have them compare the food chain shown in **Figure 3** with the food web shown in **Figure 4**.

c. If students have trouble with energy pyramids, **then** refer them to **Figure 5** and ask how many snakes they think it takes to keep an owl fed and how many mice they think it takes to keep a snake fed.

my science COACH Have students go online for help in understanding energy flow in ecosystems.

Differentiated Instruction

L1 Visualize Energy Transfers To assist students needing help visualizing energy transfers in an energy pyramid, divide the class into groups of three. Distribute scissors and graph paper. The first student, the "producer," should cut a 10-by-10 block of squares from graph paper. The block represents the total amount of food energy stored in the producer. The "producer" should then cut a row of 10 squares from the block and pass it on to the second student, the

"first-level consumer." That student should cut one square from the row and pass it to the third student, the "second-level consumer." Students will see that only a small portion of the original energy stored in the producer reaches the second-level consumer.

Name _____ Date _____ Class _____

Energy Flow in Ecosystems

Inquiry Warm-Up, *Where Did Your Dinner Come From?*
In the Inquiry Warm-Up, you investigated where certain foods come from. Using what you learned from that activity, answer the questions below.

1. **DRAW CONCLUSIONS** What is a benefit of knowing the source of a certain food? Explain.

    _____

    _____

2. **MAKE GENERALIZATIONS** Look at the lists of a few of your fellow students. Which source of food was listed the most? Which source was listed the least?

    _____

    _____

3. **COMMUNICATE** Like macaroni, some foods come from multiple sources. Draw a Venn diagram showing the source(s) for the following foods: chicken salad, green peas, bacon, fish, popcorn, beef stew.

4. **INTERPRET DATA** Which foods in the diagram are in the multiple sources category?

    _____

Assess Your Understanding

Energy Flow in Ecosystems

What Are the Energy Roles in an Ecosystem?

1a. DESCRIBE An organism's energy role is determined by how it obtains _____ and how it _____ with other organisms.

b. APPLY CONCEPTS What is the main source of energy for all three energy roles? Why? _____

_____

gotit? ··

○ **I get it!** Now I know that the energy roles in an ecosystem are _____

_____

○ **I need extra help with** _____

How Does Energy Move Through an Ecosystem?

2a. DEFINE A food (web/chain) is a series of events in which one organism eats another and obtains energy. A food (web/chain) consists of many overlapping food (webs/chains).

b. COMPARE AND CONTRAST Why is a food web a more realistic way of portraying an ecosystem than a food chain?

_____

c. RELATE CAUSE AND EFFECT Why are there usually fewer organisms at the top of an energy pyramid?

_____

_____

gotit? ··

○ **I get it!** Now I know that energy moves through an ecosystem when _____

_____

○ **I need extra help with** _____

_____

Key Concept Summaries

Energy Flow in Ecosystems

What Are the Energy Roles in an Ecosystem?

An organism's energy role is determined by how it obtains energy and how it interacts with other organisms. **Each of the organisms in an ecosystem fills the energy role of producer, consumer, or decomposer.** Energy enters most ecosystems as sunlight. An organism that can make its own food is a **producer.** Producers are the source of all the food in an ecosystem. An organism that obtains energy by feeding on other organisms is a **consumer.** Consumers that eat only plants are **herbivores;** consumers that eat only animals are **carnivores;** consumers that eat both plants and animals are **omnivores.** A **scavenger** is a carnivore that feeds on the bodies of dead organisms. **Decomposers** break down wastes and dead organisms and return the raw materials to the ecosystem. Mushrooms and bacteria are common decomposers.

How Does Energy Move Through an Ecosystem?

Energy moves through an ecosystem when one organism eats another. A **food chain** is a series of events in which one organism eats another and obtains energy. A **food web** consists of many overlapping food chains in an ecosystem. Organisms may play more than one role in an ecosystem. Just as food chains overlap and connect, food webs interconnect also. When an organism in an ecosystem eats, it obtains energy. The organism uses some of this energy to move, grow, reproduce, and carry out other life activities. These activities produce heat, a form of energy, which is then released into the environment. When heat is released, the amount of energy that is available to the next consumer is reduced. A diagram called an **energy pyramid** shows the amount of energy that moves from one feeding level to another in a food web. **The most energy is available at the producer level of the pyramid. As energy moves up the pyramid, each level has less energy available than the level below.**

On a separate sheet of paper, explain the energy roles in an ecosystem.

Energy Flow in Ecosystems

Understanding Main Ideas
Answer the following questions on a separate sheet of paper.

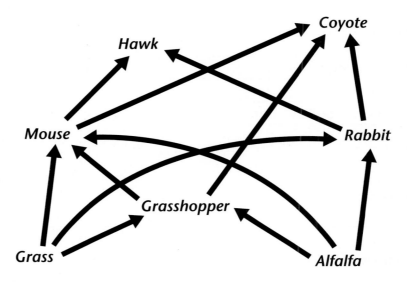

1. Which organism in the food web above is sometimes a first-level consumer and sometimes a second-level consumer? Explain.
2. Choose one food chain in the web. Name all the organisms in that chain. Start with the producer and end with the top-level consumer.
3. Draw an energy pyramid for the food chain you chose. Label the pyramid to tell how much food energy is available at each level.

Building Vocabulary
On a separate sheet of paper, write the term that fits each definition below.

4. Organisms that make their own food
5. Organisms that obtain energy by feeding on other organisms
6. Organisms that break down wastes and dead organisms and return the raw materials to the environment
7. Consumers that eat only animals
8. Consumers that eat only plants
9. Consumers that eat both plants and animals
10. Consumers that feed on the bodies of dead organisms

Name ______________________ Date ____________ Class ____________

Enrich

Energy Flow in Ecosystems

The open ocean, like all land ecosystems, has many food webs. The chart below provides a list of animals in a typical South Atlantic food web and their sources of food energy. Study the table and answer the questions that follow.

Food Webs in the Ocean

Organisms	Obtain food energy from...
Squid	shrimp, fish
Algae	make their own food by photosynthesis
Fishes	shrimp
Penguins	squid

1. Which organisms are the producers?

____

2. Which organism is a first-level consumer?

____

3. What makes the squid's role different from that of other consumers listed in the table?

____

____

4. In the space below, draw the ocean food web. Label each organism to identify its energy role in the ecosystem.

Place the outside corner, the corner away from the dotted line, in the corner of your copy machine to copy onto letter-size paper.

Name _____ Date _____ Class _____

Energy Flow in Ecosystems

If the statement is true, write *true*. If the statement is false, change the underlined word or words to make the statement true.

1. _____ A <u>food web</u> is a series of events in which one organism eats another and obtains energy.

2. _____ <u>Each of the organisms</u> in an ecosystem fills the energy role of producer, consumer, or decomposer.

3. _____ Organisms may play <u>only one role</u> in an ecosystem.

4. _____ An organism that obtains energy by feeding on other organisms is a <u>decomposer</u>.

5. _____ Energy enters most ecosystems as <u>sunlight</u>.

Fill in the blank to complete each statement.

6. An organism that can make its own food is a _____.

7. Mushrooms and bacteria are common _____.

8. _____ moves through an ecosystem when one organism eats another.

9. The most energy is available at the _____ level of the pyramid.

10. As energy moves up the pyramid, each level has _____ energy available than the level below.

Energy Flow in Ecosystems

Answer Key

After the Inquiry Warm-Up

1. Accept all reasonable responses. Students may say: Some people may become sick by or are allergic to certain foods and their ingredients. Knowing the source of a food would help them avoid discomfort or worse.

2. Accept all reasonable responses. Students may say: Animal/meat is listed the most, plant/vegetable is listed the least.

3. Sample: Students should draw a Venn diagram with at least two overlapping categories: Plant, Animal. In the Plant circle: green peas, popcorn; in the Animal circle: bacon and fish; and in the Plant/Animal overlap: chicken salad and beef stew.

4. Chicken salad and beef stew

Key Concept Summaries

An organism's energy role—producer, consumer, or decomposer—is determined by how it gets energy and interacts with other organisms. Energy enters most ecosystems as sunlight. Organisms that make their own food are producers. Organisms that get energy by feeding on other organisms are consumers. There are three types of consumers: herbivores eat only plants; carnivores eat only animals; omnivores eat both. Decomposers break down wastes and dead organisms and return the raw materials to the ecosystem.

Review and Reinforce

1. The mouse; it is a first-level consumer when it eats grass or alfalfa and a second-level consumer when it eats a grasshopper.

2. There are many different food chains in the web. Examples include grass ⟶ mouse ⟶ hawk; alfalfa ⟶ grasshopper ⟶ mouse ⟶ coyote; and grass ⟶ rabbit ⟶ hawk. All chains cited by students should start with grass or alfalfa and end with the hawk or coyote.

3. Students' diagrams should show the producer at the base and the top-level consumer at the apex. The levels should be labeled in 10-percent increments—producer, 100%; first-level consumer, 10%; second-level consumer, 1%; third-level consumer, 0.1%.

4. producers
5. consumers
6. decomposers
7. carnivores
8. herbivores
9. omnivores
10. scavengers

Enrich

1. algae

2. shrimp

3. The squid is a second-level consumer when it eats shrimp and a third-level consumer when it eats fish.

4. Students should identify algae as producers, shrimp as first-level consumers, and fishes and penguins as second-level consumers. Squid are first-level consumers and second-level consumers.

Lesson Quiz

1. food chain
2. true
3. more than one role
4. consumer
5. true
6. producer
7. decomposers
8. Energy
9. producer
10. less

Place the outside corner, the corner away from the dotted line, in the corner of your copy machine to copy onto letter-size paper.

Cycles of Matter

Lesson Pacing: 2–3 periods or 1–1$\frac{1}{2}$ blocks

🕐 **SHORT ON TIME?** To do this lesson in approximately half the time, do the Activate Prior Knowledge activity on page 50. A discussion of the key concepts on pages 50, 52, and 54 will familiarize students with the lesson content. Use the Explore the Big Q to help students trace four cycles of matter. Have students do the Quick Labs. The rest of the lesson can be completed by students independently.

Preference Navigator, in the online Planning tools, allows you to customize *Interactive Science* to your own teaching style. You can also edit lesson plans by selecting the Lesson Planner option.

Digital Teacher's Edition allows you to access your Teacher's Edition and Resource materials online.

my science online.com

Lesson Vocabulary

- evaporation
- condensation
- precipitation
- nitrogen fixation

Content Refresher

Making Nutrients Available Ecosystem cycles are critical to providing organisms with basic building blocks needed for survival. One such building block is the element nitrogen. Nitrogen is needed for the formation of amino acids, which combine to form proteins. Some proteins are enzymes, which are catalysts for an organism's chemical reactions. Other proteins are the key components of many body tissues, such as muscle and skin. However, an organism cannot use all forms of nitrogen. In an ecosystem, those organisms that are part of the nitrogen cycle make it possible for nitrogen to be converted into forms other organisms can use.

LESSON OBJECTIVES

🔑 Name and describe processes involved in the water cycle.
🔑 Explain how carbon and oxygen are recycled.
🔑 Define and describe the nitrogen cycle.

Blended Path
Active learning using Student Edition, Inquiry Path, and Digital Path

ENGAGE AND EXPLORE

To teach this lesson using a variety of resources, begin by reading **My Planet Diary** as a class. Have students share their opinions about using animals to save human lives. Then have students do the **Inquiry Warm-Up activity.** Students will investigate their part in the water cycle. Discuss the formation of evaporation of water vapor and students' part in the process. The **After the Inquiry Warm-Up worksheet** sets up a discussion about students' part in a water cycle. Have volunteers share their answers to number 4 about other cycles students may be a part of.

EXPLAIN AND ELABORATE

Teach Key Concepts by explaining the processes of evaporation, condensation, and precipitation in the water cycle.

Continue to **Teach Key Concepts** by explaining how, in an ecosystem, the processes by which carbon and oxygen are recycled are linked. Ask students to explain the roles producers, consumers, and decomposers play in these cycles. Then have students look at **Figure 2** and ask volunteers to share their answers. Students can then practice the lesson's inquiry skill in the **Apply It activity.**

Using **Figure 4, Teach Key Concepts** by asking students how free nitrogen in the air is mixed into compounds. Use the **Explore the Big Q activity** to relate carbon and oxygen, water, and nitrogen cycles and the food chain. Hand out the **Key Concept Summaries** as a review of each part of the lesson. Students can also use the online **Vocab Flash Cards** to review key terms.

EVALUATE

Have students take the **Lesson Quiz.** For an alternate assessment, see the **EXAM**VIEW® Assessment Suite, Progress Monitoring Assessments, or SuccessTracker™.

E L L Support

1 Content and Language

Compare the words *evaporation, condensation, precipitation,* and *fixation* in the vocabulary. Explain what the word parts signal. The *-ation* means a process. The word parts *evapor-, condens-, precipit-,* and *fix-* tell about the process; *evapor*—change to steam or vapor; *condens*—change to liquid; *precipit*—condense from a vapor; and *fix*—fasten or hold.

Lab zone Inquiry Path
Hands-on learning in the Lab zone

ENGAGE AND EXPLORE

Teach this lesson with an emphasis on inquiry. Begin with the **Inquiry Warm-Up activity** in which students will explore evaporation and condensation. Discuss the processes and how they differ. Have students do the **After the Inquiry Warm-Up worksheet.** Talk about students' roles in a water cycle. Have volunteers share their answers to number 4 about other cycles students may be a part of.

EXPLAIN AND ELABORATE

Focus on the **Inquiry Skill** for the lesson. Point out that when you infer, you draw a conclusion by reasoning. What conclusion can be drawn from the results of activities in the **Inquiry Warm-Up activity?** (*You can be part of a water cycle of condensation and evaporation.*) Have students do the first **Quick Lab** and then share their observations about the elements of the water cycle.

Review *producer, consumer,* and *decomposer* before beginning the **Apply It activity.** Ask volunteers to share what they know about the carbon and oxygen cycles. The **Build Inquiry activity** allows students to participate in a minds-on activity about producers and consumers. Have students do the second **Quick Lab** to explore the role of producers in the carbon and oxygen cycles.

Give students an opportunity to role-play various organisms and materials of a nitrogen cycle in the last **Quick Lab.** Students can use the online **Vocab Flash Cards** to review key terms.

EVALUATE

Have students take the **Lesson Quiz.** For an alternate assessment, see the **EXAM**VIEW® Assessment Suite, Progress Monitoring Assessments, or SuccessTracker™.

Digital Path
Online learning at my science online.com

ENGAGE AND EXPLORE

To teach this lesson using digital resources, begin by having students explore cycles of matter at **My Planet Diary** online. Have them access the Chapter Resources to find the **Unlock the Big Question activity.** There they can answer the questions and refine their responses as they continue through the lesson. You can re-assign the activity and have students submit their work so you can track their progress.

EXPLAIN AND ELABORATE

Students reading above, at, or below the lexile measure of this lesson can access basic content readings at their level at **My Reading Web.** Have students do the online **Interactive Art activity** to identify the processes of the water cycle. Have students do the first **Quick Lab** and then share their observations about the elements of the water cycle. Encourage students to use the online **Vocab Flash Cards** to preview key terms.

Review *producer, consumer,* and *decomposer* before assigning the online **Apply It activity.** Ask volunteers to share what they know about the carbon and oxygen cycles and have them submit their work to you. Have students do the second **Quick Lab** to explore the role of producers in the carbon and oxygen cycles.

Have students do the online **Interactive Art activity** to observe how energy and matter are cycled through an ecosystem. Have students do the **Quick Lab** to explore to understand the organisms and materials of a nitrogen cycle. The **Key Concept Summaries** online allow students to read a summary and see an image associated with each part of the lesson. Online remediation is available at **My Science Coach.**

EVALUATE

Have students take the **Lesson Quiz.** For an alternate assessment, see the **EXAM**VIEW® Assessment Suite, Progress Monitoring Assessments, or SuccessTracker™.

2 Frontload the Lesson
Preview the lesson visuals, labels, and captions. Ask students what they know about the words *evaporation, condensation, precipitation,* and *fixation.* Explain the specific meanings these words have in science.

3 Comprehensible Input
Have students study the visuals and their captions on pages 51, 53, and 55 to support the key concepts of the lesson.

4 Language Production
Pair or group students with varied language abilities to complete labs collaboratively for language practice. Have each student copy the completed written lab for personal reference.

5 Assess Understanding
Make true or false statements using lesson content and have students indicate if they agree or disagree with a thumbs up or thumbs down gesture to check whole-class comprehension.

LESSON 2.2

Cycles of Matter

Establish Learning Objectives

After this lesson, students will be able to:

🔑 Name and describe processes involved in the water cycle.

🔑 Explain how the carbon and oxygen cycles are related.

🔑 Define and describe the nitrogen cycle.

Engage

Activate Prior Knowledge

MY PLANET DIARY Read *Canaries and Coal* with the class. Explain that in certain extreme locations, such as at very high altitudes or below ground, it is challenging for humans to get enough oxygen. Some students may find this passage upsetting. Point out that canaries are not used in this way in coal mines any longer. Ask: **What effect does fresh circulating oxygen have in an underground space like a coal mine?** *(It makes it possible for people to breathe.)*

BIG IDEAS OF SCIENCE REFERENCE LIBRARY 📖
Have students look up the following topic: Great Lakes.

Explore

Lab Resource: Inquiry Warm-Up 🔬

L1 **ARE YOU PART OF A CYCLE?** Students will explore how they are part of the oxygen cycle.

---

2 Cycles of Matter

UNLOCK THE BIG ?

🔑 **What Processes Are Involved in the Water Cycle?**

🔑 **How Are the Carbon and Oxygen Cycles Related?**

🔑 **How Does Nitrogen Cycle Through Ecosystems?**

my planet diary   DISASTER

Canaries and Coal

Have you ever stopped to listen to a bird sing? If you were a coal miner in the early 1900s, your life may have depended on it! Sometimes miners stumbled upon pockets of carbon monoxide, a toxic, odorless gas that makes it difficult for the body to get enough oxygen. Without fresh air circulating in the mineshafts, the miners would fall asleep and eventually die. To prevent this disaster from happening, canaries were used to monitor the air quality. A singing canary indicated that all was well. If the canary stopped singing and died, the miners knew that they needed to quickly leave the mine.

Answer the question below.
Do you think it was ethical, or fair, to use canaries this way? Explain.

Sample: Yes; I think it was ethical to use canaries to save human lives.

▷ **PLANET DIARY** Go to **Planet Diary** to learn more about cycles of matter.

 Lab zone Do the Inquiry Warm-Up *Are You Part of a Cycle?*

What Processes Are Involved in the Water Cycle?

Recycling is important for ecosystems because matter is limited. To understand how matter cycles through an ecosystem, you need to know a few terms that describe the structure of matter. Matter is made up of tiny particles called atoms. Two or more atoms that are joined and act as a unit make up a molecule. For example, a water molecule consists of two hydrogen atoms and one oxygen atom.

Water is essential for life. The water cycle is the continuous process by which water moves from Earth's surface to the atmosphere and back. 🔑 **The processes of evaporation, condensation, and precipitation make up the water cycle.**

50 Ecosystems and Biomes

SUPPORT ALL READERS
Lexile Measure = 980L   Lexile Word Count = 1292

Prior Exposure to Content: May be the first time students have encountered this topic

Academic Vocabulary: *infer, observe, sequence*

Science Vocabulary: *evaporation, condensation, precipitation*

Concept Level: May be difficult for students who struggle with abstract ideas

Preteach With: My Planet Diary "Canaries and Coal" and Figure 1 activity

Go to **My Reading Web** to access leveled readings that provide a foundation for the content.

my science online.com

Vocabulary
- evaporation
- precipitation
- condensation
- nitrogen fixation

Skills
- Reading: Sequence
- Inquiry: Infer

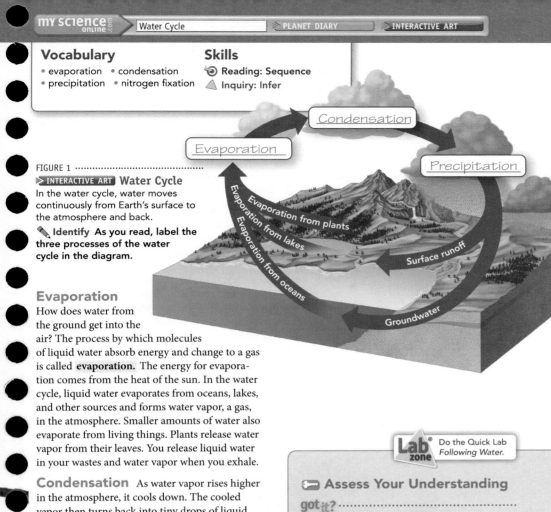

FIGURE 1 ....

> INTERACTIVE ART **Water Cycle**
In the water cycle, water moves continuously from Earth's surface to the atmosphere and back.

✎ **Identify** As you read, label the three processes of the water cycle in the diagram.

Evaporation
How does water from the ground get into the air? The process by which molecules of liquid water absorb energy and change to a gas is called **evaporation.** The energy for evaporation comes from the heat of the sun. In the water cycle, liquid water evaporates from oceans, lakes, and other sources and forms water vapor, a gas, in the atmosphere. Smaller amounts of water also evaporate from living things. Plants release water vapor from their leaves. You release liquid water in your wastes and water vapor when you exhale.

Condensation
As water vapor rises higher in the atmosphere, it cools down. The cooled vapor then turns back into tiny drops of liquid water. The process by which a gas changes to a liquid is called **condensation.** The water droplets collect around dust particles and form clouds.

Precipitation
As more water vapor condenses, the drops of water in the clouds grow larger. Eventually the heavy drops fall to Earth as **precipitation**—rain, snow, sleet, or hail. Precipitation may fall into oceans, lakes, or rivers. The precipitation that falls on land may soak into the soil and become groundwater, or run off the land, flowing back into a river or ocean.

 Lab zone Do the Quick Lab Following Water.

🔑 Assess Your Understanding
got it? ....

○ I get it! Now I know that the processes of the water cycle are _evaporation,_ _condensation, and_ _precipitation._

○ I need extra help with _See TE note._

Go to **MY SCIENCE COACH** online for help with this subject.

51

Explain

Introduce Vocabulary
To help students understand the relationship among the terms *evaporation, condensation,* and *precipitation,* point out the suffix *-tion/-ation* and explain that in these three words it means "the process of."

Teach Key Concepts 🔑
You may want to make sure that students understand the meaning of the word *cycle* and ask them for examples. *(Seasons of the year, days of the week, plants growing from seeds)* Explain to students that several processes take place in the water cycle. Draw students' attention to **Figure 1.** Ask: **What is the function of the water cycle?** *(It moves water from Earth's surface to the atmosphere and back.)* **What are the three processes that move water between Earth's surface and the atmosphere?** *(Evaporation, condensation, precipitation)* Point out to students that the process in which water evaporates from plant leaves is a type of evaporation called transpiration. **Which process includes melted snow entering rivers?** *(Surface runoff)* **How can you tell from the figure that the water cycle is continuous?** *(All three processes happen over and over again.)*

Lab Resource: Quick Lab 🧪
L2 FOLLOWING WATER Students will make a solar still and observe elements of the water cycle.

Evaluate

Assess Your Understanding
Have students evaluate their understanding by completing the appropriate sentence.

🅡🅣🅘 Response to Intervention
If students need help with the water cycle, **then** call on volunteers to describe steps in the water cycle while you diagram each of these steps on the board.

MY SCIENCE COACH Have students go online for help in understanding the water cycle.

My Planet Diary provides an opportunity for students to explore real-world connections to the carbon and oxygen cycles.

Interactive Art allows students to identify the processes of the water cycle.

MY SCIENCE online | Water Cycle

ⒺⓁⓁ Support

1 Content and Language
Ask students to identify the common suffix in *evaporation, condensation,* and *precipitation.* The suffix *-tion* means "the act or process of doing something."

2 Frontload the Lesson
To help students understand why it is called the *water cycle,* ask students to explain what a cycle is. Simplify **Figure 1** by drawing a water cycle with two parts—liquid and gas (vapor)—and arrows that form a cycle going from one to another.

3 Comprehensible Input
Explain the Explore the Big Q image and caption, restating information as needed. Have students complete the **Figure 5** activity, allowing them to draw and write according to their language proficiency level.

Explain

Teach Key Concepts 🔑

Remind students that the carbon and oxygen cycles are linked and that producers and consumers play a part in both cycles. Review the basic processes of photosynthesis and respiration. Ask: **What is the role of producers in the carbon and oxygen cycles?** *(Producers take in carbon dioxide during photosynthesis and use it to make food in the form of carbon-containing molecules. They release oxygen as a product of photosynthesis.)* **How do consumers fit into the carbon and oxygen cycles?** *(Consumers take in carbon-containing molecules by eating producers; when they break these molecules down, they release carbon dioxide. Consumers use oxygen to get energy from the food they have eaten.)* **How will depriving a closed terrarium of sunlight affect the oxygen and carbon cycles of the plants and small animals inside?** *(Without sunlight, plants can't make food and won't release oxygen; consumers will have no food sources and insufficient oxygen and will not release carbon dioxide.)*

Teach With Visuals

Tell students to look at **Figure 2.** Ask: **What two cycles are illustrated in this diagram?** *(Carbon cycle, oxygen cycle)* **How are these two cycles represented in the diagram?** *(Violet arrows and lines illustrate the processes of the carbon cycle, and yellow arrow and lines illustrate the processes of the oxygen cycle.)* You may want to point out to students a key difference between the carbon and oxygen cycles illustrated in **Figure 2** and the water cycle in **Figure 1.** The water cycle involves physical changes as water changes state. The carbon and oxygen cycles involve the chemical changes of photosynthesis and cellular respiration.

Elaborate

Apply It!

L1 Review the definitions of *producer, consumer,* and *decomposer* before beginning the activity.

⚠ **Infer** Remind students that when they infer, they use the information they are given as well as their prior knowledge to answer a question or draw a conclusion. Make sure students understand that a cow is a first-level consumer. Discuss with students how a cow obtains oxygen and carbon.

How Are the Carbon and Oxygen Cycles Related?

Carbon and oxygen are also necessary for life. Carbon is an essential building block in the bodies of living things. For example, carbon is a major component of bones and the proteins that build muscles. And most organisms use oxygen for their life processes. 🔑 **In ecosystems, the processes by which carbon and oxygen are recycled are linked. Producers, consumers, and decomposers all play roles in recycling carbon and oxygen.**

The Carbon Cycle Most producers take in carbon dioxide gas from the air during food-making or photosynthesis. They use carbon from the carbon dioxide to make food—carbon-containing molecules such as sugars and starches. As consumers eat producers, they take in the carbon-containing molecules. Both producers and consumers then break down the food to obtain energy. As the food is broken down, producers and consumers release carbon dioxide and water into the environment. When producers and consumers die, decomposers break down their remains and return carbon molecules to the soil. Some decomposers also release carbon dioxide into the air.

The Oxygen Cycle Look at **Figure 2.** Like carbon, oxygen cycles through ecosystems. Producers release oxygen as a result of photosynthesis. Most organisms take in oxygen from the air or water and use it to carry out their life processes.

Human Impact Human activities also affect the levels of carbon and oxygen in the atmosphere. When humans burn oil and other plant-based fuels, carbon dioxide is released into the atmosphere. Carbon dioxide levels can also rise when humans clear forests for lumber, fuel, and farmland. Increasing levels of carbon dioxide are a major factor in global warming. As you know, producers take in carbon dioxide during photosynthesis. When trees are removed from the ecosystem, there are fewer producers to absorb carbon dioxide. There is an even greater effect if trees are burned down to clear a forest. When trees are burned down, additional carbon dioxide is released during the burning process.

apply it!

Producers, consumers, and decomposers all play a role in recycling carbon and oxygen.

▲ **Infer** On the lines below, describe how you think a cow eating grass is part of both the carbon and oxygen cycles.

Sample: The cow takes in oxygen from the air and carbon molecules from the grass. Carbon dioxide is released by the cow as a waste product.

Digital Lesson: Assign the *Apply It* activity online and have students submit their work to you.

my science online.com ▶ **Carbon and Oxygen Cycles**

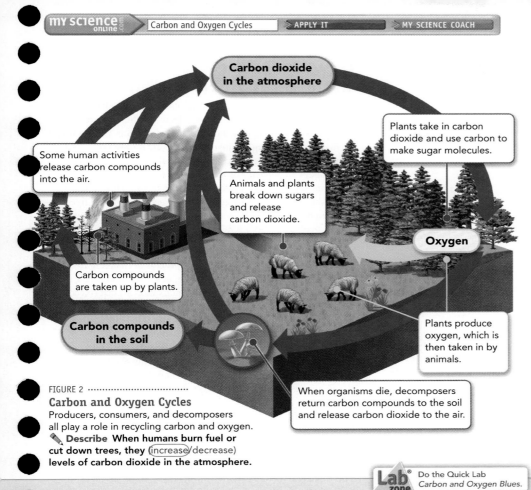

Carbon dioxide in the atmosphere

Some human activities release carbon compounds into the air.

Plants take in carbon dioxide and use carbon to make sugar molecules.

Animals and plants break down sugars and release carbon dioxide.

Oxygen

Carbon compounds are taken up by plants.

Carbon compounds in the soil

Plants produce oxygen, which is then taken in by animals.

When organisms die, decomposers return carbon compounds to the soil and release carbon dioxide to the air.

FIGURE 2 ······

Carbon and Oxygen Cycles
Producers, consumers, and decomposers all play a role in recycling carbon and oxygen.
✎ **Describe** When humans burn fuel or cut down trees, they (increase)/decrease) levels of carbon dioxide in the atmosphere.

Lab zone | Do the Quick Lab *Carbon and Oxygen Blues.*

🔧 Assess Your Understanding

1a. Identify Carbon and oxygen are both ___recycled___ in an ecosystem.

b. Develop Hypotheses How might the death of all the producers in a community affect the carbon and oxygen cycles?

The cycles would halt because
no oxygen or carbon would be
made available to consumers.

got it?

○ I get it! Now I know that the carbon and oxygen cycles are related by _the roles_
producers, consumers, and
decomposers play in
recycling them.

○ I need extra help with _See TE note._

Go to **my science** **coach** *online for help with this subject.*

53

L3 Research Effects of Carbon Dioxide in the Atmosphere Challenge students to do research to learn more about how increasing carbon dioxide levels in the atmosphere relate to global climate change. Urge students to prepare a written report and to include a list of their reference sources.

L1 Two Cycles Some students may find it helpful to look at the carbon cycle and oxygen cycle as separate cycles.

Have students diagram the oxygen cycle and then the carbon cycle on separate sheets of paper. Then have students compare their diagrams to the combined cycle diagram in **Figure 2.** If students have previously studied photosynthesis and respiration, they can apply their understanding of these processes to trace how carbon and oxygen cycle through producers, consumers, and decomposers.

Build Inquiry **Lab** zone

L2 PREDICT CARBON AND OXYGEN CYCLING

Materials none

Time 10 minutes

Review the differing roles of producers and consumers in recycling and carbon and oxygen. Describe for students a sealed jar containing guppies, plants, algae, and snails. Provide a picture if possible. (If you provide a picture, make sure that the algae are not green. Green algae are classified as plants, not protists.)

Ask: **Which organisms in the jar are producers?** *(The plants and algae)* **What do the producers release when they conduct photosynthesis?** *(Oxygen)* **What happens to the oxygen?** *(It is taken in by the guppies and snails.)* **Where do the producers get the carbon dioxide they need?** *(It is released by the guppies and snails.)* **Would you predict that this cycle would go on indefinitely? Why or why not?** *(Yes; as long as the producers receive sunlight and the guppies and snails receive food, the carbon and oxygen will continue to cycle between the producers and the consumers.)*

Lab Resource: Quick Lab **Lab** zone

L2 CARBON AND OXYGEN BLUES Students will explore the role of producers in the carbon and oxygen cycles.

Evaluate

Assess Your Understanding

After students answer the questions, have them evaluate their understanding by completing the appropriate sentence.

R T I Response to Intervention

1. If students have trouble with the carbon and oxygen cycles, **then** help them trace the path of carbon and oxygen through the diagram that shows the two cycles.

my science **coach** Have students go online for help in understanding the carbon and oxygen cycles.

Explain

Teach Key Concepts 🔑

Explain to students that the nitrogen cycle shares some characteristics with other cycles of matter, such as the carbon and oxygen cycles. Ask: **In what three places is nitrogen found?** *(In the soil, in the air, and in living things)* **What is "free" nitrogen?** *(Nitrogen gas, which is not combined with other kinds of atoms)* Remind students that most organisms cannot utilize nitrogen gas. Ask: **By what process do bacteria turn nitrogen into a usable form?** *(Nitrogen fixation)* **What organisms return simple nitrogen compounds to the soil?** *(Decomposers)*

21st Century Learning

INFORMATION LITERACY The application of nitrogen fertilizers to crops and lawns has resulted in the leaching of nitrates into groundwater. The contaminated groundwater eventually flows into streams, rivers, and lakes, affecting numerous ecosystems. This contamination affects water and habitat quality, which eventually leads to changes in the plant and animal populations. Encourage students to research the dangers of fertilizer contamination and what is now being done to help solve this problem. For instance, many local municipalities have begun to pass laws restricting when fertilizer can be applied and how much fertilizer can be used. Students can present their findings to the class in a short presentation.

How Does Nitrogen Cycle Through Ecosystems?

Like carbon, nitrogen is one of the necessary building blocks that make up living things. For example, in addition to carbon, nitrogen is also an important component of proteins. 🔑 **In the nitrogen cycle, nitrogen moves from the air into the soil, into living things, and back into the air or soil.** Since the air around you is about 78 percent nitrogen gas, you might think that it would be easy for living things to obtain nitrogen. However, most organisms cannot use nitrogen gas. Nitrogen gas is called "free" nitrogen because it is not combined with other kinds of atoms.

Nitrogen Fixation Most organisms can use nitrogen only after it has been "fixed," or combined with other elements to form nitrogen-containing compounds. The process of changing free nitrogen into a usable form of nitrogen, as shown in **Figure 4,** is called **nitrogen fixation.** Most nitrogen fixation is performed by certain kinds of bacteria. These bacteria live in bumps called nodules (NAHJ oolz) on the roots of legumes. These plants include clover, beans, peas, alfalfa, peanuts, and some trees.

The relationship between the bacteria and the legumes is an example of mutualism. Both the bacteria and the plants benefit from this relationship: The bacteria feed on the plants' sugars, and the plants are supplied with nitrogen in a usable form.

Return of Nitrogen to the Environment Once nitrogen is fixed, producers can use it to build proteins and other complex compounds. Nitrogen can cycle from the soil to producers and then to consumers many times. At some point, however, bacteria break down the nitrogen compounds completely. These bacteria then release free nitrogen back into the air, causing the cycle to continue.

FIGURE 3 ···

Growth in Nitrogen-Poor Soil
Pitcher plants can grow in nitrogen-poor soil because they obtain nitrogen by trapping insects in their tube-shaped leaves. The plants then digest the insects and use their nitrogen compounds.

✎ **Circle the correct word in each sentence.**

1. **Identify** If nitrogen in the soil isn't (fixed/free), then most organisms cannot use it.

2. CHALLENGE The relationship between the pitcher plant and the insects is an example of (competition/predation/symbiosis).

54   Ecosystems and Biomes

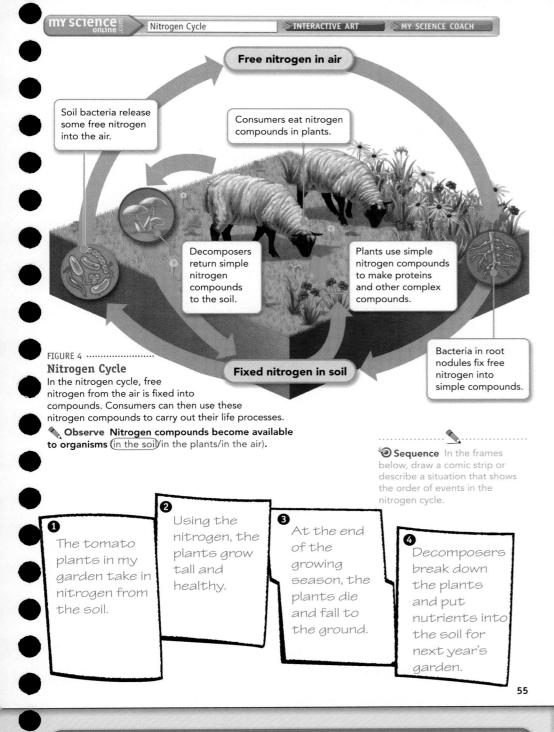

Free nitrogen in air

Soil bacteria release some free nitrogen into the air.

Consumers eat nitrogen compounds in plants.

Decomposers return simple nitrogen compounds to the soil.

Plants use simple nitrogen compounds to make proteins and other complex compounds.

Bacteria in root nodules fix free nitrogen into simple compounds.

Fixed nitrogen in soil

FIGURE 4 ·····················

Nitrogen Cycle
In the nitrogen cycle, free nitrogen from the air is fixed into compounds. Consumers can then use these nitrogen compounds to carry out their life processes.

✎ **Observe** Nitrogen compounds become available to organisms (in the soil)/in the plants/in the air).

✎ **Sequence** In the frames below, draw a comic strip or describe a situation that shows the order of events in the nitrogen cycle.

❶ The tomato plants in my garden take in nitrogen from the soil.

❷ Using the nitrogen, the plants grow tall and healthy.

❸ At the end of the growing season, the plants die and fall to the ground.

❹ Decomposers break down the plants and put nutrients into the soil for next year's garden.

55

Teach With Visuals

Have students look at **Figure 4**. Ask: **Why is nitrogen essential for living things?** *(It is used to make proteins.)* **What kinds of organisms return nitrogen compounds to the soil?** *(Bacteria and other decomposers)*

↻ **Sequence** Explain that sequencing involves organizing events or steps in a process in their correct order. Students should use the information in **Figure 4** to help them determine the correct order of events in the nitrogen cycle.

21st Century Learning

L3 **CRITICAL THINKING** Ask students to review the cycles of matter they have seen in this lesson and look for similarities and differences in the way materials move through the ecosystem. Also ask students to compare the way living things use water, carbon, oxygen, and nitrogen. Encourage students to recognize that the elements in these cycles—carbon, nitrogen, oxygen, and hydrogen (from water) are essential elements necessary to the make-up of living things. Ask: **How does the nitrogen cycle differ from the carbon and oxygen cycles?** *(Nitrogen becomes available to organisms through the soil rather than being absorbed from the air.)*

Differentiated Instruction

L1 **Illustrate Mutualism** Have pairs of students create simple diagrams to show how the relationship between bacteria and legumes represents mutualism. Students' diagrams should include labels and a simple rendering of bacteria in a nodule on the roots of a legume. Students might use arrows as well as text descriptions to convey the fact that the bacteria feed on the plant's sugars and that the plant is supplied with usable nitrogen.

L3 **Nitrogen in the Soil** Challenge students to do research to learn about the important role that nitrogen plays in agriculture. Students might focus on their region or state as they gather information that shows how farmers' economic success is dependent on their soil having sufficient nitrogen.

Explain

Teach With Visuals

Tell students to look at **Figure 5.** Point out that there are different ways to represent the cycles and the food chain in the diagram. Explain that students may use different details and may configure a cycle or food chain differently from one another. Ask: **Which two animals in the illustration are essentially interchangeable, in terms of their function in cycles of matter and food chains?** *(Pig, rabbit)*

Remind students that the plants and fungi pictured play the same role as the animals in the carbon cycle. They break down carbon-containing molecules in food, releasing carbon into the air (as carbon dioxide) and into the soil.

Elaborate

Explore the Big Q ❓ UbD

Direct students' attention to the particular details—sky, clouds, precipitation, trees, grass, water, soil, plants and their roots, fish, snake, field mouse, rabbit, pig, mushrooms—that are included in **Figure 5.** Ask: **Which of the cycles involves the atmosphere?** *(All four)* **Which of the cycles involves the roots of plants?** *(Nitrogen)* **What is the only third-level consumer in the illustration?** *(Snake)*

21st Century Learning 🇩🇰

COMMUNICATION Have students read *Great Lakes* in the **Big Ideas of Science Reference Library** and create a poster using the Great Lakes watershed to illustrate the three processes of the water cycle.

Lab Resource: Quick Lab 🔬

L1 PLAYING NITROGEN CYCLE ROLES Students will explore the processes and relationships involved in the nitrogen cycle by role-playing various materials and organisms.

Cycles of Matter

EXPLORE THE BIG ❓

How do energy and matter move through ecosystems?

FIGURE 5 ·····················

▶ **INTERACTIVE ART** Energy and matter are constantly being cycled through an ecosystem. These cycles can occur at the same time.

✎ **Interpret Diagrams** Using colored pencils, draw arrows to represent the following in the figure below: water cycle (blue), carbon cycle (purple), oxygen cycle (yellow), nitrogen cycle (orange), food chain (green). Label each cycle.

Carbon and oxygen cycle

Water cycle

Food chain

56 Ecosystems and Biomes

Interactive Art allows students to observe how energy and matter are cycled through an ecosystem.

my science online.com | **Nitrogen Cycle**

Nitrogen cycle

Lab zone® Do the Quick Lab *Playing Nitrogen Cycle Roles.*

Assess Your Understanding

2a. Describe (Fixed/~~Free~~) nitrogen is not combined with other kinds of atoms.

b. Predict What might happen in a community if farmers did not plant legume crops?

Consumers and producers would not survive because they depend on the nodules on the roots of legumes to fix nitrogen. Fixed nitrogen is needed to make the compounds they need for life processes. The nitrogen cycle would stop.

c. **ANSWER THE BIG ?** How do energy and matter move through ecosystems?

Food webs move energy through an ecosystem. Cycles move matter such as water, carbon, oxygen, and nitrogen through an ecosystem.

got **it?**

○ I get it! Now I know that the nitrogen cycle *moves nitrogen from the air into the soil, into living things, and back into the air or soil.*

○ I need extra help with *See TE note.*

Go to **MY SCIENCE S COACH** *online for help with this subject.*

57

Evaluate

Assess Your Understanding

After students answer the questions, have them evaluate their understanding by completing the appropriate sentence.

Answer the Big Q ? UbD

To help students focus on the Big Question, lead a class discussion about how energy and matter move through an ecosystem.

RTI Response to Intervention

2a, b. If students need help with the nitrogen cycle, **then** help them trace the movement of nitrogen through the ecosystem, especially the steps involving bacteria.

c. If students have trouble with cycles of matter, **then** have them review the illustrations of the cycles covered in this lesson.

MY SCIENCE S COACH Have students go online for help in understanding cycles of matter.

Differentiated Instruction

L1 Compare and Contrast Cycles Have pairs or groups of students use Venn diagrams, drawings, or tables to compare and contrast the water, carbon, oxygen, and nitrogen cycles. Encourage students to review the figures in this lesson, comparing and contrasting both the individual steps in the processes and the overall functions of each cycle.

L3 Human Effects on Cycles of Matter Challenge students to write a composition in which they describe in detail how particular human activities affect the water, carbon, oxygen, or nitrogen cycle. Students may wish to research using the Internet before beginning their compositions.

Lab zone **After the Inquiry Warm-Up**

Cycles of Matter

Inquiry Warm-Up, *Are You Part of a Cycle?*

In the Inquiry Warm-Up, you investigated your part in the water cycle. Using what you learned from that activity, answer the questions below.

1. **RELATE CAUSE AND EFFECT** What process caused the water vapor to form on the mirror?

   _____

   _____

2. **OBSERVE** What happened to the water vapor on the mirror after a few moments?

   _____

   _____

3. **USE PRIOR KNOWLEDGE** What happens to the water vapor after it evaporates into the air?

   _____

   _____

4. **USE PRIOR KNOWLEDGE** Describe one other cycle of which you are a part.

   _____

   _____

Place the outside corner, the corner away from the dotted line, in the corner of your copy machine to copy onto letter-size paper.

Assess Your Understanding

Cycles of Matter

> ### What Processes Are Involved in the Water Cycle?

got it? ···

○ **I get it!** Now I know that the processes of the water cycle are _____

_____

_____

○ **I need extra help with** _____

_____

> ### How Are the Carbon and Oxygen Cycles Related?

1a. **IDENTIFY** Carbon and oxygen are both _____ in an ecosystem.

b. **DEVELOP HYPOTHESES** How might the death of all the producers in a community affect the carbon and oxygen cycles?

_____

_____

_____

_____

got it? ···

○ **I get it!** Now I know that the carbon and oxygen cycles are related by _____

_____

_____

○ **I need extra help with** _____

_____

Name _____ Date _____ Class _____

Cycles of Matter

How Does Nitrogen Cycle Through Ecosystems?

2a. **DESCRIBE** (Fixed/Free) nitrogen is not combined with other kinds of atoms.

b. **PREDICT** What might happen in a community if farmers did not plant legume crops?

_____

_____

_____

_____

_____

c. **ANSWER** 🔍 How do energy and matter move through ecosystems?

_____

_____

_____

_____

_____

gotit? ···

O **I get it!** Now I know that the nitrogen cycle _____

_____

_____

O **I need extra help with** _____

_____

Key Concept Summaries

Cycles of Matter

What Processes Are Involved in the Water Cycle?

The water cycle is the continuous process by which water moves from Earth's surface to the atmosphere and back. **The processes of evaporation, condensation, and precipitation make up the water cycle.** The process by which molecules of liquid water absorb energy and change to a gas is called **evaporation.** In the water cycle, liquid water evaporates from oceans, lakes, plants, and other living things and forms water vapor, a gas, in the atmosphere. As water vapor rises higher in the atmosphere, it cools and turns back into liquid water. The process by which a gas changes to a liquid is called **condensation.** As more water vapor condenses, drops of water fall to Earth as **precipitation**—rain, snow, sleet, or hail.

How Are the Carbon and Oxygen Cycles Related?

Carbon is an essential building block in the bodies of living things. Most organisms use oxygen for their life processes. **In ecosystems, the processes by which carbon and oxygen are recycled are linked.** **Producers, consumers, and decomposers all play roles in recycling carbon and oxygen.** Human activities also cause the levels of carbon dioxide in the atmosphere to rise.

How Does Nitrogen Cycle Through Ecosystems?

Nitrogen is one of the necessary building blocks that make up living things. **In the nitrogen cycle, nitrogen moves from the air into the soil, into living things, and back into the air.** The air around us is about 78 percent nitrogen gas, but most organisms cannot use nitrogen gas, or "free nitrogen." The process of changing free nitrogen into a usable form of nitrogen is called **nitrogen fixation.** This process is performed by some kinds of bacteria.

On a separate sheet of paper, explain the water cycle.

Review and Reinforce

Cycles of Matter

Understanding Main Ideas
Answer the following questions on a separate sheet of paper.

1. What is the source of energy for the process of evaporation?
2. What happens to rainwater that falls on land?
3. How are oxygen and carbon cycled between plants and animals?
4. Why are nitrogen-fixing bacteria so important to other organisms?

Building Vocabulary
Answer the following question and identify labels in the spaces provided.

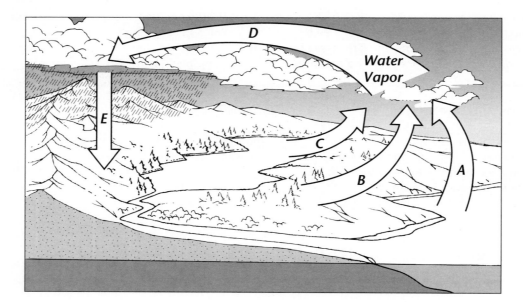

5. Which cycle is shown in the diagram above?

_____

Identify each process labeled in the diagram.

6. A _____

7. B _____

8. C _____

9. D _____

10. E _____

Enrich

Cycles of Matter

Deepa wanted to study how oxygen and carbon dioxide move through ecosystems. To do this, she set up three jars to represent consumers, producers, and consumers and producers together. She tested the jars for the presence of oxygen and carbon dioxide. Deepa's procedure and results are shown below. Study this information and then use a separate sheet of paper to answer the questions.

Testing for Oxygen and Carbon Dioxide

Procedure

Bromthymol blue (BTB) is a chemical that turns yellow in the presences of carbon dioxide. In the presence of oxygen, BTB stays blue. Deepa put the same amount of BTB in the three jars, and varied the organisms she placed in each jar. In Jar A, she put two aquatic snails. In Jar B, she put two sprigs of Elodea, an aquatic plant. In Jar C, she put two snails and two sprigs of Elodea.

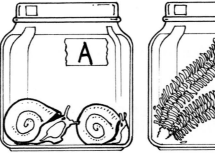

Results

Deepa examined the jars every day for three days. These are the observations she recorded.

Analyze and Conclude

1. Why did the BTB solution in Jar A turn yellow?
2. Why did the BTB solution in Jar B stay blue?
3. Why did the BTB solution in Jar C stay blue?
4. Which jar showed what happens during the carbon and oxygen cycles in nature? Describe the process that occurred in that jar.

Jar	Observations
A	The BTB solution turned yellow.
B	The BTB solution stayed blue.
C	The BTB solution stayed blue.

Lesson Quiz

Cycles of Matter

Fill in the blank to complete each statement.

1. The processes of evaporation, condensation, and precipitation make up
   _____.

2. The process by which a gas changes to a liquid is called _____.

3. In ecosystems, producers, consumers, and decomposers are linked by their roles in
   recycling carbon and _____.

4. _____ is a major component of bones and the proteins that build
   muscles.

5. The process of changing free nitrogen into a usable form of nitrogen is called
   _____.

If the statement is true, write *true*. If the statement is false, change the underlined word or words to make the statement true.

6. _____ <u>Condensation</u> is the continuous process by which water moves
   from Earth's surface to the atmosphere and back.

7. _____ In the <u>water cycle</u>, liquid water evaporates from oceans, plants,
   and other living things and forms water vapor, a gas, which rises in the atmosphere,
   then cools and turns back to drops of liquid water.

8. _____ Most organisms take in <u>nitrogen</u> from the air or water and use
   it to carry out their life processes.

9. _____ In a(n) <u>food web</u>, nitrogen moves from the air into the soil, into
   living things, and back into the air.

10. _____ The air around us is about <u>78 percent</u> nitrogen gas, but most
    organisms cannot use this "free nitrogen."

Cycles of Matter

Answer Key

After the Inquiry Warm-Up

1. condensation due to the temperature difference between the mirror and air coming out of your lungs

2. It evaporated into the air.

3. It condenses and falls to Earth as precipitation.

4. Accept all reasonable responses. Students may say: carbon cycle

Key Concept Summaries

The water cycle is the continuous process by which water moves from Earth's surface to the atmosphere and back through evaporation, condensation, and precipitation. In evaporation, molecules of liquid water absorb energy and change to water vapor, a gas, in the atmosphere. As water vapor rises higher, it cools and turns back into liquid water. This process, in which a gas changes to a liquid, is condensation. As more water vapor condenses, drops of water fall to Earth as precipitation—rain, snow, sleet, or hail.

Review and Reinforce

1. the sun

2. It soaks into the soil and becomes groundwater or runs off the land and flows into a river or ocean.

3. Plants take in carbon dioxide in the air, use the carbon to make their own food in photosynthesis, and release oxygen as a waste product. Animals take in oxygen in the air, use it in their life processes, and release carbon dioxide as a waste product.

4. Other organisms cannot use "free" nitrogen in the air. Nitrogen-fixing bacteria combine "free" nitrogen with other elements to form nitrogen-containing compounds that other organisms can use.

5. the water cycle

6. evaporation from oceans

7. evaporation from plants

8. evaporation from lakes

9. condensation

10. precipitation

Enrich

1. The change from blue to yellow indicated the addition of carbon dioxide, which was released by the snails.

2. No color change indicated that no carbon dioxide was added to the solution. Plants release oxygen, which would not change the solution's color.

3. The amount of oxygen released by the plants was equal to or greater than the amount of carbon dioxide released by the snails.

4. Jar C: The snails released carbon dioxide as a waste product; the plants used carbon dioxide to make their own food during photosynthesis and released oxygen as a waste product; the snails used oxygen dissolved in the water for their life processes.

Lesson Quiz

1. the water cycle

2. condensation

3. oxygen

4. Carbon

5. nitrogen fixation

6. the water cycle

7. true

8. oxygen

9. nitrogen cycle

10. true

3 How do energy and matter move through ecosystems?

Lesson Pacing: 2–3 periods or 1–1½ blocks

🕐 **SHORT ON TIME?** To do this lesson in approximately half the time, do the Activate Prior Knowledge activity on page 58. A discussion of the key concepts on page 58 will familiarize students with the lesson content. Have students do the Quick Lab. The rest of the lesson can be completed by students independently.

> **Preference Navigator,** in the online Planning tools, allows you to customize Interactive Science to your own teaching style. You can also edit lesson plans by selecting the Lesson Planner option.
>
> **Digital Teacher's Edition** allows you to access your Teacher's Edition and Resource materials online.

MY SCIENCE online.com

Lesson Vocabulary

- biome
- climate
- desert
- rain forest
- emergent layer
- canopy
- understory
- grassland
- savanna
- deciduous tree
- boreal forest
- coniferous tree
- tundra
- permafrost

Content Refresher
Professional Development Note

Climate and Biomes Although many factors determine the types of organisms that live in a biome, climate is especially important. The two main characteristics that determine the climate of an area are temperature and precipitation. In temperate and tropical regions, the various biomes are distinguished more by amounts of precipitation than by temperature. Temperate rain forests and temperate deserts experience very different amounts of precipitation, and therefore, they vary greatly in their physical conditions and species compositions. Both tundra and boreal forests have similar levels of yearly precipitation, but their temperatures, and therefore, their organisms, differ vastly.

LESSON OBJECTIVE

 Name the six major biomes found on Earth.

Blended Path
Active learning using Student Edition, Inquiry Path, and Digital Path

ENGAGE AND EXPLORE

Teach this lesson using a variety of resources. Begin by reading **My Planet Diary** as a class. Have students share ideas about animals that live in their region whose habits change according to seasonal changes. Then have students do the **Inquiry Warm-Up activity.** Students will investigate the amount of rain that falls in four different regions. The **After the Inquiry Warm-Up worksheet** sets up a discussion about the amount of rain falling in different regions and its effect on organisms. Have volunteers share their graphs to number 4, a bar graph that includes the annual precipitation for their state.

EXPLAIN AND ELABORATE

Teach Key Concepts by explaining the terms *climate* and *biome* and how *climate* helps determine the six *biomes*: desert, rain forest, grassland, deciduous forest, boreal forest, and tundra. Continue to **Teach Key Concepts** by describing each of the biomes. Ask students to describe animal adaptations for each biome. **Lead a Discussion** about precipitation and temperature in desert biomes. **Lead a Discussion** about locations and climates of the two types of rain forests. Use the **Support the Big Q** to illustrate the amazing variety of consumers in the tropical rain forest. Discuss how the rain forest supports these consumers. **Lead a Discussion** about grassland, deciduous forest, boreal forest, and tundra biomes. Have students describe locations, climates, and animal adaptations in these biomes. **Lead a Discussion** about how mountains are not classified to one biome and offer unique ecosystems. Then have students practice the inquiry skill in the **Apply It activity.** Hand out the **Key Concept Summaries** as a review of the lesson. Students can also use the online **Vocab Flash Cards** to review key terms.

EVALUATE

Have students take the **Lesson Quiz.** For an alternate assessment, see the **EXAM**VIEW® Assessment Suite, Progress Monitoring Assessments, or SuccessTracker™.

ELL Support

1 Content and Language

Three of the more difficult vocabulary words—*boreal, coniferous,* and *deciduous*—have Latin roots. *Boreal* comes from a Latin word north or northwind, *coniferous* comes from a Latin word meaning cone bearing, and *deciduous* comes from a Latin word meaning to fall from or fall off.

Lab zone Inquiry Path
Hands-on learning in the Lab zone

Digital Path
Online learning at **my science online**.com

ENGAGE AND EXPLORE

To teach this lesson with an emphasis on inquiry, begin with the **Inquiry Warm-Up activity.** Students will investigate and compare rainfall amounts for different regions. Lead a discussion about how the regions differ. Have students do the **After the Inquiry Warm-Up worksheet.** Talk about student predictions in numbers 1 and 4. Have volunteers share their graphs for number 4, which include precipitation in their state.

EXPLAIN AND ELABORATE

Focus on the **Inquiry Skill** for the lesson. Point out that when you draw a conclusion, you make a judgment after considering information or data. What conclusion can be drawn from the graph in the **Inquiry Warm-Up activity?** *(Different regions receive different amounts of precipitation. These amounts can be arranged in order from least to greatest.)* Use the **Support the Big Q** illustrate how organisms interact in tropical rain forests. Have students **Build Inquiry** by reminding them that a habitat offers an organism the means to live, grow, and reproduce. **Build Inquiry** by having students illustrate how mountain habitats represent different biomes. Review the world maps noting the colors assigned to certain biomes before beginning the **Apply It activity.** Ask volunteers to share their descriptions. Have students do the **Quick Lab** to reinforce understanding of forest climates and share their results. Students can use the online **Vocab Flash Cards** to review key terms.

EVALUATE

Have students take the **Lesson Quiz.** For an alternate assessment, see the **EXAM**VIEW® Assessment Suite, Progress Monitoring Assessments, or SuccessTracker™.

ENGAGE AND EXPLORE

Teach this lesson using digital resources. Begin by having students explore biomes and animal adaptations at **My Planet Diary** online. Have them access the Chapter Resources to find the **Unlock the Big Question activity.** There they can answer the questions and refine their responses as they continue through the lesson. You can re-assign the activity and have students submit their work so you can track their progress.

EXPLAIN AND ELABORATE

Students reading above, at, or below the lexile measure of this lesson can access basic content readings at their level at **My Reading Web.** Have students use the online **Vocab Flash Cards** to preview key terms. Have students do the **Quick Lab** to reinforce understanding of forest climates and then ask students to share their results.

Have students do the online **Interactive Art activity** to recognize that mountains and ice are not part of any major biome. Assign the **Do the Math activity** online and have students submit their work to you. Review the world maps noting the colors assigned to certain biomes before assigning the online **Apply It activity.** Ask volunteers to share their descriptions. Have students submit their work to you. The **Key Concept Summaries** online allow students to read a summary and see an image associated with each part of the lesson. Online remediation is available at **My Science Coach.**

EVALUATE

Have students take the **Lesson Quiz.** For an alternate assessment, see the **EXAM**VIEW® Assessment Suite, Progress Monitoring Assessments, or SuccessTracker™.

2 Frontload the Lesson
Preview the lesson visuals, labels, and captions. Ask students to relate any real-world experiences of the six major biomes to the class.

3 Comprehensible Input
Have students study the visuals and their captions on pages 59–66 to support the key concepts of the lesson.

4 Language Production
Pair or group students with varied language abilities to complete labs collaboratively for language practice. Have each copy the completed written lab for personal reference.

5 Assess Understanding
Make true or false statements about each of the six major biomes and have students indicate if they agree or disagree by raising their right hands for agreement and left for disagreement to check whole-class comprehension.

LESSON 2.3

Biomes

Establish Learning Objective

After this lesson, students will be able to:

 Name the six major biomes found on Earth.

Engage

Activate Prior Knowledge

MY PLANET DIARY Read *That's Super Cool!* with the class. Point out that animals hibernate in other places besides the Arctic. Encourage students to think of examples of animals in your region that are not evident at certain times of year. Explain that animals' movements and habits may change according to seasonal changes. Ask: **Why might arctic ground squirrels hibernate for such long stretches of time?** *(To survive when food is scarce)*

BIG IDEAS OF SCIENCE REFERENCE LIBRARY 📖
Have students look up the following topics: Atacama Desert, Rainforest.

Explore

Lab Resource: Inquiry Warm-Up 🔬

L2 HOW MUCH RAIN IS THAT? Students will use data in a table to create a bar graph representing amounts of rainfall in four different biomes.

LESSON

3 Biomes

🔑 **What Are the Six Major Biomes?**

MY PLANET DIARY

That's Super Cool!

Misconception: It is always fatal when body temperatures drop below freezing.

Fact: In the tundra, arctic ground squirrels hibernate up to eight months a year. During this time, a squirrel's body temperature drops below freezing! This is called supercooling and gives the squirrel the lowest body temperature of any mammal. Without waking, a squirrel will shiver for several hours every couple of weeks to increase its body temperature.

MISCONCEPTION

Answer the question below.
What do you think are the advantages of supercooling?

Sample: Supercooling allows an organism to use minimal energy during the winter so that it doesn't have to wake up and eat food.

▶ **PLANET DIARY** Go to **Planet Diary** to learn more about biomes.

🔬 Do the Inquiry Warm-Up *How Much Rain Is That?*

What Are the Six Major Biomes?

Imagine that you are taking part in an around-the-world scientific expedition. On this expedition you will collect data on the typical climate and organisms of each of Earth's biomes. A **biome** is a group of ecosystems with similar climates and organisms.

🔑 **The six major biomes are desert, rain forest, grassland, deciduous forest, boreal forest, and tundra.** It is mostly the **climate**—the average annual temperature and amount of precipitation—in an area that determines its biome. Climate limits the species of plants that can grow in an area. In turn, the species of plants determine the kinds of animals that live there.

SUPPORT ALL READERS
Lexile Measure = 930L   Lexile Word Count = 2325

Prior Exposure to Content: Most students have encountered this topic in earlier grades

Academic Vocabulary: *compare, contrast, explain, interpret*

Science Vocabulary: *biome, climate*

Concept Level: Generally appropriate for most students in this grade

Preteach With: My Planet Diary "That's Super Cool!" and Figure 1 activity

Go to **My Reading Web** to access leveled readings that provide a foundation for the content.

my science online.com

Vocabulary

- biome
- climate
- desert
- rain forest
- emergent layer
- canopy
- understory
- grassland
- savanna
- deciduous tree
- boreal forest
- coniferous tree
- tundra
- permafrost

Skills

↪ Reading: Compare and Contrast

△ Inquiry: Draw Conclusions

Desert Biomes The first stop on your expedition is a desert. You step off the bus into the searing heat. A **desert** is an area that receives less than 25 centimeters of rain per year. Some of the driest deserts may not receive any precipitation in a year! Deserts often undergo large shifts in temperature during the course of a day. A scorching hot desert like the Namib Desert in Africa cools rapidly each night when the sun goes down. Other deserts, such as the Gobi in central Asia, have a yearly average temperature that is below freezing.

Organisms that live in the desert, like the fennec in **Figure 1,** must be adapted to little or no rain and to extreme temperatures. For example, the stem of a saguaro cactus has folds that are similar to the pleats in an accordion. The stem expands to store water when it is raining. Gila monsters can spend weeks at a time in their cool underground burrows. Many other desert animals are most active at night when the temperatures are cooler.

FIGURE 1 ....

Desert

Organisms must be adapted to live in the desert.

✏ **Complete these tasks.**

1. CHALLENGE How do you think the fennec's ears and fur are adaptations to the desert's extreme temperatures?

   Big ears get rid of
   extra heat; fur keeps
   it warm.

2. **List** Write five things you'll need to be well adapted to desert conditions. Pack carefully!

Supply List

○ wide-brimmed hat
○ Sample: sunblock
○ Sample: water
○
○
○

Desert Biomes
▢ Desert

59

1 Content and Language

Write and define the word *adaptation.* Have students conduct a picture walk of the lesson and discuss how they would dress if they lived in each of the six biomes. Relate this idea to the fact that animals and plants must be adapted to the biomes in which they live.

2 Frontload the Lesson

List the six biomes on the board. Then have students conduct a picture walk of

the lesson, asking them to use detailed words to describe each biome based on the visual aids shown.

3 Comprehensible Input

Guide students back to the text to help them fill in the labels in **Figure 3.** Have students describe how the words *tallest, underneath,* and *below* help indicate the order of each of the tree layers.

Explain

Introduce Vocabulary

Explain that *weather* is the condition outside at any particular time and place, whereas *climate* is the weather conditions of a place over a long period.

Teach Key Concepts 🗝

Explain to students that a group of ecosystems with similar climates and similar organisms makes up a biome. Ask: **What are the six major biomes on Earth?** (*Desert, rain forest, grassland, deciduous forest, boreal forest, tundra*) **In which biome do you live?** (*Students should indicate the local biome.*) **Which other biome have you ever been in?** (*Accept all reasonable responses.*) Invite students who have been in other biomes to describe the conditions in those biomes.

Lead a Discussion

DESCRIBE DESERT BIOMES Ask students who have visited a desert to describe it. Remind students that climate incorporates both temperature and precipitation. Indicate to students that the areas indicated on the map in **Figure 1** represent only hot and dry deserts. Ask: **What can you say about precipitation and evaporation in the desert?** (*Deserts receive less than 25 centimeters of precipitation each year; evaporation is greater than precipitation.*) **How might desert temperatures vary over a 24-hour day?** (*Deserts are hot during the day, but they can be cold at night.*)

Address Misconceptions

L1 **DESERTS** It is a common misconception that all deserts are hot. Several deserts, such as the Atacama Desert in South America and the Gobi Desert in Asia, are actually cold. Reinforce the idea that deserts are characterized by minimal precipitation, and not hot climates. Students may be surprised to learn that the biggest desert in the world is Antarctica. In fact, the majority of the world's desert area is cold and dry.

21st Century Learning   DK

CREATIVITY Have students read *Atacama Desert* in the **Big Ideas of Science Reference Library** and create a humorous real estate brochure to try to attract settlers to the area.

My Planet Diary provides an opportunity for students to explore real-world connections to a tundra biome.

my science online.com Biomes

Explain

Lead a Discussion

RAIN FORESTS Tell students that tropical and temperate rain forests share many traits but differ in location and temperatures. Display a world map or globe and help students locate these biomes. Students should refer to the biome map on this page. Ask: **Where are the world's tropical rain forests located?** *(All are located at or near the equator.)* **How do the location and climate of temperate rain forests differ from tropical rain forests?** *(Temperate rain forests are much farther north and much cooler.)* **How are temperate and tropical rain forests similar?** *(Both are humid, receive a lot of rain, and have a large variety of plant and animal species.)*

Compare and Contrast Explain that when you compare and contrast, you look for similarities and differences. Remind students that the qualities shared by both temperate and tropical rain forests belong in the overlapping section of the diagram.

Compare and Contrast As you read about temperate and tropical rain forests, fill in the Venn diagram.

Temperate

Huge trees
U.S. Pacific Northwest
Moderate temperature

Wet
Lots of plants
Lots of animals

Humid; tree layers
Hot temperature
Near equator

Tropical

FIGURE 2 ....

Temperate Rain Forests
The sugar pine is the tallest kind of pine tree, reaching heights of 53 to 61 meters. It also produces the largest pine cones. A sugar pine cone can reach a length of 30 to 56 centimeters. The sugar pine cone shown here is actual size!

Identify What conditions do you think allow a tree to grow so tall?

Moderate temperatures
and the large amount
of rain the area
receives

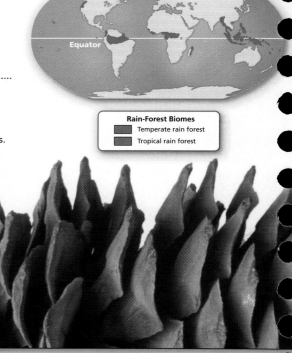

Rain-Forest Biomes The second stop on your expedition is a rain forest. **Rain forests** are forests in which large amounts of rain fall year-round. This biome is living up to its name—it's pouring! After a short shower, the sun reappears. However, very little sunlight reaches the ground.

Plants are everywhere in the rain forest. Some plants, like the vines hanging from tree limbs, even grow on other plants! And animals are flying, creeping, and slithering all around you.

Temperate Rain Forests You may think that a rain forest is a warm, humid "jungle" in the tropics. But there is another type of rain forest. The Pacific Northwest of the United States receives more than 300 centimeters of rain a year. Huge trees grow there, including redwoods, cedars, and firs. Many ecologists refer to this ecosystem as a temperate rain forest. The term *temperate* means "having moderate temperatures."

Equator

Rain-Forest Biomes
■ Temperate rain forest
■ Tropical rain forest

60 Ecosystems and Biomes

Professional Development Note **Teacher to Teacher**

Survivor Project Students assume the roles of rescued plane crash survivors. Having survived in one of the six major biomes, their job is to record what they learned in a Survival Manual. Students begin with a description of an ecosystem in one of the biomes. Chapters in their manual include: vegetation, animals (predator/prey relationships, where survivors acted on the food web), type of shelter built (using available resources). One chapter describes how organisms interacted with each other and with the nonliving environment. Students conclude their publication with a description of the effect they had on the ecosystem.

📧 *Emily Compton*
Park Forest Middle School
Baton Rouge, LA

Tropical Rain Forests As you can see on the map, tropical rain forests are found in regions close to the equator. The climate is warm and humid all year long, and there is a lot of rain. Because of these climate conditions, an amazing variety of plants grow in tropical rain forests.

Trees in the rain forest form several distinct layers. The tallest layer of the rain forest which receives the most sunlight and can reach up to 70 meters, is the **emergent layer.** Underneath, trees up to 50 meters tall form a leafy roof called the **canopy.** Below the canopy, a layer of shorter trees and vines, around 15 meters high, form an **understory.** Understory plants grow well in the shade formed by the canopy. The forest floor is nearly dark, so only a few plants live there. Look at the tree layers in **Figure 3.**

The abundant plant life in tropical rain forests provides habitats for many species of animals. Ecologists estimate that millions of species of insects live in tropical rain forests. These insects serve as a source of food for many reptiles, birds, and mammals. Many of these animals, in turn, are food sources for other animals. Although tropical rain forests cover only a small part of the planet, they probably contain more species of plants and animals than all the other biomes combined.

Emergent layer

Canopy

Understory

Forest floor

FIGURE 3 ···

Tropical Rain Forests
On the edge of this tropical rain forest, an amazing variety of organisms can be found in the different layers.

✎ **Relate Text and Visuals** Based on your reading, label the four distinct layers of the tropical rain forest in the boxes above.

Support the Big Q ❓ UbD

CONSUMERS IN THE RAIN FOREST Discuss with students the abundance of animals in tropical rain forests. Ask: **What do many of the reptiles, birds, and mammals feed on in tropical rain forests?** *(Insects)* **What do you think the insects feed on?** *(Plants)* **Why does the tropical rain forest support so many species of animals?** *(There are many plant species that provide habitats for various animals and are the producers in a food chain.)*

21st Century Learning

CRITICAL THINKING Point out that the layers of trees found in a tropical rain forest demonstrate a series of causes and effects. Ask: **What causes the trees of the emergent layer to grow tallest?** *(They receive the most sun.)* **How does the presence of the trees in the emergent layer affect the trees below?** *(The emergent layer creates shade, which prevents trees below from growing as high as those in the top layer.)* **How does the presence of the trees in the canopy affect the trees below?** *(The canopy creates even more shade, which prevents trees below from growing as high as those in the top two layers.)* **How does the presence of the trees in the understory affect the trees and plants below?** *(The understory creates still more shade, which prevents vegetation below from growing very high.)*

Teach With Visuals

Have students look at **Figure 3.** Have students identify the layers of the rain forest shown. You may wish to have students add height information to their labels. Ask: **How much open space is there below the emergent layer?** *(Very little)* **How much open space is there below the canopy?** *(There is a large open space below the canopy and above the understory.)*

61

Differentiated Instruction

L1 Define Terms Relating to Tropical Rain Forests Have pairs of students work with a dictionary to find meanings for the terms *emergent* and *canopy.* Then have them break apart the compound word *understory* in order to analyze the two words that comprise it.

L3 Identify Main Ideas About Tropical Rain Forests Call on students to state the main idea of each paragraph about tropical rain forests.

L1 Compare Biomes Pair students to assist each other. Assign three headings: *Temperate rain forest, Tropical rain forest, Both,* and a list of words from these pages: *firs, rain, trees, equator, warm, cool.* Have students read the text and place the terms under the appropriate headings *(Temperate rain forest—firs, cool; Tropical rain forest—warm, equator; Both—rain, trees).*

Explain

Lead a Discussion

GRASSLANDS Describe grasslands as widely distributed ecosystems that have moderate climates and are dominated by grasses. Have students use a world map or globe to locate countries that have large areas of grasslands. Also have students locate prairie areas in the United States. Ask: **What parts of Earth do not have grasslands?** *(Land areas in the extremes of the Northern Hemisphere and of the Southern Hemisphere)* **Which is the only continent without a grasslands biome?** *(Antarctica)* **How do savannas differ from prairies?** *(Savannas are closer to the equator; they receive more rain.)*

Teach With Visuals

Tell students to look at **Figure 4.** Ask: **What typical features of grassland biomes are visible in Figure 4?** *(Tall grass, large grassland birds)* **What kinds of plants are not found in grasslands?** *(Trees)* **What characteristics do the three birds have in common?** *(They are large and have long legs.)*

FIGURE 4 ······································

Grasslands
The rhea, cassowary, and ostrich are grassland birds that live on different continents.

✎ **Interpret Maps** On the world map, identify the continents in which these three birds are located. List three characteristics that these grassland birds all share.

Sample: long, slender
necks; long legs; large
bodies

_____

_____

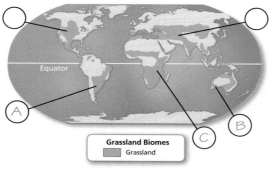

Equator

Grassland Biomes
Grassland

Grassland Biomes The third stop on the expedition is a grassy plain called a prairie. Temperatures are more comfortable here than they were in the desert. The breeze carries the scent of soil warmed by the sun. This rich soil supports grasses as tall as you. Startled by your approach, sparrows dart into hiding places among the waving grass stems.

Although the prairie receives more rain than a desert, you may notice only a few scattered areas of trees and shrubs. Ecologists classify prairies, which are generally found in the middle latitudes, as grasslands. A **grassland** is an area that is populated mostly by grasses and other nonwoody plants. Most grasslands receive 25 to 75 centimeters of rain each year. Fires and droughts are common in this biome. Grasslands that are located closer to the equator than prairies are known as savannas. A **savanna** receives as much as 120 centimeters of rain each year. Scattered shrubs and small trees grow on savannas, along with grass.

Grasslands are home to many of the largest animals on Earth— herbivores such as elephants, bison, antelopes, zebras, giraffes, kangaroos, and rhinoceroses. Grazing by these large herbivores maintains the grasslands. Their grazing keeps young trees and bushes from sprouting and competing with the grass for water and sunlight. You can see some grassland birds in **Figure 4.**

Deciduous Forest Biomes Your trip to the fourth biome takes you to another forest. It is now late summer. Cool mornings here give way to warm days. Several members of the expedition are busy recording the numerous plant species. Others are looking through binoculars, trying to identify the songbirds.

You are now visiting a deciduous forest biome. Many of the trees in this forest are **deciduous trees** (dee SIJ oo us), trees that shed their leaves and grow new ones each year. Oaks and maples are examples of deciduous trees. Deciduous forests receive enough rain to support the growth of trees and other plants, at least 50 centimeters of rain per year. Temperatures can vary greatly during the year. The growing season usually lasts five to six months.

The variety of plants in a deciduous forest creates many different habitats. Many species of birds live in different parts of the forest, eating the insects and fruits in their specific areas. Mammals such as chipmunks and skunks live in deciduous forests. In a North American deciduous forest you might also see wood thrushes and white-tailed deer.

If you were to return to this biome in the winter, you would not see much wildlife. Many of the bird species migrate, or fly great distances, to warmer areas. Some of the mammals hibernate, or enter a state of greatly reduced body activity similar to sleep. Look at **Figure 5**. During the winter months, animals that hibernate get energy from fat stored in their bodies.

did you know?

How far would you be willing to migrate? The bobolink has one of the longest songbird migration routes. The birds travel south from southern Canada and the northern United States to northern Argentina. This migration route is approximately 20,000 kilometers round trip!

Equator

Deciduous Forest Biomes
Deciduous forest

FIGURE 5 ··
Deciduous Forest
Most of the trees in a deciduous forest have leaves that change color and drop to the forest floor each autumn. In the leaves, this dormouse hibernates through the winter.

✎ **Infer** Is hibernation an adaptation to life in a deciduous forest? Explain your answer.

Sample: Yes; hibernation is an adaptation because it allows organisms to survive the winter months.

63

Differentiated Instruction

L1 Review Geographical Terms and Names Have students review basic geographical terms and names in order to clarify the information shown in the two world maps. As necessary, help students understand terms such as *equator*, *hemisphere*, and *pole*, as well as the names and locations of the planet's seven continents.

L3 Research a Grasslands Bird Challenge students to do research on one or more of the grasslands birds shown in this section. Students can gather and organize information about a bird's habitat, diet, physical characteristics, predators, and life span.

Lead a Discussion

DECIDUOUS FORESTS Tell students that deciduous forests experience seasonal changes to which organisms are adapted. Ask: **What is the climate like in a deciduous forest?** *(Temperatures vary greatly during the year; there is enough rainfall to support trees.)* **How are trees adapted to seasonal changes in this biome?** *(They shed their leaves and grow new ones each year.)* **How are animals adapted?** *(Many birds migrate in winter; some mammals hibernate.)* **How do the many animal species coexist in a deciduous forest?** *(The different plants create a mix of habitats within the forest.)*

Teach With Visuals

Tell students to look at **Figure 5**. Help students find the curled-up dormouse. Point out that this image is a close-up of the forest floor. If possible, show students photographs of deciduous trees from a field guide. Ask: **What plant materials can you see around the dormouse?** *(Pieces of leaves, ferns, and grass.)* Help students identify the green and greenish-yellow lichens growing nearby.

Elaborate

Build Inquiry **Lab zone**

L2 MAKE MODELS OF A DECIDUOUS FOREST

Materials none

Time 20 minutes

Remind students that a habitat provides the things an organism needs to live, grow, and reproduce.

Ask: **Suppose you want to model a rotting-log habitat on the forest floor. What abiotic materials would you need?** *(Soil, a source of filtered light, water, a rotting log, dead leaves or other dead plant material)* **What organisms would you place in the model habitat?** *(Mosses, ferns, fungi, earthworms, sow bugs, crickets, salamanders or toads)*

Have students draw a model of a rotting-log habitat. Ask: **What other deciduous forest habitats can you name?** *(Bird roosts and squirrel nests in trees, chipmunk burrows, bear dens, deer grazing areas, and the like)*

Explain

Lead a Discussion

EXPLORE A COLD CLIMATE Tell students that boreal forests are found in northern locations that have cold climates. Ask: **Why is water availability a challenge in boreal forests?** *(Temperatures are low enough that water is frozen much of the year.)* **How do plants in boreal forests adapt to lack of water?** *(Coniferous trees have thick, waxy needles that prevent water loss.)* **Can you describe a boreal forest food chain?** *(Producers—seeds and bark of coniferous trees; first-level consumers—red squirrel, insects, birds, snowshoe hare, moose, beaver; second-level consumers—wolf, bear, lynx, great horned owl)*

Teach With Visuals

Have students examine the map of boreal forest biomes on this page. Ask: **Where are most boreal forests located?** *(Boreal forests are located in the Northern Hemisphere in a band at latitudes where the climate is too cold for deciduous forests.)* **Why are there no boreal forests in the Southern Hemisphere?** *(There are no large landmasses in the Southern Hemisphere at the appropriate latitude below the equator.)*

FIGURE 6 ··

Boreal Forest

✎ This lynx and snowshoe hare are adapted to life in the boreal forest.

1. **Infer** Choose the best answer. The feet of each animal are an adaptation to its
   - ◯ food.
   - ◯ climate.
   - ◯ predators.
   - ⦿ all of the above

2. **Explain** Defend your answer.

   <u>Sample: Large feet allow each</u>
   <u>animal to run across snow to</u>
   <u>get food or escape predators.</u>
   <u>The fur also keeps the feet</u>
   <u>warm in cold climates.</u>

64 Ecosystems and Biomes

Boreal Forest Biomes
Boreal forest

Boreal Forest Biomes Now the expedition heads north to a colder biome, the boreal forest. The term *boreal* means "northern," and **boreal forests** are dense forests found in upper regions of the Northern Hemisphere. The expedition leaders claim they can identify a boreal forest by its smell. When you arrive, you catch a whiff of the spruce and fir trees that blanket the hillsides. Feeling the chilly early fall air, you pull a jacket and hat out of your bag.

Boreal Forest Plants Most of the trees in the boreal forest are **coniferous trees** (koh NIF ur us), trees that produce their seeds in cones and have leaves shaped like needles. The boreal forest is sometimes referred to by its Russian name, the *taiga* (TY guh). Winters in these forests are very cold. The snow can reach heights well over your head! Even so, the summers are rainy and warm enough to melt all the snow.

Tree species in the boreal forest are well adapted to the cold climate. Since water is frozen for much of the year, trees must have adaptations that prevent water loss. Coniferous trees, such as firs and hemlocks, all have thick, waxy needles that prevent water from evaporating.

Boreal Forest Animals Many of the animals of the boreal forest eat the seeds produced by the coniferous trees. These animals include red squirrels, insects, and birds such as finches. Some herbivores, such as moose and beavers, eat tree bark and new shoots. The variety of herbivores in the boreal forest supports many predators, including lynx, otters, and great horned owls. **Figure 6** shows an herbivore and its predator.

Tundra Biomes As you arrive at your last stop, the driving wind gives you an immediate feel for this biome. The **tundra** is extremely cold and dry. Expecting deep snow, many are surprised to learn that the tundra may receive no more precipitation than a desert.

Most of the soil in the tundra is frozen all year. This frozen soil is called **permafrost**. During the short summer, the top layer of soil thaws, but the underlying soil remains frozen. Because rainwater cannot soak into the permafrost, shallow ponds and marshy areas appear in the summer.

Tundra Plants Mosses, grasses, and dwarf forms of a few trees can be found in the tundra. Most of the plant growth takes place during the long days of the short summer season. North of the Arctic Circle, the sun does not set during midsummer.

Tundra Animals In summer, the insects are abundant. Insect-eating birds take advantage of the plentiful food by eating as much as they can. But when winter approaches, these birds migrate south. Mammals of the tundra include caribou, foxes, and wolves. The mammals that remain on the tundra during the winter grow thick fur coats. What can these animals find to eat on the tundra in winter? The caribou scrape snow away to find lichens. Wolves follow the caribou and look for weak members of the herd to prey upon.

FIGURE 7

Tundra
Although the ground is frozen for most of the year, mosses, grasses, and dwarf willow trees grow here.

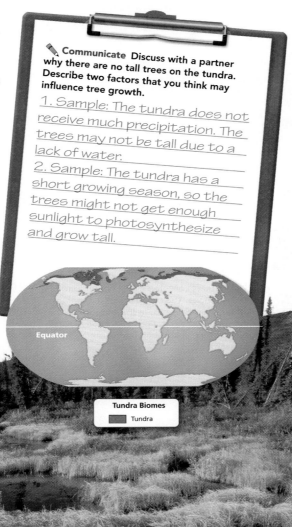

✎ **Communicate** Discuss with a partner why there are no tall trees on the tundra. Describe two factors that you think may influence tree growth.

1. Sample: The tundra does not receive much precipitation. The trees may not be tall due to a lack of water.

2. Sample: The tundra has a short growing season, so the trees might not get enough sunlight to photosynthesize and grow tall.

Equator

Tundra Biomes

☐ Tundra

65

Lead a Discussion

TUNDRA BIOMES Tell students that the term *tundra* comes from a Sami word meaning "marshy plain." Explain that the Sami are the indigenous people of northern Europe. Direct students' attention to **Figure 7.** Have them locate the tundra areas of northern Europe. Ask: **What does the land look like in this photograph of the tundra?** *(It is flat and marshy.)* **Do you think "marshy plain" is a good description of the tundra?** *(Students will probably indicate that the description seems apt, citing the flat land and the wet areas.)*

Elaborate

21st Century Learning

CRITICAL THINKING Explain that because the permafrost does not allow water to drain from the soil and because the low temperatures slow evaporation, the tundra's soil is constantly saturated with water, even though the area receives little precipitation. Ask: **Why are insects, such as mosquitoes, so common on the tundra in summer?** *(Many insects breed in the standing water that cannot sink into the permafrost.)*

Differentiated Instruction

L1 Permafrost Help students solidify their understanding of the word *permafrost* by pointing out the fact that the word combines *frost* with the root of the word *permanent*. Have students use a dictionary to find the definition of *permanent*. Then have them explain to a partner how this word contributes to the meaning of *permafrost*.

L3 Compare and Contrast Biomes Have students create a detailed compare/contrast table showing rainfall and temperature differences among the six major biomes. Encourage students to do additional research to present a fuller picture of conditions in each biome.

Explain

Lead a Discussion

HIGH-ALTITUDE HABITATS Explain that mountains and ice do not fit into one biome classification, but they have unique ecosystems. Ask: **Is the habitat at the bottom of a mountain the same as at the top?** *(No, the habitats change with altitude.)* **What countries or continents are covered with ice?** *(Antarctica; most of Greenland)* **Can ice sheets support organisms?** *(Yes)* **What are some examples?** *(Polar bears and leopard seals)*

Elaborate

Build Inquiry

L1 **DRAW MOUNTAIN HABITATS**

Materials paper and pencils

Time 10 minutes

Have students illustrate mountain habitats representing different biomes. Divide students into small groups. Have each group draw a side-view diagram of a mountain and label it with the biome names given in the text: grassland at the base, deciduous forest next, then boreal forest, and finally tundra at the top.

Ask: **Why do the biomes vary at different locations on a mountain?** *(Climate becomes colder from the base of a mountain to its top.)* **From what you know about this mountain's biomes, does the top of the mountain receive much rain?** *(No, because it is tundra habitat, which is dry)*

Do the Math!

L1 Point out that this line graph makes it possible to see how the average temperature changes or remains the same over twelve months of time. In addition to allowing students to analyze average temperatures in two different locations, the graph also lets students compare and contrast the two locations. Ask students to identify the highest average temperature and the lowest average temperature for each location.

▲ **Draw Conclusions** Remind students that drawing a conclusion involves making a statement that sums up what they have learned about a topic or question.
See *Math Skill and Problem-Solving Activities* for support.

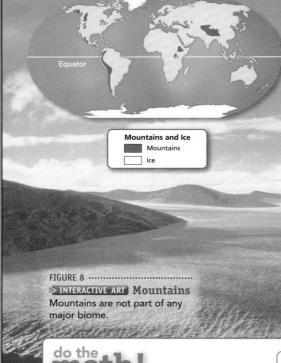

Equator

Mountains and Ice
- ■ Mountains
- □ Ice

FIGURE 8 ································
▷ **INTERACTIVE ART** **Mountains**
Mountains are not part of any major biome.

Mountains and Ice Some land areas are not classified as biomes. Recall that biomes are defined by abiotic factors such as climate and soil, and by biotic factors such as plant and animal life. Because the organisms that live in these areas vary, mountain ranges and land covered with thick ice sheets are not considered biomes.

The climate of a mountain changes from its base to its summit. If you were to hike all the way up a tall mountain, you would pass through a series of biomes. At the base, you might find grasslands. As you climbed, you might pass through deciduous forest and then boreal forest. As you neared the top, your surroundings would resemble the cold, dry tundra.

Other places are covered year-round with thick ice sheets. Most of Greenland and Antarctica fall into this category. Organisms that are adapted to life on ice include leopard seals and polar bears.

do the math!

Biome Climates

An ecologist collected climate data from two locations. The graph shows the monthly average temperatures in the two locations. The total yearly precipitation in Location A is 250 centimeters. In Location B, the total yearly precipitation is 14 centimeters.

① **Read Graphs** Provide a title for the graph. What variable is plotted on the horizontal axis? On the vertical axis?

Month; temperature

② **Interpret Data** Study the graph. How would you describe the temperature over the course of a year in Location A? In Location B?

Location A temperatures are steady; Location B temperatures rise and fall.

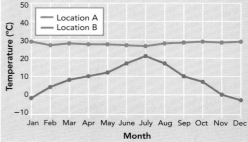

Average Monthly Temperatures

— Location A
— Location B

Temperature (°C)

Month: Jan Feb Mar Apr May June July Aug Sep Oct Nov Dec

③ **Draw Conclusions** Given the precipitation and temperature data for these locations, in which biome would you expect each to be located?

Based on the temperatures and the amount of precipitation, Location A is a tropical rain forest and Location B is a desert.

66 Ecosystems and Biomes

Interactive Art allows students to recognize that mountains and ice are not part of any major biome.

Digital Lesson
- Assign the *Do the Math* activity online and have students submit their work to you.
- Assign the *Apply It* activity online and have students submit their work to you.

MY SCIENCE online.com | **Biomes**

apply it!

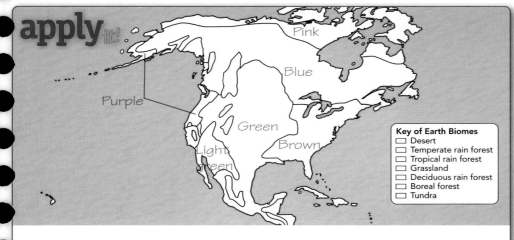

Pink

Blue

Purple

Green

Brown

Light green

Key of Earth Biomes
- ☐ Desert
- ☐ Temperate rain forest
- ☐ Tropical rain forest
- ☐ Grassland
- ☐ Deciduous rain forest
- ☐ Boreal forest
- ☐ Tundra

❶ Interpret Maps Using the colors shown in the biome maps throughout this lesson, color in the key above. Use the key to color in the areas on the map of North America.

❷ Draw Conclusions Where are most of the boreal forests located? Why are there no boreal forests in the Southern Hemisphere?

Boreal forests are located far
from the equator in cold climates.
There are no boreal forests in the
Southern Hemisphere because
there is not enough land at the
appropriate latitudes.

❸ Describe Mark the area in which you live with an *X* on the map. What is the climate like where you live? How do you think your climate affects which organisms live there?

Accept all reasonable answers.

Lab zone® Do the Quick Lab *Inferring Forest Climates.*

🔑 Assess Your Understanding

1a. Review _Temperature_ and _precipitation_ are the two main factors that determine an area's biome.

b. Infer What biome might you be in if you were standing on a bitterly cold, dry plain with only a few, short trees scattered around?

Tundra

got it? ....

○ I get it! Now I know that the six major biomes are _desert, rain forest, grassland,_ _deciduous forest, boreal forest, and tundra._

○ I need extra help with _See TE note._

Go to my science 🅢 COACH *online for help with this subject.*

67

Apply It!

L1 Review each of the world maps shown in this lesson, noting the colors assigned to certain biomes before beginning the activity. Then have them use colored pencils to fill in the key and to color the map of North America using the same colors to signify specific biomes presented in the lesson.

🔺 **Draw Conclusions** As they draw conclusions, students must decide whether or not the data they collected supports their hypothesis.

Lab Resource: Quick Lab

L2 **INFERRING FOREST CLIMATES** Using a globe, students will mark locations of deciduous and boreal forests.

Evaluate _____

Assess Your Understanding

After students answer the questions, have them evaluate their understanding by completing the appropriate sentence.

RTI Response to Intervention

1a. If students have trouble naming factors that determine a biome, **then** ask volunteers to describe climate conditions in various biomes.

b. If students need help identifying a specific biome, **then** review with them the major biomes and eliminate those that do not fit the description.

my science 🅢 COACH Have students go online for help in understanding biomes.

Differentiated Instruction

L1 **Altitude and Latitude** Help students understand the changes in biomes going up a mountain by comparing an increase in altitude with an increase in latitude. The latitude of the equator is 0°. As they go "up" from the equator to the North Pole, they see the climate change from hot to cold. As they go up a mountain, they see similar changes.

L3 **Identify Biome Distribution** Have students use biome maps and a world atlas or globe to locate biomes for a given continent. Provide each student or group an outline map of that continent. If possible, assign a different continent to each student or group. Students should refer to the map resources to sketch the locations of the various biomes found on their continent.

Name _____ Date _____ Class _____

 After the Inquiry Warm-Up

Biomes

Inquiry Warm-Up, *How Much Rain Is That?*

In the Inquiry Warm-Up, you investigated rainfall amounts for different regions. Using what you learned from that activity, answer the questions below.

1. **PREDICT** Ignoring all other factors, will an organism that requires abundant moisture, such as an amphibian, survive better in the Mojave Desert or the Costa Rican rain forest? Explain.

   _____

   _____

2. **CALCULATE** How many more times precipitation fell in the Great Smoky Mountains than in the Mojave Desert?

   _____

3. **INFER** Obviously, if 350 centimeters of precipitation fell all at once, people wouldn't be able to live in or near the Costa Rican rain forest. Over what period of time were these precipitation measurements most likely taken—a day, a week, a year, or a century?

   _____

4. **GRAPH** Predict the amount of precipitation that falls each year in the state in which you live. Then using reference materials recommended by your teacher, check to see how close you came to the correct answer. Draw a simple bar graph that includes the four locations shown in the lab and your state, arranged from lowest to highest precipitation amounts.

Assess Your Understanding

Biomes

What Are the Six Major Biomes?

1a. REVIEW _____ and _____ are the two main factors that determine an area's biome.

b. INFER What biome might you be in if you were standing on a bitterly cold, dry plain with only a few, short trees scattered around?

_____

got it? ....

○ **I get it!** Now I know that the six major biomes are _____

_____

_____

_____

○ **I need extra help with** _____

_____

Name _____ Date _____ Class _____

Biomes

What Are the Six Major Biomes?

A **biome** is a group of ecosystems with similar climates and organisms. **The six major biomes are desert, rain forest, grassland, deciduous forest, boreal forest, and tundra.** It is mostly the **climate**—the average annual temperature and amount of precipitation—in an area that determines its biome. Climate limits the species of plants that can grow in an area. The species of plants determine the kinds of animals that live there.

A **desert** is an area that receives less than 25 centimeters of rain per year. Organisms that live in the desert must be adapted to little or no rain and to extreme temperatures. **Rain forests** are forests in which large amounts of rain fall year-round. The Pacific Northwest of the U.S. is home to a temperate rain forest, where over 300 centimeters of rain falls yearly. Tropical rain forests are found close to the equator. The climate is warm, and there is a lot of rain. Trees form several layers. The tallest layer of the rain forest that receives the most sunlight and can reach up to 70 meters, is the **emergent layer.** Underneath, trees up to 50 meters tall form a leafy roof called the **canopy.** Below the canopy, a layer of shorter trees and vines, around 15 meters high, form an **understory.** Although tropical rain forests cover only a small part of the planet, they probably contain more species of plants and animals than all other biomes combined. A **grassland** is an area that is populated mostly by grasses and other nonwoody plants. A prairie is a grassland in the middle latitudes that receives between 25 and 75 centimeters of rain yearly. Grasslands located closer to the equator are called savannas. A **savanna** receives as much as 120 centimeters of rain each year. Grasslands are home to many of the largest animals on Earth.

In a deciduous forest biome, many trees are **deciduous trees** that shed their leaves and grow new ones each year. Oaks and maples are examples of deciduous trees. Deciduous forests receive at least 50 centimeters of rain a year, and temperatures vary greatly. Many species of plants, birds, mammals, and insects live in different parts of the forest. The term *boreal* means "northern," and **boreal forests** are dense forests found in upper regions of the Northern Hemisphere. Most of the trees in the boreal forest are **coniferous trees,** trees that produce their seeds in cones and have leaves shaped like needles. Winters are cold and snowy, and summers are rainy and fairly warm. Many of the animals of the boreal forest eat seeds produced by coniferous trees. The sixth biome, the **tundra,** is extremely cold and dry. The tundra often receives the same amount of precipitation as a desert. The soil in the tundra that is frozen most of the year is called **permafrost.** Mosses, grasses, and dwarf forms of a few trees grow on the tundra, as well as insects, birds, and a few mammals live on the tundra.

On a separate sheet of paper, identify Earth's six major biomes and briefly describe each one.

Biomes

Understanding Main Ideas

Answer the following questions on a separate sheet of paper.

1. How does climate affect the type of biome found in an area?
2. What are two adaptations that enable mammals to survive cold winters?
3. Why are tropical rain forests such rich habitats for many species of animals?
4. Why does a deciduous forest have a variety of habitats?

Building Vocabulary

Name each biome described in the table below.

	Biome	Climate and Organisms
5.		warm summers, cold winters; receives at least 50 cm of precipitation per year; trees shed their leaves and grow new ones each year
6.		hot in daytime, cool or cold at night; very dry; organisms are adapted to extreme temperatures and dry conditions
7.		warm, rainy summers; very cold winters with heavy snow; trees produce cones with seeds that are eaten by many animals
8.		warm temperatures do not vary much throughout the year; very wet and humid; greater variety of species than any other biome
9.		extremely cold winters, 10.warmer summers; windy; very dry; no trees, only low-growing plants
10.		receives between 25 and 75 centimeters of rain each year; populated by grasses and many large herbivores

Name _____ Date _____ Class _____

Biomes

The map below shows the six major biomes on Earth. Examine the map carefully. Then follow the instructions below.

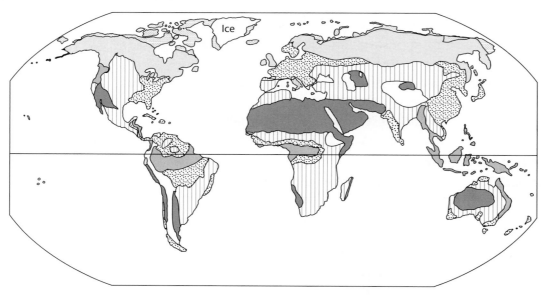

Key:

 _____    _____

_____   _____

_____   _____

1. Label North America, South America, Europe, Asia, Africa, and Australia on the map.
2. Color each block in the key a different color.
3. Color the biomes on the map, using the same colors you used in the key.
4. Write the names of the biomes in the key.
5. Mark a red dot where you live. In which biome do you live?

_____

6. Locate the equator on the map. Which biome is most common along the equator?

_____

Lesson Quiz

Biomes

If the statement is true, write *true*. If the statement is false, change the underlined word or words to make the statement true.

1. _____ A group of animals limits the species of plants that can grow in an area.

2. _____ The Pacific Northwest is home to a temperate rain forest, where over 300 centimeters of rain falls yearly.

3. _____ Tropical rain forests cover a small part of the planet, yet they contain more species of plants and animals than all other biomes combined.

4. _____ Rain forests are home to many of the largest animals on Earth.

5. _____ In a boreal forest biome, many trees shed their leaves and grow new ones each year.

Fill in the blank to complete each statement.

6. A biome is a group of ecosystems with similar _____ and organisms.

7. Organisms that live in the _____ must be adapted to little or no rain and to extreme temperatures.

8. Prairies and savannas are two types of _____.

9. A _____ biome is a dense forest found in upper regions of the Northern Hemisphere.

10. Mosses, grasses, dwarf forms of a few trees, insects, birds, and a few mammals live on the _____ biome.

Biomes

Answer Key

After the Inquiry Warm-Up

1. Sample: Amphibians and other organisms that require abundant moisture, would do better in the rain forest than the desert, because there's more precipitation in the rain forest.

2. The Great Smoky Mountains get twelve (12) times as much precipitation as does the Mojave Desert.

3. a year

4. Sample: Bar graph with five bars. Your state should be positioned according to its precipitation amount relative to the other four locations.

Key Concepts Summaries

The six major biomes are desert, rain forest, grassland, deciduous forest, boreal forest, and tundra. A desert receives little rain, and organisms must be adapted to little rain and to extreme temperatures. Rain forests receive large amounts of rainfall year-round, and often contain several layers of tree growth. Tropical rain forests contain a huge number of plant and animal species. A grassland is an area of grasses and other nonwoody plants, as well as many large animals. A deciduous forest contains deciduous trees, which shed their leaves and grew new ones each year, as well as many species of plants, birds, mammals, and insects. A boreal forest is a dense forest of coniferous trees found in upper regions of the Northern Hemisphere. The tundra is extremely cold and dry, and its soil that stays frozen most of the year is called permafrost.

Review and Reinforce

1. It is mostly the climate conditions—temperature and precipitation—that determine the plants that grow in a region. The plants determine the animals, and both determine the ecosystems.

2. hibernation, thick fur

3. The number and variety of plants in a rain forest provide food for many different species.

4. It has a wide variety of plant life.

5. deciduous forest   6. desert

7. boreal forest   8. tropical rain forest

9. tundra   10. grassland

Enrich

1. Check that students have labeled the continents correctly.

2. Make sure students have coded each biome with the same color on both the key and the map.

3. Make sure students have coded each biome with the same color on both the key and the map.

4. Students should include the following biomes in their keys: tundra, rain forest, grassland, deciduous forest, boreal forest, desert.

5. Answers will depend on your location.

6. tropical rain forest

Lesson Quiz

1. Climate   2. true

3. true   4. Grasslands

5. deciduous forest biome 6. climates

7. desert   8. grasslands

9. boreal forest   10. tundra

Place the outside corner, the corner away from the dotted line, in the corner of your copy machine to copy onto letter-size paper.

Aquatic Ecosystems

4 How do energy and matter move through ecosystems?

Lesson Pacing: 1–2 periods or $\frac{1}{2}$–1 block

🕐 **SHORT ON TIME?** To do this lesson in approximately half the time, do the Activate Prior Knowledge activity on page 68. A discussion of the key concept on page 68 will familiarize students with the lesson content. Have students do the Quick Lab. The rest of the lesson can be completed by students independently.

Preference Navigator, in the online Planning tools, allows you to customize Interactive Science to your own teaching style. You can also edit lesson plans by selecting the Lesson Planner option.

Digital Teacher's Edition allows you to access your Teacher's Edition and Resource materials online.

MY SCIENCE online.com

Lesson Vocabulary

• estuary • intertidal zone • neritic zone

Content Refresher

Land and Sea Estuaries are marine ecosystems that serve as transitions between freshwater and saltwater habitats. They can include bays, marshes, sounds, mangrove forests, swamps, and other habitats. Because estuaries are linked to the ocean, they are tidal. They receive and trap large deposits of decaying plant matter from the adjacent land as currents move the materials toward the ocean. Thus, typical estuaries offer nutrient-rich soils that support a wide array of organisms. Estuaries provide a buffer between land and ocean. Estuaries absorb the impact of storms and floods, reducing potential damage to coastal communities. Estuaries also act as filters, containing river pollutants before they are released to the ocean.

LESSON OBJECTIVE

🔑 Name the two major types of aquatic ecosystems.

Blended Path
Active learning using Student Edition, Inquiry Path, and Digital Path

ENGAGE AND EXPLORE

Teach this lesson using a variety of resources. Begin by reading **My Planet Diary** as a class. Have students share ideas about real-world connections, such as Alvin, to aquatic ecosystems. Then have students do the **Inquiry Warm-Up activity.** Students will investigate how an organism's structure helps it survive in its habitat. The **After the Inquiry Warm-Up worksheet** sets up a comparison of students' structures and those of a fish. Have volunteers share and compare their answers to number 4 to identify the many structures of a fish.

EXPLAIN AND ELABORATE

Teach Key Concepts by explaining the terms intertidal and neritic. *Inter-* means between, so *intertidal* means between the highest high tide line and the lowest low tide line. *Neritic* may be derived from the Latin word for marine snails to describe their habitat and refer to the shallow water below the lowest low tide line that extends over the continental shelf. Continue to **Teach Key Concepts** by explaining that there are two major aquatic ecosystems. Ask students to name these ecosystems and tell how they differ. Use the **Support the Big Q** to distinguish among the living organisms in the intertidal and neritic zones and among the organisms in these two zones and the open ocean. **Lead a Discussion** to have students share their experiences with aquatic ecosystems, such as swimming or fishing. Then have students practice the inquiry skill in the **Apply It activity.** Hand out the **Key Concept Summaries** as a review of the lesson. Students can also use the online **Vocab Flash Cards** to review key terms.

EVALUATE

Have students take the **Lesson Quiz.** For an alternate assessment, see the **EXAM**VIEW® Assessment Suite, Progress Monitoring Assessments, or SuccessTracker™.

E L L Support

1 Content and Language
Explain that the word *estuary* means a place where the fresh water of a river or stream meets the salt water of an ocean. It is often found between fresh water ecosystems and marine ecosystems.

Lab zone Inquiry Path
Hands-on learning in the Lab zone

ENGAGE AND EXPLORE

Teach this lesson with an emphasis on inquiry. Begin with the **Inquiry Warm-Up activity** in which students will investigate how an organism's structure helps it survive in its habitat. Lead a discussion about these structures. Have students do the **After the Inquiry Warm-Up worksheet.** Talk about student hand and speaking gestures. Have volunteers share their answers to number 4 about structures that help fish swim through the water.

EXPLAIN AND ELABORATE

Focus on the **Inquiry Skill** for the lesson. Point out that when you communicate, you share information. What might students communicate from the **Inquiry Warm-Up activity?** *(Information about fish structures and how they help fish in their habitats.)* Use the **Support the Big Q** to distinguish among the organisms in the intertidal and neritic zones and among the organisms in these two zones and the open ocean. Have students **Build Inquiry** by discussing what kind of organism a coral is and what a coral structure is. Review **Figure 2** before beginning the **Apply It activity.** Ask volunteers to name organisms likely to be found on the ocean floor. Have students do the **Quick Lab** to understand how oxygen dissolves. Students can use the online **Vocab Flash Cards** to review key terms.

EVALUATE

Have students take the **Lesson Quiz.** For an alternate assessment, see the **EXAM**VIEW® Assessment Suite, Progress Monitoring Assessments, or SuccessTracker™.

Digital Path
Online learning at my science online.com

ENGAGE AND EXPLORE

To teach this lesson using digital resources, begin by having students explore aquatic ecosystems at **My Planet Diary** online. Have them access the Chapter Resources to find the **Unlock the Big Question activity.** There they can answer the questions and refine their responses as they continue through the lesson. You can re-assign the activity and have students submit their work so you can track their progress.

EXPLAIN AND ELABORATE

Students reading above, at, or below the lexile measure of this lesson can access basic content readings at their level at **My Reading Web.** Have students use the online **Vocab Flash Cards** to preview key terms. Have students do the **Quick Lab** on dissolved oxygen and then ask students to share their results. Review **Figure 2** before assigning the online **Apply It activity.** Ask volunteers to name organisms likely to be found on the ocean floor. Have students submit their work to you. The **Key Concept Summaries** online allow students to read a summary and see an image associated with each part of the lesson. Online remediation is available at **My Science Coach.**

EVALUATE

Have students take the **Lesson Quiz.** For an alternate assessment, see the **EXAM**VIEW® Assessment Suite, Progress Monitoring Assessments, or SuccessTracker™.

2 Frontload the Lesson

Preview the lesson visuals, labels, and captions. Ask students what they know about the words *marine* and *freshwater.* Explain the specific meanings these words have in science. Some students may have heard the word *marine* used to describe saltwater or ocean water.

3 Comprehensible Input

Have students study the visuals and their captions on pages 70–71 to support the key concepts of the lesson.

4 Language Production

Pair or group students with varied language abilities to present oral reports on additional plants and animals found in freshwater and marine ecosystems.

5 Assess Understanding

Have students take notes during oral presentations and then summarize the notes in concise paragraphs to check comprehension.

LESSON 2.4

Aquatic Ecosystems

Establish Learning Objective

After this lesson, students will be able to:

🔑 Name and describe the two major types of aquatic ecosystems.

Engage ────────

Activate Prior Knowledge

MY PLANET DIARY Read *Underwater* Alvin with the class. Point out that the deepest and most remote regions of the ocean are all but impossible for scuba divers to explore. Ask: **What characteristics of an HOV make it an excellent way to explore the ocean floor?** *(Sample: An HOV can go deeper and farther than a scuba diver.)*

BIG IDEAS OF SCIENCE REFERENCE LIBRARY 📖
Have students look up the following topics:
Bay of Fundy, Beaches, Deep Sea Vents, Everglades.

Explore ────────

Lab Resource: Inquiry Warm-Up 🧪

L1 **WHERE DOES IT LIVE?** Students will look at photos and determine where the organisms that are depicted live.

LESSON
4 Aquatic Ecosystems

🔑 **What Are the Two Major Aquatic Ecosystems?**

my planet Diary

TECHNOLOGY

Underwater *Alvin*

Meet *Alvin*, an HOV (Human-Occupied Vehicle). Equipped with propulsion jets, cameras, and robotic arms, *Alvin* helps scientists gather data and discover ecosystems that exist deep in the ocean. Built in 1964, *Alvin* was one of the world's first deep-ocean submersibles and has made more than 4,500 dives. *Alvin* is credited with finding a lost hydrogen bomb, exploring the first known hydrothermal vents, and surveying the wreck of the *Titanic*.

Calculate Suppose that on each of the 4,500 dives *Alvin* has made, a new pilot and two new scientists were on board. How many scientists have seen the deep ocean through *Alvin's* windows? How many people, in total, traveled in *Alvin*?

9,000 scientists;
13,500 people total

▷ **PLANET DIARY** Go to **Planet Diary** to learn more about aquatic ecosystems.

 Lab zone Do the Inquiry Warm-Up *Where Does It Live?*

What Are the Two Major Aquatic Ecosystems?

Since almost three quarters of Earth's surface is covered with water, many living things make their homes in and near water. 🔑 **There are two types of aquatic, or water-based, ecosystems: freshwater ecosystems and marine (or saltwater) ecosystems.** All aquatic ecosystems are affected by the same abiotic, or nonliving, factors: sunlight, temperature, oxygen, and salt content. Sunlight is an important factor in aquatic ecosystems because it is necessary for photosynthesis in the water just as it is on land. Half of all oxygen produced on Earth comes from floating algae called phytoplankton. Because water absorbs sunlight, there is only enough light for photosynthesis to occur near the surface or in shallow water.

68 Ecosystems and Biomes

SUPPORT ALL READERS
Lexile Measure = 960L   Lexile Word Count = 864

Prior Exposure to Content: May be the first time students have encountered this topic

Academic Vocabulary: *classify, outline*

Science Vocabulary: *estuary, intertidal zone, neritic zone*

Concept Level: Generally appropriate for most students in this grade

Preteach With: My Planet Diary "Underwater *Alvin*" and Figure 2 activity

Go to **My Reading Web** to access leveled readings that provide a foundation for the content.

my science online.com

Vocabulary
- estuary
- intertidal zone
- neritic zone

Skills
- Reading: Outline
- Inquiry: Communicate

Freshwater Ecosystems No worldwide expedition would be complete without exploring Earth's waters. Even though most of Earth's surface is covered with water, only 3 percent of the volume is fresh water. Freshwater ecosystems include streams, rivers, ponds, and lakes. On this part of your expedition, you'll find that freshwater biomes provide habitats for a variety of organisms.

Streams and Rivers At the source of a mountain stream, the water flows slowly. Plants take root on the bottom, providing food for insects and homes for frogs. These consumers then provide food for larger consumers. Stream currents increase as streams come together to make larger streams, often called rivers. Animals here are adapted to strong currents. For example, trout have streamlined bodies to swim in the rushing water. As the current speeds up, it can become cloudy with sediment. Few plants or algae grow in this fast-moving water. Consumers such as snails feed on leaves and seeds that fall into the stream. At lower elevations, streams are warmer and often contain less oxygen, affecting the organisms that can live in them.

Ponds and Lakes Ponds and lakes are bodies of still, or standing, fresh water. Lakes are generally larger and deeper than ponds. Ponds are often shallow enough that sunlight can reach the bottom, allowing plants to grow there. In large ponds and most lakes, however, algae floating at the surface are the major producers. Many animals are adapted for life in still water. Dragonflies, snails, and frogs live along the shores of ponds. In the open water, sunfish feed on insects and algae close to the surface. Scavengers such as catfish live near the bottoms of ponds. Bacteria and other decomposers also feed on the remains of other organisms.

Outline As you read, make an outline on a separate sheet of paper that includes the different types of aquatic ecosystems. Use the red headings for the main ideas and the black headings for the supporting details.

FIGURE 1
Freshwater Ecosystems
Water lilies live in ponds and lakes.

✎ **Answer the questions.**

1. **Identify** What are two abiotic factors that can affect water lilies?

   Water temperature
   and amount of
   sunlight

2. **CHALLENGE** What adaptations do fish have that allow them to live in water?

   Sample: gills for
   breathing oxygen
   in water, fins, tails,
   scales for insulation
   and protection

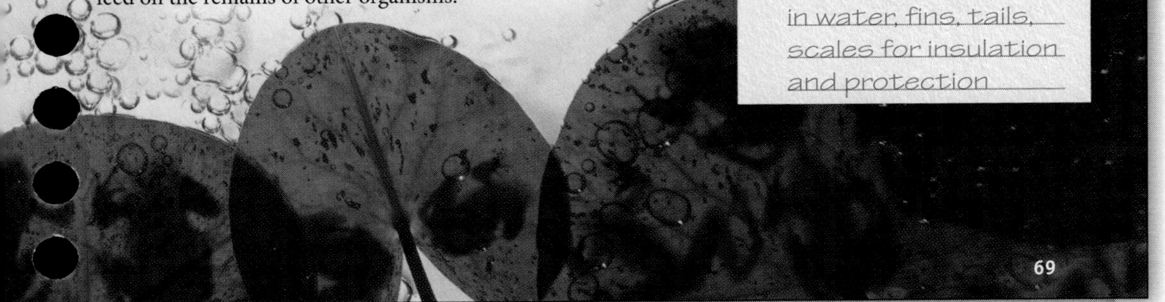

69

Explain

Introduce Vocabulary

Explain that the word *intertidal* combines a form of the word *tide* with a prefix (*inter-*) meaning "between." The intertidal zone of the ocean is the area between the waterline at high tide and at low tide.

Explain

Teach Key Concepts 🔑

Explain to students that water-based ecosystems are called aquatic ecosystems. Ask: **What two major categories are aquatic ecosystems divided into?** *(Freshwater ecosystems and saltwater, or marine, ecosystems)* The source of most freshwater on Earth is in glaciers and in water underground. In fact, 99% of liquid freshwater is found underground. Almost half of the world's lake water is saltwater, such as the Great Salt Lake of Utah. Saltwater lakes can be up to ten times saltier than the ocean. Point out that sunlight, temperature, oxygen, and salt content are factors that affect all aquatic ecosystems. Ask: **Why is sunlight important to aquatic ecosystems?** *(Sunlight is needed for photosynthesis.)* **Where does most photosynthesis take place?** *(Near the surface or in shallow water where there is light)* **What are two groups of freshwater ecosystems?** *(Flowing water and standing water)*

21st Century Learning

CRITICAL THINKING Help students compare and contrast types of aquatic ecosystems. Ask: **What are two examples of flowing water ecosystems?** *(Streams and rivers)* **How do these ecosystems differ?** *(Streams tend to be smaller and the water flows slowly near their source. Rivers tend to be wider, deeper, and faster-moving.)* **What are two examples of standing water ecosystems?** *(Ponds and lakes)* **How do these ecosystems differ?** *(Lakes are larger and deeper than ponds. Sunlight can reach the bottom of many ponds, but not lakes.)*

Outline Outlining helps organize information in a visual way that makes it easier to see the relationships between ideas. Make sure students follow the proper format for an outline.

My Planet Diary provides an opportunity for students to explore real-world connections to aquatic ecosystems.

my science online.com › **Aquatic Ecosystems**

ELL Support

1 Content and Language
Allow students to create entries for the vocabulary terms in their own science glossaries. Students should briefly define each word, draw a picture, and include the word in their native language if needed.

2 Frontload the Lesson
Have students name organisms they have seen in marine ecosystems, even at an aquarium. Have students cooperatively discuss the habitats of these organisms.

3 Comprehensible Input
Have students suggest other marine organisms they have seen that are not shown in **Figure 2**. Ask students to hypothesize the depth at which the organism can be found.

Explain

Support the Big Q ? UbD

PRODUCERS IN THE OCEAN Ask students to look at the intertidal zone in **Figure 2**. Ask: **What difference do you see in what is living here compared to the other zones?** *(This zone has plants attached to the bottom and the others do not.)* Ask: **In which other zones do algae live?** *(Neritic zone and surface zone of the open ocean)* **Why are these organisms important to marine ecosystems?** *(They produce oxygen and are food for other organisms.)* Help students appreciate the importance of producers in the ocean by explaining that floating algae called phytoplankton produce half of Earth's oxygen.

Lead a Discussion

Invite students to share their knowledge of water-based ecosystems, which may have come from experiences such as swimming, fishing, boating, or observing from shore. Ask: **What aquatic ecosystems have you seen?** *(Students will likely name ponds, lakes; rivers, streams; bays, or open oceans.)* **What plants and animals did you observe?** *(Students will likely mention green algae, water lilies, marsh grasses, "seaweed," fish, frogs, turtles, waterfowl, or other birds.)* Encourage students who have seen different aquatic ecosystems to share differences and similarities between the ecosystems.

21st Century Learning

CRITICAL THINKING Discuss with students the differences and similarities among marine ecosystems in location, water depth, amount of salt in water, organisms, and sunlight. Ask: **How are an estuary and the intertidal zone different?** *(Different organisms live in them; the water in the intertidal zone is saltier than the water in an estuary; the estuary has few waves.)* **How are an estuary and the intertidal zone alike?** *(In both, the land is sometimes covered with water and at other times exposed to the air and sunlight.)*

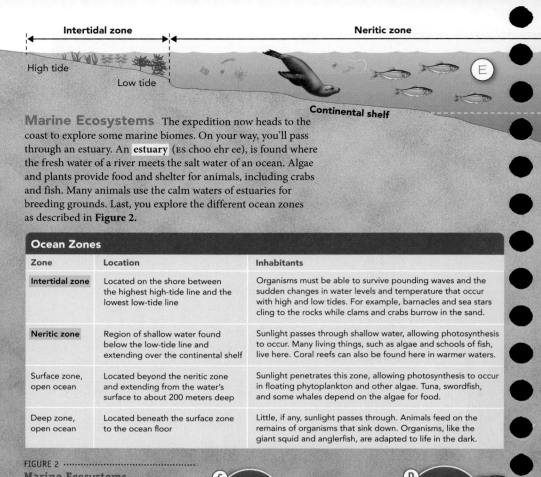

Marine Ecosystems The expedition now heads to the coast to explore some marine biomes. On your way, you'll pass through an estuary. An **estuary** (ES choo ehr ee), is found where the fresh water of a river meets the salt water of an ocean. Algae and plants provide food and shelter for animals, including crabs and fish. Many animals use the calm waters of estuaries for breeding grounds. Last, you explore the different ocean zones as described in **Figure 2**.

Ocean Zones

Zone	Location	Inhabitants
Intertidal zone	Located on the shore between the highest high-tide line and the lowest low-tide line	Organisms must be able to survive pounding waves and the sudden changes in water levels and temperature that occur with high and low tides. For example, barnacles and sea stars cling to the rocks while clams and crabs burrow in the sand.
Neritic zone	Region of shallow water found below the low-tide line and extending over the continental shelf	Sunlight passes through shallow water, allowing photosynthesis to occur. Many living things, such as algae and schools of fish, live here. Coral reefs can also be found here in warmer waters.
Surface zone, open ocean	Located beyond the neritic zone and extending from the water's surface to about 200 meters deep	Sunlight penetrates this zone, allowing photosynthesis to occur in floating phytoplankton and other algae. Tuna, swordfish, and some whales depend on the algae for food.
Deep zone, open ocean	Located beneath the surface zone to the ocean floor	Little, if any, sunlight passes through. Animals feed on the remains of organisms that sink down. Organisms, like the giant squid and anglerfish, are adapted to life in the dark.

FIGURE 2 ·················

Marine Ecosystems
The ocean is home to a number of different ecosystems.

✎ **Classify** Using the clues, determine at which depth each organism belongs. In the circles in the ocean, write the letter for each organism in the correct zone.

Yellowfin Tuna
Found in open waters and has been known to eat squid

Blue Whale
Feeds on shrimplike creatures at depths of more than 100 meters during the day

Anglerfish
Females have a lighted lure to help them attract prey in the dark.

Tripod Fish
This fish has three elongated fins to help it stand.

Swordfish
Often seen jumping out of the water to stun smaller fish

70 Ecosystems and Biomes

Digital Lesson: Assign the *Apply It* activity online and have students submit their work to you.

my science online.com | Aquatic Ecosystems

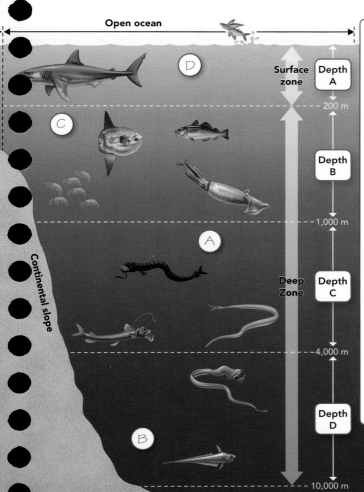

Open ocean

Continental slope

Surface zone

Depth A

200 m

Depth B

1,000 m

Deep Zone

Depth C

4,000 m

Depth D

10,000 m

D

C

A

B

apply it!

While on a deep sea exploration, you discover a new marine organism on the ocean floor.

Communicate Draw or describe the new organism below. Identify the structures and adaptations it has to live in the deep zone.

Sample: The organism is very small so it doesn't require much food. It is very strong to withstand the pressure of the water. Big eyes help it see in the dark.

 Lab zone Do the Quick Lab Dissolved Oxygen.

🔑 Assess Your Understanding

1a. List The four abiotic factors that affect all aquatic ecosystems are

sunlight, temperature, oxygen, and salt content.

b. Make Generalizations Why is sunlight important to all aquatic ecosystems?

Sunlight is needed for producers to make food and oxygen.

got it?

○ **I get it!** Now I know that the two major types of aquatic ecosystems are _freshwater and marine._

○ **I need extra help with** _See TE note._

Go to MY SCIENCE ⑤ COACH online for help with this subject.

71

Differentiated Instruction

L1 Draw the Ocean's Four Zones Have each student draw a diagram showing the ocean's four zones and label each zone without referring to the illustration in this section. Have students check their work when they have finished their diagrams. Students' diagrams might be displayed on a classroom or hallway bulletin board.

L3 Aquatic Photos Challenge students to find photographs of two

different aquatic ecosystems. Have them take notes on the similarities and differences between the ecosystems and the organisms that live in them. Students can then explain those characteristics to the class. Remind students of the factors to consider in comparing the ecosystems: salty water or fresh water, amount of available sunlight, still or moving water, types of organisms, and so on.

Elaborate

Build Inquiry

L1 INFER CORAL STRUCTURE

Materials coral

Time 10 minutes

Ask students if a coral is a plant or an animal *(Animal)* Provide samples of different types of coral for students to examine. Emphasize that these pieces of coral are not the animals, which are soft, but the structures they produced and left behind when they died.

Ask: **Where do you think the coral animals lived?** *(Inside the tiny holes)* **How do you think this hard structure helps coral animals survive?** *(It provides protection for the animals' soft bodies and also anchors them to the ocean floor.)*

Apply It!

L1 Review details listed in the Ocean Zones table and the Marine Ecosystems illustrations before beginning the activity. Make sure students understand that the new organism should have structures and adaptations that are appropriate for the deep zone of the open ocean. Point out that students might "borrow" one or more characteristics from several existing organisms in order to create a new kind of organism.

Communicate Tell students that including details will help them convey their ideas more clearly.

Lab Resource: Quick Lab **Lab zone**

L2 DISSOLVED OXYGEN Students will explore how oxygen is dissolved in water.

Evaluate

Assess Your Understanding

After students answer the questions, have them evaluate their understanding by completing the appropriate sentence.

RTI Response to Intervention

1a. If students have trouble listing factors that affect aquatic ecosystems, **then** call on volunteers to list factors that affect land ecosystems. Then ask students which of these factors affect aquatic ecosystems, and to add any additional factors.

b. If students need help with the importance of sunlight, **then** ask them which kinds of organisms require sunlight and why.

MY SCIENCE ⑤ COACH Have students go online for help in understanding aquatic ecosystems.

Lab **zone** After the Inquiry Warm-Up

Aquatic Ecosystems

Inquiry Warm-Up, *Where Does It Live?*

In the Inquiry Warm-Up, you investigated how an organism's structure helps it survive in its habitat. Using what you learned from that activity, answer the questions below.

1. **USE PRIOR KNOWLEDGE** Are their structures in your hand that help you survive? List at least two structures in your hand and their functions.

   _____

   _____

2. **USE PRIOR KNOWLEDGE** List all the structures of your body necessary in order for you to say a word.

   _____

   _____

3. **COMMUNICATE** Draw a simple diagram of a fish. Label as many different structures on the fish as you can.

4. **EXPLAIN** List all the structures of the fish that help it swim through water.

   _____

   _____

   _____

   _____

Assess Your Understanding

Aquatic Ecosystems

> ## What Are the Two Major Aquatic Ecosystems?

1a. LIST The four abiotic factors that affect all aquatic ecosystems are

_____

b. MAKE GENERALIZATIONS Why is sunlight important to all aquatic ecosystems?

_____

got it? ···

○ **I get it!** Now I know that the two major types of aquatic ecosystems are _____

_____

○ **I need extra help with** _____

_____

Key Concept Summaries

Aquatic Ecosystems

What Are the Two Major Aquatic Ecosystems?

There are two types of aquatic, or water-based, ecosystems: freshwater ecosystems and marine (or saltwater) ecosystems. All aquatic ecosystems are affected by the same abiotic, or nonliving factors: sunlight, temperature, oxygen, and salt content.

Most of Earth's surface is covered with water, yet only 3 percent is fresh water. Freshwater ecosystems include streams, rivers, ponds, and lakes. Freshwater biomes provide habitats for a variety of organisms. Few plants or algae can grow in this fast-moving water. Slower moving water in rivers is warmer and contains less oxygen, so different organisms are adapted to life there. Plants take root on the river bottom, providing food for insects and homes for frogs. These consumers provide food for larger consumers. Ponds and lakes are bodies of still fresh water. Usually lakes are larger and deeper than ponds. In large ponds and most lakes, algae floating at the surface are major producers. Many animals are adapted for life in still water, such as dragonflies, snails, frogs, sunfish, and catfish. Bacteria and other decomposers also feed on the remains of other organisms.

An **estuary** is found where the fresh water a river meets the salt water of an ocean. Algae and plants provide food and shelter for animals, including crabs and fish. Many animals use the calm waters of estuaries for breeding grounds. Marine ecosystems have different ocean zones. There are four ocean zones. Located on the shore between the highest high-tide line and the lowest low-tide line, the **intertidal zone** is home to organisms, such as barnacles, clams, and crabs, that survive pounding waves and sudden changes in water levels and temperature, The **neritic zone** is a shallow water region found below the low-tide line and extending over the continental shelf. Living things, such as algae and fish, live here. The surface zone is open ocean located beyond the neritic zone and extending from the water's surface to a few hundred meters deep. Tuna, swordfish, and some whales feed on algae here. The deep zone is the deeper, darker water below the surface zone. Animals feed on the remains of organisms that sink down. Organisms, like the giant squid and anglerfish, are adapted to life in the dark.

On a separate sheet of paper, identify the categories into which freshwater ecosystems and marine ecosystems are divided.

Review and Reinforce

Aquatic Ecosystems

Understanding Main Ideas
Answer the following question in the spaces provided.

1. What are the four main types of freshwater ecosystems?

   _____

   _____

2. What conditions to organisms face in the intertidal zone?

   _____

   _____

   _____

   _____

3. Why is the neritic zone particularly rich in living things?

   _____

   _____

   _____

Building Vocabulary
Fill in the blank to complete each statement.

4. The _____ zone is the point along the shoreline between the highest high-tide line and the lowest low-tide line.

5. The point where the fresh water of a river meets the salt water of the ocean is called a(n) _____.

6. The _____ zone is out in the open ocean where light penetrates only to a depth of a few hundred meters.

7. The _____ zone is a region of shallow water below the low-tide line that extends over the continental shelf.

8. The _____ zone is almost totally dark.

Enrich

Aquatic Ecosystems

> A hydrothermal vent is a place very hot water from Earth's crust rises to the ocean floor and is released into the surrounding seawater through cracks in the ocean floor. Read the passage and then answer the questions on a separate sheet of paper.

Hydrothermal Vent Communities

There are many ecosystems within the marine environment including estuaries, the intertidal zone, and the open ocean. Within each of these ecosystems, life is rich and diverse. The open ocean can be divided into two main zones, the surface zone, where light penetrates water to a depth of a few hundred meters, and the deep zone, where there is little to no light. In the surface zone, algae are the producers, using light energy from the sun to undergo photosynthesis and produce glucose, an energy-rich compound. In the deepest areas of the ocean, where there is no light, photosynthesis cannot take place. Although vast areas of the deep-ocean floor are empty of life, one unique community of organisms exists in some of the deepest areas of the ocean, around hydrothermal vents.

At hydrothermal vents, the hot water is rich in minerals, including sulfur compounds. Certain types of bacteria can produce glucose from the sulfur compounds through a process called *chemosynthesis*. These bacteria are producers. Like algae in the surface zone that use light energy to produce glucose, the bacteria use the energy in the sulfur compounds to do the same.

These communities have been found as deep as 2.2 km below the ocean surface. The bacteria in a hydrothermal vent community can live on rocks that are heated to temperatures of 110°C from the water gushing out of cracks in the ocean floor. They coat the hot rocks and are grazed on by shrimp. The shrimp and other grazers are eaten by crabs and fishes.

1. What process do producers in the surface zone undergo to produce glucose?
2. What are hydrothermal vent communities?
3. Which organisms are the producers in a hydrothermal vent community? What process do these organisms undergo to produce glucose?
4. How can these bacteria produce glucose without light energy from the sun?
5. Predict what would happen if the hot, sulfur-containing water stopped entering the surrounding ocean water.

Name _____ Date _____ Class _____

Aquatic Ecosystems

Fill in the blank to complete each statement.

1. _____ ecosystems include streams, rivers, ponds, and lakes.

2. A(n) _____ is found where the fresh water of a river meets the salt water of an ocean.

3. Located on the shore, the _____ zone is home to organisms that can survive pounding waves and sudden changes in water levels and temperature.

4. There are two types of aquatic ecosystems: freshwater biomes and _____ biomes.

5. Organisms like the giant squid and anglerfish are adapted to life in the dark of the _____ zone.

If the statement is true, write *true*. If the statement is false, change the underlined word or words to make the statement true.

6. _____ All <u>aquatic ecosystems</u> are affected by the same nonliving factors: sunlight, temperature, oxygen, and salt content.

7. _____ Most of Earth's surface is covered with water, yet only <u>30 percent</u> is fresh water.

8. _____ Usually lakes are <u>smaller and shallower</u> than ponds.

9. _____ Tuna, swordfish, and some whales feed on algae in the <u>intertidal</u> zone.

10. _____ The <u>neritic zone</u> is a region of shallow water where many living things, such as algae and schools of fish, live.

Aquatic Ecosystems

Answer Key

After the Inquiry Warm-Up

1. Accept all reasonable responses. Students may say: Yes, fingers help to grip, nails for scratching or picking at something.

2. Accept all reasonable responses. Students may say: mouth, tongue, vocal cords, and lungs.

3. Sample: Simple line drawing of a fish with labeled structures, such as: eye, gills, fin, tail, etc.

4. Sample: Gills for breathing underwater, fins for turning and stability, tail for propulsion.

Key Concept Summaries

Freshwater ecosystems and marine ecosystems are the two types of aquatic ecosystems. Freshwater ecosystems include streams, rivers, ponds, and lakes. Streams tend to be fast-moving and cold, and rivers tend to be slower and warmer. Ponds and lakes are bodies of still fresh water. Usually lakes are larger and deeper than ponds. An estuary is found where the fresh water of a river meets the salt water of an ocean. The ocean is divided into four zones. The intertidal zone is located on the shore between the highest high-tide line and the lowest low-tide line. The neritic zone is shallow water found below the low-tide line and extending over the continental shelf.

The surface zone is open ocean located beyond the neritic zone and extending from the water's surface to a few hundred meters deep. The deep zone is the deeper, darker water below the surface zone.

Review and Reinforce

1. streams, rivers, ponds, lakes

2. They face pounding waves as well as sudden changes in water levels and temperature that occur with high and low tides.

3. It is rich in organisms because sunlight passes through its shallow water enabling photosynthesis to occur.

4. intertidal

5. estuary

6. surface

7. neritic

8. deep

Enrich

1. photosynthesis

2. communities of organisms that form near areas of the deep ocean floor where super-heated water that contains sulfur compounds is released into surrounding ocean water from Earth's crust

3. bacteria; chemosynthesis

4. Since sunlight does not penetrate to the deep-ocean floor, these bacteria use the energy in the sulfur compounds in place of light energy to produce glucose, a process called chemosynthesis.

5. The bacteria would not be able to undergo chemosynthesis without a source of energy and have to move to a new vent area or die. Since the bacteria are the producers supporting the entire community, the consumers would have to find another food source, move to a new vent, or die.

Lesson Quiz

1. Freshwater
2. estuary
3. intertidal
4. marine
5. deep
6. true
7. 3 percent
8. larger and deeper
9. surface
10. true

Place the outside corner, the corner away from the dotted line, in the corner of your copy machine to copy onto letter-size paper.

How do energy and matter move through ecosystems?

Lesson Pacing: 1–2 periods or $\frac{1}{2}$–1 block

SHORT ON TIME? To do this lesson in approximately half the time, do the Activate Prior Knowledge activity on page 72. A discussion of the key concept on page 73 will familiarize students with the lesson content. Have students do the Quick Lab. The rest of the lesson can be completed by students independently.

Preference Navigator, in the online Planning tools, allows you to customize Interactive Science to your own teaching style. You can also edit lesson plans by selecting the Lesson Planner option.

Digital Teacher's Edition allows you to access your Teacher's Edition and Resource materials online.

Lesson Vocabulary

- biogeography
- continental drift
- dispersal
- exotic species

Content Refresher

Dispersal Barriers Continental drift and volcanic eruptions have resulted in landmasses separated by large bodies of water. These bodies of water act as barriers to the dispersal of organisms from one landmass to another. As a result, many isolated areas have developed their own unique organisms. Today humans can overcome these expanses of water and other natural physical barriers that once prevented the dispersal of species. Inadvertent dispersal through travel by air or ocean and purposeful dispersal through cultivation of exotic species are two ways that humans can overcome previous barriers to dispersal. As humans have accelerated the dispersal of species, new species can be introduced into areas, and native species that previously did not have to compete for resources now must do so. Often the native species are displaced.

LESSON OBJECTIVE

Identify what factors affect species dispersal.

Blended Path
Active learning using Student Edition, Inquiry Path, and Digital Path

ENGAGE AND EXPLORE

Teach this lesson using a variety of resources. Begin by reading **My Planet Diary** as a class. Have students share ideas about animals that live in Australia and how they are unique. Then have students do the **Inquiry Warm-Up activity.** Students will investigate how seeds are transported. Discuss the different ways of dispersal of seed types. The **After the Inquiry Warm-Up worksheet** sets up a discussion about seed dispersal. Have volunteers share their answers to number 4 about disadvantages to seed dispersal.

EXPLAIN AND ELABORATE

Teach Key Concepts by explaining the term *biogeography* and *dispersal. Biogeography* relates to the study of where living things are found on Earth. *Dispersal* is the process of spreading organisms from one place to another. Continue to **Teach Key Concepts** by explaining factors that affect dispersal. Have students identify these factors as a means of distribution or limits of dispersal. Ask students to name factors in dispersal. Use the **Support the Big Q** to illustrate why a population of an introduced species might increase rapidly. Use **Figure 2** to illustrate a dispersal factor. Then have students practice the inquiry skill in the **Apply It activity.** Hand out the **Key Concept Summaries** as a review of each part of the lesson. Students can also use the online **Vocab Flash Cards** to review key terms.

EVALUATE

Have students take the **Lesson Quiz.** For an alternate assessment, see the **EXAM**VIEW® Assessment Suite, Progress Monitoring Assessments, or SuccessTracker™.

ELL Support

1 Content and Language

Identify the words *exotic species* in the vocabulary. Explain that although students may think of an exotic species as an interesting animal in a country far from home, it has a scientific meaning—a non-native organism introduced to a new habitat.

Lab zone Inquiry Path
Hands-on learning in the Lab zone

ENGAGE AND EXPLORE

To teach this lesson with an emphasis on inquiry, begin with the **Inquiry Warm-Up activity.** Students will investigate how seeds are transported. Discuss with students the different ways of dispersal and seed types. Have students do the **After the Inquiry Warm-Up worksheet.** Talk about seed dispersal. Have volunteers share their answers to number 4 about disadvantages to seed dispersal.

EXPLAIN AND ELABORATE

Focus on the **Inquiry Skill** for the lesson. Point out that when you predict, you foretell or indicate in advance. What predictions can be made in the **Inquiry Warm-Up activity?** *(Food sources can be grouped into categories based on the type of organism they come from.)* Review means of dispersal before beginning the **Apply It activity.** Ask volunteers to identify the means by which rats were dispersed. Have students do the **Quick Lab** to reinforce understanding of dispersal by continental drift. Students can use the online **Vocab Flash Cards** to review key terms.

EVALUATE

Have students take the **Lesson Quiz.** For an alternate assessment, see the **EXAM**VIEW® Assessment Suite, Progress Monitoring Assessments, or SuccessTracker™.

Digital Path
Online learning at my science online.com

ENGAGE AND EXPLORE

Teach this lesson using digital resources. Begin by having students explore biogeography at **My Planet Diary** online. Have them access the Chapter Resources to find the **Unlock the Big Question activity.** There they can answer the questions and refine their responses as they continue through the lesson. You can re-assign the activity and have students submit their work so you can track their progress.

EXPLAIN AND ELABORATE

Students reading above, at, or below the lexile measure of this lesson can access basic content readings at their level at **My Reading Web.** Have students use the online **Vocab Flash Cards** to preview key terms. Have students do the online **Interactive Art activity** to observe continental drift and how is affects the dispersal of organisms. Review means of dispersal before assigning the online **Apply It activity.** Ask volunteers to identify the means by which rats were dispersed. Have students submit their work to you. Do the **Quick Lab** and then ask students to share their results. The **Key Concept Summaries** online allow students to read a summary and see an image associated with each part of the lesson. Online remediation is available at **My Science Coach.**

EVALUATE

Have students take the **Lesson Quiz.** For an alternate assessment, see the **EXAM**VIEW® Assessment Suite, Progress Monitoring Assessments, or SuccessTracker™.

2 Frontload the Lesson
Preview the lesson visuals, labels, and captions. Ask students what they know about continental drift. Use **Figure 1** to explain this dispersal factor.

3 Comprehensible Input
Have students study the visuals and their captions on pages 73–75 to support the key concepts of the lesson.

4 Language Production
Pair or group students with varied language abilities to complete labs collaboratively for language practice. Have each student copy the completed written lab for personal reference.

5 Assess Understanding
Make true or false statements using lesson content and have students indicate if they agree or disagree with a thumbs up or thumbs down gesture to check whole-class comprehension.

LESSON 2.5

Biogeography

Establish Learning Objective

After this lesson, students will be able to:

🔑 Identify what factors affect species dispersal.

Engage

Activate Prior Knowledge

MY PLANET DIARY Read *Australia's Animals* with the class. Point out that kangaroos have powerful hind legs, long feet, short forelimbs, and long, muscular tails, all of which make them well adapted for hopping and maintaining balance on the vast Australian plains. Ask: **How does a kangaroo's pouch help this species survive in its environment?** *(The pouch keeps young safe in an area that has few places to hide or protect them.)*

BIG IDEAS OF SCIENCE REFERENCE LIBRARY 📖 Have students look up the following topic: Plant Invasion.

Explore

Lab Resource: Inquiry Warm-Up 🧪

L1 **HOW CAN YOU MOVE A SEED?** Students will list ways in which seeds can be moved from place to place.

---

5 Biogeography

🔑 **What Factors Affect Species Dispersal?**

MY PLANET DiARY

Australia's Animals

When you think of Australia, what animal comes to mind? Most likely, you think of a kangaroo or a koala. Did you know that these animals are marsupials, mammals that carry their young in a pouch? You might be surprised to learn that most marsupials exist only in Australia. Now, can you name any monotremes, or mammals that lay eggs? The only monotremes that exist are platypuses and echidnas, both native to Australia. Lots of unique animals are native to Australia because it is completely surrounded by water.

FUN FACT

Communicate **Answer the following questions with a classmate.**

1. What are two types of mammals that are common in Australia?

   <u>Marsupials and monotremes</u>

2. Would you ever expect a platypus to move from Australia to the United States? Explain.

   <u>Sample: No, because Australia is surrounded by water. It would be too difficult for a platypus to swim such a long distance.</u>

▶ **PLANET DIARY** Go to **Planet Diary** to learn more about biogeography.

🧪 Do the Inquiry Warm-Up *How Can You Move a Seed?*

72 Ecosystems and Biomes

SUPPORT ALL READERS

Lexile Measure = 980L   Lexile Word Count = 873

Prior Exposure to Content: May be the first time students have encountered this topic

Academic Vocabulary: *cause, effect, predict*

Science Vocabulary: *biogeography, dispersal*

Concept Level: Generally appropriate for most students in this grade

Preteach With: My Planet Diary "Australia's Animals" and Figure 1 activity

Go to **My Reading Web** to access leveled readings that provide a foundation for the content.

Vocabulary
- biogeography
- dispersal
- continental drift
- exotic species

Skills
- Reading: Relate Cause and Effect
- Inquiry: Predict

What Factors Affect Species Dispersal?

Do you think all of the people who live in your hometown were born there? Some of them may have come from different cities, states, or countries. Just as humans do, different plants and animals live in different parts of the world. The study of where organisms live and how they got there is called **biogeography**. Biogeographers also study factors that have led to the worldwide distribution of species that exist today.

The movement of the Earth's continents is one factor that has affected how species are distributed. The continents are parts of huge blocks of solid rock, called plates, that make up Earth's surface. These plates have been moving very slowly for millions of years. As the plates move, the continents move with them in a process called **continental drift**. **Figure 1** shows how the continents have moved over time. Notice that about 225 million years ago, all of the continents were part of one huge landmass, called Pangaea.

Continental drift has had a great impact on species distribution. For example, Australia drifted away from the other landmasses millions of years ago. Organisms from other parts of the world could not reach the isolated island and unique Australian species developed in this isolation.

🔑 Continental drift, wind, water, and living things are all means of distributing species. Other factors, such as physical barriers, competition, and climate, can limit species dispersal.

FIGURE 1 ·····················
▶ **INTERACTIVE ART** **Continental Drift**
The movement of landmasses is one factor affecting the distribution of organisms.

✎ **Observe** How has Australia's location changed over time?

Sample: Australia moved eastward and away from Antarctica less than 115 million years ago.

225 Million Years Ago

115 Million Years Ago

Earth Today

73

Explain

Introduce Vocabulary

To help students understand the term *dispersal*, point out that the verb form, *disperse*, comes from a Latin word meaning "scatter" along with the prefix *dis-*, meaning "away."

Teach Key Concepts 🔑

Explain to students that there are several reasons why species have been spread around the world. Other reasons have limited the way species are distributed. Ask: **What are four causes of species distribution?** *(Continental drift, wind, water, living things)* **Which of these causes takes place most slowly?** *(Continental drift)* **What are three factors that can limit species distribution?** *(Climate, competition among species, physical barriers)*

Teach With Visuals

Tell students to look at **Figure 1.** Explain to students that the changes shown took place over hundreds of millions of years. Ask: **Why is the western coast of Africa shaped like it is?** *(Continental drift separated it from what is now the eastern coast of South America. These two coastlines once fitted together snugly.)* **Where was present-day Europe located when Pangaea existed?** *(Side by side with what is now northeastern North America.)* **Have North America and South America always been connected since the breakup of Pangaea?** *(No)*

My Planet Diary provides an opportunity for students to explore real-world connections to species dispersal.

Interactive Art shows how the movement of the continents is one factor affecting the distribution of organisms.

my science online.com | Species Dispersal

LESSON 2.5

ⒺⓁⓁ Support

1 Content and Language
Define *continental drift* using maps (for *continent*) and pantomime (for *drift*) to help students understand each word's meaning. Ask them to explain how knowing these words helps one understand the term *continental drift*.

2 Frontload the Lesson
Break the term *biogeography* into two parts: *bio-* and *geography*. Ask students to define *geography* (i.e., the study of the characteristics of places on Earth). Then ask students to explain how adding the prefix *bio-*, meaning "life," changes the meaning of the word.

3 Comprehensible Input
Simplify the information discussed in "Limits to Dispersal" by creating a graphic organizer. Use synonyms. In the center circle, write *limits to movement* with branches for *barriers*, *competition*, and *climate*.

Explain

Teach With Visuals

Have students look at **Figure 2.** Ask: **What are some ways that organisms can be dispersed?** *(By wind and by other living things)* **When might seed dispersal not be beneficial for the species?** *(When seeds are carried to an area where they cannot grow)* **Why were rats considered an exotic species on Rat Island in 1780?** *(There were no rats on the island before people from the Japanese ship unintentionally introduced the rats to the island.)*

Support the Big Q ❓ UbD

INTRODUCED SPECIES Discuss with students the paragraph in the *Apply It* activity. Explain that introduced species, also known as nonnative species, enter an ecosystem and can interfere with local food chains. Ask: **Why might the population of an introduced species increase rapidly?** *(There might not be any predators to feed on them and control their numbers.)*

Make Analogies

L1 MODES OF TRANSIT To help students understand the concept of means of dispersal of organisms, compare an ecosystem to a city or town. Describe how at the end of a workday, people come out of office buildings and stores to travel to their homes. Ask: **What methods might people use to go their separate ways?** *(Walking, bicycling, riding in a bus or train or boat or airplane, driving a car)* **What do all of these methods have in common?** *(They disperse people and move them from one place to another.)* **How do human travel methods compare to wind, water, or living things causing dispersal of organisms?** *(In both cases, there are different ways or devices or processes that accomplish a similar effect, dispersal of organisms.)*

Elaborate

Apply It!

L1 Review the information in the photograph and have students think about places they might expect to see rats before beginning the activity. Encourage them to speculate on how some organism might be dispersed unexpectedly to an ecosystem that is very different from its usual one.

🔺 **Predict** Remind students that when they predict, they use their observations and knowledge to make an inference about a future event.

FIGURE 2
▶ INTERACTIVE ART **Means of Dispersal**
Seeds can be dispersed by the wind or by organisms like this blue jay.

Means of Dispersal The movement of organisms from one place to another is called **dispersal.** Dispersal can be caused by gravity, wind, water, or living things, such as the blue jay in **Figure 2.**

Wind and Water Many animals move into new areas on their own. But plants and small organisms need help in moving from place to place. Wind can disperse seeds, fungi spores, tiny spiders, and other small, light organisms. Birds use the wind to fly to new locations. Similarly, water transports objects that float, such as coconuts and leaves. Small animals, such as insects or snails, may get a ride to a new home on top of these floating rafts. Water also transports organisms like fish and marine mammals.

Other Living Things Organisms can also be dispersed by other living things. If your dog or cat has ever come home covered with sticky plant burs, you have seen an example of dispersal. Humans have sped up the dispersal of organisms, both intentionally and unintentionally, as they travel around the world. An **exotic species** is an organism that is carried into a new location by people. Exotic species have contributed to the decline or elimination of native species.

In 1780, a Japanese ship ran aground on one of Alaska's uninhabited Aleutian Islands. Rats from the ship swam to the island. Since then, the rats on this island, now called Rat Island, have preyed upon and destroyed seabird populations and the overall ecosystem. "Rat spills" from ships are one of the leading causes of seabird extinctions on islands worldwide.

❶ **Communicate** With a partner, identify ways in which sailors can control rats on board their ships and prevent them from going ashore.

Sample: have rat traps set at all times; keep food and trash in sealed containers

❷ 🔺 **Predict** Do you think the role of humans in the dispersal of species will increase or decrease in the next 50 years? Defend your answer.

Sample: Humans' role will increase as people travel more freely around the world, including to previously isolated or unexplored regions.

Interactive Art demonstrates the dispersal of seeds as they move from one area to another.

Digital Lesson: Assign the *Apply It* activity online and have students submit their work to you.

MY SCIENCE online.com ▶ | Species Dispersal

Limits to Dispersal With all these means of dispersal, you might expect to find the same species in many places around the world. Of course, that's not so. Three factors that limit distribution of a species are physical barriers, competition, and climate.

Physical Barriers (Water and mountains) form barriers that are hard to cross. These features <u>can limit the movement of organisms.</u> For example, once Australia became separated from the other continents, organisms could not easily move to or from Australia.

Competition When an organism enters a new area, it must (compete for resources with the species that already live there) To survive, the organism must find a unique niche, or role. <u>Existing species may outcompete the new species.</u> In this case, competition is a barrier to dispersal. Sometimes, in certain situations, <u>new species outcompete and displace the existing species.</u>

Climate The typical weather pattern in an area over a long period of time is the area's climate. (Climate differences can limit dispersal.) For example, the climate changes greatly as you climb a tall mountain. <u>The warm, dry mountain base, the cooler and wetter areas higher up, and the cold, windy top all support different species.</u> Those species that thrive at the base may not survive at the top.

FIGURE 3 ....

Limits to Dispersal
Physical barriers, like the Grand Canyon and the Colorado River, can make it difficult for species to move around.

✎
↩ **Relate Cause and Effect**
In the paragraphs at the left, circle the factors that can limit dispersal. Then underline the effects of these limits.

Lab zone® Do the Quick Lab *Relating Continental Drift to Dispersal.*

🔑 **Assess Your Understanding**

1a. Explain What role do humans play in the dispersal of species?
<u>Humans intentionally and accidentally disperse species as they travel.</u>

b. |CHALLENGE| Suppose that a new species of insect were introduced to your area. Explain how competition might limit its dispersal.
<u>Accept all well-reasoned responses. Sample: Local insect species would outcompete an introduced species.</u>

got_{it}? ....

○ I get it! Now I know that species dispersal is affected by <u>continental drift, wind, water, other living things, physical barriers, competition, and climate.</u>

○ I need extra help with <u>See TE note.</u>

Go to MY SCIENCE 🅢 COACH *online for help with this subject.*

75

Differentiated Instruction

L3 **Illustrate Climate's Effect on Dispersal** Have students study the paragraph on climate's effect on species dispersal. Then challenge students to do additional research in order to create a detailed illustration of a mountain, showing the distribution of plant species on different parts of the mountain. Students might label the gradually higher levels of the mountain with names of species such as *desert scrub,*

grassland, oak woodland, pine-oak, mixed conifer, spruce-fir, and *alpine.* Urge students to include detailed sketches of each plant species.

L1 **Identify Dispersal Methods** Connect the lesson's Inquiry Warm-Up activity to the section's content for students who need extra help. Ask them to identify the dispersal methods they modeled when they moved the corn kernels.

21st Century Learning

CRITICAL THINKING Have students reread the paragraph under the red head *Limits to Dispersal.* Point out that each of the three boldfaced headings—*physical barriers, competition,* and *climate*—are causes that limit dispersal. Ask: **How can water have the effect of limiting dispersal?** *(An organism may be unable to cross the water.)* **How does competition for resources cause limited dispersal?** *(Sample: There may not be enough food in an ecosystem to support existing organisms and an organism that moves there.)* **How can climate differences cause limited dispersal?** *(A species might be unable to survive in a certain climate.)*

Lab Resource: Quick Lab Lab zone

L1 **RELATING CONTINENTAL DRIFT TO DISPERSAL** Students will explore how continental drift caused the dispersal of species.

Evaluate

Assess Your Understanding

After students answer the questions, have them evaluate their understanding by completing the appropriate sentence.

R T I Response to Intervention

1. If students need help with factors that affect dispersal, **then** call on volunteers to describe ways seeds or small animals can be dispersed naturally, then list ways humans can cause dispersal.

MY SCIENCE 🅢 COACH Have students go online for help in understanding dispersal of species.

Lab zone After the Inquiry Warm-Up

Biogeography

> **Inquiry Warm-Up, *How Can You Move a Seed?***
> In the Inquiry Warm-Up, you investigated how seeds are transported. Using what you learned from that activity, answer the questions below.

1. **COMPARE AND CONTRAST** Dandelion seeds are small, light weight, and have feathery structures. Compared to a corn kernel, which seed is better adapted to being dispersed by the wind?

   _____

2. **INFER** Coconuts are large but mostly hallow. Explain how this characteristic helps the coconut palm tree survive and thrive on small, isolated islands in the ocean.

   _____

   _____

3. **INFER** Describe the type of habitat where dispersing seeds by clinging to animal fur or clothing is a better dispersal method than wind.

   _____

   _____

   _____

   _____

4. **DRAW CONCLUSIONS** What is one disadvantage to seed dispersal? Explain

   _____

   _____

   _____

   _____

Assess Your Understanding

Biogeography

What Factors Affect Species Dispersal?

1a. EXPLAIN What role do humans play in the dispersal of species?

_____

_____

b. CHALLENGE Suppose that a new species of insect were introduced to your area. Explain how competition might limit its dispersal.

_____

_____

gotit? ....

○ **I get it!** Now I know that species dispersal is affected by _____

_____

_____

_____

○ **I need extra help with** _____

_____

Key Concept Summaries

Biogeography

What Factors Affect Species Dispersal?

Different plants and animals live in different parts of the world. The study of where organisms live and how they got there is called **biogeography.** Biogeographers study what factors have led to the worldwide distribution of species that exists today.

One factor that has affected how species are distributed is the movement of the Earth's continents, which are parts of huge blocks of solid rock called plates. As the plates move, the continents move with them in a process called **continental drift.** About 225 million years ago, all of the continents were part of one huge landmass, Pangaea. Continental drift has had a great impact on species distribution, since organisms from one part of the world could not reach continents in other parts of the world.

Continental drift, wind, water, and living things are all means of distributing species. The movement of organisms from one place to another is called **dispersal.** Dispersal can be caused by gravity, wind, water, or living things, including humans. Plants and small animals need help in moving from place to place. Wind disperses seeds, fungi spores, spiders, and other small, light organisms. Water transports objects that float, such as coconuts and leaves. Small animals may travel on top of these floating "rafts." Of course, water also transports organisms like fish and marine mammals. Organisms can be dispersed by other living things. Humans can also disperse organisms, both intentionally and unintentionally, as they travel around the world. An **exotic species** is an organism that is carried into a new location by people.

With so many means of dispersal, you might expect to find the same species to be in many places around the world. **Factors such as physical barriers, competition, and climate, can limit species distribution.** Water and mountains form barriers that can limit the movement of organisms. When an organism enters a new area, it must compete for resources with the species that already live there. Climate differences can also limit dispersal.

On a separate sheet of paper, explain the factors that cause species dispersal and the factors that limit it.

Review and Reinforce

Biogeography

Understanding Main Ideas
Complete the concept map below by writing your answers in the spaces.

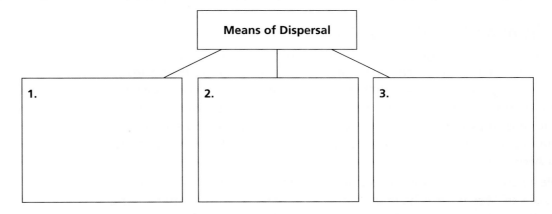

Answer the following questions on a separate sheet of paper.

4. Describe three ways plant seeds are dispersed by other organisms.

5. How does competition limit the dispersal of organisms?

6. What is the difference between weather and climate?

Building Vocabulary
Fill in the blank to complete each statement.

7. A species that is carried into a new location by people is called a(n)

   _____ species.

8. The study of where organisms live is called _____.

9. The movement of organisms from one place to another is called _____.

10. The very slow movement of the continents is called _____.

Name _____ Date _____ Class _____

Biogeography

Continental drift takes place over thousands of centuries and can affect where in the world organisms are located. Read the following descriptions. Then answer the questions on a separate sheet of paper.

Organisms and Continental Drift

1. Madagascar is a large island located about 400 kilometers off the southeast coast of Africa. Madagascar is home to about 15 species of monkeylike animals called lemurs that are found nowhere else in the world. Lemurs are related to the ancient ancestors of monkeys and apes that live in Africa today. What does this tell you about Madagascar's location millions of years ago? Why are there no lemurs in Africa today?

2. *Mesosaurus* was an aquatic reptile that lived in lakes and estuaries. Fossils of *Mesosaurus* have been found in eastern South America and southwestern Africa, as shown on the map below. No *Mesosaurus* fossils have been found anywhere else in the world. What could explain the existence of *Mesosaurus* fossils only in eastern South America and southwestern Africa?

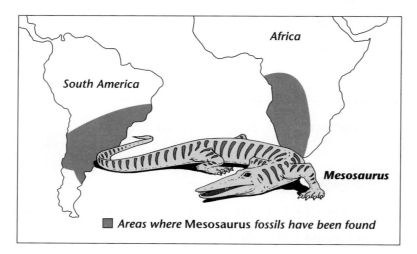

■ *Areas where* **Mesosaurus** *fossils have been found*

3. Continental drift is still occurring today. For example, the western part of California moves north along the San Andreas fault at a rate of about 3.4 centimeters per year. Examine a map and find where the western part of California will be in 100 million years. How might that location affect the types of organism that now live in the western part of California? (Assume that the climate of the new location will be the same in 100 million years as it is today.)

Lesson Quiz

Biogeography

If the statement is true, write *true*. If the statement is false, change the underlined word or words to make the statement true.

1. _____ About 225 million years ago, <u>North America and South America</u> were part of one huge landmass, Pangaea.

2. _____ Continental drift had <u>little</u> impact on organisms from one part of the world reaching other parts of the world.

3. _____ Organisms can be dispersed by <u>other living things</u>.

4. _____ <u>Water and mountains</u> form barriers that can limit the movement of organisms.

5. _____ When an organism enters a new area, it <u>enjoys all of</u> the resources with the species that already live there.

Fill in the blank to complete each statement.

6. The study of where organisms live and how they got there is called

_____.

7. As Earth's plates move, the continents move with them in a process called

_____.

8. The movement of organisms from one place to another is called _____.

9. _____ transports objects such as coconuts and leaves, small animals that travel on these "rafts," as well as organisms like fish and marine mammals.

10. A(n) _____ species is an organism that is carried into a new location by people.

Biogeography

Answer Key

After the Inquiry Warm-Up

1. dandelion

2. Accept all reasonable responses. Students may say: The chances of a seed landing in water are high on a small, isolated island. Being mostly hallow, the coconuts float on water, eventually washing up on a beach and growing there.

3. Sample: Clinging to fur or clothing would be better where there's not a lot of wind (i.e., low to the ground or in thick vegetation).

4. Sample: Seeds will not always end up in suitable habitats. Seeds that end up in unstable habitats are wasted.

Key Concept Summaries

Several factors, including continental drift, gravity, wind, water, and living things, have caused species to become dispersed throughout the world. Continental drift separated one land mass into seven continents, distributing organisms around the world. Organisms travel from place to place by floating on water, riding on other organisms, or being blown by the wind, or falling to the Earth from gravity. Distribution of species is limited by physical barriers (such as mountains or bodies of water), competition with other organisms for resources, and climate.

Review and Reinforce

(Answers 1–3 in any order)

1. wind
2. water
3. other living organisms

4. An organism may eat fruit containing the seeds and deposit them somewhere else in its wastes. Seeds with burs can stick to another organism and be carried someplace else. Humans may carry plant seeds into a new area, either intentionally or accidentally.

5. When organisms enter a new area, they must compete for resources with existing species. If the existing species are thriving, they may outcompete the new organisms.

6. Weather is the day-to-day conditions in an area. Climate is the typical weather pattern in an area over a long period of time.

7. exotic
8. biogeography
9. dispersal
10. continental drift

Enrich

1. Madagascar must have been connected to Africa. While the "ancient ancestors" were still living in Africa, Madagascar broke off and drifted away. Over millions of years, the ancestors developed into monkeys and apes in Africa and into lemurs in Madagascar. The ocean area between Africa and Madagascar prevented lemurs from dispersing.

2. When *Mesosaurus* existed, eastern South America and southwestern Africa must have been connected because *Mesosaurus* could not have swum across the Atlantic Ocean.

3. The western part of California's new location would be 3,400 kilometers farther north. Its climate would be much colder. Many species in western California today are adapted to its warmer climate. If they could not survive in a colder climate, they would become extinct in that area.

Lesson Quiz

1. Pangaea
2. great
3. true
4. true
5. must compete for
6. biogeography
7. continental drift
8. dispersal
9. Water
10. exotic

Study Guide

Review the Big Q ? UbD

Have students complete the statement at the top of the page. These Key Concepts support their understanding of the chapter's Big Question. Have students return to the chapter opener question. What is different about how students view the image of the owl and the mouse now that they have completed the chapter? Thinking about this will help them prepare for the *Apply the Big Q* activity in the Review and Assessment.

Partner Review

Have partners review definitions of vocabulary terms by using the Study Guide to quiz each other. Students could read the Key Concept statements and leave out words for their partner to fill in, or change a statement so that it is false and then ask their partner to correct it.

Class Activity: Poster

Have students work in groups to create an illustrated, labeled poster that shows the six major biomes, the two major types of aquatic ecosystems, four cycles of matter, and energy flow through ecosystems. Encourage students to integrate these subjects in the poster as much as possible. For example, the water cycle could be shown as part of the illustration for a biome such as deciduous forest or grassland or rain forest. Students should include an explanation of how the lesson's title relates to the Big Idea, as well as key terms and concepts. Urge students to use the following questions to help them organize their ideas:

- What are the energy roles in an ecosystem?
- How does energy move through an ecosystem?
- What processes are involved in the water cycle?
- How are the carbon and oxygen cycles related?
- How does nitrogen cycle through ecosystems?
- What are the six major biomes?
- What are the two major aquatic ecosystems?

My Science Coach allows students to complete the *Practice Test* online.

The Big Question allows students to complete the *Apply the Big Q* activity about how energy and matter cycle through an ecosystem.

Vocab Flash Cards offer a way to review the chapter vocabulary words.

my science online.com **Ecosystems and Biomes**

CHAPTER 2 Study Guide

Producers, <u>consumers</u>, and <u>decomposers</u> help to cycle energy through ecosystems.

LESSON 1 Energy Flow in Ecosystems

🔑 Each of the organisms in an ecosystem fills the energy role of producer, consumer, or decomposer.

🔑 Energy moves through an ecosystem when one organism eats another.

🔑 The most energy is available at the producer level of the pyramid. As energy moves up the pyramid, each level has less energy available than the level below.

Vocabulary
- producer • consumer • herbivore • carnivore • omnivore
- scavenger • decomposer • food chain • food web • energy pyramid

LESSON 2 Cycles of Matter

🔑 The processes of evaporation, condensation, and precipitation make up the water cycle.

🔑 The processes by which carbon and oxygen are recycled are linked. Producers, consumers, and decomposers play roles in recycling both.

🔑 Nitrogen moves from the air into the soil, into living things, and back into the air or soil.

Vocabulary
- evaporation • condensation
- precipitation • nitrogen fixation

LESSON 3 Biomes

🔑 The six major biomes are desert, rain forest, grassland, deciduous forest, boreal forest, and tundra.

Vocabulary
- biome • climate • desert • rain forest
- emergent layer • canopy • understory
- grassland • savanna • deciduous tree
- boreal forest • coniferous tree • tundra
- permafrost

LESSON 4 Aquatic Ecosystems

🔑 There are two types of aquatic, or water-based, ecosystems: freshwater ecosystems and marine (or saltwater) ecosystems.

Vocabulary
- estuary
- intertidal zone
- neritic zone

LESSON 5 Biogeography

🔑 Continental drift, wind, water, and living things are all means of distributing species. Other factors, such as physical barriers, competition, and climate, can limit species dispersal.

Vocabulary
- biogeography • continental drift
- dispersal • exotic species

ELL Support

4 Language Production

Divide the class into small groups with one student acting as recorder. Ask the Big Question and give students time to think about answers. Then have members of the groups share responses with one another, and have their responses written down by the recorder.

Beginning
LOW/HIGH Allow students to answer with single words or short phrases.

Intermediate
LOW/HIGH Have students draft sentences to answer the Big Question.

Advanced
LOW/HIGH Have students assist by acting as the recorder in each group.

Review and Assessment

LESSON 1 Energy Flow in Ecosystems

1. A diagram that shows how much energy is available at each feeding level in an ecosystem is a(n)

a. food web.   b. food chain.

c. water cycle.   **d.** energy pyramid.

2. A(n) <u>herbivore</u> is a consumer that eats only plants.

3. Interpret Diagrams Which organisms in the illustration are producers? Consumers?

<u>Producers: the</u>
<u>plants;</u>
<u>consumers: the</u>
<u>fish and snails</u>

4. Compare and Contrast How are food chains and food webs different?

<u>A food chain shows only one</u>
<u>possible path of energy flow,</u>
<u>while a food web shows many</u>
<u>food chains.</u>

5. **Write About It** Think about your own food web. Name the producers and consumers that make up your diet.

<u>Sample: The main producers in</u>
<u>my diet are wheat, rice, broccoli,</u>
<u>tomatoes, corn, and squash.</u>
<u>Chickens, cows, and fish are</u>
<u>consumers in my diet.</u>
<u>See TE rubric.</u>

LESSON 2 Cycles of Matter

6. When drops of water in a cloud become heavy enough, they fall to Earth as

a. permafrost.   b. evaporation.

c. precipitation.   d. condensation.

7. Evaporation, condensation, and precipitation are the three main processes in the

<u>water cycle.</u>

8. Infer Which process is responsible for the droplets visible on the glass below? Explain.

<u>Condensation;</u>
<u>water vapor</u>
<u>in the air</u>
<u>condenses on</u>
<u>the glass.</u>

9. Classify Which group of organisms is the source of oxygen in the oxygen cycle? Explain.

<u>Producers; they release oxygen</u>
<u>as a result of photosynthesis.</u>

10. Make Generalizations Describe the roles of producers and consumers in the carbon cycle.

<u>Producers use carbon dioxide</u>
<u>to produce food (carbon</u>
<u>compounds) via photosynthe-</u>
<u>sis. Producers and consumers</u>
<u>break down food and release</u>
<u>carbon dioxide as a waste</u>
<u>product.</u>

11. Draw Conclusions What would happen if all the nitrogen-fixing bacteria disappeared?

<u>Free nitrogen from the air would</u>
<u>not be changed into a form</u>
<u>that other organisms could use</u>
<u>and organisms would die.</u>

77

Review and Assessment

Assess Understanding

Have students complete the answers to the Review and Assessment questions. Have a class discussion about what students find confusing. Write Key Concepts on the board to reinforce knowledge.

RTI Response to Intervention

3. If students have trouble identifying producers and consumers, **then** remind students that the words' non-scientific meanings provide clues about the role of each type of organism: a producer "makes" and "assembles" while a consumer "eats" or "devours."

11. If students cannot explain the importance of nitrogen-fixing bacteria, **then** review with them the nitrogen cycle as shown in **Figure 4** in the lesson.

Alternate Assessment

L1 DESIGN A SCREEN SAVER Have students design and produce a series of images—illustrations, diagrams, or other graphic devices—to appear as a screen-saver loop on an idle computer display. Each image should convey key ideas and terms having to do with energy flow, cycles of matter, biomes, and aquatic ecosystems. Challenge students to create each image so that its information can be absorbed in 15 or 20 seconds, before it is replaced by another image.

CHAPTER 2

Write About It Assess student's writing using this rubric.

SCORING RUBRIC	SCORE 4	SCORE 3	SCORE 2	SCORE 1
Identify producers and consumers in diet	Names producers and consumers accurately	Names some producers and some consumers accurately	Inaccurately names producers and consumers	Does not name producers and consumers
Relate personal diet to food web	Recognizes place in food web and applies this knowledge with clarity and detail	Recognizes place in food web, but omits details about the web	Struggles to recognize place in food web and applies knowledge in general way	Does not recognize place in food web

Review and Assessment, Cont.

RTI Response to Intervention

13. If students cannot explain what a biome is, **then** have them scan the text in Lesson 3 for the highlighted term and review the definition.

16. If students have trouble identifying the neritic zone, **then** review with them the information on the table in **Figure 2**.

19. If students cannot define biogeography, **then** have them look for the highlighted term and review the definition.

Apply the Big Q ? UbD

TRANSFER Students should be able to demonstrate understanding of how energy and matter move through ecosystems by answering this question. See the scoring rubric below.

Connect to the Big Idea ? UbD

BIG IDEA Living things interact with their environment.

Send students back to the Big Ideas of Science at the beginning of their student edition. Have them read what they wrote about interactions of living things and their environment before they started the chapter. Lead a class discussion about how their thoughts have changed. If all chapters have been completed, have students fill in the bottom section for the Big Idea.

L3 WRITING IN SCIENCE Ask students to write a voice-over narration for a science video explaining how the cycles that occur in ecosystems show how living things interact on Earth.

LESSON 3 Biomes

12. Little precipitation and extreme temperatures are main characteristics of which biome?

a. desert   **b.** grassland
c. boreal forest   **d.** deciduous forest

13. A _biome_ is a group of ecosystems with similar climates and organisms.

14. Compare and Contrast How are the tundra and desert similar? How are they different?
Sample: Both biomes have similar rainfall amounts. They have different latitudes, with the tundra much farther north. The desert is much hotter than the tundra.

LESSON 4 Aquatic Ecosystems

15. In which ocean zone would you find barnacles, sea stars, and other organisms tightly attached to rocks?

a. neritic zone   **b.** intertidal zone
c. estuary ecosystem   **d.** freshwater ecosystem

16. Coral reefs are found in the shallow, sunny waters of the _neritic zone._

17. Compare and Contrast How are a pond and lake similar? How do they differ?
Ponds and lakes are both fresh-water ecosystems. In both cases, floating algae are major producers. Ponds are smaller and shallower than lakes, so sunlight may reach the bottom.

78 Ecosystems and Biomes

LESSON 5 Biogeography

18. What is a likely method of dispersal for seeds that are contained within a small berry?

a. wind   **b.** water
c. an animal   **d.** continental drift

19. The study of where organisms live and how they got there is called
biogeography.

20. Predict When might seed dispersal not be beneficial?
Sample: when seeds are carried to an area where you do not want them to grow

How do energy and matter cycle through ecosystems?

21. Many acres of the Amazon rain forest have been destroyed to create farmland. Describe how the amount of energy in the food web for this area might be affected. How might the carbon and oxygen cycle also be affected?
Sample: If the vegetation is destroyed, then there will be fewer producers. Without producers to capture and use energy, there will be less energy in the food web for the consumers. Fewer produc-ers means there will be fewer organisms to absorb carbon dioxide and release oxygen into the environment. See TE rubric.

How do living things affect one another?
Assess student's response using this rubric.

SCORING RUBRIC	SCORE 4	SCORE 3	SCORE 2	SCORE 1
Describe how energy might be affected	Describes specific effects on producers and consumers	Describes effects but doesn't name energy roles	Describes effects with inaccuracies about energy	Does not describe effects on food web
Describe how carbon and oxygen cycle might be affected	Describes specific effects on carbon and oxygen cycling	Describes effects without details to carbon and oxygen cycles	Describes effects with inaccuracies on carbon and oxygen cycles	Does not describe effects on carbon and oxygen cycles

Standardized Test Prep

Multiple Choice

Circle the letter of the best answer.

1. At which level of this energy pyramid is the *least* energy available?

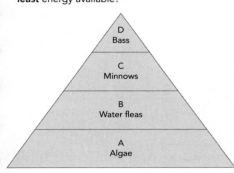

D
Bass

C
Minnows

B
Water fleas

A
Algae

A Level A **B** Level B
C Level C **ⓓ** Level D

2. You are in an area in Maryland where the fresh water of the Chesapeake Bay meets the Atlantic Ocean. Which of the following terms describes where you are?

A tundra **ⓑ** estuary
C neritic zone **D** intertidal zone

3. Which pair of terms could apply to the same organism?

A carnivore and producer
ⓑ consumer and carnivore
C scavenger and herbivore
D producer and omnivore

4. Many Canadian forests contain coniferous trees, such as fir and spruce. The winter is long and cold. Which term describes this biome?

A tundra **B** grassland
ⓒ boreal forest **D** deciduous forest

5. Organisms can be dispersed in all of the following ways *except* by

A wind. **B** water.
ⓒ temperature. **D** other organisms.

Constructed Response

Use the diagram below and your knowledge of science to help you answer Question 6. Write your answer on a separate piece of paper.

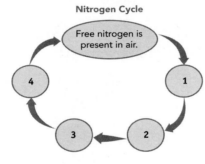

Nitrogen Cycle

Free nitrogen is present in air.

4

1

3

2

6. Describe each numbered part of the cycle shown in the diagram above.

See TE note.

79

Science Matters

Museum of Science

Have students read *Clothing that Fights Back*. Point out that humans sometimes need protection from their environments, much as animals do. For example. some animals have heavy coats of fur to protect them from extreme cold. The fur is an adaptation that helps the animal survive in its environment. Animals that lack thick fur might not survive in a cold climate. Humans have invented things like protective clothing to help them survive in climates to which they are not naturally adapted.

Have students examine the photograph. Point out that the woman in the photo is exercising outdoors. Her long-sleeved jacket and long pants are protecting her skin from UV radiation. They are also most likely lightweight to keep her cool, since she is running on a sunny day.

As students attempt to design their protective garment, ask them to think about the conditions in their chosen biome that humans might need to be protected from. Is it very hot or very cold? Is there normally a lot of sunshine in their biome? Are there a lot of insects or other wildlife they may need protection from living in their biome? Is it very wet or very dry?

Ask: **What are some of the protective clothes you already own and what conditions do they protect you from?** *(Sample: coat protects you from cold, long sleeves and long pants protect from insect bites, hats protect from sunburn)* **What kind of jobs could someone have that might require special protective clothing?** *(Sample: military personnel, constructions workers, park rangers, fire fighters)*

SCIENCE MATTERS

TECH & DESIGN

Museum of Science

Clothing
That
FIGHTS
BACK

Humans live in every biome on Earth, even some harsh environments that our bodies are not adapted for—deserts, rain forests, and tundra. In less extreme climates, we also face risks from our surroundings. But we have learned to protect ourselves by building shelters and wearing clothing.

UV (ultraviolet) radiation from the sun can damage your skin and cause cancer. A plain T-shirt offers some protection, but not as much as you might think—it may still allow between 7 and 20 percent of the sun's UV radiation through. Now, you can choose clothing made with chemicals that absorb UV radiation. These clothes offer better protection against the sun because they have a higher UPF (ultraviolet protection factor). They are also lightweight, so they're not as sticky in warm weather.

Design It Sun protection is not the only area in which science has helped people develop protective clothing. Scientists have created bug-repellent clothing, waterproof-breathable clothing, and insulated clothing. Research the climate in a biome of your choosing. List characteristics of that climate that might make survival difficult. Design an item of clothing that could help protect humans in that climate. What materials would your garment need in order to work?

Museum of Science.

80 Ecosystems and Biomes

Quick Facts

The Arbor Day Foundation created a program called Tree City USA®. This program encourages, supports, and recognizes community forestry programs. Any city, town, or community can become a Tree City. They must have a Tree Board or Department, a Tree Care Ordinance, a Forestry program with a certain minimum budget, and an Arbor Day Observance and Proclamation. Over 3,000 communities participate in the Tree City USA program and receive help and education for developing their forestry program. Sometimes Tree City USA communities are given money by the government for developing their forestry programs because of their Tree City status. Have students do an Internet search to determine whether your community is a Tree City. If so, find out how your students can help out. If not, research what is needed for your community to become a Tree City.

Trees: Environmental Factories

Some of the most important members of your community don't volunteer. They consume huge amounts of water and they make a mess. Despite these drawbacks, these long-standing community members do their share. Who are these individuals? They're trees!

Keeping it clean: Trees remove pollutants from the air. Some researchers have calculated the value of the environmental cleaning services that trees provide. One study valued the air-cleaning service that trees in the Chicago area provide at more than $9 million every year.

Keeping it cool: Trees provide shade and lower air temperature by the process of transpiration. Pollutants, like ozone and smog, form more easily when air temperatures are high, so by keeping the air cool, trees also keep it clean.

Acting locally and globally: Trees help fight global environmental problems such as climate change. Trees remove carbon dioxide from the air and store the carbon as they grow. Experts estimate that urban trees in the United States remove more than 700 million tons of carbon from the air every year.

Helping the local economy: Trees are also good for business. One study found that shoppers spend more money in urban areas where trees are planted than they do in similar areas that don't have trees!

Research It Examine a topographical map of the area where you live. Compare it to an aerial photograph from a library or local archive. Identify areas with a lot of trees, and areas that you think could benefit from more trees. Create a proposal to plant trees in one of the areas you identified. What kinds of trees will you plant? What do those trees need in order to grow well?

Schools, clubs, and civic groups all over the United States volunteer to plant trees in their communities. ▶

81

Science and Society

Have students read *Trees: Environmental Factories*. Point out that trees provide many benefits to a community. The benefits shown are mostly from trees in urban areas. In the suburbs, trees are often planted at the edges of property. Along streets, this can create a beautiful shady path for drivers. In backyards, trees can provide privacy and mark the border between neighboring properties. They can also provide fun places for a parent to hang a swing for their child to play on.

In rural communities, trees can provide an economic benefit. Many fruits grow on trees. Farmers harvest these fruits and sell them at local farmer's markets. In wooded areas, trees provide habitats for animals. Wooded areas are also nice places for a fun day of exercise or hiking. Have students volunteer ways they think the trees in their community benefit them.

If possible, have students compare a current or recent aerial photograph to an older photograph. Ask them what they notice about the change in the number of trees and suggest possible reasons for that change.

Ask: **Why might a community choose to plant trees near a factory or a heavily traveled highway?** *(Sample: Factories and cars that travel on highways create a lot of pollution and trees help eliminate pollution from the air.)* **Why would a community choose to plant trees in a local park?** *(Sample: Trees provide shade, providing a cool place for people to relax on a sunny day.)*

Resources and Living Things

Introduce the Big Q UbD

Have students look at the image and read the Engaging Question and description. Ask them to make an inference about the basic things the chick needs to live, based on the information in the text and what they already know. Point out that some needs, such as the need for food, are common to all living things. Ask: **How are the resources that you need to survive like those that the macaw chick needs?** *(Sample: Like the macaw chick, I need sunlight, food, water, and a place to live.)* **What are some materials that Earth provides that you use to meet your needs for survival?** *(Sample: Fuels such as oil and gas, water from streams or lakes, plants for food)* **What are some ways that humans can make Earth's resources last longer?** *(Sample: Not wasting water, reducing air pollution and conserving fossil fuels by bicycling or car pooling, recycling, preserving habitats for species like the macaw chick)*

Untamed Science Video

THE GREAT MACAW DEBATE Before viewing, invite students to suggest some ways in which humans and animals compete for resources. Then play the video. Lead a class discussion and make a list of questions that this video raises. You may wish to have students view the video again after they have completed the chapter to see if their questions have been answered.

To access the online resources for this chapter, search on or navigate to *Resources and Living Things.*

Untamed Science Video shows what happens when a treasured animal's habitat is also valuable land.

The Big Question allows students to answer the Engaging Question about the Macaw chick's basic needs.

my science online.com **Resources and Living Things**

---

82   Resources and Living Things

WHAT DOES THIS MACAW CHICK NEED TO SURVIVE?

 How do people use Earth's resources?

People aren't the only living things that need resources to survive. How we use our planet's resources has an impact on all of Earth's species. Small and helpless, this baby scarlet macaw cannot live on its own. This chick was born featherless and with its eyes closed. Macaw parents feed the chick until it is at least three months old. **Infer What basic things does this chick need to live?**

Sample: food, shelter, protection from
other animals that could eat it

▶ UNTAMED SCIENCE Watch the **Untamed Science** video to learn more about natural resources.

Professional Development Note   **From the Author**

My son Brian served in the United States Peace Corps in Costa Rica, living in the town of Puerto Jimenez, right on the edge of Corcovado National Park. According to one source, the park contains about 140 species of mammals, 367 birds, and 117 amphibians and reptiles. In comparison, the whole United States, while having more than 150 times as much territory as all of Costa Rica, has just 205 species of mammals, 279 birds and 442 reptiles and amphibians. Much of the Costa Rican economy is related to tourism. A challenge Costa Ricans face and that my son experienced in his work is how to retain the economic benefits of tourism while preserving biodiversity, especially in critical places like Corcovado.

✏ *Michael Padilla*

Resources and Living Things

CHAPTER 3

Chapter at a Glance

CHAPTER PACING: 9–14 Periods, $4\frac{1}{2}$–7 Blocks

INTRODUCE THE CHAPTER: Explore the Engaging Question and the opening image with students. Activate prior knowledge and preteach vocabulary using the Getting Started pages.

Lesson 1: Introduction to Environmental Issues

Lesson 2: Introduction to Natural Resources

Lesson 3: Human Population Growth

Lesson 4: Forests and Fisheries

Lesson 5: Biodiversity

ASSESSMENT OPTIONS: Chapter Test, **EXAM**VIEW® Assessment Suite, Performance Assessment, Progress Monitoring Assessments, SuccessTracker™

Preference Navigator, in the online Planning tools, allows you to customize *Interactive Science* to your own teaching style. You can also edit lesson plans by selecting the Lesson Planner option.

Digital Teacher's Edition allows you to access your Teacher's Edition and Resource materials online.

my science online

Differentiated Instruction

L1 Macaw Chicks Make sure that students understand that there is nothing wrong with this chick. Birds of this species are not fully developed when they hatch. Students may not have seen an adult scarlet macaw, a large bright red parrot. You may wish to look for images of adult macaws in pet magazines or on the Internet and show students these images. Have students compare and contrast the chick with an adult.

L3 Research Macaws Tell students that macaws are a threatened species native to rain forests in South and Central America. Have students work in pairs to find out why they are threatened and identify efforts to help preserve this species. Students can present their findings in an oral report to the class. Encourage students to use visual aids in their presentations.

Getting Started

Check Your Understanding

This activity assesses students' understanding of the terms *ecology* and *ecosystem*. After students have shared their answers, point out that the two terms share the Greek root *eco*, meaning home or environment. *Ecology* is the study of the environment and interaction among living things. An *ecosystem* is a community of interacting organisms and their physical environment.

Preteach Vocabulary Skills

Explain to students that learning related forms of a word can help determine the meanings of unknown words and help increase their vocabularies. Related words usually share the same root but contain different prefixes or suffixes. As students read, challenge them to identify related word forms for each vocabulary term.

---

3 Getting Started

Check Your Understanding

1. **Background** Read the paragraph below and then answer the question.

> Ed is observing his **ecology** project for the tenth day in a row. He holds the bottle up to see the **habitat** inside. The snails, fish, and plants inside the bottle all look healthy. He can even see some baby snails. It is a whole **ecosystem** in a bottle!

Ecology is the study of how organisms interact with each other and their environment.

A **habitat** is an environment that provides the things a specific organism needs to live, grow, and reproduce.

An **ecosystem** is the community of organisms that live in a particular area, along with their nonliving environment.

* How are the terms *ecosystem* and *ecology* related?

  Ecology is the study of ecosystems and the interactions that take place in them.

▶ **MY READING WEB** If you had trouble completing the question above, visit **My Reading Web** and type in *Resources and Living Things.*

Vocabulary Skill

Identify Related Word Forms You can increase your vocabulary by learning related forms of a word. For example, if you know the verb *produce* means "to make," you can figure out that the meaning of the noun *product* is "something that is made." The table below shows two vocabulary words in this chapter and their related word forms.

Verb	Noun	Adjective
pollute to contaminate Earth's land, water, or air	**pollution** the contamination of Earth's land, water, or air	**pollutive** contaminating Earth's land, water, or air
conserve to manage resource use wisely	**conservation** the practice of managing resource use wisely	**conservational** managing resource use wisely

2. **Quick Check** Complete the sentence with the correct form of the word from the table above.

* Air _pollution_ is a problem in many of the world's major cities.

84 Resources and Living Things

My Reading Web offers leveled readings related to chapter content.

Vocab Flash Cards offer extra practice with the chapter vocabulary words.

Digital Lesson

* Assign the *Check Your Understanding* activity online and have students submit their work to you.
* Assign the *Vocabulary Skill* activity online and have students submit their work to you.

my science online.com **Resources and Living Things**

natural resource

nonrenewable resource

exponential growth

keystone species

Chapter Preview

LESSON 1
- natural resource
- pollution • point source
- nonpoint source
- environmental science
- 🔁 Relate Cause and Effect
- △ Draw Conclusions

LESSON 2
- renewable resource
- nonrenewable resource
- sustainable use
- ecological footprint
- conservation
- 🔁 Relate Text and Visuals
- △ Calculate

LESSON 3
- exponential growth
- 🔁 Identify the Main Idea
- △ Predict

LESSON 4
- clear-cutting
- selective cutting
- sustainable yield
- fishery
- aquaculture
- 🔁 Summarize
- △ Communicate

LESSON 5
- biodiversity • keystone species
- gene • extinction
- endangered species
- threatened species
- habitat destruction
- habitat fragmentation
- poaching • captive breeding
- 🔁 Compare and Contrast
- △ Infer

> VOCAB FLASH CARDS For more help with vocabulary, visit **Vocab Flash Cards** and type in *Resources and Living Things.*

85

Preview Vocabulary Terms

Have students create word webs to show the relationships between the vocabulary terms for the chapter. Tell students to draw a few empty word webs. After previewing the vocabulary terms, discuss with students categories and concepts that they can write in the center of each word web. Be sure to discuss and analyze each term before students add words to their webs. As the class progresses through the chapter, students can add new words to existing webs or create new webs for a group of terms. A list of Academic Vocabulary for each lesson can be found in the Support All Readers box at the start of the lesson.

L1 Have students look at the images on this page as you pronounce the vocabulary term. Have students repeat the word after you. Then read the definition. Use the sample sentence in italics to clarify the meaning of the term.

natural resource *(NACH ur ul REE sawrs)* Anything that occurs naturally in the environment and is used by people. *This meadow contains many natural resources, including trees, grasses, flowers, and wildlife.*

nonrenewable resource *(nawn REE noo a bul REE sawrs)* Resources that are not replaced in a useful time frame. *Gold is a nonrenewable resource, which helps explain why gold jewelry is so costly.*

exponential growth *(ik spoh NEN shul grohth)* The situation that arises when a population grows at an ever-increasing rate. *The exponential growth of a species can exhaust the supply of water or other renewable resources.*

keystone species *(KEE stohn SPEE sheez)* Species that influences the survival of many other species in an ecosystem. *The sea otter is a keystone species in a kelp forest ecosystem.*

CHAPTER 3

E L L Support

Have students work in pairs to complete the word webs for the Preview Vocabulary Terms activity. Discuss multiple-meaning words such as *competition* and *host* in their proper science contexts with students.

Beginning
LOW Complete the webs using a combination of visuals and words in the native language.

HIGH Use a word or phrase to describe the vocabulary terms in each web.

Intermediate
LOW/HIGH Provide definitions for the vocabulary terms in each web.

Advanced
LOW/HIGH Write a sentence for the vocabulary terms in each web.

Introduction to Environmental Issues

1 How do people use Earth's resources?

Blended Path
Active learning using Student Edition, Inquiry Path, and Digital Path

Lesson Pacing: 2–3 periods or 1–1½ blocks

🕐 **SHORT ON TIME?** To do this lesson in approximately half the time, do the Activate Prior Knowledge activity on page 86. A discussion of the key concepts on pages 87 and 90 will familiarize students with the lesson content. Have students do the Quick Labs. The rest of the lesson can be completed by students independently.

Preference Navigator, in the online Planning tools, allows you to customize *Interactive Science* to your own teaching style. You can also edit lesson plans by selecting the Lesson Planner option.

Digital Teacher's Edition allows you to access your Teacher's Edition and Resource materials online.

Lesson Vocabulary

- natural resource
- pollution
- point source
- nonpoint source
- environmental science

Content Refresher

Environmental Laws Environmental issues have been with us for a long time. In approximately A.D. 80, the Roman senate passed laws designed to protect the city's supply of clean water for drinking and bathing. Laws in fourteenth-century England prohibited burning coal within the city limits of London. In the United States in the late seventeenth century, William Penn decreed that Pennsylvania would set aside one acre of forest for every five acres cleared for settlement.

LESSON OBJECTIVES

🔑 Identify the general categories of environmental issues.

🔑 Describe how decision makers balance opposing needs and concerns.

ENGAGE AND EXPLORE

To teach this lesson using a variety of resources, begin by reading **My Planet Diary** as a class. Have students share their ideas and feelings about nature. Discuss agreements and disagreements. Then have students do the **Inquiry Warm-Up activity.** Students will discuss pressing environmental issues and decision-making about these issues. Have students do the **After the Inquiry Warm-Up worksheet.** Have volunteers share their answers to number 4 about whether personal interest plays an important role in making decisions about the environment.

EXPLAIN AND ELABORATE

Teach Key Concepts by explaining the terms *natural resource, pollution, point source,* and *nonpoint source.* Have student use **Figures 1** and **2** to discuss the pros and cons of developing Antarctica and everyday natural resources such as land, water, and fuel. Use the **Support the Big Q** to discuss how population growth may affect natural resources

Continue to **Teach Key Concepts** by explaining how different needs are balanced when legislators make environmental decisions. Have students consider costs and benefits in the **Apply It activity.**

Hand out the **Key Concept Summaries** as a review of each part of the lesson. Students can also use the online **Vocab Flash Cards** to review key terms.

EVALUATE

Have students take the **Lesson Quiz.** For an alternate assessment, see the **EXAM**VIEW® Assessment Suite, Progress Monitoring Assessments, or SuccessTracker™.

ELL Support

1 Content and Language
Have students talk about what they know about resolving environmental issues. Document the results of their discussion with a KWL chart.

DIFFERENTIATED INSTRUCTION KEY
L1 Struggling Students or Special Needs
L2 On-Level Students **L3** Advanced Students

LESSON PLANNER 3.1

Lab zone Inquiry Path
Hands-on learning in the Lab zone

ENGAGE AND EXPLORE

To teach this lesson with an emphasis on inquiry, begin with the **Inquiry Warm-Up activity.** Students will discuss decisions about important environmental issues and their impact. Discuss environmental issue decision-making. Have students do the **After the Inquiry Warm-Up worksheet.** Talk about each question and the student or group response. Have volunteers share and compare their answers to number 4 about whether personal interest plays an important role in making decisions about the environment.

EXPLAIN AND ELABORATE

Focus on the **Inquiry Skill** for the lesson. Point out that when you draw conclusions, you use information you already know to reach a decision. Have students do the **Quick Lab** to explore environmental issues and then share their results.

Review costs and benefits before beginning the **Apply It activity.** Use the **Support the Big Q** to discuss how population growth may affect natural resources. Have students do the second **Quick Lab** to compare more costs and benefits about environmental issues.

Students can use the online **Vocab Flash Cards** to review key terms.

EVALUATE

Have students take the **Lesson Quiz.** For an alternate assessment, see the **EXAM**VIEW® Assessment Suite, Progress Monitoring Assessments, or SuccessTracker™.

Digital Path
Online learning at **my science online**.com

ENGAGE AND EXPLORE

To teach this lesson using digital resources, begin by having students explore different approaches to environmental issues at **My Planet Diary** online. Have them access the Chapter Resources to find the **Unlock the Big Question activity.** There they can answer the questions and refine their responses as they continue through the lesson. You can re-assign the activity and have students submit their work so you can track their progress.

EXPLAIN AND ELABORATE

Students reading above, at, or below the lexile measure of this lesson can access basic content readings at their level at **My Reading Web.** Have students use the online **Vocab Flash Cards** to preview key terms. Do the **Quick Lab** and then ask students to share their results.

Review *costs* and *benefits* before assigning the online **Apply It activity.** Ask volunteers to share what they know about resolving environmental issues. Have students submit their work to you. Have students do the online **Interactive Art activity** for **Figure 3** to draw conclusions about offshore drilling. Then have them do the **Quick Lab** to continue their costs and benefits analysis. The **Key Concept Summaries** online allow students to read a summary and see an image associated with each part of the lesson. Online remediation is available at **My Science Coach.**

EVALUATE

Have students take the **Lesson Quiz.** For an alternate assessment, see the **EXAM**VIEW® Assessment Suite, Progress Monitoring Assessments, or SuccessTracker™.

2 Frontload the Lesson
Preview the lesson visuals, labels, and captions. Ask students what they know about environmental issues. You may want to relate the topic to students' lives through the use of local examples.

3 Comprehensible Input
Have students study the visuals and graphic organizers on pages 87–89 and 91 to support the key concepts of the lesson. Point out that many of these graphic organizers are used to compare.

4 Language Production
Pair or group students with varied language abilities to complete the letter writing activity on page 91 collaboratively for language practice. Have each student copy the completed written letter for personal reference.

5 Assess Understanding
Have students role-play protesters and company executives for the **Apply It activity** on page 90.

Introduction to Environmental Issues

Establish Learning Objectives

After this lesson, students will be able to:

🔑 Identify the general categories of environmental issues.

🔑 Describe how decision makers balance opposing needs and concerns.

Engage

Activate Prior Knowledge

MY PLANET DIARY Read *How Do You Feel About Nature?* with the class. Point out that the scuba diver and commercial fisherman want the same thing—preservation of coral reefs—for different reasons. Ask: **How can a common desire or need for nature bring different groups of people together?** *(Sample answer: People like the scuba diver and commercial fisherman, who might not have much in common, may decide to work together to achieve a shared goal.)*

BIG IDEAS OF SCIENCE REFERENCE LIBRARY 📖
Have students look up the following topics: Fuel Cell Cars, Population Growth, Seed Bank, Skywalk.

Explore

Lab Resource: Inquiry Warm-Up

L2 **HOW DO YOU DECIDE?** Students will identify and discuss pressing environmental issues.

LESSON 1

Introduction to Environmental Issues

🔑 What Are the Types of Environmental Issues?

🔑 How Are Environmental Decisions Made?

UNLOCK THE BIG ?

my planeT DiaRY

CAREER

How Do You Feel About Nature?

You have probably heard of scientists who study animals, plants, rocks, and everything else in an ecosystem. Social scientists study an often-overlooked but very important part of any ecosystem—the people who use it! These scientists study how people value nature. They study how much people would be willing to pay to preserve nature. They also study how different age groups, genders, races, and social groups use nature. For example, a scuba diver wants coral reefs to remain beautiful and full of all kinds of organisms to enjoy in future dives. A commercial fisherman cares more about a coral reef supporting the kind of fish he wants to catch. You might care about coral reefs because you want to visit one someday.

Communicate Discuss the question with a group of classmates. Then write your answer below.

Do you think it is important to consider how people value nature? Explain.

Sample: Yes; considering people's values about nature helps scientists and lawmakers decide how to meet the needs of different groups.

▷ PLANET DIARY Go to **Planet Diary** to learn more about environmental issues.

Lab zone Do the Inquiry Warm-Up *How Do You Decide?*

86 Resources and Living Things

SUPPORT ALL READERS
Lexile Measure = 900L   Lexile Word Count = 1253

Prior Exposure to Content: May be the first time students have encountered this topic

Academic Vocabulary: *cause, effect*

Science Vocabulary: *natural resource, pollution*

Concept Level: Generally appropriate for most students in this grade

Preteach With: My Planet Diary "Feel About Nature" and Figure 1 activity

Go to **My Reading Web** to access leveled readings that provide a foundation for the content.

my science online.com

Vocabulary
- natural resource • pollution • point source
- nonpoint source • environmental science

Skills
- Reading: Relate Cause and Effect
- Inquiry: Draw Conclusions

What Are the Types of Environmental Issues?

Here is a riddle for you: what place is bigger than the United States and Mexico combined? This place is covered with ice more than two kilometers thick. It is a habitat for many animals and is a source of oil, coal, and iron. Stumped? The answer is Antarctica. Some people think of Antarctica as a useless, icy wasteland, but there are unique wildlife habitats in Antarctica. There are also valuable minerals beneath its thick ice.

What is the best use of Antarctica? Many people want access to its rich deposits of minerals and oil. Others worry that mining will harm its delicate ecosystems. Some people propose building hotels, parks, and ski resorts. Others think that Antarctica should remain undeveloped. Who should decide Antarctica's fate?

In 1998, 26 nations agreed to ban mining and oil exploration in Antarctica for at least 50 years. As resources become more scarce elsewhere in the world, the debate will surely continue.

Antarctica's future is just one environmental issue that people face today. 🔑 **Environmental issues fall into three general categories: population growth, resource use, and pollution.** Because these three types of issues are interconnected, they are very difficult to study and resolve.

FIGURE 1 ···

Arguing Over Antarctica
Some people want to leave Antarctica wild. Others want it developed.

✎ **Summarize** Fill in the boxes with points outlining each argument.

Argument One: Keep Antarctica Wild	Argument Two: Develop Antarctica
Sample: • unique wildlife and habitats • building resorts is expensive • building and visiting resorts is dangerous in Antarctica's weather conditions	Sample: • need oil and mineral deposits • get money from building hotels, resorts, and attractions • provides jobs

87

Explain

Introduce Vocabulary

Explain to students that *point source* and *nonpoint source* both refer to sources of pollution. They can distinguish between the terms by asking themselves whether a person could literally point to the source of pollution. If so, that would be a point source.

Teach Key Concepts 🔑

Draw students' attention to the three general categories of environmental issues. Ask a volunteer to read the sentence immediately following the Key Concept statement. Ask: **What is an issue?** (*A problem or question about which people disagree*) **Why are interconnected issues hard to study and resolve?** (*Samples: You need specialists from different fields to provide data on interconnected issues; agencies with the power to resolve one type of issue, such as water pollution, may have no authority over a related issue, such as the use of water resources.*)

21st Century Learning

COMMUNICATION Have students read the caption for **Figure 1**. Point out that drilling in Antarctica is just one of many hotly contested environmental issues. Ask students to think of other major environmental issues that they have read about or viewed on television. Encourage students to outline opposing arguments on one of the major issues that they identify.

My Planet Diary provides an opportunity for students to explore real-world connections to ecosystems and environmental issues.

ELL Support

1 Content and Language
Help students preview the vocabulary by pointing out related word pairs—*point source/nonpoint source, renewable resource/nonrenewable resource, clear-cutting/selective cutting,* and *endangered species/threatened species.* Ask students which prefix makes two of these word pairs antonyms.

2 Frontload the Lesson
Ask students to define the words *survive* and *resources*. After completing a picture walk, ask them to explain how the two are related.

3 Comprehensible Input
Help students fill in the **My Resources Journal** by explaining the ways in which you have used resources today. For each, explain what you did and how it involved resources. Have students orally repeat each resource, and identify if they, too, used similar resources.

Explain

Teach With Visuals

Tell students to look at **Figure 2.** Ask: **What are some specific ways in which a trip to the beach uses land, water, and fuel?** *(Samples: Land—walking on sand beaches and through dunes, which can increase erosion; water—swimming, drinking; fuel— transportation to and from beaches)*

Support the Big Q ? UbD

POPULATION GROWTH AND RESOURCES Ask students if they have seen evidence of growth in the population of their community. Students may mention seeing new homes built or increased traffic on local streets. Ask: **How might an increase in the local population affect your community?** *(Sample: Schools might become crowded; there would be less space for recreation; there might not be enough space for people to park their cars.)* **What is a natural resource?** *(Anything that occurs naturally in the environment and is used by people)* **In addition to water, what other natural resources are in increased demand because of population growth?** *(Sample: Oil, as world population grows and more nations industrialize)*

21st Century Learning

INFORMATION LITERACY Give students an example of conflicts that arise when a natural resource is scarce or used in a way that people feel is unfair; for example, conflicts within or between Montana and Wyoming over water rights. Ask students how they can become well-informed about such an issue. *(Samples: Look for and read regional news sources online; use a search engine to research the general issue before reading about the specifics)*

Vocabulary Identify Related Word Forms The word *conflict* means a disagreement between people, ideas, or interests. What causes conflicting opinions about natural resource use?

Sample: People have conflicting opinions over resource use when they think the resource is scarce or used in an unfair or harmful way.

FIGURE 2 ··········
Everyday Natural Resources
We use natural resources many times a day without even realizing it! A trip to the beach uses land, water, fuel, and many other resources.

✎ **List** On the journal page, list all the ways you have used natural resources so far today. For example, this book is made of paper that started as a tree.

Population Growth The human population grew very slowly until about A.D. 1650. Around that time, improvements in medicine, agriculture, and waste disposal led to people's living longer. The human population has been growing faster and faster since then.

When a population grows, the demand for resources also grows. Has your town or city ever experienced a water shortage? If so, you might have noticed that people have been asked to restrict their water use. This sometimes happens in areas with fast-growing populations. The water supplies in such areas were designed to serve fewer people than they now do, so shortages can occur during unusually dry weather.

Resource Use Earth provides many materials people use throughout their lives. Anything that occurs naturally in the environment and is used by people is called a **natural resource.** Natural resources include trees, water, oil, coal, and other things. However, people do not use resources in the same way. In some areas of the world, people use a wide variety of resources. In other areas, people have little or no access to certain natural resources. For example, people in central Asia live too far away from ocean waters that provide fish and other resources. Conflict arises when a natural resource is scarce or used in a way that people feel is unfair.

My Resources Journal

Accept all reasonable answers.
Sample: breakfast foods, water in the shower, clothes made from cotton, gas in the school bus or car, pencil made from wood, drinking water

---

Professional Development Note — Teacher to Teacher

Introduction to Environmental Issues The best introduction to environmental issues enables students to view data scientists uncovered that led them to recognize environmental problems. The Keeling Curve is on the Scripps CO_2 Program Web site with the title Mauna Loa Record. Show a copy of the graph, making sure to cover the descriptions on each axis. Once students discuss the graph, uncover the axis labels. Most students are astounded by the growth in CO_2 levels, especially when viewed alongside graphs showing the past 1,000 years of temperature data. "What's Up With the Weather?" from the PBS program *NOVA,* has video footage of Charles David Keeling recounting his reaction to the data.

✉ *James Kuhl*
Central Square Middle School
Central Square, NY

Pollution Many environmental factors can contribute to less than ideal conditions on Earth for people or other organisms. The contamination of Earth's land, water, or air is called **pollution.** Pollution can be caused by wastes, chemicals, noise, heat, light, and other sources. Pollution can destroy wildlife and cause human health problems.

Pollution is usually related to population growth and resource use. As you probably know, the burning of gasoline releases pollutants into the air. With more cars on the road, more gasoline is used, so more pollutants are released into the air. As populations grow and more people need to be fed, more fertilizers and other chemicals may be used to produce that food. As these chemicals run off the land, they can pollute bodies of water.

Pollution sources can be grouped into two categories. A **point source** is a specific pollution source that can be identified. A pipe gushing polluted water into a river is an example of a point source. A nonpoint source of pollution is not as easy to identify. A **nonpoint source** is widely spread and cannot be tied to a specific origin. For example, the polluted air that can hang over urban areas comes from vehicles, factories, and other polluters. The pollution cannot be tied to any one car or factory.

✏️ **Relate Cause and Effect**
Use what you have read about pollution so far to fill in the boxes below.

Some Causes of Pollution

Sample: wastes,
noise, heat, light,
and chemicals
_____
_____

Some Effects of Pollution

Sample: destroys
wildlife, destroys
habitat, causes
health problems,
reduces quality of
natural resources

Lab zone
Do the Quick Lab
Environmental Issues.

🔑 **Assess Your Understanding**

1a. Define What is a natural resource?

A natural resource is anything
that occurs naturally in the
environment and is used by
people.

b. Make Generalizations How is population growth related to resource use and pollution?

Sample: As the population
increases, so will the amount of
resources people use and the
pollution they cause.

got it? ......

○ I get it! Now I know that the types of environmental issues are population growth,
  resource use, and pollution.

○ I need extra help with See TE note.

Go to MY SCIENCE ⑤ COACH *online for help with this subject.*

89

Differentiated Instruction

L1 Everyday Natural Resources If students have difficulty completing the list for **Figure 2,** have them review the examples of natural resources under the red head *Resource Use.* Then ask students clarifying questions, such as "What foods grow on trees?" "How do people use wood?" "What fuel do cars and buses use?" and "How do you personally use water?"

L3 Research and Report Invite pairs of students to research Jane Goodall or Chico Mendes, activists who influenced the way that many people think about environmental issues. Tell students to present their information in the form of an interview in which one student plays the role of the activist and the other student is the interviewer.

Elaborate

Make Analogies

L1 POINT AND NONPOINT SOURCES To help students understand point and nonpoint sources, compare them to a mixture and solution. Ask: **What is a key difference between a mixture, such as a salad, and a solution, such as lemonade?** *(Sample answer: You can easily see the parts of a salad, but the substances in lemonade are so evenly mixed that you can't see them.)* **How is this like the difference between a point and nonpoint pollution source?** *(A point source can be easily identified; a nonpoint source cannot be pinned to a particular origin.)*

🔄 **Relate Cause and Effect** Explain that a cause is the reason why something happens. The effect is what happens as a result of the cause. Students should identify the things that create pollution and the conditions that result from pollution.

Lab Resource: Quick Lab

L2 ENVIRONMENTAL ISSUES Students will pose questions about environmental issues.

Evaluate

Assess Your Understanding

After students answer the questions, have them evaluate their understanding by completing the appropriate sentence.

RTI Response to Intervention

1a. If students have trouble defining natural resource, **then** have them find and reread the highlighted term.

1b. If students cannot relate population growth, resource use, and pollution, **then** have them review the material under the red head *Population Growth.*

MY SCIENCE ⑤ COACH Have students go online for help in understanding the types of environmental issues.

Explain

Teach Key Concepts 🗝

Explain to students that different, perhaps even opposing, needs can have equal weight in a debate on an environmental issue. Ask: **How do decision-makers resolve an environmental issue when compelling arguments and proposals are presented by both sides?** *(Sample: Decision makers weigh the costs and benefits of each course of action or inaction.)* **What needs must be balanced when deciding whether to drill for oil in a wildlife refuge?** *(Sample answer: The need to protect the ecosystem, the need for fuel)*

Teach With Visuals

Have students look at **Figure 3.** Ask: **Which cost do you think represents the greatest problem? Which benefit do you think is the most important? Explain your choice.** *(Accept all responses as long as they are supported logically.)*

Elaborate

Apply It!

L1 Review the Key Concept statement and the photographs of the factory and park before beginning the activity.

21st Century Learning

COMMUNICATION Have students form small groups to research an environmental issue. Have each group create a skit based on their research. Ask groups to present different viewpoints and proposed solutions. Suggest that each group include a photograph, graphic organizer, or other visual to help their audience better understand the group's position on the issue.

21st Century Learning   📖

COMMUNICATION Have students read *Fuel Cell Cars* in the **Big Ideas of Science Reference Library.** Assignment: You have been asked to speak at the National Hydrogen Association's annual conference. You can write your speech from the perspective of an automaker, a NASA executive, or a member of another organization that is engaged in fuel cell research. Focus your talk on ways that your organization has decreased carbon emissions.

How Are Environmental Decisions Made?

Dealing with environmental issues means making decisions. Decisions can be made at many levels. Your decision to walk to your friend's house rather than ride in a car is made at a personal level. A town's decision about how to dispose of its trash is made at a local level. A decision about whether the United States should allow oil drilling in a wildlife refuge is made on a national level. Decisions about how to protect Earth's atmosphere are made on a global level. Your personal decisions have a small impact. But when the personal decisions of millions of people are combined, they have a huge impact on the environment.

Balancing Different Needs Lawmakers work with many groups to make environmental decisions. One such group is environmental scientists. **Environmental science** is the study of natural processes in the environment and how humans can affect them. Data provided by environmental scientists are only part of the decision-making process. Environmental decision making requires a balance between the needs of the environment and the needs of people. 🗝 **To help balance the different opinions on an environmental issue, decision makers weigh the costs and benefits of a proposal for change before making a decision.**

Suppose you are a member of a city planning board. A company wants to buy a piece of land outside the city and build a factory on it. When you go into work one day, you are met by protesters demanding that the land be turned into a wildlife park.

❶ Solve Problems How should you decide what to do with the land?

Sample: I would weigh the costs and benefits of both proposals to see which best meets the needs of people and the environment.

❷ CHALLENGE What are some ways you could find out people's opinions about the issue?

Sample: hold public meetings; have an Internet campaign; take an online, phone, or mail survey; interview people in person

Digital Lesson: Assign the *Apply It* activity online and have students submit their work to you.

Interactive Art allows students to weigh the costs and benefits of environmental decisions.

MY SCIENCE online.com › **Making Environmental Decisions**

Types of Costs and Benefits

Costs and benefits are often economic. Will a proposal provide jobs? Will it cost too much money? Costs and benefits are not measured only in terms of money. For example, suppose a state must decide whether to allow logging in a certain area. Removing trees changes the ecosystem, which is an ecological cost. However, the wood and jobs provided by the logging are economic benefits.

It is also important to consider the short-term and long-term costs and benefits of an environmental decision. A plan's short-term costs might be outweighed by its long-term benefits.

Costs of Offshore Drilling	Benefits of Offshore Drilling
• Setting up sites is expensive.	• Creates jobs
• Transporting the oil is risky and expensive.	• A larger oil supply lowers oil prices.
• Oil supply is limited and will not meet energy demands.	• Provides new oil supply to fight shortages
• Oil spills and leaks harm marine organisms and the environment.	• Reduces dependence on foreign oil

FIGURE 3 ·····························
> INTERACTIVE ART Weighing Costs and Benefits
Once you have identified the potential costs and benefits of a decision, you must analyze them.
✎ **Draw Conclusions** Read the chart. Based on these costs and benefits, write a brief letter to your senator explaining your opinion either in favor of or against offshore drilling.

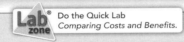
Accept letters of both opinions. Students should provide reasons to support their opinions. Sample letter: Dear Senator, I am writing to encourage you to vote in favor of offshore drilling. This country needs more oil to meet its needs, and we can get oil off our shores. It will also create jobs and could lower prices. People shouldn't have to spend so much money on gas or oil for their cars or homes. Offshore drilling is a good way to fix this problem.

Lab zone Do the Quick Lab
Comparing Costs and Benefits.

🔑 **Assess Your Understanding**

got it? ·····························

○ I get it! Now I know that environmental decisions are made by <u>weighing the costs and benefits of a proposal.</u>

○ I need extra help with <u>See TE note.</u>

Go to my science **coach** *online for help with this subject.*

91

△ **Draw Conclusions** In order to draw a conclusion, students must use the information in the chart with information they already know to reach a decision on the topic.

Lab Resource: Quick Lab

L2 COMPARING COSTS AND BENEFITS Students will develop a cost versus benefit table for one of the environmental issues mentioned in the text.

Evaluate

Assess Your Understanding

Have students evaluate their understanding by completing the appropriate sentence.

RTI Response to Intervention

If students need help explaining how environmental decisions are made, **then** review the material under the red head *Balancing Different Needs*.

my science **coach** Have students go online for help in understanding how environmental decisions are made.

Differentiated Instruction

L1 Review Vocabulary If students have difficulty composing a letter for **Figure 3,** go over each item listed in the table. Explain or call on volunteers to explain potentially challenging vocabulary such as *expensive, transporting, marine organisms,* and *dependence on foreign oil.* You may also wish to review the correct format for a formal letter.

L3 Multimedia Presentation Ask groups of students to choose a local or regional environmental issue and identify two proposals to resolve it. Have groups create a multimedia presentation to explain the issue and showing the costs and benefits of each proposal.

Lab zone **After the Inquiry Warm-Up**

Introduction to Environmental Issues

Inquiry Warm-Up, *How Do You Decide?*
In the Inquiry Warm-Up, you investigated making decisions about environmental issues. Using what you learned from that activity, answer the questions below.

1. **APPLY CONCEPTS** What was the main reasoning within your group for deciding which issue was most important?

_____

_____

2. **MAKE JUDGMENTS** Should the importance of an environmental issue be exclusively based on the number of people it affects? Explain.

_____

_____

3. **FORM OPERATIONAL DEFINITIONS** Compare your definition of *environmental issue* with those of other students. Make any revisions to your definition you feel are necessary to better explain what you believe to be an environmental issue. Write your revised definition below.

_____

_____

_____

_____

4. **MAKE JUDGMENTS** How important a part should personal interests play in making decisions about environmental issues? Explain.

_____

_____

_____

Name _____ Date _____ Class _____

Introduction to Environmental Issues

What Are the Types of Environmental Issues?

1a. DEFINE What is a natural resource?

_____

_____

b. MAKE GENERALIZATIONS How is population growth related to resource use and pollution?

_____

_____

gotit? ....

○ **I get it!** Now I know that the types of environmental issues are _____

_____

○ **I need extra help with** _____

_____

How Are Environmental Decisions Made?

gotit? ....

○ **I get it!** Now I know that environmental decisions are made by _____

_____

○ **I need extra help with** _____

_____

Key Concept Summaries

Introduction to Environmental Issues

What Are the Types of Environmental Issues?

Environmental issues fall into three general categories: population growth, resource use, and pollution. Because these three types of issues are interconnected, they are very difficult to study and resolve.

Anything that occurs naturally in the environment and is used by people is called a **natural resource.** Natural resources include trees, water, oil, coal, and other things. Conflict arises when a natural resource is scarce or used in a way that people feel is unfair. The demand for resources grows when population grows.

Certain environmental factors, such as pollution, can lower the quality of life on Earth for people or other organisms. **Pollution** is the contamination of land, water, or air. It can be caused by wastes, chemicals, noise, heat, light, and other sources. It can destroy wildlife and cause human health problems.

Pollution sources are grouped in two categories. A **point source** is a specific pollution source that can be identified. A **nonpoint source** is widely spread and cannot be tied to a specific origin.

How Are Environmental Decisions Made?

Environmental science is the study of natural processes in the environment and how humans can affect them. Lawmakers work with environmental scientists to make environmental decisions. However, data provided by environmental scientists are only part of the decision-making process. **To help balance the**

different opinions on an environmental issue and make a decision, decision makers weigh the costs and benefits of a proposal. Costs and benefits are often economic. A plan's short-term costs might be outweighed by its long-term benefits.

On a separate sheet of paper, make a graphic organizer showing the categories of environmental issues. Then write a sentence summarizing how decisions about environmental issues are made.

Review and Reinforce

Introduction to Environmental Issues

Understanding Main Ideas

Decision–makers use a Costs-and-Benefits table to organize the positives and negatives of a proposal. Use the table to answer the question below. Consider both short-term and long-term costs and benefits.

Costs	Benefits

1. Suppose a town wants to buy a polluted marsh on an abandoned factory's land, clean up the marsh, and use the area as a nature center for the town. What are two costs and two benefits of the town's proposal?

   _____

   _____

   _____

   _____

Building Vocabulary

Answer the following questions in the spaces provided.

2. Give three examples of natural resources.

   _____

3. Define *environmental science*. Use your own words.

   _____

   _____

Enrich

Introduction to Environmental Issues

Cities around the world are looking for ways to control the problem of traffic. Exhaust from cars adds to air pollution. Sounds of engines and horns add to noise pollution. And the stress of sitting in a car stuck in traffic is bad for the health of drivers and passengers. Read the passage below about one attempt to reduce city traffic. Then use a separate sheet of paper to answer the questions that follow the passage.

Congestion Pricing

Several cities, such as London England and Stockholm Sweden, are using congestion pricing to reduce traffic in the city center. Congestion pricing means charging a fee to every motorist who drives beyond a certain point and enters the center of a large city. The idea behind congestion pricing is that people who do not want to pay the fee will take public transportation instead of driving into the city. As a result there will be fewer cars on the roads. In London, city-center traffic was reduced by about 10-15 percent. In Stockholm, it was reduced by 30 percent. Air quality also improved.

If fewer cars are on the roads, then motorists will move faster instead of stopping in traffic. People who favor congestion pricing point out that fewer cars on the road allows emergency services to get where they are needed. Shorter response times for ambulances and fire engines can save lives.

Another expected benefit of congestion pricing is that the fees collected from drivers will help to pay for improvements in public transportation. People who choose not to drive into the city center will benefit from more frequent trains, buses, and subways, and additional routes and newer vehicles to ride in.

Opponents of congestion pricing say that it is an unfair tax, placing too much burden on the poorest people. Some people who cannot afford to pay the fee do not live near a subway or bus route. They have a long and difficult trip to and from work each day. People who can afford to pay the fee get to go to work in the comfort of their own cars.

Some people say the system costs too much to set up. Every road that leads into the city center must have toll booths or devices to monitor traffic. In London, traffic cameras photograph license plates so that the owners of the cars can be charged. Because many cameras were already in place as safety monitors, London did not have to install too much equipment. But a city that does not already have such camera systems, the cost of installing the system would consume many years' worth of fees.

1. One issue raised by congestion pricing is people who drive as close to the city center as possible, then change to public transportation to avoid the congestion fee. How might a city deal with this situation?

2. Should any vehicles be allowed to drive into the city center without paying the congestion fee? Explain your answer.

3. Do you think congestion pricing is a good way to control traffic? Explain your answer.

Lesson Quiz

Introduction to Environmental Issues

If the statement is true, write *true*. If the statement is false, change the underlined word or words to make the statement true.

1. _____ Because the three types of environmental issues are interconnected, they are <u>easy</u> to resolve.

2. _____ Air pollution in Los Angeles is a <u>nonpoint</u> source.

3. _____ A(n) <u>environmental resource</u> occurs naturally in the environment and is used by people.

4. _____ The <u>condition</u> of Earth's land, water, or air is called pollution.

5. _____ Decisions about how to protect Earth's atmosphere are made on a <u>local</u> level.

6. _____ Data provided by environmental scientists are <u>part of</u> what decision-makers consider when resolving an environmental issue.

Fill in the blank to complete each statement.

7. When a population grows, the demand for resources _____.

8. Three general categories of environmental issues are related to pollution, resource use, and _____.

9. _____ of an environmental proposal are often economic.

10. _____ can be grouped in two categories, point source and nonpoint source.

Introduction to Environmental Issues

Answer Key

After the Inquiry Warm-Up

1. Accept all reasonable responses. Students may say: Most members felt the issue was most important because it affects the greatest number of people.

2. Sample: No, other factors should be considered, such as, the severity of an issue's effects, or to a lesser degree, the economic cost of ignoring or addressing the issue.

3. Accept all reasonable responses. Students may revise definition to make it broader or narrower in scope.

4. Accept all reasonable responses. Students may say: Personal interests should play an important but not determining part when making decisions about environmental issues. Personal interests can strongly encourage people to address an issue.

Key Concept Summaries

Sample: Graphic organizers may comprise a large box with three smaller boxes below it. Text in large box: Environmental Issues; text in smaller boxes: Population Growth; Resource Use; Pollution.

Accept all reasonable summaries. Sample: Lawmakers and other decision makers, in collaboration with environmental scientists, weigh the costs and benefits of proposals for resource use.

Review and Reinforce

1. Accept any two reasonable costs and benefits. Sample response: *Costs*—Costs of buying the marsh, cleaning it up, loss of land for business use and tax money to town; *Benefits*—Organisms that could not live in the polluted marsh would return; the restored land would be beautiful and could be enjoyed; the nature center could be used for education programs.

2. Accept three of the following: trees, water, oil, coal

3. Sample: the study of the environment and how humans affect it

Enrich

1. Sample: One solution might be to establish parking lots near bus stops. The city could charge a fee to park to help pay for the construction and maintenance of the parking lot.

2. Accept all reasonable responses. Students will likely say that police and other emergency vehicles should be exempt from the fees. Students may also include buses or carpool vans.

3. Accept all responses that are well supported.

Lesson Quiz

1. difficult
2. true
3. natural resource
4. contamination
5. global
6. true
7. grows
8. population growth
9. Costs and benefits
10. Pollution

Place the outside corner, the corner away from the dotted line, in the corner of your copy machine to copy onto letter-size paper.

Introduction to Natural Resources

2 How do people use Earth's resources?

Blended Path
Active learning using Student Edition, Inquiry Path, and Digital Path

Lesson Pacing: 2–3 periods or 1–1½ blocks

🕐 **SHORT ON TIME?** To do this lesson in approximately half the time, do the Activate Prior Knowledge activity on page 92. A discussion of the key concepts on pages 93 and 95 will familiarize students with the lesson content. Have students do the Quick Lab. The rest of the lesson can be completed by students independently.

Preference Navigator, in the online Planning tools, allows you to customize *Interactive Science* to your own teaching style. You can also edit lesson plans by selecting the Lesson Planner option.

Digital Teacher's Edition allows you to access your Teacher's Edition and Resource materials online.

MY SCIENCE ONLINE.com

Lesson Vocabulary

- renewable resource
- nonrenewable resource
- sustainable use
- ecological footprint
- conservation

Content Refresher
Professional Development Note

Rachel Carson Rachel Carson set off a national and international uproar with the publication of *Silent Spring* in 1962. Carson did not advocate banning pesticides entirely; she argued against their abuse—specifically, against indiscriminate spraying, which not only kills "pests" but poisons entire food chains and ecosystems.

Carson effectively addressed the general public and scientific community. The chemical industry, however, was not pleased with Carson's presentation and interpretation. Carson said, "As a writer, my interest is divided between the presentation of facts and the interpretation of their significance, with emphasis, I think, toward the latter."

LESSON OBJECTIVES

🔑 Explain what natural resources are and distinguish between renewable and nonrenewable resources.

🔑 Explain why natural resources are important.

ENGAGE AND EXPLORE

To teach this lesson using a variety of resources, begin by reading **My Planet Diary** as a class. Have students share ideas about protecting natural resources. Then have students do the **Inquiry Warm-Up activity.** Students will investigate some of the natural resources they use in the course of a day. Discuss how important each resource is. The **After the Inquiry Warm-Up worksheet** continues to investigate natural resource use. Have volunteers share their answers to 4 about steps that can be taken to use less electricity daily.

EXPLAIN AND ELABORATE

Teach Key Concepts by explaining the terms *renewable* and *nonrenewable resources* and how a resource can be both.

Continue to **Teach Key Concepts** by explaining that some resources are essential for human life. Use the **Support the Big Q** to help students distinguish between essential and nonessential natural resources. Use **Figure 2** to discuss the use of resources in Sierra Leone, China, and Iceland. Then have students practice the inquiry skill in the **Apply It activity.** Ask students about how much larger is the ecological footprint of a person from the United States than that of a person from China. *(about 6 times)* **Lead a Discussion** on conservation and the "3 Rs" strategies.

Hand out the **Key Concept Summaries** as a review of each part of the lesson. Students can also use the online **Vocab Flash Cards** to review key terms.

EVALUATE

Have students take the **Lesson Quiz.** For an alternate assessment, see the **EXAM**VIEW® Assessment Suite, Progress Monitoring Assessments, or SuccessTracker™.

E L L Support

1 Content and Language
The terms *renewable* and *nonrenewable* are opposites since the prefix *non-* before a word indicates *no* or *not*. The prefix *re-* means *again* so *renewable* is *new again.*

DIFFERENTIATED INSTRUCTION KEY
L1 Struggling Students or Special Needs
L2 On-Level Students **L3** Advanced Students

LESSON PLANNER 3.2

Lab zone Inquiry Path
Hands-on learning in the Lab zone

ENGAGE AND EXPLORE

To teach this lesson with an emphasis on inquiry, begin with the **Inquiry Warm-Up activity.** Students will investigate natural resources they use in a typical day. Discuss the types of resources mentioned. Have students do the **After the Inquiry Warm-Up worksheet.** Talk about the most important and most used resources. Have volunteers share their answers to number 4 about steps that can be taken to use less electricity daily.

EXPLAIN AND ELABORATE

Focus on the **Inquiry Skill** for the lesson. Point out that when you calculate, you often find new information from existing information. Have students do the **Quick Lab** to further investigate natural resources and then share their results.

Use the **Support the Big Q** to help students distinguish between essential and nonessential natural resources. Review *ecological footprints* before beginning the **Apply It activity.** Ask volunteers to write another problem using the data in the table. Have students do the **Lab Investigation** to reinforce understanding of recycling paper. Students can use the online **Vocab Flash Cards** to review key terms.

EVALUATE

Have students take the **Lesson Quiz.** For an alternate assessment, see the **EXAM**VIEW® Assessment Suite, Progress Monitoring Assessments, or SuccessTracker™.

Digital Path
Online learning at **my science online**.com

ENGAGE AND EXPLORE

To teach this lesson using digital resources, begin by having students learn more about natural resources at **My Planet Diary** online. Have them access the Chapter Resources to find the **Unlock the Big Question activity.** There they can answer the questions and refine their responses as they continue through the lesson. You can re-assign the activity and have students submit their work so you can track their progress.

EXPLAIN AND ELABORATE

Students reading above, at, or below the lexile measure of this lesson can access basic content readings at their level at **My Reading Web.** Have students use the online **Vocab Flash Cards** to preview key terms. Have students do the **Quick Lab** and then share their examples of natural resources.

Review *ecological footprints* before assigning the online **Apply It activity.** Ask volunteers to share their ideas about nations with large and smaller ecological footprints. Have students submit their work to you.

Have students do the online **Lab Investigation** about recycling paper. The **Key Concept Summaries** online allow students to read a summary and see an image associated with each part of the lesson. Online remediation is available at **My Science Coach.**

EVALUATE

Have students take the **Lesson Quiz.** For an alternate assessment, see the **EXAM**VIEW® Assessment Suite, Progress Monitoring Assessments, or SuccessTracker™.

2 Frontload the Lesson
Preview the lesson visuals, labels, and captions. Ask students what they know about the words *ecological footprint.* Explain the specific meanings that *footprint* has in science.

3 Comprehensible Input
Have students study the visuals and their captions on page 93 to support the key concepts of the lesson and understanding of renewable and nonrenewable resources.

4 Language Production
Pair or group students with varied language abilities to complete the **Lab Investigation** collaboratively for language practice. Have each student copy the completed written lab for personal reference.

5 Assess Understanding
Have students make their own illustrations of an *ecological footprint* and explain its meaning.

LESSON 3.2

Introduction to Natural Resources

Establish Learning Objectives

After this lesson, students will be able to:

🔑 Explain what natural resources are and distinguish between renewable and nonrenewable resources.

🔑 Explain why natural resources are important.

Engage

Activate Prior Knowledge

MY PLANET DIARY Read *Voices from History* with the class. Tell students that before writing *Silent Spring,* Carson wrote several articles, including "Help Your Child to Wonder," that helped people learn about and appreciate nature. Ask: **What other people have you heard of who raised people's awareness of environmental issues?** *(Possible responses: Henry David Thoreau, Chief Seattle)*

BIG IDEAS OF SCIENCE REFERENCE LIBRARY 📖
Have students look up the following topic: Georges Bank.

Explore

Lab Resource: Inquiry Warm-Up 🧪

L2 USING RESOURCES Students will make lists of everything they use, eat, and throw away.

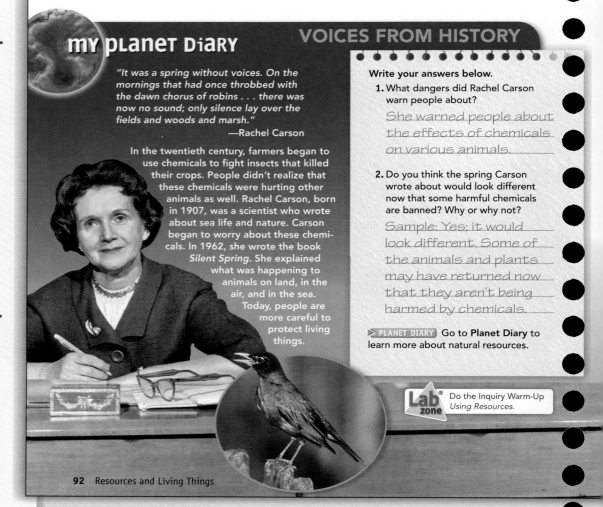

LESSON 2

Introduction to Natural Resources

UNLOCK THE BIG ?

🔑 **What Are Natural Resources?**

🔑 **Why Are Natural Resources Important?**

my planeT DiaRY

VOICES FROM HISTORY

"It was a spring without voices. On the mornings that had once throbbed with the dawn chorus of robins . . . there was now no sound; only silence lay over the fields and woods and marsh."

—Rachel Carson

In the twentieth century, farmers began to use chemicals to fight insects that killed their crops. People didn't realize that these chemicals were hurting other animals as well. Rachel Carson, born in 1907, was a scientist who wrote about sea life and nature. Carson began to worry about these chemicals. In 1962, she wrote the book *Silent Spring.* She explained what was happening to animals on land, in the air, and in the sea. Today, people are more careful to protect living things.

Write your answers below.

1. What dangers did Rachel Carson warn people about?

   She warned people about the effects of chemicals on various animals.

2. Do you think the spring Carson wrote about would look different now that some harmful chemicals are banned? Why or why not?

   Sample: Yes; it would look different. Some of the animals and plants may have returned now that they aren't being harmed by chemicals.

▶ **PLANET DIARY** Go to **Planet Diary** to learn more about natural resources.

🧪 **Lab zone** Do the Inquiry Warm-Up *Using Resources.*

SUPPORT ALL READERS

Lexile Measure = 910L   Lexile Word Count = 1077

Prior Exposure to Content: Most students have encountered this topic in earlier grades

Academic Vocabulary: *calculate, categorizing, summarize*

Science Vocabulary: *renewable resource, nonrenewable resource*

Concept Level: Generally appropriate for most students in this grade

Preteach With: My Planet Diary and Figure 1 activity

Go to **My Reading Web** to access leveled readings that provide a foundation for the content.

my science online.com

LESSON 3.2

Vocabulary
- renewable resource • nonrenewable resource
- sustainable use • ecological footprint • conservation

Skills
- ⊙ Reading: Relate Text and Visuals
- △ Inquiry: Calculate

What Are Natural Resources?

Did you turn on a light or use an alarm clock today? Flush a toilet or take a shower? Ride in a car or bus? Eat some food? Use any paper—other than this page that you are reading right now? All of these things—and so much more—depend on Earth's resources.

Recall that anything that occurs naturally in the environment and is used by people is called a natural resource. 🔑 **Natural resources include organisms, water, sunlight, minerals, and oil.**

Renewable Resources A **renewable resource** is either always available or is naturally replaced in a relatively short time. Some renewable resources, like wind and sunlight, are almost always available. Other renewable resources, like water and trees, are renewable only if they are replaced as fast as they are used.

Original trees on land

Trees after first harvest

Trees after replanting

✏️

⊙ **Relate Text and Visuals** The trees in the first diagram are being harvested for wood. The landowner tells you the trees are a renewable resource. Based on the number of trees being harvested and replanted, is the landowner right? Why?

This landowner is wrong. These trees are not being treated as a renewable resource. The trees are being used faster than they are being replanted.

93

Explain

Introduce Vocabulary

Point out that the term *ecological footprint* is a way of describing someone's effect on the environment. Compare this to the way footprints show someone's affect on the floor they walk on.

Teach Key Concepts 🔑

Draw students' attention to the six examples of natural resources. Ask: **What other natural resources can you name?** *(Samples: Coal, soil, trees)* **What are some kinds of minerals?** *(Samples: Silver, gold, copper, platinum)* **What is a renewable resource?** *(A resource that is always available or is naturally replaced in a relatively short time.)*

Teach With Visuals

Tell students to look at the images on this page. If students have difficulty answering the question, ask: **How many trees were there before the harvest?** *(Ten)* **How many trees were there after the harvest?** *(Three)* **How many trees were there after the replanting?** *(Six)* **Were all the trees that were cut down replaced?** *(No)*

⊙ **Relate Text and Visuals** Explain that relating text and visuals shows how the two elements work together to convey information. Remind students that visuals may include photographs, charts, tables, and illustrations along with labels and captions.

My Planet Diary provides an opportunity for students to explore real-world connections to natural resources.

my science ONLINE | Introduction to Natural Resources

E L L Support

1 Content and Language
Write the following cloze sentence on the board: _____ is a renewable/nonrenewable resource because _____. As students fill in the table in **Figure 1,** instruct them to use the sentence to orally identify renewable and nonrenewable resources.

2 Frontload the Lesson
Ask students to explain why a tree is a renewable resource. Be sure students

mention that a resource is renewable only if replaced as fast as it is used.

3 Comprehensible Input
Students may know the word *fuel* in relation to an automobile. Explain that *fuel* refers to any substance used as a source of energy. Reiterate that all fuels are resources; some are renewable, and some are not. Display photos of different fuels and have students identify each as renewable or nonrenewable.

Elaborate

Make Analogies

L1 **RENEWABLE RESOURCES** Ask for volunteers who have made yogurt or who know how yogurt is made. Ask: **What is a starter?** *(Sample: A little bit of yogurt that you use to make more yogurt)* **How is yogurt like a renewable resource?** *(Sample: If you save some yogurt from each batch, you can use the part you saved as a starter to make more. In the same way, if we conserve trees and other renewable resources by not overusing them, the resources can replenish themselves.)*

Lab Resource: Quick Lab

L1 **NATURAL RESOURCES** Students will explore examples of natural resources.

Evaluate

Assess Your Understanding

After students answer the questions, have them evaluate their understanding by completing the appropriate sentence.

R T I Response to Intervention

1a. If students need help with defining *renewable resource,* **then** have them locate the heading *Renewable Resources* and review the definition below it.

b. If students have trouble comparing and contrasting resources, **then** have them skim the section to find where sunlight and trees are discussed in the text and use the discussion to help them.

MY SCIENCE **COACH** Have students go online for help in understanding renewable and nonrenewable resources.

Nonrenewable Resources Over millions of years, natural processes changed the remains of organisms into the substances now called oil and coal. Today's world is powered by these fuels. Humans use these resources much faster than they are naturally replaced. Resources that are not replaced in a useful time frame are **nonrenewable resources.** Metals and minerals are also nonrenewable. Remember that some resources, such as trees, may be renewable or nonrenewable, depending on how quickly they are replaced.

FIGURE 1 ··

Categorizing Resources
Resources are grouped into two main categories: renewable and nonrenewable. Gold, shown above, is nonrenewable.

✎ **Summarize** Use what you have read to fill in the table comparing renewable and nonrenewable resources.

Renewable Resources	Nonrenewable Resources	Both
Replaced in a short time or always available	Not replaced in a useful time frame	Fits both natural resource categories
Examples: _____ sunlight, wind _____	Examples: _____ metals, oil, minerals, coal, natural gas	Examples: _____ water, trees, food crops _____

 Do the Quick Lab
Natural Resources.

🔑 **Assess Your Understanding**

1a. Define What is a renewable resource?
A renewable resource is almost always available or is naturally replaced in a short time.

b. Compare and Contrast Sunlight and trees are both natural resources. How are they different?
Sunlight cannot be used up, but trees can be if they are used faster than they are replaced.

got it? ·······································

○ **I get it!** Now I know that natural resources include *organisms, water, sunlight, minerals, and oil.*

○ **I need extra help with** *See TE note.*

Go to **MY SCIENCE** **COACH** *online for help with this subject.*

94 Resources and Living Things

Why Are Natural Resources Important?

Humans cannot live without some natural resources, such as sunlight and fresh water. Others, such as metals, are necessary to sustain modern life. **Humans depend on Earth's natural resources for survival and for development.**

How People Use Resources Around the world, people rely on natural resources for the same basic needs. Not all resources are equally available in all parts of the world. In some areas, there is a plentiful supply of clean fresh water. In other areas, water is scarce. In some places, pollution threatens the water supply.

Globally, fuels are used for cooking, heating, and power. Different fuels are common in different parts of the world. Coal is plentiful in some areas of the world and oil is plentiful in others. See **Figure 2.** In some areas, wood is the main fuel, not coal or oil.

FIGURE 2 ....
Resources Around the World
People use natural resources in different ways around the world.

✎ **Describe** In the blank box below, draw or describe one way you use natural resources.

In Sierra Leone, entire communities get their drinking water from a main well.

In China, coal is delivered to homes by bicycle to be burned for heat.

In Iceland, most homes get hot water and heat from the energy of the hot, liquidlike rock under Earth's surface.

> Accept all reasonable answers. Sample: I eat fruits and vegetables from a community garden during the summer. The bus that brings me to school runs on diesel fuel.

95

Differentiated Instruction

L1 Using Natural Resources To help students answer the question, have them think about the steps in their typical daily routines, paying careful attention to any natural resources they might use during each step. You can extend this activity by having students keep a journal for a week to record the different resources they use. Remind them to think about the resources that were used to make or power the objects they use daily.

L1 Read a Map To help students understand the unequal distribution of natural resources, show them a map from an atlas or the Internet that depicts the global distribution of forest, freshwater, or energy resources.

L3 Formation of a Fuel Have students research online to find and evaluate diagrams showing how coal or oil was formed. Encourage students to use their findings and analysis to make their own diagrams.

Explain

Teach Key Concepts 🔑

Explain to students that people are absolutely dependent on some natural resources and rely on others to make daily life better and more convenient than it would be without them. Ask: **What are some examples of the ways people use natural resources for development?** *(Samples: People use marble to make sculptures, steel to make skyscrapers, fur to line or decorate warm or fancy clothing)*

Support the Big Q ❓ UbD

Help students distinguish between essential and nonessential natural resources. Ask: **What natural resources do you use to help you grow and survive?** *(Samples: Fresh water for drinking; plants for food)* **What natural resources do you enjoy having that aren't essential to your survival?** *(Samples: Silver for earrings, silicon for computer chips)*

Teach With Visuals

Tell students to look at **Figure 2.** Ask: **How does the way the community in Sierra Leone gets its drinking water differ from the way your community gets its drinking water?** *(Sample: Children are involved in getting drinking water in Sierra Leone but not in my community. In my community, water is stored in a large reservoir and carried through pipes to every home, while the community in Sierra Leone gets its drinking water from a single well.)* **What is one disadvantage of burning coal to heat homes?** *(Sample: Burning coal produces air pollution and can harm human health.)* **How does the photograph of Iceland support the statement that different fuels are common in different parts of the world?** *(Sample response: In the United States, we do not have hot, liquid-like rock to use for generating electricity.)* Iceland only gets about a quarter of its electricity from geothermal sources. Nearly the rest comes from hydroelectric power. However, Iceland does get most of its heating and hot water from geothermal sources.

Explain

21st Century Learning

CRITICAL THINKING Help students understand that the sustainable use of a resource can be hard to determine and that sustainable use affects people and other parts of an ecosystem differently. Ask: **How might regulating motor traffic on a river affect the quality of the river over time?** *(Sample: Regulating motor traffic could decrease the amount of pollutants discharged into the river, but even regulated motor traffic could harm river species and habitat.)*

Teach With Visuals

Tell students to look at **Figure 3.** Ask: **What are some activities that make up this ecological footprint?** *(Airplane travel, electricity generation and transport, motor vehicle travel, wastewater treatment, satellite data reception, commercial fishing, cattle raising, solid waste removal, irrigation)* List students' responses on the board. Discuss how important or unimportant each activity on the list is in students' lives. Rewrite the list in order from most important to least important. Explain to students that the units used for measuring an ecological footprint are global hectares (gha). According to the Global Footprint Network, a global hectare is a common unit that encompasses the average productivity of all the biologically productive land and sea area in the world in a given year. Biologically productive areas include cropland, pastures, forests, and fishing grounds. For reference, tell students that a hectare is a unit of area that is equivalent to the size of a soccer field.

Lead a Discussion

CONSERVATION Tell students that conservation is a part of the "3 Rs" strategy: Reduce, Reuse, and Recycle. Ask: **Which of the three Rs best describes resource conservation?** *(Possible response: Reduce)* **Why?** *(Sample: When you reduce your use of one resource, such as petroleum products in plastic bottles, you not only conserve the resources used to make the bottle but also the energy needed to recycle it.)*

FIGURE 3 ·······························
Ecological Footprint
Everything you do contributes to your ecological footprint, from how you travel, to the food you eat, to the home you live in. Ecological footprints vary among individuals and among nations, depending on how people live.

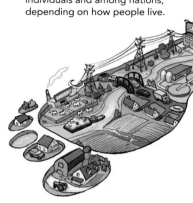

Sustainable Use How long a resource lasts depends on how people use it. **Sustainable use** of a resource means using it in ways that maintain the resource at a certain quality for a certain period of time. For example, a city may want to manage a river. Does the city want the water to be clean enough to drink or clean enough to swim in? Does the city want the water to be clean for fifty years, two hundred years, or indefinitely? The answers to these questions define what would be considered sustainable use of the river. However, it may not be sustainable from an ecological perspective even if it meets human needs. Other cities farther down the river may have different answers to those questions, but their plans could also be considered sustainable if they met their goals. Because of these differences, policymakers and lawmakers struggle to define sustainable use. The struggle adds to the challenge of regulating resources.

Ecological Footprint The amount of land and water that individuals use to meet their resource needs and absorb the waste they produce is called an **ecological footprint.** A high level of resource use means a larger footprint. A low level of resource use means a smaller footprint. Refer to **Figure 3.**

apply it!

The chart below gives the average ecological footprints for the people of several countries. It also gives the footprint for each country as a whole. Ecological footprints are measured in global hectares. A global hectare (gha) is a unit of area. It is adjusted to compare how much life different places on Earth can support.

Country	Average Ecological Footprint (gha/person)	Total Ecological Footprint (million gha)
United States	9.6	2,819
United Kingdom	5.6	333
Germany	4.5	375
Mexico	2.6	265
China	1.6	2,152

1 **Interpret Tables** Which country has the largest ecological footprint? <u>United States</u>

2 **Calculate** About how many times larger is the average ecological footprint per person in the United States than per person in Mexico? <u>About 3.7 times</u>

3 **CHALLENGE** China has a smaller ecological footprint per person than the United Kingdom, but a much larger total ecological footprint. Why?

<u>China's ecological footprint per person may be smaller, but it is multiplied over a much larger population.</u>

96 Resources and Living Things

Digital Lesson: Assign the *Apply It* activity online and have students submit their work to you.

my science online.com ▷ **Importance of Natural Resources**

Conservation While we cannot avoid using resources, there are better ways to use them. Resource **conservation** is the practice of managing the use of resources wisely so the resources last longer. Conservation cannot make resources last forever, but it can make resources last longer.

Governments and industries greatly affect resource conservation. Even individuals can make a difference. Walking, riding a bike, or riding the bus conserves fuel resources. People can also conserve resources when they turn off lights and unplug equipment that they are not using. Taking shorter showers saves water. When many people make small changes, the results can be huge.

did you know?

If everyone on Earth lived like the average American, it would take the resources of five planets to support us!

Resource Conservation at My School

Sample: recycling when possible;
having students write on both sides of
sheets of paper; turning off lights and
computers when they are not in use;
encouraging people to carpool, take the
bus, or ride bikes to school

FIGURE 4 ·····································
Conserving Resources at School
Students like you can take action to conserve natural resources.

 List On the notebook paper, write ways your school can conserve resources.

Lab zone Do the Lab Investigation *Recycling Paper.*

🔑 **Assess Your Understanding**

2a. Review Resources (are/~~are not~~) equally available around the world.

b. Summarize What two factors determine whether or not a resource is being used sustainably?

Resource quality and time

c. Evaluate the Impact on Society As the human population continues to grow, how do you think it will affect the use of natural resources?

Sample: More people will use
more resources. We may run
out of nonrenewable resources.

got it? ··

○ **I get it!** Now I know that natural resources are important because humans depend on them for survival and development.

○ **I need extra help with** See TE note.

Go to **MY SCIENCE COACH** *online for help with this subject.*

97

Elaborate ──────────────

Apply It!

L1 Review the table before beginning the activity. Make sure students understand the kinds of data given in columns 2 and 3.

🔺 **Calculate** Have students find a clue word or phrase that tells what operation they should use to solve the problem. *(The clue words "times larger" tell you to divide.)*

Lab Resource: Lab Investigation

L2 **RECYCLING PAPER** Students will explore if paper is a renewable or nonrenewable resource.

Evaluate ──────────────

Assess Your Understanding

After students answer the questions, have them evaluate their understanding by completing the appropriate sentence.

RTI Response to Intervention

2a. If students cannot describe the availability of resources, **then** have them review the first paragraph under the red head *How People Use Resources*.

b. If students have trouble with indicators of sustainable use, **then** have them locate and review the sentence with the highlighted vocabulary term *sustainable use*.

c. If students need help identifying population growth and resource use, **then** draw a vertical arrow, with the head at the top. Tell students the arrow represents human population growth. Have a volunteer come to the board and draw a second arrow showing the commensurate growth in use of natural resources. *(The second arrow should also have the head at the top.)*

MY SCIENCE COACH Have students go online for help in understanding natural resources.

Differentiated Instruction

L1 **Ecological Footprints and Food Choices** Have students imagine a trip to the grocery store. Challenge them to identify two items that maximize and two items that help minimize their ecological footprint. *(Sample: Maximize—Individually wrapped fruit rolls in a plastic bag, individual serving of soup in a plastic bowl with plastic-wrapped seasonings; Minimize—locally grown fruit or vegetables.)*

L1 **Calculate Your Ecological Footprint** Have students work in pairs to calculate their ecological footprints. Tell students to search the Internet using the key words *ecological footprint calculator*. Remind students to follow prescribed guidelines for Internet use.

L3 **Sustainable Harvest** Have students research sustainable harvest practices for trees or a crop. Invite students to share their information with the class.

Lab zone After the Inquiry Warm-Up

Introduction to Natural Resources

Inquiry Warm-Up, *Using Resources*

In the Inquiry Warm-Up, you investigated some of the resources you use in a typical day. Using what you learned from that activity, answer the questions below.

1. **MAKE JUDGMENTS** Was the resource used most also the most important resource used? Why or why not?

_____

_____

_____

_____

2. **OBSERVE** List four different resources you use to get ready in the morning for a typical school day.

_____

_____

_____

_____

3. **USE PRIOR KNOWLEDGE** What are two steps you could take to use less water in your daily routine?

_____

_____

4. **APPLY CONCEPTS** What are two steps you could take to use less electricity in your daily routine?

_____

_____

Name _____ Date _____ Class _____

Introduction to Natural Resources

What Are Natural Resources?

1a. **DEFINE** What is a renewable resource?

_____

_____

b. **COMPARE AND CONTRAST** Sunlight and trees are both natural resources. How are they different?

_____

_____

got it? ··

○ **I get it!** Now I know that natural resources include _____

_____

○ **I need extra help with** _____

_____

Why Are Natural Resources Important?

2a. **REVIEW** Resources (are/are not) equally available around the world.

b. **SUMMARIZE** What two factors determine whether or not a resource is being used sustainably?

_____

c. **EVALUATE THE IMPACT ON SOCIETY** As the human population continues to grow, how do you think it will affect the use of natural resources?

_____

_____

got it? ··

○ **I get it!** Now I know that natural resources are important because _____

_____

○ **I need extra help with** _____

_____

Name _____ Date _____ Class _____

Introduction to Natural Resources

What Are Natural Resources?

Anything that occurs naturally in the environment and is used by people is called a natural resource. **Natural resources include water, wind, sunlight, minerals, oil, and gas.**

A **renewable resource** is always available or is naturally replaced in a relatively short time. Resources that are not replaced in a useful time frame are **nonrenewable resources.** Oil, coal, metals, and minerals are nonrenewable.

Why Are Natural Resources Important?

Humans depend on Earth's natural resources for survival and for development. Humans cannot live without some natural resources, such as sunlight and fresh water. Other natural resources, such as metals, are necessary to sustain modern life.

Not all resources are equally available in all parts of the world. For example, different fuels, such as coal and oil, are common in different parts of the world. In some areas, wood is the main fuel.

How long a resource lasts depends on how people use it. **Sustainable use** means using a resource in

ways that maintain the resource at a certain quality for a certain period of time.

The amount of land and water that individuals use to meet their resource needs and absorb the waste they produce is called an **ecological footprint.** A high level of resource use makes a larger ecological footprint. A low level of resource use makes a smaller footprint.

Resource **conservation** is the practice of managing the use of resources wisely so they last longer. Governments and industries greatly affect resource conservation.

On a separate sheet of paper, describe the ecological footprint you want to make. Include the terms renewable resource, nonrenewable resource, sustainable use, **and** conservation.

Introduction to Natural Resources

Understanding Main Ideas
Answer the following questions in the spaces provided.

1. Explain how renewable resources and nonrenewable resources are different. Give two examples of each.

   _____

   _____

   _____

2. What is similar and different about how natural resources are used in different parts of the world?

   _____

   _____

   _____

Building Vocabulary
Match each term with its definition by writing the letter of the correct definition in the right column on the line beside the term in the left column.

3. ___ sustainable use

4. ___ natural resource

5. ___ ecological footprint

6. ___ nonrenewable resource

7. ___ conservation

8. ___ renewable resource

A wind

B. allows you to maintain a resource at a certain quality over a certain period of time

C. amount of land and water individuals use

D. managing resource use so that resources last longer

E. occurs naturally in the environment and is used by people

F. coal

Name _____ Date _____ Class _____

Introduction to Natural Resources

Read the passage below. Then use a separate sheet of paper to answer the questions that follow the passage.

Keeping Water Clean

Clean water is an essential natural resource. Prior to 1987, the Clean Water Act was the primary government tool for controlling water pollution from point sources of pollution. The government defines a point source as "any discernable, confined and discrete source of pollution." Point sources include factories and waste-treatment facilities. Businesses like these are monitored by the government. If a business is found to be releasing more than an acceptable level of pollution, the company must pay fines. In some cases, company executives have to serve jail sentences.

As such point sources of pollution began to be controlled, water quality improved. But it became clear that factories, waste-treatment facilities, and other industries were not the only sources of water pollution. In 1987, Congress recognized the need to control additional kinds of pollution. More rules were added to the Clean Water Act for the purpose of controlling nonpoint sources of pollution.

Nonpoint sources of pollution cannot be traced to a specific source. They are detected in bodies of water, but it is impossible to tell exactly how they got there. Pollutants in storm water runoff are considered nonpoint sources. Household activities that contribute to pollution include dumping used motor oil or pet waste into a storm drain. Fertilizers and pesticides used on lawns become nonpoint sources of pollution when storm runoff carries these chemicals into bodies of water.

Since nonpoint sources cannot be identified, the government has to rely on voluntary cooperation by citizens, rather than the fines that industries face. The government educates citizens about the importance of reducing pollution. Guidelines for use of fertilizers and pesticides have been developed. Many communities have passed laws prohibiting the release of pet waste and oil into the environment. Efforts by individuals have contributed significantly to the improvement of water quality.

1. If you dump the oil you removed from your lawnmower down a storm drain, the oil entered the water from a specific point. Why is this not considered point source pollution?
2. Why is 1987 such an important year in pollution control?
3. The pollution from an average household is much less than that released by a factory. Why is it important to control the pollution released by an individual household?

Name _____ Date _____ Class _____

Introduction to Natural Resources

Write the letter of the correct answer on the line at the left.

1. ___ Natural resources include
   A fresh water
   B television
   C ovens
   D computers

2. ___ Humans depend on natural resources for
   A health and welfare
   B art and leisure
   C survival and development
   D growth and maturity

3. ___ Globally, fuels are used for
   A power and trade
   B weapons and travel
   C research and development
   D cooking and heating

4. ___ Ecological footprints are measured in
   A square miles
   B global hectares
   C square meters
   D English units

If the statement is true, write *true*. If the statement is false, change the underlined word or words to make the statement true.

5. _____ Resource conservation can make resources last <u>forever</u>.

6. _____ A high level of resource use makes a <u>larger</u> ecological footprint.

7. _____ Sustainable use means using a resource in ways that maintain the resource at a certain quality for a <u>generation</u>.

8. _____ Some renewable resources are renewable only if they are replaced <u>a little more slowly than</u> they are used.

9. _____ Oil and coal were formed over <u>hundreds</u> of years.

10. _____ <u>Not all</u> resources are available equally in all parts of the world.

Introduction to Natural Resources

Answer Key

After the Inquiry Warm-Up

1. Accept all reasonable responses. Students may say: No, while energy was used the most, it can be acquired from a number of alternative sources, whereas alternative sources of fresh water are much more limited.

2. Accept all reasonable responses. Students may say: Electricity for lights and my alarm clock; water to bathe myself and brush my teeth; natural or synthetic fibers for clothing, food, gas and/or electricity to make breakfast, etc.

3. Sample: Take shorter showers, turn off the water when brushing my teeth.

4. Sample: Turn lights off when not using a room, don't run electronic devises unless in use

Key Concept Summaries

Accept all reasonable answers. Sample: I want to make an ecological footprint that minimizes the use of nonrenewable resources, such as oil. That means I ride my bike or walk when I can, instead of riding in a car. I want to make an ecological footprint that uses renewable resources, such as trees, in a sustainable way. Conservation is important in the ecological footprint I want to make, because conserving resources makes them last longer.

Review and Reinforce

1. Sample: Renewable resources are either always available or are naturally replaced in a relatively short time; whereas, nonrenewable resources are not replaced in a useful time frame. Examples of renewable resources include sunlight and trees. Examples of nonrenewable resources include coal and oil.

2. Sample: People around the world use natural resources to meet the same basic needs. However, not all resources are equally available in all parts of the world. For example, people in some parts of the world mainly use coal for fuel. In other parts of the world, people mainly use oil.

3. B	4. E
5. C	6. F
7. D	8. A

Enrich

1. When the oil reaches a tested water body it can not be traced to you or identified as your oil.

2. Sample: The year 1987 is important because as pollution from factories declined the importance of simple family activities such as fertilizer overuse was recognized.

3. Although the individual household releases very little pollution, there are many households in a community, and the combined releases are significant.

Lesson Quiz

1. A	2. C
3. D	4. B
5. longer	6. true
7. certain period of time	8. as fast as
9. millions	10. true

Place the outside corner, the corner away from the dotted line, in the corner of your copy machine to copy onto letter-size paper.

Human Population Growth

 How do people use Earth's resources?

Lesson Pacing: 1–2 periods or $\frac{1}{2}$–1 block

🕐 **SHORT ON TIME?** To do this lesson in approximately half the time, do the Activate Prior Knowledge activity on page 98. A discussion of the key concepts on pages 99 and 100 will familiarize students with the lesson content. Have students do the Quick Labs. The rest of the lesson can be completed by students independently.

Preference Navigator, in the online Planning tools, allows you to customize *Interactive Science* to your own teaching style. You can also edit lesson plans by selecting the Lesson Planner option.

Digital Teacher's Edition allows you to access your Teacher's Edition and Resource materials online.

my science online.com

Lesson Vocabulary

• exponential growth

 Content Refresher

Human Population Studies The field of population studies encompasses many disciplines, including biology, biochemistry, applied mathematics, sociology, history, and economics. Together, these fields of inquiry can illuminate the economic, social, and ecological implications of anticipated changes in human population.

In 1789 the British scholar Thomas Malthus predicted that human population would grow past the ability of Earth's resources to sustain it. After Malthus' time, unforeseeable gains in food production were realized together with improvements in medical care and sanitation, which resulted in a near quadrupling of global human population in the twentieth century.

LESSON OBJECTIVES

🔑 Explain how the human population has grown over time.

🔑 Identify factors that affect the rate of human population growth.

Blended Path
Active learning using Student Edition, Inquiry Path, and Digital Path

ENGAGE AND EXPLORE

To teach this lesson using a variety of resources, begin by reading **My Planet Diary** as a class. Have students share ideas about the exponential nature of human population growth. Then have students do the **Inquiry Warm-Up activity.** Students will use tables of population growth to answer questions. Discuss the **After the Inquiry Warm-Up worksheet** and the mathematics required to solve number 4 about whether unchecked population growth is beneficial or harmful to a species.

EXPLAIN AND ELABORATE

Teach Key Concepts by explaining the term *exponential growth*. It means the rate of growth is increasing.

Continue to **Teach Key Concepts** by discussing the human species' unique ability to support population growth. **Lead a Discussion** on increasing and decreasing populations with respect to trees. Ask who or what can affect tree survival. Use the **Support the Big Q** to illustrate how increasing human population may tax resources. Then have students interpret tables in the **Apply It activity.** Use **Figure 1** to explain the population density of Hong Kong.

Hand out the **Key Concept Summaries** as a review of each part of the lesson. Students can also use the online **Vocab Flash Cards** to review key terms.

EVALUATE

Have students take the **Lesson Quiz.** For an alternate assessment, see the **EXAM**VIEW® Assessment Suite, Progress Monitoring Assessments, or SuccessTracker™.

E L L Support

1 Content and Language

The only vocabulary term is *exponential growth*. Give an example of the use of an exponent, for example, 3^2. The 2 indicates that 3 is multiplied by itself: $3 \times 3 = 9$, so $3^2 = 9$. Exponents usually indicate rapid increase or growth.

Lab zone Inquiry Path
Hands-on learning in the Lab zone

ENGAGE AND EXPLORE

To teach this lesson with an emphasis on inquiry, begin with the **Inquiry Warm-Up activity.** Students will investigate exponential growth and limitations of natural resources such as food and water. Discuss the limitations of natural resources. Have students do the **After the Inquiry Warm-Up worksheet.** Talk about the mathematics needed to solve numbers 2 and 3. Have volunteers share their answers to number 4 and make lists of harmful effects of unchecked population growth.

EXPLAIN AND ELABORATE

Focus on the **Inquiry Skill** for the lesson. Point out that when you predict, you use existing information or data to indicate or tell in advance. Prediction is often used in interpreting graphs. Have students do the **Quick Lab** to see how the human population has grown over time and then share their results.

Review the meanings of birth and death rates before beginning the **Apply It activity.** Ask volunteers to explain how they know which countries had decreasing populations. *(Death rate is larger than birth rate.)* Use the **Support the Big Q** to illustrate how growing human population affects both natural and technological resources. Do the **Quick Lab** to reinforce understanding of population density around the world. Students can use the online **Vocab Flash Cards** to review key terms.

EVALUATE

Have students take the **Lesson Quiz.** For an alternate assessment, see the **EXAM**VIEW® Assessment Suite, Progress Monitoring Assessments, or SuccessTracker™.

Digital Path
Online learning at **my science online**.com

ENGAGE AND EXPLORE

To teach this lesson using digital resources, begin by having students explore the exponential nature of human population growth at **My Planet Diary** online. Have them access the Chapter Resources to find the **Unlock the Big Question activity.** There they can answer the questions and refine their responses as they continue through the lesson. You can re-assign the activity and have students submit their work so you can track their progress.

EXPLAIN AND ELABORATE

Students reading above, at, or below the lexile measure of this lesson can access basic content readings at their level at **My Reading Web.** Encourage students to use the online **Vocab Flash Cards** to preview key terms. Have students do the **Quick Lab** and then ask students to share their results.

Review *exponential growth* before assigning the online **Apply It activity.** Ask volunteers to share their methods for solving number 1. Have students submit their work to you. Have students do the online **Interactive Art activity** to visualize the population density of Hong Kong. Assign the **Do the Math activity** online and have students submit their work to you. Have students do the online **Quick Lab** to investigate populations around the world. The **Key Concept Summaries** online allow students to read a summary and see an image associated with each part of the lesson. Online remediation is available at **My Science Coach.**

EVALUATE

Have students take the **Lesson Quiz.** For an alternate assessment, see the **EXAM**VIEW® Assessment Suite, Progress Monitoring Assessments, or SuccessTracker™.

2 Frontload the Lesson
Relate the idea of exponential growth rate to the speed and acceleration of a motor vehicle so that students understand that this rate increases quickly.

3 Comprehensible Input
Have students study the graph and its labels on page 99 to support the key concepts of the lesson.

4 Language Production
Pair or group students with varied language abilities to complete the two labs collaboratively for language practice. Have each student copy the completed written lab for personal reference.

5 Assess Understanding
Have students review the chart on page 101 and indicate the effect of each condition on human population by thumbs up or thumbs down gestures.

Lexile Measure = 920L

Human Population Growth

Establish Learning Objectives

After this lesson, students will be able to:

🔑 Explain how the human population has grown over time.

🔑 Identify factors that affect the rate of human population growth.

Engage

Activate Prior Knowledge

MY PLANET DIARY Read *Dangerous Disease* with the class. Ask students to think about dangerous diseases that people can avoid by getting vaccinated. Ask: **What dangerous diseases are people in the United States vaccinated against?** *(Sample response: Smallpox, tuberculosis)* **Can you think of a dangerous disease for which there is no vaccine?** *(Sample response: Lung cancer)*

BIG IDEAS OF SCIENCE REFERENCE LIBRARY 📖 Have students look up the following topic: Population Growth.

Explore

Lab Resource: Inquiry Warm-Up

L2 DOUBLING TIME Students will calculate how long it takes for populations to double.

Human Population Growth

🔑 How Has the Human Population Grown Over Time?

🔑 What Factors Allow the Human Population to Grow?

MY PLANET DIARY

DISASTERS

Dangerous Disease

In the mid-1300s, nearly one third of the European population died from a disease known as "black plague." Around 25 million people died, reducing the regional population from 75 million to 50 million. No treatment was available, and the disease spread. Today, the disease can be treated.

Plague is carried by rodents and rodent fleas. It can be passed to humans by a bite from a rodent flea or by handling infected rodents. The most recent outbreak in the United States occurred in 1925. Since then, only 10 to 15 cases have been reported in the United States each year. Around the world, 1,000 to 3,000 cases are reported annually.

Communicate Discuss the question with a group of classmates. Then write your answer below.

Is plague a concern today?

Cases are reported each year but not at the same rate as in the 1300s. Only a handful of cases occur in the United States each year and most can be treated.

▷ **PLANET DIARY** Go to **Planet Diary** to learn more about human population growth.

Lab zone Do the Inquiry Warm-Up *Doubling Time.*

◀ Rodent flea

98 Resources and Living Things

SUPPORT ALL READERS

Lexile Measure = 920L   Lexile Word Count = 532

Prior Exposure to Content: May be the first time students have encountered this topic

Academic Vocabulary: *predict, main idea*

Science Vocabulary: *exponential growth*

Concept Level: May be difficult for students who struggle with math

Preteach With: My Planet Diary "Dangerous Disease" and the *Do the Math* activity

Go to **My Reading Web** to access leveled readings that provide a foundation for the content.

MY SCIENCE online.com

Vocabulary
- exponential growth

Skills
- 🔁 Reading: Identify the Main Idea
- 🔺 Inquiry: Predict

How Has the Human Population Grown Over Time?

Five hundred years ago, there were approximately 480 million people on Earth. Today, there are more than 6.7 billion people.

Exponential growth occurs when a population grows at an ever-increasing rate. In exponential growth, the larger a population gets, the faster it grows. 🔑 **Over time, the human population has grown exponentially.** Today, the human population continues to grow, but the growth rate is decreasing. Some experts predict that the human population will stop growing, and possibly decline in the future. Other experts strongly disagree.

do the math!

❶ Interpret Graphs What is the predicted world population for the year 2050?

Nine billion

❷ 🔺Predict How might this graph look in 500 years?

Sample: The population will keep
growing until the planet cannot
support growth anymore, and then
it will decrease.

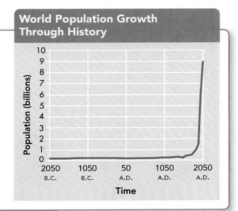

World Population Growth Through History

Population (billions) vs *Time* (2050 B.C., 1050 B.C., 50 A.D., 1050 A.D., 2050 A.D.)

Lab zone Do the Quick Lab
Human Population Growth.

🔑 Assess Your Understanding

got it? ....

○ I get it! Now I know that the human population has grown exponentially over time.

○ I need extra help with See TE note.

Go to **my science** **COACH** *online for help with this subject.*

99

E L L Support

1 Content and Language
Help students understand that while the *population* is still increasing, the *rate* at which it grows is decreasing. Draw a sample line graph that shows what this trend might look like.

2 Frontload the Lesson
To help students understand *exponential growth*, point out where the year 1550 A.D. (population of 480 million). Then, identify the present day on the graph

(6.7 billion). Note that the world's population reached 6 billion in 1999.

3 Comprehensible Input
Have students model exponential growth using a piece of notebook paper. Students should fold the paper in half again and again and note that the thickness doubles with each fold.

Explain

Introduce Vocabulary

Explain to students that, for *exponential growth*, the larger a quantity gets, the faster it grows.

Teach Key Concepts 🔑

Explain to students that the human population has grown exponentially over time but that its growth rate is currently decreasing. Ask: **How could experts disagree about human population growth in the future?** *(Sample answer: Experts' opinions could be swayed by their beliefs. Different experts may also be using different data or interpreting the data using different methods.)*

Elaborate

Do the Math!

Point out that the graph makes it possible to see trends in world population growth. If students have trouble interpreting the graph, show them how to find 2050 A.D. on the *x*-axis and move a finger up to find the corresponding number on the *y*-axis.

🔺 **Predict** Making an accurate prediction involves looking at the relationship between the values of each year shown to project what will happen in the future.

See *Math Skill and Problem-Solving Activities* for support.

Lab Resource: Quick Lab

L2 HUMAN POPULATION GROWTH Students will explore how the population has grown over time.

Evaluate

Assess Your Understanding

Have students evaluate their understanding by completing the appropriate sentence.

R T I Response to Intervention

If students have trouble with population growth, **then** have them reread the blue heading question and look for the highlighted vocabulary term.

my science COACH Have students go online for help in understanding human population growth.

My Planet Diary provides an opportunity for students to explore real-world connections to human population growth.

Digital Lesson: Assign the *Do the Math* activity online and have students submit their work to you.

Explain

Teach Key Concepts 🔑

Explain that the human population has grown exponentially over time. Ask: **How is the human species uniquely able to support its own population growth?** (Sample: Humans have the unique mental capacity to develop technologies and medicines, which has allowed the population to grow exponentially.) **What do the human population's birthrate and death rate have in common?** (Both are calculated per 1,000 people.) **How are the birthrate and death rate different?** (The birthrate measures the rate of birth, whereas the death rate measures the rate of death.)

Lead a Discussion

INCREASING AND DECREASING POPULATIONS
Have students recall what can threaten the survival of living things. Ask: **What can decrease a tree population in a forest?** (Samples: Fire, logging, root rot or other diseases) **What can foster growth in a tree population?** (Samples: Fire prevention, ample rainfall, designating the forest a wilderness area where commercial harvesting is prohibited) **Could a tree population in a forest grow to be too large?** (Yes. A population of one tree species could grow so large that it crowds out other species.)

Support the Big Q ❓ UbD

USING RESOURCES Discuss with students how an increasing population uses more and more resources, both natural resources and technological resources. Ask: **What are some natural resources that can be limited as the human population grows?** (Samples: food, fresh water, oil, clean air) **What are some technological resources that can be limited as the human population grows?** (Samples: health care, housing)

Teach With Visuals

Explore **Figure 1** with students. Ask: **What kinds of challenges does a city like Hong Kong, with such a large population, face?** (Sample: Air, land, light, and noise pollution)

What Factors Allow the Human Population to Grow?

A population needs food and other resources to survive. Health and disease can determine life or death. Over time, people have affected these conditions of human survival. 🔑 **Advances in medicine and technology have improved human health and allowed for exponential human population growth.**

Birth and Death Rates A population's birthrate is the number of babies born each year per 1,000 people. The death rate of a population is the number of people who die each year per 1,000 people. The global population grows because more people are born each year than die each year. In most areas of the world today, people also live longer than ever before in human history.

apply it!

❶ **Interpret Tables** Circle the countries in the table with decreasing populations.

❷ CHALLENGE Larger populations use more resources. Why do you think some countries are still encouraging population growth?

Sample: Countries may be worried they could lose their traditions.

Country	Birthrate (per 1,000 people)	Death Rate (per 1,000 people)
⟨Japan⟩	7.9	9.2
United States	14.0	8.2
⟨Italy⟩	8.4	10.6
Argentina	18.1	7.4
Egypt	22.1	5.1

100   Resources and Living Things

Digital Lesson: Assign the *Apply It* activity online and have students submit their work to you.

Art in Motion allows students to explore a visual representation of human population growth.

my science online.com ▷ | Population Growth Factors |

Medical Care and Technology Today human survival has increased greatly because of advances in medical care and technology. Antibiotics, vaccines, sanitation, and improved nutrition have lowered death rates and increased birthrates. New technologies have allowed people to build cities, maintain clean water supplies, and produce and distribute more food than ever anticipated. As a result, today's population size is much larger than most experts in the past had predicted.

Population Growth and Natural Resources As the human population grows, so does the demand for natural resources. If current trends continue, humans will be using resources twice as fast as Earth can replace them within this century. New technologies may allow for a larger human population than ever imagined, but Earth does not have an endless supply of resources. At some point, if it isn't already, the population size will be too large for Earth to support.

FIGURE 1 ·············
> ART IN MOTION **Crowded City**
The photo across these pages is of Hong Kong, China. More than seven million people live in this city of only about 1,100 square kilometers. That's more than 6,000 people per square kilometer!

Healthcare technology	↑	Population	↑
Death rate	↑	Population	↓
Food production and distribution	↑	Population	↑
Population	↑	Natural resources	↓
Birthrate	↑	Population	↑

✎
⟲ Identify the Main Idea
Draw arrows in the chart to show the effect of each condition on the human population or natural resources. For example, as healthcare technology improves, the population will increase.

Lab zone® Do the Quick Lab *Comparing Populations.*

▭ Assess Your Understanding
got it? ·············
○ I get it! Now I know that the human population has grown exponentially because of ___ advances in medicine and technology that have improved human health.
○ I need extra help with *See TE note.* ___
  Go to **my science** ⓢ **coach** *online for help with this subject.*

101

Elaborate ————————
Apply It!
L1 Review the concept of exponential growth before beginning the activity. Ask: **Why is the death rate for Egypt so much lower than that for the U.S. or Italy?** *(The population is so much younger in countries with high birth rates.)*

21st Century Learning
INTERPERSONAL SKILLS Have students work in small groups to identify and discuss what kinds of public policies could help slow population growth to keep pace with Earth's limited supply of resources.

⟲ **Identify the Main Idea** When students read, they encounter many ideas and concepts. Good readers try to find the most important or biggest idea. That is the main idea of the passage.

Lab Resource: Quick Lab **Lab zone**
L3 **COMPARING POPULATIONS** Students will compare populations and population densities of different countries around the world.

Evaluate ————————
Assess Your Understanding
Have students evaluate their understanding by completing the appropriate sentence.

R T I Response to Intervention
If students cannot explain exponential population growth, **then** have them review the Key Concept statement for this section.

my science ⓢ **coach** Have students go online for help in understanding factors that allow the human population to grow.

Differentiated Instruction

L1 **Medical Care and Human Survival** Review the following vocabulary to make sure students understand the text: *antibiotics, vaccines, sanitation,* and *nutrition.* Call on volunteers to read each word aloud and explain what it means. Then ask students to explain how these examples of medical care and technology make it possible for populations to grow.

L3 **Research Public Policy** Have students research the use of urban growth boundaries (UGBs) to control urban sprawl in cities such as Portland, Oregon. Students should address the pros and cons of controlling growth through public policy and to support their ideas with facts and details from their research. Have students share their findings with the class.

Lab zone **After the Inquiry Warm-Up**

Human Population Growth

Inquiry Warm-Up, *Doubling Time*
In the Inquiry Warm-Up, you investigated exponential population growth. Using what you learned from that activity, answer the questions below.

1. **PREDICT** Assume Population B is able to grow enough food for 50 people in Year 1. They are able to increase food production by 10 each year after that. In what year would Population B be unable to produce enough food to feed itself? Explain.

   _____

   _____

   _____

2. **CALCULATE** Based on your results in the data table in the Inquiry Warm-Up, about how many times faster is Population B growing than Population A?

   _____

3. **CALCULATE** Assume each person in Population A uses 3 units of water per year. What is the percent increase in water usage by Population A from Year 1 to Year 9?

   _____

4. **MAKE JUDGMENTS** Based on the results of the Inquiry Warm-Up and your prior knowledge of the limitations of natural resources, do you believe unchecked exponential population growth is ultimately beneficial or harmful to a species? Explain.

   _____

   _____

   _____

   _____

Name _____ Date _____ Class _____

Human Population Growth

How Has the Human Population Grown Over Time?

gotit? ....

○ **I get it!** Now I know that the human population _____

_____

○ **I need extra help with** _____

_____

What Factors Allow the Human Population to Grow?

gotit? ....

○ **I get it!** Now I know that the human population has grown exponentially because of

_____

_____

○ **I need extra help with** _____

_____

Key Concept Summaries

Human Population Growth

How Has the Human Population Grown Over Time?

Over time, the human population has grown exponentially. Exponential growth occurs when a population grows at an ever-increasing rate. In exponential growth, the larger a population gets, the faster it grows.

Today, the human population continues to grow, but the growth rate is decreasing. Some experts predict that the human population will stop growing—possibly even decline. Other experts strongly disagree.

What Factors Allow the Human Population to Grow?

A population needs food and other resources. Over time, people have affected these factors of human survival. **Advances in medicine and technology have improved human health and allowed for exponential human population growth.**

increased birthrates. New technologies have allowed people to maintain clean water supplies and produce and distribute more food than people ever thought possible. As a result, human population is today much larger than most experts in the past predicted.

The global population grows when more people are born each year than die each year. In most areas of the world people live longer than ever before.

As the human population grows, so does the demand for natural resources. If current trends continue, within this century humans will be using resources twice as fast as Earth can replace them. At some point, the size of the human population will be too large for Earth to support.

Advances in medical care and technology have helped increase human survival. New medicines and improved sanitation and nutrition have lowered death rates and

On a separate sheet of paper, explain why the world's population has grown so dramatically in recent years.

Name _____ Date _____ Class _____

Human Population Growth

Understanding Main Ideas
Answer the following questions in the spaces provided.

1. In one word, describe how human population has grown over time.

   _____

2. What has affected the factors for human survival?

   _____

   _____

3. Explain how birthrate, death rate, and population growth are related.

   _____

   _____

   _____

4. How is human population growth related to resource use?

   _____

   _____

Building Vocabulary
Write a definition for the term on the lines below.

5. exponential growth

   _____

   _____

Enrich

Human Population Growth

Almost one-third of the world's human population is under age 15. The table below lists the percentage of the population under age 15 in six different countries. Study the table and then use a separate sheet of paper to answer the questions.

Future Population Growth

Population Under Age 15	
Country	**Percent of Population under Age 15**
Kenya	38.0
India	33.6
France	18.0
Nicaragua	40.2
United States	21.6
Brazil	26.4

1. List the countries in order from the one with the highest percentage of population under age 15 to the one with the lowest percentage
2. Use the data in the table to make a bar graph on a sheet of graph paper. Arrange the countries in order from the highest to the lowest percentage.
3. Which country do you think will have the greatest increase in its total population in the next 20 years? Why?
4. Is the increase in the total population of the United States likely to be larger or smaller than most other countries?
5. Why is the percentage of population under age 15 important for predicting future population growth?

Name _____ Date _____ Class _____

Human Population Growth

Write the letter of the correct answer on the line at the left.

1. ___ Health and disease can determine a population's
   A life or death
   B hopes and dreams
   C happiness or discontent
   D religious beliefs or politics

2. ___ Today the human population of Earth is
   A more than 10 billion
   B more than 6.7 billion
   C less than 7 million
   D less than 9.9 million

3. ___ Experts strongly disagree over
   A how to define exponential population growth
   B the predicted world population for the year 2050
   C whether the human population will stop growing
   D how much the human population has grown in the last 500 years

4. ___ In most areas of the world today
   A people are richer than ever in human history
   B people are smarter than ever in human history
   C people weigh more than ever in human history
   D people live longer than ever in human history

If the statement is true, write _true_. If the statement is false, change the underlined word or words to make the statement true.

5. _____ Dramatic growth occurs when a population grows at an ever-increasing rate.

6. _____ Today the growth rate of the human population is decreasing.

7. _____ Advances in arts and science have improved human health and allowed for tremendous population growth.

8. _____ As the human population grows, the demand for natural resources stays the same.

9. _____ If population and the demand for natural resources continue to grow at the present rate, the human population will be too large for Earth to support.

10. _____ The United States' population grows when more people are born worldwide each year than die worldwide each year.

Human Population Growth

Answer Key

After the Inquiry Warm-Up

1. Sample: Population B will be unable to feed itself by Year 3. In Year 2, they have just enough food for their population, but by Year 3, they are short 2 units.

2. about twice (2 times) as fast

3. 321% increase

4. Accept all reasonable responses. Students may say: Harmful, because a population can quickly out grow available resources or its ability to acquire those resources.

Key Concept Summaries

Sample: The human population has grown exponentially in recent years because of advances in medicine and technology. New medicines and improved sanitation and nutrition have lowered death rates and increased birthrates. New technologies have allowed people to maintain clean water supplies and produce more food than anyone would have thought possible a long time ago.

Review and Reinforce

1. exponentially

2. people affect the factors for human survival in terms of population growth, death and birth rates, making advances in medicine and technology.

3. if the birth rate is greater than the death rate in a given period of time, then there is population growth

4. As the human population grows, people use more resources.

5. dramatic expansion that occurs when a population grows at an ever-increasing rate

Enrich

1. Nicaragua, Kenya, India, Brazil, United States, France

2. Bar graphs should show the countries in the order listed in Question 1. The bars for Nicaragua and Kenya should be more than twice the height of the bar for France.

3. Nicaragua or Kenya; these countries have the most young people who will reproduce and cause the population to grow.

4. Smaller; its population under 15 is smaller.

5. Students' answers should demonstrate understanding that the higher the percentage of population under 15, the greater the potential for population growth when those people reach their reproductive years.

Lesson Quiz

1. A
2. B
3. C
4. D
5. Exponential growth
6. true
7. medicine and technology
8. increases
9. true
10. global

Place the outside corner, the corner away from the dotted line, in the corner of your copy machine to copy onto letter-size paper.

Forests and Fisheries

 How do people use Earth's resources?

Lesson Pacing: 2–3 periods or 1–1½ blocks

🕐 **SHORT ON TIME?** To do this lesson in approximately half the time, do the Activate Prior Knowledge activity on page 102. A discussion of the key concepts on pages 103 and 106 will familiarize students with the lesson content. Have students do the Quick Labs. The rest of the lesson can be completed by students independently.

> **Preference Navigator,** in the online Planning tools, allows you to customize *Interactive Science* to your own teaching style. You can also edit lesson plans by selecting the Lesson Planner option.
>
> **Digital Teacher's Edition** allows you to access your Teacher's Edition and Resource materials online.

my science online.com

Lesson Vocabulary

- clear-cutting
- selective cutting
- sustainable yield
- fishery
- aquaculture

 Professional Development Note

Content Refresher

Deforestation and Climate Change Deforestation can have a profound effect on regional and global climates. During transpiration, a tree returns to the air about 97 percent of the water that the roots absorb from the ground. This water eventually returns to Earth through the water cycle. Deforestation can reduce rainfall in a region and increase the frequency of droughts.

Deforested tropical rain forests may also contribute to an increase of global temperatures. As felled trees are burned, they add carbon dioxide to the atmosphere, which increases the amount of heat the atmosphere retains. In addition, fewer trees absorb less carbon dioxide from the atmosphere.

LESSON OBJECTIVES

🗝 Describe how forests can be managed as renewable resources.

🗝 Describe how fisheries can be managed for a sustainable yield.

Blended Path
Active learning using Student Edition, Inquiry Path, and Digital Path

ENGAGE AND EXPLORE

To teach this lesson using a variety of resources, begin by reading **My Planet Diary** as a class. Have students share ideas about the destruction of forests. Then have students do the **Inquiry Warm-Up activity.** Students will investigate the decline of the Western Atlantic Bluefin Tuna and make a graph. Discuss the line graphs. The **After the Inquiry Warm-Up worksheet** uses prior knowledge and graphs to help students understand changes in a tuna population. Have volunteers share their answers to number 4 and discuss their conclusions based on graphs.

EXPLAIN AND ELABORATE

Teach Key Concepts by explaining the terms *clear-cutting* and *selective cutting.* **Lead a Discussion** on forest products that are familiar to students. Introduce a few products students may not know. Use the **Support the Big Q** to direct students to **Figure 2** and a discussion of logging methods. Then have students practice the inquiry skill in the **Apply It activity.**

Continue to **Teach Key Concepts** by explaining how fisheries can be managed for a sustainable yield. Ask students to describe strategies for this. Have students use **Figure 3** to describe the costs and benefits of aquaculture.

Hand out the **Key Concept Summaries** as a review of each part of the lesson. Students can also use the online **Vocab Flash Cards** to review key terms.

EVALUATE

Have students take the **Lesson Quiz.** For an alternate assessment, see the **EXAM**VIEW® Assessment Suite, Progress Monitoring Assessments, or SuccessTracker™.

ELL Support

1 Content and Language
Review the meaning of *renewable resources* with students. Ask how this term might be applied to forests or fisheries.

Lab zone Inquiry Path
Hands-on learning in the Lab zone

ENGAGE AND EXPLORE

To teach this lesson with an emphasis on inquiry, begin with the **Inquiry Warm-Up activity.** Students will make a line graph to show the decline of a tuna population. Discuss the reasons for this decline. Have students do the **After the Inquiry Warm-Up worksheet.** Talk about how graphs and percents can show this decline. Have volunteers share their answers to number 4 and discuss their interpretation of the data on the graphs.

EXPLAIN AND ELABORATE

Focus on the **Inquiry Skill** for the lesson. Point out that when you communicate, you share or transfer information. Use the **Support the Big Q** to direct students to **Figure 2** where they will label two methods of tree harvesting. Review the definition of *sustainable wood* before beginning the **Apply It activity.** Have students do the **Quick Lab** to model shelterwood cutting and then share their results.

Use **Figure 3** to help students explain costs and benefits. Do the **Quick Lab** to reinforce understanding of managing fisheries. Students can use the online **Vocab Flash Cards** to review key terms.

EVALUATE

Have students take the **Lesson Quiz.** For an alternate assessment, see the **EXAM**VIEW® Assessment Suite, Progress Monitoring Assessments, or SuccessTracker™.

Digital Path
Online learning at my science online.com

ENGAGE AND EXPLORE

To teach this lesson using digital resources, begin by having students discuss declining tree populations at **My Planet Diary** online. Have them access the Chapter Resources to find the **Unlock the Big Question activity.** There they can answer the questions and refine their responses as they continue through the lesson. You can re-assign the activity and have students submit their work so you can track their progress.

EXPLAIN AND ELABORATE

Students reading above, at, or below the lexile measure of this lesson can access basic content readings at their level at **My Reading Web.** Have students do the online **Interactive Art activity** to distinguish between two methods of harvesting. Encourage students to use the online **Vocab Flash Cards** to preview key terms. Have students do the **Quick Lab** and then ask students to share their results. Review *sustainable wood* before assigning the online **Apply It activity.** Ask volunteers to share their slogans and logos. Have students submit their work to you.

Have students do the online **Quick Lab** on managing fisheries. The **Key Concept Summaries** online allow students to read a summary and see an image associated with each part of the lesson. Online remediation is available at **My Science Coach.**

EVALUATE

Have students take the **Lesson Quiz.** For an alternate assessment, see the **EXAM**VIEW® Assessment Suite, Progress Monitoring Assessments, or SuccessTracker™.

2 Frontload the Lesson
Before teaching the lesson on forests and fisheries, some students might need an explanation of the role of local, state, and federal governments in regulating logging and fishing.

3 Comprehensible Input
Display actual products made from wood and actual products or photographs of fish products in the classroom.

4 Language Production
Pair or group students with varied language abilities to complete the **Apply It activity** collaboratively for language practice.

5 Assess Understanding
Make true or false statements using lesson content about forests and fisheries and their management. Have students indicate their agreement or disagreement by raising right hands for agreement and left for disagreement.

LESSON 3.4

Forests and Fisheries

Establish Learning Objectives

After this lesson, students will be able to:

🔑 Describe how forests can be managed as renewable resources.

🔑 Describe how fisheries can be managed for a sustainable yield.

Engage

Activate Prior Knowledge

MY PLANET DIARY Read *What Happened to All the Trees?* with the class. Tell students that in this lesson they will learn how forests can be preserved. Ask: **What new information did you learn in the Planet Diary?** *(Sampler: Every two seconds a piece of forest the size of a soccer field is destroyed.)* **What words come to mind when you look at the picture of the forest and cut trees?** *(Samples: Sad, chop, logging)*

BIG IDEAS OF SCIENCE REFERENCE LIBRARY 📖 Have students look up the following topic: Forestry.

Explore

Lab Resource: Inquiry Warm-Up

L2 **WHAT HAPPENED TO THE TUNA?** Students will make a line graph showing changes in a tuna population during a 30-year period.

LESSON

4 Forests and Fisheries

🔑 **How Can Forests Be Managed as Renewable Resources?**

🔑 **How Can Fisheries Be Managed for a Sustainable Yield?**

my planet diary

SCIENCE STATS

What happened to all the trees?

We get all kinds of things from forests, from food to oxygen to medicine to beautiful places for exploring. The world's forests are disappearing at an alarming rate. We lose a piece of forest the size of a soccer field every two seconds. In a year, that's about an area as big as the state of Illinois! Many people are trying to save the forests. Some countries have passed laws to stop farmers, miners, loggers, and ranchers from cutting down the forests. And some organizations are replanting trees.

Communicate Discuss the questions with a group of classmates. Then write your answers below.

1. Why should people care about losing trees?

   We get so many good and useful things from forests so trees should be protected.

2. How could your class raise awareness about the importance of trees in your community?

   Sample: distribute flyers, host speakers, design a Web site

▸ **PLANET DIARY** Go to **Planet Diary** to learn more about forests and fisheries.

Lab zone Do the Inquiry Warm-Up *What Happened to the Tuna?*

102 Resources and Living Things

SUPPORT ALL READERS

Lexile Measure = 950L   Lexile Word Count = 1314

Prior Exposure to Content: May be the first time students have encountered this topic

Academic Vocabulary: *communicate, summarize*

Science Vocabulary: *sustainable yield, aquaculture*

Concept Level: Generally appropriate for most students in this grade

Preteach With: My Planet Diary "All the Trees" and Figure 1 activity

Go to **My Reading Web** to access leveled readings that provide a foundation for the content.

my science online

Vocabulary
- clear-cutting • selective cutting • sustainable yield
- fishery • aquaculture

Skills
- Reading: Summarize
- Inquiry: Communicate

How Can Forests Be Managed as Renewable Resources?

Forests contain many valuable resources. Many products are made from the fruits, seeds, and other parts of forest plants. Some of these products, such as maple syrup, rubber, and nuts, come from living trees. Other products, such as lumber and wood pulp for making paper, require cutting trees down. Coniferous trees, including pine and spruce, are used for construction and for making paper. Hardwoods, such as oak, cherry, and maple, are used for furniture because of their strength and beauty. Some products made from trees are shown in **Figure 1**.

Trees and other plants produce oxygen that organisms need to survive. They also absorb carbon dioxide and many pollutants from the air. Trees help prevent flooding and control soil erosion. Their roots absorb rainwater and hold the soil together.

There are about 300 million hectares of forests in the United States. That's nearly a third of the nation's area! Many forests are located on public land. Others are owned by individuals or by private timber and paper companies. Forest industries in the United States provide jobs for more than 1.5 million people.

Because new trees can be planted to replace trees that are cut down, forests can be renewable resources. The United States Forest Service and environmental organizations work with forestry companies to conserve forest resources. They try to develop logging methods that maintain forests as renewable resources.

FIGURE 1 ·······································

Forest Products
Many common products have at least one thing in them that came from trees. The soles on the shoes below came from the sap of the rubber tree.

✏ **Identify** Besides the shoes, circle the three items that were made from tree products. Pick one of the items and explain why you think it contains tree products.

Accept all reasonable
answers. Sample: The
basketball is made of
rubber.

103

Explain

Introduce Vocabulary

Write on the board the terms *clear-cutting* and *selective cutting*. Tell students that the first word in each compound word holds a clue to what the term means. If a forest is cleared, all trees are cut down. In selective cutting, only some trees are selected for removal.

Teach Key Concepts 🗝

Remind students that forests are valuable resources. Ask: **Why are forests considered renewable resources?** *(Because new trees can be planted to replace trees that are cut down)* **What are some products that come from forests?** *(Possible answers: Nuts, lumber, rubber, maple syrup, pulp for paper)* **Why else are forests important?** *(Plants in forests produce oxygen, absorb pollutants, help prevent flooding, and control soil erosion.)*

Lead a Discussion

FOREST PRODUCTS Have students to look around the classroom and ask them to list as many items they see in the room as they can within one minute. Ask: **What are some things made from trees in this classroom?** *(Sample responses: Writing paper, cardboard, poster board, paper towels, textbooks, wood furniture, pencils, chairs)*

21st Century Learning

INTERPERSONAL SKILLS Have students read *Forestry* in the **Big Ideas of Science Reference Library.** Assignment: You are a park ranger with the National Park Service. Choose one of the parks. What are your ideas for preserving land? Share your ideas with a partner and present them in a multimedia format that includes images from your chosen park.

My Planet Diary provides an opportunity for students to explore real-world connections to managing forests.

my science online | Managing Forests

(E)(L)(L) Support

1 Content and Language
To help students understand *sustainable yield*, count off students by "1s" and "2s." Ask all 1s to stand up. This represents the existing forest. For each "1" you ask to sit down (i.e., a tree being cut down), have a "2" stand up.

2 Frontload the Lesson
Read aloud the first subhead/question: *How Can Forests Be Managed as Renewable Resources?* Ask students to

use this title to predict what they will learn about on the page.

3 Comprehensible Input
Help students identify words signaling advantages and disadvantages in the second paragraph of *Logging Methods*. Note that in informational text, advantages are often listed first; to indicate that text is switching to disadvantages or visa versa, words such as *but* and *however* are used.

Explain

Support the Big Q ? UbD

Explain to students that, if used carefully, forests can be renewable resources. Direct students' attention to **Figure 2**. Ask: **How can you describe the original forest after clear-cutting?** *(No trees are left in the area that was clear-cut.)* **How can you describe the forest after selective cutting?** *(There is a mix of trees remaining.)* **Which final stage—replanted growth or diverse growth—is more like the original forest?** *(Diverse growth)*

Teach With Visuals

L1 Tell students to look at **Figure 2**. In certain areas, clear-cutting can be used to provide habitat for grassland and prairie bird species. Ask: **Would people in areas with little forest likely choose to use the strategy of clear-cutting to provide habitat?** *(No)* **Why not?** *(The forest ecosystem is needed. Areas that are heavily forested are better candidates for clear-cutting to increase habitat diversity.)*

Logging Methods There are two major methods of logging: clear-cutting and selective cutting. **Clear-cutting** is the process of cutting down all the trees in an area at once. Cutting down only some trees in a forest and leaving a mix of tree sizes and species behind is called **selective cutting**. See **Figure 2**.

Each logging method has advantages and disadvantages. Clear-cutting is usually quicker and cheaper than selective cutting. It may also be safer for the loggers. In selective cutting, the loggers must move the heavy equipment and logs around the remaining trees in the forest. But selective cutting is usually less damaging to the forest environment than clear-cutting. When an area of forest is clear-cut, the ecosystem changes. After clear-cutting, the soil is exposed to wind and rain. Without the protection of the trees, the soil is more easily blown or washed away. Soil washed into streams may harm the fish and other organisms that live there. However, clear-cutting can provide habitats for species such as rabbits and some birds.

FIGURE 2 ·····················
▶ **INTERACTIVE ART** **Tree Harvest**
Clear-cutting and selective cutting are two methods of tree harvesting.

✎ **Relate Text and Visuals** Based on what you have read, label the original forest, the clear-cut forest, and the selectively cut forest.

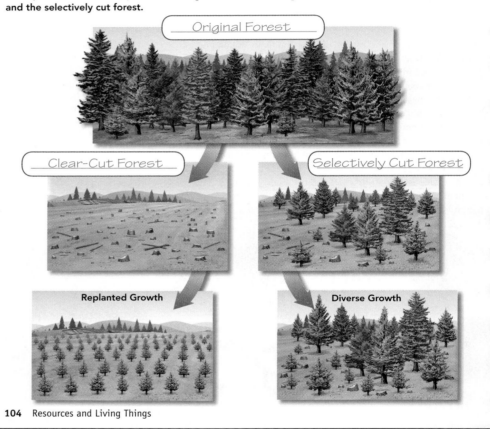

Original Forest

Clear-Cut Forest

Selectively Cut Forest

Replanted Growth

Diverse Growth

104 Resources and Living Things

Interactive Art demonstrates the effect of clear-cutting and selective cutting on a forest.

Digital Lesson: Assign the *Apply It* activity online and have students submit their work to you.

my science online.com **Managing Forests**

Sustainable Forestry Forests can be managed to provide a sustainable yield. A **sustainable yield** is an amount of a renewable resource such as trees that can be harvested regularly without reducing the future supply. Sustainable forestry works sort of like a book swap: as long as you donate a book each time you borrow one, the total supply of books does not change. Planting a tree to replace one that was cut down is like donating a book to replace a borrowed one.

In sustainable forestry, after trees are harvested, young trees are planted. Trees must be planted frequently enough to keep a constant supply. Different species grow at different rates. Forests containing faster-growing trees, such as pines, can be harvested and replanted every 20 to 30 years. On the other hand, some forests containing hardwood trees, such as hickory, oak, and cherry, may be harvested only every 40 to 100 years. One sustainable approach is to log small patches of forest. This way, different sections of forest can be harvested every year.

Certified Wood The Forest Stewardship Council is an international organization dedicated to sustainable forest management. This organization oversees certification of forests that are well managed and that provide good working conditions for their employees. Once a forest is certified, its wood may carry a "well-managed" label. This label allows businesses and individuals to select wood from forests that are managed for sustainable yields.

---

apply it!

You are an advertising writer for a company that makes products from sustainable wood.

❶ **Communicate** Write a slogan to help sell the products.

Accept all reasonable
slogans. Sample:
Sustainable chopping
is smart shopping.

❷ Design a company logo.

Accept all
reasonable designs.

Lab zone Do the Quick Lab
Shelterwood Cutting.

🔑 Assess Your Understanding

1a. Define What is a sustainable yield of a natural resource like trees?

The amount of trees that can
be harvested regularly without
reducing the future supply

b. CHALLENGE Should the government buy only certified wood for construction projects? Why?

Sample: The government
should use certified wood to
protect forests.

---

got it? ....

○ **I get it!** Now I know that forests can be managed as renewable resources by _planting_
  young trees to replace trees that were harvested.

○ I need extra help with _See TE note._

  Go to MY SCIENCE 💬 COACH *online for help with this subject.*

105

Elaborate

Apply It!

L1 Review the material under *Sustainable Forestry* and *Certified Wood* before beginning the activity.

🔺 **Communicate** Tell students that an effective advertisement makes a compelling appeal to consumers. A slogan is usually a clever, easy-to-remember phrase that makes people want to buy the product.

Lab Resource: Quick Lab

L2 **SHELTERWOOD CUTTING** Students will model shelterwood cutting.

Evaluate

Assess Your Understanding

After students answer the questions, have them evaluate their understanding by completing the appropriate sentence.

RTI Response to Intervention

1a. If students have trouble defining sustainable yield, **then** have them locate the highlighted term in the text and read its definition.

b. If students cannot make a judgment about certified wood, **then** have them review the subsection describing forest certification.

MY SCIENCE 💬 COACH Have students go online for help in understanding forest management.

Differentiated Instruction

L1 **Make Three-Dimensional Models** Insert wooden dowels of various lengths into clay to represent an original forest as shown in **Figure 2.** Have groups of students prepare four other models with clay and dowels to represent the other images in **Figure 2.** Then have groups refer to the models as they discuss the processes of clear-cutting and selective cutting.

L3 **Forest Ecosystems** Have students make diagrams showing the water cycle in a temperate forest ecosystem. Encourage students to use library resources to help them. Completed diagrams could include the terms *rainfall, snowmelt, infiltration, absorption, transpiration,* and *evaporation.* When students have completed their diagrams, have them write a paragraph explaining some of the negative effects of unsustainable forestry.

105

Explain

Teach Key Concepts 🔑

Explain to students that even though fisheries are renewable resources, they must be managed for sustainable yields—or the supply of fish will run out. Ask: **How can people manage fisheries for a sustainable yield?** *(By setting fishing limits, changing fishing methods, developing aquaculture techniques, and finding new resources)* **How can setting limits on the size of fish that can be caught help maintain fish populations?** *(Sample: Young fish will be more likely to survive and reproduce.)* **What are some fishing methods that have been outlawed?** *(Poisoning fish and exploding dynamite underwater are outlawed because they harm all the fish in the area.)* **What steps do you think scientists might take to convince the public to eat different species of ocean organisms?** *(Sample responses: Educating the public about the different species and the need to find different sources for food; persuading supermarkets to advertise and purchase different species; introducing influential food writers and chefs to different species)*

🔄 **Summarize** Explain that students' summaries should only contain the most important ideas and details about the effects of large-scale fishing.

Make Analogies

L1 OVERFISHING Write the word *overexert* on the board. Call on a volunteer to read the word and tell what it means. Explain that you can quickly overexert yourself by using up all your energy, especially after you have been ill. Ask: **How is overexertion like overfishing?** *(Sample: If you catch too many cod and create a situation of overfishing, the supply of cod runs out. If you overexert yourself after you've been ill, you have so little energy and feel so tired that you have to go back to bed.)*

How Can Fisheries Be Managed for a Sustainable Yield?

Fish are an important global food resource. An area with a large population of valuable ocean organisms is called a **fishery.**

Until recently, fisheries seemed to have unlimited resources. The waters held such huge schools of fish, and fish reproduce in incredible numbers. A single codfish can lay as many as nine million eggs in one year! But people have discovered that this resource has limits. After many years of big catches, the number of sardines off the California coast suddenly declined. The same thing happened to the huge schools of cod off the New England coast. What caused these changes?

The fish were caught faster than they could breed, so the population decreased. This situation is known as overfishing. Scientists estimate that 70 percent of the world's major fisheries have been overfished. But if fish populations recover, a sustainable yield can again be harvested. 🔑 **Managing fisheries for a sustainable yield includes strategies such as setting fishing limits, changing fishing methods, developing aquaculture techniques, and finding new resources.**

Fishing Limits Laws can ban the fishing of certain species. Laws can also limit the number or size of fish that can be caught. These laws ensure that all of the largest adult fish aren't caught and that young fish survive long enough to reproduce. If a fishery has been severely overfished, however, the government may ban fishing completely until the populations recover.

✏️ **Summarize** Explain the effect of large-scale fishing (as in the scene below) on major fish populations.

Sample: After people harvest many fish over a long period of time, the populations decrease. The fish are caught faster than they can reproduce.

Fishing Methods Today many fishing crews use nets with a larger mesh size that allow small, young fish to escape. Many other fishing practices are also regulated by laws. Some harmful fishing methods have been outlawed. These methods include poisoning fish with cyanide and stunning them by exploding dynamite under water. These techniques harm all the fish in an area rather than targeting certain fish.

Aquaculture The practice of raising fish and other water-dwelling organisms for food is called **aquaculture.** The fish may be raised in artificial ponds or bays. Salmon, catfish, and shrimp are farmed in this way in the United States.

However, aquaculture is not a perfect solution. The artificial ponds and bays often replace natural habitats such as salt marshes. Maintaining the farms costs money, and the farms can cause pollution and spread diseases into wild fish populations.

New Resources Today about 9,000 different fish species are harvested for food. More than half the animal protein eaten by people throughout the world comes from fish. One way to help feed a growing human population is to fish for new species. Scientists and chefs are working together to introduce people to deep-water species such as monkfish and tile fish, as well as easy-to-farm freshwater fish such as tilapia.

FIGURE 3 ·······················

Aquaculture
Fish like tilapia, shown below, can be farmed.

 Analyze Costs and Benefits Fill in the boxes to explain the costs and benefits of aquaculture.

Benefits of Aquaculture

Sample: Fish are available where they don't occur naturally. Fish with low wild populations can still be eaten if farmed.

Costs of Aquaculture

Sample: Farms can cause pollution and spread disease. Natural habitats are destroyed. Farms are expensive.

 Do the Quick Lab
Managing Fisheries.

🗝 **Assess Your Understanding**

got it? ·······················

○ I get it! Now I know managing fisheries for a sustainable yield includes setting fishing limits, changing methods, developing aquaculture, and finding new resources.

○ I need extra help with See TE note.

Go to MY SCIENCE COACH online for help with this subject.

107

21st Century Learning

INFORMATION LITERACY Tell students to look at **Figure 3.** Explain that farmed fish like tilapia have been introduced into the wild where they compete with native species, often successfully.
Ask: **How can introduced species harm native species?** (Sample: By pressuring native species into smaller areas as the species compete for habitat)

Elaborate

Lab Resource: Quick Lab

L2 **MANAGING FISHERIES** Students will model fishery management practices.

Evaluate

Assess Your Understanding

Have students evaluate their understanding by completing the appropriate sentence.

RTI **Response to Intervention**

If students cannot explain how to manage fisheries, **then** have them reread the key concept statement and the subsections that elaborate on it.

MY SCIENCE COACH Have students go online for help in understanding managing fisheries sustainably.

Differentiated Instruction

L1 **Aquaculture** To help students understand the concept of aquaculture, have them identify the meaning of the term *agriculture*, and then discuss the similarities between agriculture and aquaculture.

L1 **Compare and Contrast** Have students discuss how overfishing and clear-cutting are similar and different. Encourage students to use a Venn

diagram to help them compare and contrast the practices.

L3 **Research Fishery Management** Have students research to find if and how fisheries are being managed for a sustainable yield in a coastal area such as California, New England, or the Pacific Northwest. Invite students to share their findings orally.

Name ______________________ Date __________ Class __________

Lab zone After the Inquiry Warm-Up

Forests and Fisheries

Inquiry Warm-Up, *What Happened to the Tuna?*
In the Inquiry Warm-Up, you investigated the decline in the Western Atlantic Bluefin Tuna population. Using what you learned from that activity, answer the questions below.

1. **USE PRIOR KNOWLEDGE** Besides a line graph, which type of graph could be used to show changes in the tuna population?

____

2. **USE PRIOR KNOWLEDGE** Why is a line graph the best way to show the data in the table from the Inquiry Warm-Up?

____

____

____

____

3. **CALCULATE** What was the percent change in the tuna population between 1975 and 1980?

____

4. **INTERPRET DATA** Based on the data presented in the Inquiry Warm-Up, do you believe the tuna population can increase as quickly as it decreased from 1975 to 1980? Explain.

____

____

____

____

Place the outside corner, the corner away from the dotted line, in the corner of your copy machine to copy onto letter-size paper.

Assess Your Understanding

Forests and Fisheries

How Can Forests Be Managed as Renewable Resources?

1a. DEFINE What is a sustainable yield of a natural resource like trees?

_____

_____

b. CHALLENGE Should the government buy only certified wood for construction projects? Why?

_____

_____

got it? ···

○ **I get it!** Now I know that forests can be managed as sustainable resources by _____

_____

○ **I need extra help with** _____

_____

How Can Fisheries Be Managed for a Sustainable Yield?

got it? ···

○ **I get it!** Now I know managing fisheries for a sustainable yield includes _____

_____

○ **I need extra help with** _____

_____

Key Concept Summaries

Forests and Fisheries

How Can Forests Be Managed as Renewable Resources?

Many products are made from the fruit, seeds, and other parts of forest plants. Some of these products, such as maple syrup, rubber, and nuts, come from living trees. Making other products, such as lumber and wood pulp, requires cutting trees down.

The United States Forest Service and environmental organizations work with forestry companies to conserve forest resources. They try to develop logging methods that maintain forests as renewable resources. **Because new trees can be planted to replace trees that are cut down, forests can be renewable resources.**

There are two major methods of logging: clear-cutting and selective cutting. **Clear-cutting** means cutting down all the trees in a forest at once. **Selective cutting** involves cutting down only some trees in a forest and leaving a mix of tree sizes and species.

Forests can be managed to provide a **sustainable yield,** an amount of a renewable resource that can be harvested regularly without reducing the future supply. In sustainable forestry, young trees are planted after older trees are harvested. Trees must be planted frequently enough to keep a constant supply

How Can Fisheries Be Managed for a Sustainable Yield?

An area with a large population of valuable ocean organisms is called a **fishery.** Fisheries may seem like an unlimited resource; however, fish have been caught faster than they can breed. An estimated 70 percent of the world's major fisheries have been overfished.

Managing fisheries for a sustainable yield includes strategies such as setting fishing limits, changing fishing methods, developing aquaculture techniques, and finding new resources. Aquaculture is the practice of raising fish and other water-dwelling organisms for food.

On a separate sheet of paper, explain how forests and fisheries can be managed for a sustainable yield.

Review and Reinforce

Forests and Fisheries

Understanding Main Ideas
Complete the concept map below.

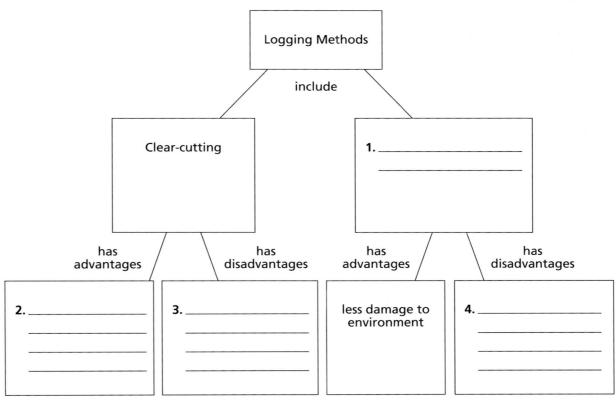

Answer the following questions on a separate sheet of paper.

5. What are three reasons that forests are valuable to people?

6. Describe how setting fishing limits can help protect fish species.

Building Vocabulary
Answer the following questions on a separate sheet of paper.

7. What is sustainable yield?

8. What is a fishery?

9. What is aquaculture?

Enrich

Forests and Fisheries

The illustration below shows four kinds of equipment used by commercial fishing crews. Read the descriptions and study the illustration. Then use a separate sheet of paper to answer the questions that follow the illustration.

Modern Fishing Equipment

Trawl bag: A net shaped like a bag that is dragged along the ocean floor. a trawl bag gathers crabs, shrimp, flounder, and other bottom dwellers.

Longline: A very long line with baited hoots at intervals. Each hook catches a single fish or other ocean organism.

Drift net: A long, straight net that drifts behind a fishing boat. Fish of all kinds get tangled in the net as they swim by.

Purse-Seine net: A huge circular net that is placed around a large number of fish. The net is they closed, capturing the fish and other animals swimming near them.

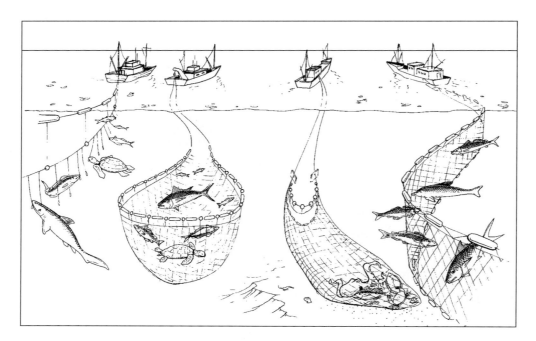

1. Identify the four kinds of fishing equipment shown above. List your answers in order from left to right.
2. Compare a trawl bag, a longline, and a purse-seine net. Do you think each device catches only the desired fish? How else do you think each device might affect ocean ecosystems?
3. Drift nets are not banned by most countries. Why do you think they have been banned?

Name _____ Date _____ Class _____

Forests and Fisheries

Fill in the blank to complete each statement.

1. An area with a large population of valuable ocean organisms is called a(n) _____.

2. Raising fish for food in an artificial pond is known as _____.

3. Because new trees can be planted to replace trees that are cut down, forests can be _____.

4. _____ involves cutting down only some trees in a forest and leaving a mix of tree sizes and species behind.

5. A(n) _____ label on wood signifies that the forest that produced the wood is managed for sustainable yields.

6. Setting _____ is an approach to managing fisheries that can involve banning or restricting fishing of certain species.

Write the letter of the correct answer on the line at the left.

7. ___ Fishing methods that have been outlawed, to manage resources for a sustainable yield, include
   A using nets with a large mesh size
   B poisoning fish with cyanide
   C maintaining aquaculture bays
   D fishing off the California and New England coasts

8. ___ Erosion is one disadvantage of
   A selective cutting
   B sustainable yield
   C certified wood
   D clear-cutting

9. ___ Trees help other organisms by producing oxygen and absorbing
   A carbon dioxide
   B carbon monoxide
   C hydrochloric acid
   D hydrogen peroxide

10. ___ The proportion of the United States' land area made up of forests is about
    A one fourth
    B one half
    C one third
    D two thirds

Forests and Fisheries

Answer Key

After the Inquiry Warm-Up

1. Sample: a bar graph

2. Sample: A line graph best shows changes in a variable over time, whereas a bar graph is best for comparing and contrasting multiple variables, sometimes over time.

3. 82% decrease

4. Accept all reasonable responses. Students may say: No, the data seems to show that the tuna population is slow to recover after drastic decreases.

Key Concept Summaries

Sample: Young trees can be planted in a forest after older trees are harvested to provide a sustainable yield. Replanting can be designed to maintain the variety of tree species in a forest. Fisheries can be managed for a sustainable yield by adopting strategies such as setting fishing limits, changing fishing methods, developing aquaculture techniques, and finding new resources.

Review and Reinforce

1. selective cutting

2. quicker and cheaper (than selective cutting)

3. destroys habitats; washes away soil

4. more difficult (for loggers to move equipment and logs around the remaining trees) and more expensive

5. Sample: Trees produce oxygen and absorb carbon dioxide and many air pollutants; have roots that hold soil and absorb rainwater; and are the source of many products.

6. Sample: Laws that limit the number or size of fish that can be caught can ensure that young fish live long enough to reproduce and that all of the adult fish in a species aren't caught.

7. an amount of renewable resource that can be harvested regularly without reducing the future supply

8. an area with a large population of valuable ocean organisms

9. the practice of raising fish and other water-dwelling organisms for food

Enrich

1. long line, purse-seine, trawl bag, drift net

2. A trawl bag can catch other organisms besides bottom-feeding fish and shrimp; pulling the bag across the ocean floor can damage habitats there. Both a longline and a purse-seine net can also catch organisms other than the desired fish, but they do not damage habitats.

3. Sample: Drift nets have been banned because these huge nets catch large numbers of different organisms indiscriminately.

Lesson Quiz

1. fishery
2. aquaculture
3. renewable resources
4. Selective cutting
5. "well-managed"
6. fishing limits
7. B
8. D
9. A
10. C

Place the outside corner, the corner away from the dotted line, in the corner of your copy machine to copy onto letter-size paper.

Biodiversity

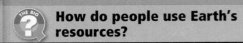

How do people use Earth's resources?

Lesson Pacing: 1–2 periods or $\frac{1}{2}$–1 block

🕐 **SHORT ON TIME?** To do this lesson in approximately half the time, do the Activate Prior Knowledge activity on page 108. A discussion of the key concepts on pages 109, 111, and 114 will familiarize students with the lesson content. Use the Explore the Big Q to help students understand how different land uses affect biodiversity. Have students do the Quick Labs and the Virtual Lab online. The rest of the lesson can be completed by students independently.

Preference Navigator, in the online Planning tools, allows you to customize *Interactive Science* to your own teaching style. You can also edit lesson plans by selecting the Lesson Planner option.

Digital Teacher's Edition allows you to access your Teacher's Edition and Resource materials online.

my science online.com

Lesson Vocabulary

- biodiversity
- keystone species
- gene
- extinction
- endangered species
- threatened species
- habitat destruction
- habitat fragmentation
- poaching
- captive breeding

Content Refresher

Professional Development Note

Pollution by DDT Pesticides such as DDT can threaten biodiversity by endangering animal species. At one time, DDT was applied for crop protection and insect control. DDT killed vast numbers of insects quickly and offered protection for months. But it also created problems. DDT passed through food chains, with increasing concentrations at each level, a mechanism called biological magnification. One study found DDT concentrations increased more than 400 times from producer to top carnivore in the local food chain. Scientists also learned humans were accumulating it. DDT was banned from general use in the U.S. in the late 1970s.

LESSON OBJECTIVES

- Explain the value of biodiversity.
- Identify the factors that affect biodiversity.
- Identify ways that human activity threatens and protects biodiversity.

Blended Path
Active learning using Student Edition, Inquiry Path, and Digital Path

ENGAGE AND EXPLORE

Teach this lesson using a variety of resources. Begin by reading **My Planet Diary** as a class. Have students share ideas about how they could protect and encourage wildlife. Then have students do the **Inquiry Warm-Up activity.** Students will investigate the biodiversity of different ecosystems. Discuss the differences in relation to the ecosystems temperatures. The **After the Inquiry Warm-Up worksheet** compares diversities in different ecosystems and asks students to make inferences. Have volunteers share their answers to number 4. If there are two different points of view, ask students to defend each point of view.

EXPLAIN AND ELABORATE

Teach Key Concepts by explaining the terms economic value and ecological value. Use **Figure 1** to discuss the wide diversity of insect species. **Lead a Discussion** about local biodiversity.

Continue to **Teach Key Concepts** by describing how climate area and diversity of niches affect the biodiversity of an ecosystem. Use **Figure 3** to estimate areas of circles, rectangles, and irregular figures. **Lead a Discussion** to remind students of what climate is and how it affects an ecosystem. Before beginning the **Apply It activity,** discuss how crops that lack a diverse gene pool may respond to changes.

Teach Key Concepts by asking students how they think people affect biodiversity both negatively and positively. Use the **Explore the Big Q** to have students consider the benefits and costs of different human choices. Use the **Answer the Big Q** to have students give reasons for the use of Earth's resources.

Hand out the **Key Concept Summaries** as a review of each part of the lesson. Students can also use the online **Vocab Flash Cards** to review key terms.

EVALUATE

Have students take the **Lesson Quiz.** For an alternate assessment, see the **EXAM**VIEW® Assessment Suite, Progress Monitoring Assessments, or SuccessTracker™.

ELL Support

1 Content and Language

Have students make a vocabulary notebook for the vocabulary words in this lesson. Have students define the terms in their own words.

Lab zone Inquiry Path
Hands-on learning in the Lab zone

ENGAGE AND EXPLORE

To teach this lesson with an emphasis on inquiry, begin with the **Inquiry Warm-Up activity.** Students will investigate various ecosystems and their biodiversity. Discuss with students what might lead to greater diversity in an ecosystem. Have students do the **After the Inquiry Warm-Up worksheet.** Talk about number 4. You might want students to list human activities beneficial and harmful to an ecosystem.

EXPLAIN AND ELABORATE

Focus on the **Inquiry Skill** for the lesson. Point out that when you infer, you use prior knowledge to make an inference. What inference could be made from the **Inquiry Warm-Up activity?** (Wider variety of tree species can support a greater variety of organisms that depend of the trees for survival) Have students do the **Quick Lab** to model keystone species using building blocks and then share their results.

Use **Build Inquiry** to help students identify factors that contribute to diversity. Review how lack of diversity may contribute to a plant's response to change before beginning the **Apply It activity.** Ask volunteers to give another example similar to Ireland's potato famine. Do the **Quick Lab** to reinforce understanding of the concept of gene pool.

Use the **Explore the Big Q** to encourage students to investigate benefits and costs of different uses of land. Use the **Answer the Big Q** to help students understand that humans use resources to meet their needs and that these needs may vary. Have students do the **Quick Lab** so they can identify ways that humans affect biodiversity positively and negatively. Students can use the online **Vocab Flash Cards** to review key terms.

EVALUATE

Have students take the **Lesson Quiz.** For an alternate assessment, see the **EXAM**VIEW® Assessment Suite, Progress Monitoring Assessments, or SuccessTracker™.

Digital Path
Online learning at my science online.com

ENGAGE AND EXPLORE

Teach this lesson using digital resources, begin by having students learn more about diversity at **My Planet Diary** online. Have them access the Chapter Resources to find the **Unlock the Big Question activity.** There they can answer the questions and refine their responses as they continue through the lesson. You can re-assign the activity and have students submit their work so you can track their progress.

EXPLAIN AND ELABORATE

Students reading above, at, or below the lexile measure of this lesson can access basic content readings at their level at **My Reading Web.**

Have students use the online **Vocab Flash Cards** to preview key terms. Have students do the first **Quick Lab.** Ask students to share their results modeling keystone species.

Review the effects of a lack of diversity in gene pools before assigning the online **Apply It activity.** Ask volunteers to share their ideas for preventing famine. Have students submit their work to you. Have students do the **Quick Lab** to identify gene pools.

Use the **Virtual Lab** to **Explore the Big Q** to have students learn how populations in an environment level out to support diversity. Use the **Answer the Big Q** to help students understand why humans use resources. Have students do the **Quick Lab** to identify how humans can affect diversity. The **Key Concept Summaries** online allow students to read a summary and see an image associated with each part of the lesson. Online remediation is available at **My Science Coach.**

EVALUATE

Have students take the **Lesson Quiz.** For an alternate assessment, see the **EXAM**VIEW® Assessment Suite, Progress Monitoring Assessments, or SuccessTracker™.

2 Frontload the Lesson
Preview the lesson visuals, labels, and captions. Ask students what they know about *endangered* and *threatened species.* Explain the specific meanings these words have in science.

3 Comprehensible Input
Have students study the visuals and their captions on pages 109–111 and 113–117 to support the key concepts of the lesson.

4 Language Production
Pair or group students with varied language abilities to complete **Virtual Lab** on pages 116–117 collaboratively for language practice. Have each student copy the completed written lab for personal reference.

5 Assess Understanding
Divide the class into small groups. Have each student identify a key concept from the lesson to discuss in his or her group. After the discussions, have students talk about the key concepts as a group.

LESSON 3.5

Biodiversity

Establish Learning Objectives

After this lesson, students will be able to:

🔑 Explain the value of biodiversity.

🔑 Identify the factors that affect biodiversity.

🔑 Identify ways that human activity threatens and protects biodiversity.

Engage

Activate Prior Knowledge

MY PLANET DIARY Read *Max's Blog* with the class. Tell students that all the species in an ecosystem are connected to one another. Ask: **How are the brown bat, tree, and mosquito connected?** *(Sample: The tree helps provide habitat for the bat; the bat and mosquito are predator and prey)*

BIG IDEAS OF SCIENCE REFERENCE LIBRARY 📖 Have students look up the following topics: Biodiversity, Frozen Zoo, Insects.

Explore

Lab Resource: Inquiry Warm-Up

L1 HOW MUCH VARIETY IS THERE? Students will compare the variety of tree species in a tropical rain forest and deciduous forest.

LESSON

5 Biodiversity

🔑 What Is Biodiversity's Value?

🔑 What Factors Affect Biodiversity?

🔑 How Do Humans Affect Biodiversity?

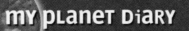

BLOG

Posted by: Max

Location: Hagerstown, Maryland

I went to summer camp to learn about wildlife and how to protect it. One of the activities that I liked the most was making "bat boxes." These are wooden homes for brown bats, which often need places to nest. Making these houses is important, because without brown bats, there would be too many mosquitoes. I hope the bats like their new homes as much as I loved making them.

Communicate Discuss the question with a group of classmates. Then write your answers below.

How do you think helping the bats in an area helps other species nearby?

Sample: If there were not enough bats to eat bugs, there would be too many bugs. Too many bugs could also affect other species. Species that eat bats would also be in trouble.

▶ PLANET DIARY Go to **Planet Diary** to learn more about biodiversity.

 Do the Inquiry Warm-Up *How Much Variety Is There?*

What Is Biodiversity's Value?

No one knows exactly how many species live on Earth. As you can see in **Figure 1**, scientists have identified more than 1.6 million species so far. The number of different species in an area is called the area's **biodiversity.** It is difficult to estimate the total biodiversity on Earth because many areas have not been thoroughly studied.

108 Resources and Living Things

SUPPORT ALL READERS

Lexile Measure = 950L   Lexile Word Count = 1698

Prior Exposure to Content: Many students may have misconceptions on this topic

Academic Vocabulary: *compare, contrast, infer*

Science Vocabulary: *biodiversity, keystone species, extinction*

Concept Level: Generally appropriate for most students in this grade

Preteach With: My Planet Diary and Figure 1 activity

Go to **My Reading Web** to access leveled readings that provide a foundation for the content.

my science online.com

Vocabulary
- biodiversity • keystone species • gene • extinction
- endangered species • threatened species
- habitat destruction • habitat fragmentation
- poaching • captive breeding

Skills
- Reading: Compare and Contrast
- Inquiry: Infer

There are many reasons why preserving biodiversity is important. One reason to preserve biodiversity is that wild organisms and ecosystems are a source of beauty and recreation. 🔑 **In addition, biodiversity has both economic value and ecological value within an ecosystem.**

Economic Value Many plants, animals, and other organisms are economically valuable for humans. These organisms provide people with food and supply raw materials for clothing, medicine, and other products. No one knows how many other useful species have not yet been identified. Ecosystems are economically valuable, too. Many companies now run wildlife tours to rain forests, savannas, mountains, and other places. This ecosystem tourism, or ecotourism, is an important source of jobs and money for such nations as Brazil, Costa Rica, and Kenya.

Ecological Value All the species in an ecosystem are connected to one another. Species may depend on each other for food and shelter. A change that affects one species can affect all the others.

Some species play a particularly important role in their ecosystems. A **keystone species** is a species that influences the survival of many other species in an ecosystem. Sea otters, as shown in **Figure 2,** are one example of a keystone species.

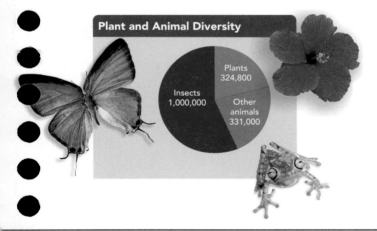

Plant and Animal Diversity

Plants 324,800

Insects 1,000,000

Other animals 331,000

FIGURE 1 ·····························

Species Diversity

There are many more species of insects than plant or other animal species on Earth!

✎ **Calculate** What percentage of species shown on the pie graph do insects represent? Round your answer to the nearest tenth.

_60.4%_

109

Explain

Introduce Vocabulary

Point out the term *poaching.* Students may already know this word as a way to cook eggs or snowboarding in a ski area where snowboarding is prohibited. Explain that in environmental science, *poaching* means illegally killing wildlife or removing wildlife from their habitats.

Teach Key Concepts 🔑

Explain to students that biodiversity can make the world more beautiful and provide opportunities to make money. Have students describe the different organisms in some of their favorite areas.

Ask: **How can entire ecosystems, such as rain forests and mountain ranges, be used to generate sources of money?** *(They can be used for ecotourism, which creates jobs and brings in money from people who visit the sites.)* **What might happen if the biodiversity of some of these ecosystems is disrupted?** *(Other species might die out; the area might not be as attractive to tourists)* **How might this affect the economy of the area?** *(Fewer people might visit the sites, resulting in loss of jobs and revenue.)*

Make Analogies

L1 **KEYSTONE SPECIES** Tell students that the term *keystone species* comes from the way a stone arch is built. Ask students if they have ever seen an arch where the stone at the center of the arch was larger than other stones. That is the keystone. If the keystone is removed, the arch will fall down. Ask: **What is a keystone species?** *(A species that influences the survival of many other species in an ecosystem)* **What would happen if the keystone species is removed from an ecosystem?** *(The ecosystem would be greatly changed.)*

Teach With Visuals

Point out to students that **Figure 1** shows known species. The number of species for bacteria, archaea, protists, and fungi are not included because their numbers are too uncertain. In addition, some organisms have not been classified or even discovered yet. Ask: **Do you think the number of species shown in Figure 1 are accurate?** *(No, new species may have been recently discovered or have yet to be classified.)*

My Planet Diary provides an opportunity for students to explore real-world connections to biodiversity.

my science online | Value of Biodiversity

ⒺⓁⓁ Support

1 Content and Language
Explain that the graph in **Figure 1** indicates the number of *species* that exist, as opposed to species *populations.*

2 Frontload the Lesson
Ask students to read aloud the red subheads, *Damaging Biodiversity* and *Protecting Biodiversity.* Ask students to predict which section will discuss the positive effects humans have on biodiversity, and which will discuss negative effects.

3 Comprehensible Input
Read aloud the captions in **Figure 2,** and then draw a cause and effect graphic organizer on the board. Reread the comic, asking students to identify the cause (sea otter population decreases) and effect (sea urchin population explodes).

Explain

Lead a Discussion

BIODIVERSITY Have students name organisms that thrive in the area where they live. Encourage students to consider a wide variety of organism types, including insects, worms, mosses, algae, plants, and bacteria, as well as mammals, birds, fish, reptiles, and amphibians. Ask: **Would you say that there is a great deal of diversity among the species living here?** *(Sample: Yes, especially if we consider plants, too.)*

Elaborate

Lab Resource: Quick Lab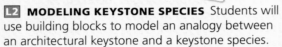

L2 MODELING KEYSTONE SPECIES Students will use building blocks to model an analogy between an architectural keystone and a keystone species.

Evaluate

Assess Your Understanding

Have students evaluate their understanding by completing the appropriate sentence.

RTI Response to Intervention

If students cannot explain the importance of biodiversity, **then** have them locate and reread the boldface Key Concept statement and the sentences that precede it.

MY SCIENCE ● **COACH** Have students go online for help in understanding the importance of biodiversity.

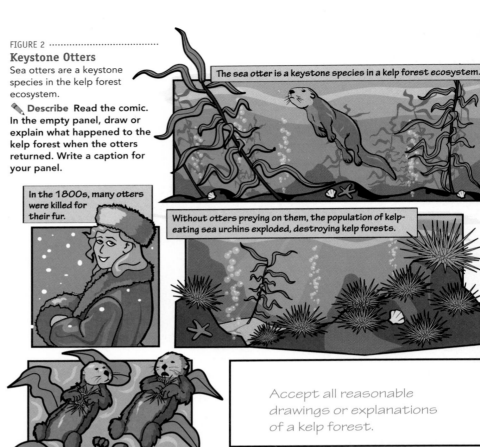

FIGURE 2
Keystone Otters
Sea otters are a keystone species in the kelp forest ecosystem.

✎ **Describe** Read the comic. In the empty panel, draw or explain what happened to the kelp forest when the otters returned. Write a caption for your panel.

The sea otter is a keystone species in a kelp forest ecosystem.

In the 1800s, many otters were killed for their fur.

Without otters preying on them, the population of kelp-eating sea urchins exploded, destroying kelp forests.

Accept all reasonable drawings or explanations of a kelp forest.

The sea otters reduced the urchin population. The kelp forest recovered.

Under new laws that banned the hunting of sea otters, the sea otter population grew again.

 Do the Quick Lab
Modeling Keystone Species.

⚷ **Assess Your Understanding**

got it? ....

O **I get it!** Now I know that biodiversity has *economic and ecological value within an ecosystem.*

O **I need extra help with** *See TE note.*

Go to **MY SCIENCE** ● **COACH** online for help with this subject.

What Factors Affect Biodiversity?

Biodiversity varies from place to place on Earth. **Factors that affect biodiversity in an ecosystem include climate, area, niche diversity, genetic diversity, and extinction.**

Climate The tropical rain forests of Latin America, southeast Asia, and central Africa are the most diverse ecosystems in the world. The reason for the great biodiversity in the tropics is not fully understood. Many scientists hypothesize that it has to do with climate. For example, tropical rain forests have fairly constant temperatures and large amounts of rainfall throughout the year. Many plants grow year-round. This continuous growing season means that food is always available for other organisms.

Area See **Figure 3.** Within an ecosystem, a large area will usually contain more species than a small area. For example, you would usually find more species in a 100-square-meter area than in a 10-square-meter area.

did you know?

Rain forests cover only about seven percent of the Earth's land surface. But they contain more than half of the world's species, including the chimpanzee!

FIGURE 3 ·······························
Park Size
A park manager has received three park plans. The dark green area represents the park.

✏️ Complete each task.

1. **Identify** Circle the plan the manager should choose to support the most biodiversity.

2. **Calculate** Suppose that 15 square meters of the park could support seven species of large mammals. About how many species could the park you circled support?

933 species

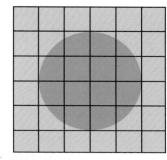

10 m
10 m

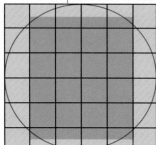

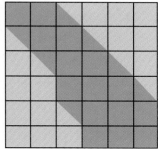

111

Explain ———————

Teach Key Concepts 🔑

Explain that five main factors—climate, area, niche, genetic diversity, and extinction—affect the level of biodiversity in an ecosystem. Ask: **What kind of climate fosters biodiversity in an ecosystem?** *(A warm sunny climate with ample precipitation)* **Which probably has greater biodiversity, a 100-square-meter area of desert or a 10-square-meter area of desert?** *(A 100-square-meter area)* **Why?** *(The larger area of an ecosystem usually contains more species.)* **Why does a tropical rain forest have such a diverse ecosystem?** *(A tropical rain forest has a climate that allows many species to survive and supports many different niches.)*

Lead a Discussion

CLIMATE Remind students that climate is the typical weather pattern—precipitation and temperature—of an area over a long period of time. Ask: **Which area is more likely to have greater biodiversity, a tropical rain forest or an area closer to Earth's poles?** *(A rain forest)* **Why?** *(Plants in a rain forest can grow year-round, making food available all year to other organisms.)* **What might happen to the biodiversity of an area if its climate becomes colder?** *(Its biodiversity might decrease.)*

Teach With Visuals

Tell students to look at **Figure 3.** After students have examined the diagram, point out that it shows how the land area of a forest affects biodiversity. Explain that the diagram does not take into account the vegetation in the park. Ask: **How does a forest with trees of varying heights affect biodiversity?** *(Sample: A forest with trees of varying heights can support more bird species than a forest with trees of mostly the same height. Raptors can nest in the high trees. Birds that eat insects can forage at lower levels.)*

Differentiated Instruction

L3 Research Keystone Species Have students do research to find a keystone species in an area near their home. You may wish to have students search on the Internet. Remind students to follow prescribed guidelines for internet use. If students have difficulty searching, suggest that they use key words such as "keystone species California forest." Encourage students to find an image of the keystone species to share with the class.

L1 Apply Vocabulary Review the meanings of the terms *area* (space covered), *climate* (the typical weather pattern in an area over a long period), and *niche* (an organism's unique role in an ecosystem). Point out the red heads that contain each term. Have students work in pairs to read aloud and identify the main idea under each heading.

Explain

Lead a Discussion

DIVERSITY AND GENES Point out that members of the same species can vary; for example, dogs of the same breed can vary in color and size. Tell students that genes determine some of an organism's characteristics. Ask: **What is the gene pool of a species?** *(All the shared and differing genes among individuals in a species)*

21st Century Learning

INFORMATION LITERACY The greatest genetic diversity exists at the single-cell level. Archaea, which are similar to bacteria, possess genes in a circular form but lack a nucleus or organelles. They use sugar, hydrogen gas, and sunlight, among others, as sources of energy. Archaea can be found in harsh environments such as hot springs and salt lakes as well as oceans and marshlands. They play an important role in the carbon and nitrogen cycles. Some archaea are found in humans and aid in food digestion. Have students do research to get more information about archaea.

Teach With Visuals

Look at **Figure 4.** Ask: **Which of the animals pictured are extinct?** *(None, all are endangered.)* **How do endangered species differ from threatened species?** *(Endangered species are in danger of becoming extinct. Threatened species could become endangered in the near future.)* **Where are endangered species found?** *(On every continent and in every ocean)*

Address Misconceptions

L1 NEWLY EXTINCT SPECIES Some people believe that all extinct animals lived long ago and became extinct under mysterious circumstances. In fact, in the past few centuries, the rate of extinction of species has increased dramatically. Ask: **What has caused the extinction of some species in relatively recent times?** *(Sample: Human actions like hunting and habitat destruction)*

Elaborate

Apply It!

L1 Review information about genetic diversity before beginning the activity. Point out that any time a large area is used to grow a single crop, the risk of loss due to disease is greater than if a variety of crops are grown.

Niche Diversity Coral reefs are the second most diverse ecosystems in the world. Found only in shallow, warm waters, coral reefs are often called the rain forests of the sea. A coral reef supports many different niches. Recall that a niche is the role of an organism in its habitat, or how it makes its living. A coral reef enables a greater number of species to live in it than a more uniform habitat, such as a flat sandbar, does.

Genetic Diversity Diversity is very important within a species. The greatest genetic diversity exists among species of unicellular organisms. Organisms in a healthy population have diverse traits such as color and size. **Genes** are located within cells and carry the hereditary information that determines an organism's traits. Organisms inherit genes from their parents.

The organisms in one species share many genes. But each organism also has some genes that differ from those of other individuals. Both the shared genes and the genes that differ among individuals make up the total gene pool of that species. Species that lack a diverse gene pool are less able to adapt to and survive changes in the environment.

apply it!

New potato plants are created from pieces of the parent plant. So a potato crop has the same genetic makeup as the parent plant. In 1845, Ireland was struck by a potato famine. A rot-causing fungus destroyed potato crops, which were an important part of the Irish diet. Many people died of starvation, and many more left the country to find food.

❶ Apply Concepts How did a potato crop without a variety of different genes lead to the Irish potato famine of 1845?

Because the potato crop did not have a large variety of different genes, a fungus was able to destroy the whole crop.

❷ CHALLENGE What could farmers do to prevent another potato famine?

Sample: Farmers could increase the genetic diversity of their crops by planting different types of potatoes.

Digital Lesson: Assign the *Apply It* activity online and have students submit their work to you.

my science online.com ▶ **Factors Affecting Biodiversity**

Extinction of Species The disappearance of all members of a species from Earth is called **extinction.** Extinction is a natural process that occurs when organisms do not adapt to changes in their environment. In the last few centuries, the number of species becoming extinct has increased dramatically. Once a population drops below a certain level, the species may not recover. People have directly caused the extinction of many species through habitat destruction, hunting, or other actions.

Species in danger of becoming extinct in the near future are called **endangered species.** Species that could become endangered in the near future are called **threatened species.** Endangered and threatened species are found on every continent and in every ocean.

Green sea turtle ▲

FIGURE 4 ·····················
Endangered Species
Large animals, like the green sea turtle, are the most publicized endangered species. Did you know insects and plants can also be endangered? ✏ **Infer** Why do you think some endangered species get more attention than others?

Sample: People know more about them due to media exposure. People may not know that insects and plants can be endangered.

Blackburn's ▲
sphinx moth

Hawaiian alula ▲

Lab Do the Quick Lab
zone Grocery Gene Pool.

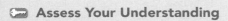

⚷ Assess Your Understanding

1a. Review A (smaller/larger) area will contain more species than a (smaller/larger) area.

b. Explain How is biodiversity related to niches?
The more niches, the greater the biodiversity.

c. ⟳ Compare and Contrast What is the difference between an endangered species and a threatened species?
A threatened species is not yet endangered but could be in the near future.

got it? ··

○ I get it! Now I know that the factors that affect biodiversity include *climate, area, niche diversity, genetic diversity and extinction.*

○ I need extra help with *See TE note.*

Go to **MY SCIENCE ⓢ COACH** *online for help with this subject.*

113

Differentiated Instruction

L3 **Research Extinct Species** Provide students with a list of species that have become extinct within the past 300 years. Examples include the quagga, dodo, moa, Tasmanian wolf (thylacine), Santa Barbara song sparrow, great auk, Hawaii oo, and passenger pigeon. Invite pairs of students to research one of those species. Suggest that students find a description of the species and its habitat and the factors that researchers believe caused the extinction.

L1 **Endangered Species** Help students understand the difference between endangered and threatened species. Ask students what it means to be "in danger." Ask students what they do when they are threatened. Help students relate their answers to the meaning of the terms.

Build Inquiry **Lab**

L2 **COMPARE BIODIVERSITY**

Materials photographs of ecosystems

Time 15 minutes

Display pictures of different types of ecosystems. Have students analyze the pictures to determine the number and types of organisms shown.

Ask: **What are the abiotic, or nonliving, factors in this ecosystem?** *(Sample: Air, light, water, temperature, soil)* **Which ecosystems have the greatest biodiversity?** *(Sample: The rain forest and coral reef)* **What factors most likely contribute to the diversity?** *(Climate, area, and diversity of niches)*

Lab Resource: Quick Lab **Lab**

L1 **GROCERY GENE POOL** Students will infer whether a fruit or vegetable has a diverse gene pool, based on the variety of the fruit or vegetable available for sale.

△ **Infer** Remind students that they should use prior knowledge to help them make an inference about the attention different endangered species receive.

Evaluate ──────────

Assess Your Understanding

After students answer the questions, have them evaluate their understanding by completing the appropriate sentence.

R T I Response to Intervention

1a, b. If students have trouble explaining factors that affect biodiversity, **then** have them review the material under *Area* and *Niche Diversity.*

c. If students cannot contrast endangered species and threatened species, **then** have them review the two boldfaced terms and definitions.

MY SCIENCE ⓢ COACH Have students go online for help in understanding factors that affect biodiversity.

Explain

Teach Key Concepts 🔑

Explain to students that humans can negatively or positively affect biodiversity. Ask: **What are four ways in which humans can negatively affect biodiversity?** *(Through habitat destruction, poaching, pollution, and introducing exotic species)* **How does habitat fragmentation contribute to extinction?** *(Sample: Clearing forests can expose trees to wind damage; animals may not be able to find enough resources in a smaller area.)* **What is the illegal removal of wildlife called?** *(Poaching)* **How can pollution contribute to species extinction?** *(Pollution can weaken organisms, kill them, or cause birth defects.)* **What are four positive ways in which humans can affect biodiversity?** *(Though captive breeding, laws and treaties, and habitat preservation)*

Make Analogies

L1 HABITAT DESTRUCTION To help students understand the concept of habitat destruction, compare an animal's habitat to a human's town or city. Ask: **What resources that you need to survive are provided, or can be purchased, in your town?** *(A place to live, food, water, clothing)* **Suppose you are out of town and your town is destroyed by a natural disaster, such as a hurricane, flood, earthquake, or volcanic eruption. Compare and contrast how this would affect you to how clearing a forest would affect a bear that lives there.** *(Like the bear after the forest is cleared, if my town were destroyed in a natural disaster, I would have no home—nowhere to sleep and no way to get the things I need to survive, such as food and water. Unlike the bear, I could move fairly easily to another place that would meet my basic needs.)*

How Do Humans Affect Biodiversity?

Humans interact with their surroundings every day. The many choices people make impact the environment and affect species. 🔑 **Biodiversity can be negatively or positively affected by the actions of humans.**

Damaging Biodiversity A natural event, such as a hurricane, can damage an ecosystem, wiping out populations or even entire species. Human activities can also threaten biodiversity and cause extinction. These activities include habitat destruction, poaching, pollution, and the introduction of exotic species.

FIGURE 5

Habitat Fragmentation

Breaking habitats into pieces can have negative effects on the species that live there.

✏️ **Interpret Diagrams** In the first diagram below, a road divides a habitat in two. On the second diagram, redraw the road so it divides the habitat's resources equally.

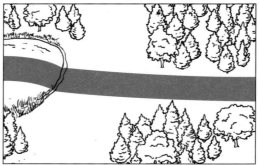

Habitat Destruction The major cause of extinction is **habitat destruction,** the loss of a natural habitat. Clearing forests or filling in wetlands changes those ecosystems. Breaking larger habitats into smaller, isolated pieces, or fragments, is called **habitat fragmentation.** See **Figure 5.** Some species may not survive such changes to their habitats.

Poaching The illegal killing or removal of wildlife from their habitats is called **poaching.** Some endangered species are valuable to poachers. Animals can be sold as pets or used to make jewelry, coats, belts, or shoes. Plants can be sold as houseplants or used to make medicines.

Pollution Some species are endangered because of pollution. Pollution may reach animals through the water they drink, the air they breathe, or the food they eat. Pollutants may kill or weaken organisms or cause birth defects.

Exotic Species Introducing exotic species into an ecosystem can threaten biodiversity. Exotic species can outcompete and damage native species. The gypsy moth was introduced into the United States in 1869 to increase silk production. Gypsy moth larvae have eaten the leaves off of millions of acres of trees in the northeastern United States.

114 Resources and Living Things

Protecting Biodiversity Some people who preserve biodiversity focus on protecting individual endangered species. Others try to protect entire ecosystems. Three methods of protecting biodiversity are captive breeding, laws and treaties, and habitat preservation.

Captive Breeding **Captive breeding** is the mating of animals in zoos or on wildlife preserves. Scientists care for the young, and then release them into the wild. Much of the sandhill crane habitat in the United States has been destroyed. To help the population, some cranes have been taken into captivity. The young are raised and trained by volunteers to learn the correct behaviors, such as knowing how and where to migrate. They are then released into the wild.

✏️

⊙ **Compare and Contrast**
The photos on top show young sandhill cranes being raised by their parents. The photos on the bottom show humans copying this process to increase the crane population. What is a possible disadvantage of the human approach?

Sample: The cranes could become used to people and endanger themselves by approaching people.

115

21st Century Learning

CRITICAL THINKING Have students look at the images of captive breeding. Ask: **How do you think scientists learned how to raise young cranes?** *(By observing cranes or other wading birds)* **What interactions do you think occurred over time between scientists and cranes?** *(Sample: You could say that by "allowing" scientists to observe them, the cranes helped humans learn, and the humans used that knowledge to help the cranes and the ecosystem.)*

⊙ **Compare and Contrast** Explain to students they should contrast the two processes to determine possible disadvantages of the human approach.

Teach With Visuals

Explain that the garment worn by the workers has a beak-like "glove" that resembles the head of a bird. The garment masks the body of the worker, allowing the worker to mimic an adult bird training the young birds.

Lead a Discussion

WILDLIFE PROTECTION CAREERS Discuss with students whether they think they might like to work as a scientist helping to protect biodiversity. Ask: **What kinds of scientists might be involved in protecting biodiversity?** *(Sample: Biologists, botanists)* **What kinds of places might a scientist work where he or she could help protect biodiversity?** *(Sample: In a zoo, in a wildlife rehabilitation facility, with a wildlife protection agency such as the World Wildlife Fund)* Have students write a job advertisement for a company that wants to hire a scientist to help protect biodiversity.

Differentiated Instruction

L1 Compare and Contrast Remind students that when you compare, you find similarities. When you contrast, you find differences. Students should think about how humans might affect the young cranes differently than actual parent cranes. Have students consider how a crane becoming used to people might negatively affect the animal in the future. Encourage students to answer the question using a graphic organizer, such as a Venn diagram.

L3 Species Competition Encourage students to research introduced species that compete with native species in the United States. Have students report on where competition is prevalent and describe the consequences to the native species. Example species include purple loosestrife, kudzu, leafy spurge, flathead catfish, sea lamprey, zebra mussel, gypsy moth, fire ant, brown tree snake, and starling.

Explain

21st Century Learning

ACCOUNTABILITY Call on students to briefly explain the three ways of protecting biodiversity presented in the text. *(Help endangered or threatened species reproduce and survive through captive breeding, for example, mating of animals in zoos or wildlife preserves; pass laws and sign treaties to protect threatened and endangered species; preserve habitat by setting aside wildlife habitats as parks and refuges)*

Elaborate

Explore the Big Q ? UbD

Direct students' attention to the two contrasting images of Wyoming. Point out the cattle ranch. Ask: **What economic demand makes cattle ranching profitable?** *(The demand for beef)* **What other ways can land be used to produce food?** *(People can grow plant crops for use as food.)* **What are some costs and benefits of using the land in that way?** *(Sample: Costs—The supply of beef decreases, so the price of beef rises; beef, a high-quality source of protein, is less available; Benefits— Raising plant crops uses fewer resources, including water and fossil fuels, and does not degrade the land by trampling of the soil and overgrazing)* **What might be a problem in converting ranches to farms?** *(Sample: Ranch land might not be suitable for growing crops.)*

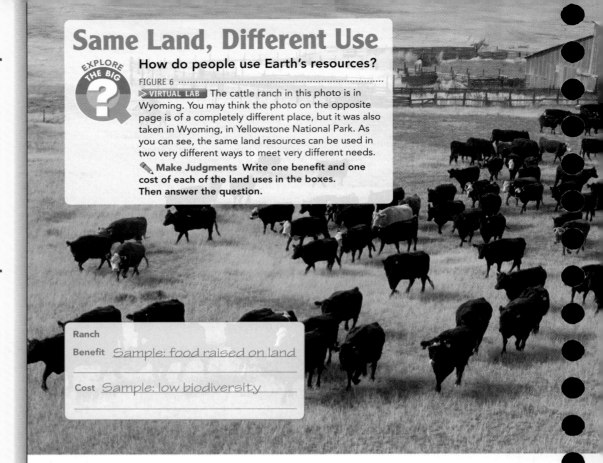

Same Land, Different Use

EXPLORE THE BIG ? **How do people use Earth's resources?**

FIGURE 6 ....

> VIRTUAL LAB The cattle ranch in this photo is in Wyoming. You may think the photo on the opposite page is of a completely different place, but it was also taken in Wyoming, in Yellowstone National Park. As you can see, the same land resources can be used in two very different ways to meet very different needs.

✎ **Make Judgments** Write one benefit and one cost of each of the land uses in the boxes. Then answer the question.

Ranch

Benefit _Sample: food raised on land_

Cost _Sample: low biodiversity_

Laws and Treaties In the United States, the Endangered Species Act prohibits trade of products made from threatened or endangered species. This law also requires the development of plans to save endangered species. The Convention on International Trade in Endangered Species is an international treaty that lists more than 800 threatened and endangered species that cannot be traded for profit or other reasons anywhere in the world.

Habitat Preservation The most effective way to preserve biodiversity is to protect whole ecosystems. Protecting whole ecosystems saves endangered species, the species they depend upon, and those that depend upon them. Many countries have set aside wildlife habitats as parks and refuges. Today, there are about 7,000 nature parks, preserves, and refuges in the world.

Virtual Lab allows students to explore the impact humans have on biodiversity.

my science online.com **Human Impact on Biodiversity**

National Park

Benefit _Sample: preserves endangered species and their habitats_

Cost _Sample: costs money to maintain park and enforce rules_

Do you think we should preserve our resources, use them, or have a balance of both? Explain your answer.

Sample: Both; we need resources to survive, but we also need to protect them for future generations.

 Do the Quick Lab
Humans and Biodiversity.

Assess Your Understanding

2a. Define What is poaching?
Poaching is the illegal killing or removal of wildlife from their habitats.

b. How do people use Earth's resources?
People use resources in ways that meet their needs and help them survive.

got it? ....

O **I get it!** Now I know that humans affect biodiversity _either positively or negatively, depending on their actions._

O **I need extra help with** _See TE note._

Go to **my science COACH** *online for help with this subject.*

117

Lab Resource: Quick Lab

L2 HUMANS AND BIODIVERSITY Students will explore how humans both protect and threaten biodiversity.

Evaluate

Assess Your Understanding

After students answer the questions, have them evaluate their understanding by completing the appropriate sentence.

Answer the Big Q ? UbD

To help students focus on the Big Question, have a class discussion about how people use Earth's resources.

RTI Response to Intervention

2a. If students need help defining poaching, **then** have them locate and reread the sentence in which the boldfaced term appears.

b. If students cannot describe uses of resources, **then** have them skim the blue questions throughout the chapter to locate sections that describe use of resources.

my science COACH Have students go online for help in understanding how humans affect biodiversity.

Differentiated Instruction

L1 Interpret Maps To enhance students' exploration of the Big Question, display a land use map of the United States. Then have a volunteer locate Wyoming. Show students where Yellowstone National Park is located. Call on volunteers to point out areas used for ranching.

L3 How People Use Land Have students research how land is used in their state. Allow them to choose whether to share their findings in a map, circle graph, multimedia presentation, or oral report. Students could start an internet search by looking at the state's official website. Remind students to follow prescribed guidelines for internet use.

117

Name _____ Date _____ Class _____

Biodiversity

> **Inquiry Warm-Up,** *How Much Variety Is There?*
> In the Inquiry Warm-Up, you investigated the biodiversity of various ecosystems. Using what you learned from that activity, answer the questions below.

1. **USE PRIOR KNOWLEDGE** Give a reason why you think a tropical rain forest would have greater diversity than a deciduous forest. Explain.

   _____

   _____

   _____

2. **INTERPRET DATA** Based solely on the results from the Inquiry Warm-Up, approximately how many times more types of trees exist in a tropical rain forest than a deciduous forest?

   _____

3. **INFER** What can you infer about the biodiversity of cold, polar regions relative to a tropical rain forest or a deciduous forest? Explain.

   _____

   _____

   _____

   _____

4. **DRAW CONCLUSIONS** Human activities can often drastically decrease the biodiversity of an area. In the context of the Inquiry Warm-Up, are such activities beneficial or harmful to an ecosystem? Explain.

   _____

   _____

   _____

Name _____ Date _____ Class _____

Biodiversity

> What Is Biodiversity's Value?

got it? ···

○ **I get it!** Now I know that biodiversity has _____

_____

○ **I need extra help with** _____

_____

> What Factors Affect Biodiversity?

1a. **REVIEW** A (smaller/larger) area will contain more species than a
(smaller/larger) area.

b. **EXPLAIN** How is biodiversity related to niches?

_____

_____

_____

c. **COMPARE AND CONTRAST** What is the difference between an
endangered species and a threatened species?

_____

_____

_____

got it? ···

○ **I get it!** Now I know that the factors that affect biodiversity include _____

_____

○ **I need extra help with** _____

_____

Name _____ Date _____ Class _____

Biodiversity

How Do Humans Affect Biodiversity?

2a. DEFINE What is poaching?

_____

_____

b. ANSWER How do people use Earth's resources?

_____

_____

got it? ....

○ **I get it!** Now I know that humans affect biodiversity _____

_____

○ **I need extra help with** _____

_____

Place the outside corner, the corner away from the dotted line, in the corner of your copy machine to copy onto letter-size paper.

Biodiversity

What Is Biodiversity's Value?

The number of different species in an area is called the area's **biodiversity.** One reason to preserve biodiversity is that wild organisms and ecosystems are a source of beauty and recreation. **In addition, biodiversity has both economic value and ecological value within an ecosystem.** Many plants, animals and other organisms are economically valuable to humans. Also, all the species in an ecosystem are connected to one another. A **keystone species** is a species that influences the survival of many other species in an ecosystem.

What Factors Affect Biodiversity?

Factors that affect biodiversity in an ecosystem include climate, area, and diversity of niches. Tropical rain forests are the most diverse ecosystems in the world. Many scientists hypothesize that the reason for the great biodiversity in the tropics has to do with climate. Coral reefs are the second most diverse ecosystems. A coral reef supports many different niches.

Species need genetic diversity. Organisms in a healthy population have diverse traits such as color and size. **Genes** are located within cells and carry the hereditary information that determines an organism's traits. Species that lack a diverse gene pool are less able to adapt and survive changes in the environment.

The disappearance of all members of a species from Earth is called **extinction.** Species in danger of becoming extinct in the near future are called **endangered species.** Species that could become endangered in the near future are called **threatened species.**

How Do Humans Affect Biodiversity?

Biodiversity can be negatively or positively affected by the actions of humans. The major cause of extinction is **habitat destruction,** the loss of a natural habitat. Breaking larger habitats into smaller, isolated pieces is called **habitat fragmentation.** The illegal killing or removal of wildlife from their habitats is called **poaching.**

Three methods of protecting biodiversity are captive breeding, laws and treaties, and habitat preservation. **Captive breeding** is the mating of animals in zoos or wildlife preserves.

On a separate sheet of paper, explain the value of biodiversity and tell how humans can positively or negatively affect it.

Biodiversity

Understanding Main Ideas

Answer the following questions in the spaces provided. Use a separate sheet of paper if you need more room.

1. What three factors affect the biodiversity of an ecosystem?

   _____

   _____

2. What is one reason coral reefs are such diverse ecosystems?

   _____

   _____

3. How does having a diverse gene pool help a species survive?

   _____

   _____

4. Name and describe three ways to protect the world's biodiversity.

   _____

   _____

Building Vocabulary

Write a definition for each of these terms on a separate sheet of paper.

5. keystone species

6. extinction

7. endangered species

8. habitat fragmentation

9. poaching

10. captive breeding

Biodiversity

> The table below lists the number of endangered species in the United States and worldwide in 2000. Study the data in the table. Then use a separate sheet of paper to answer the questions that follow the table.

Endangered Species

Category	United States	World
Mammals	53	301
Birds	74	227
Reptiles	16	74
Amphibians	6	14
Fishes	53	64
Snails	3	4
Clams	37	39
Crustaceans	8	8
Insects	11	12
Arachnids	3	3
Plants	179	180

1. Which category had the highest number of endangered species in 2000?
2. Which category of animals had the highest number of endangered species in the United States? Which had the highest number worldwide?
3. In which categories did the United States have all the endangered species?
4. How many endangered animal species were there in the United States in 2000? How many endangered animal species were there worldwide?

Lesson Quiz

Biodiversity

If the statement is true, write *true*. If the statement is false, change the underlined word or words to make the statement true.

1. _____ The major cause of extinction is <u>habitat fragmentation</u>.

2. _____ Species that could become endangered in the near future are called <u>extinct species</u>.

3. _____ The <u>Threatened Species Act</u> prohibits trade or products made from threatened or endangered species.

4. _____ Protecting <u>whole ecosystems</u> is the most effective way to preserve biodiversity.

Fill in the blank to complete each statement.

5. Biodiversity has both _____ and ecological value within an ecosystem.

6. The sea otter is a _____ that influences the survival of many other species in its ecosystem.

7. Climate, area, and _____ affect biodiversity in an ecosystem.

8. _____ are the most diverse ecosystems in the world.

9. _____ are the second most diverse ecosystems in the world.

10. Scientists think people have directly caused the extinction of some species through habitat destruction, _____, or other actions.

Biodiversity

Answer Key

After the Inquiry Warm-Up

1. Sample: The tropics receive a greater amount of sunlight (being nearer to the equator) and are usually wetter and warmer on average than other climates. These factors help support a greater variety of plant and animal life all year around unlike yearly seasonal climate changes in other parts of the world further from the equator (i.e., Northern Hemisphere summers versus winters).

2. Approximately 2 times as many types of trees.

3. Sample: Since polar regions receive less sunlight than a tropical rain forest or a deciduous forest, I believe there should be less biodiversity near the Earth's poles.

4. Sample: A decrease in biodiversity of an area narrows the variety of organisms that the area can support, making the ecosystem more vulnerable to collapse, and in extreme cases, the extinctions of species.

Key Concept Summaries

Sample: Biodiversity has ecological and economic value. Humans can positively affect biodiversity through habitat preservation, treaties and laws, and captive breeding. Humans can negatively affect biodiversity through poaching, habitat fragmentation, and habitat destruction.

Review and Reinforce

1. area, climate, and niche diversity

2. Coral reefs provide many different niches for organisms, so more species can live there than in a more uniform ecosystem.

3. A species with a diverse gene pool is better able to adapt and survive changes in the environment.

4. Sample: Habitat preservation, setting aside entire ecosystems, can protects biodiversity against the threat of habitat destruction. Captive breeding can protect biodiversity. It involves breeding and raising animals in zoos or wildlife preserves and then releasing the young animals into the wild. Laws and treaties can protect threatened and endangered species by, for example, forbidding people from trading them for profit.

5. a species that influences the survival of many other species in an ecosystem

6. the disappearance of all members of a species from Earth

7. species in danger of becoming extinct in the near future

8. breaking larger habitats into smaller, isolated pieces

9. the illegal killing or removal of wildlife from their habitats

10. the mating of animals in zoos or wildlife preserves for release into the wild

Enrich

1. plants

2. birds; mammals

3. crustaceans and arachnids

4. 264, 746

Lesson Quiz

1. habitat destruction
2. threatened species
3. Endangered Species Act
4. true
5. economic
6. keystone species
7. diversity of niches
8. Tropical rain forests
9. Coral reefs
10. hunting

Study Guide

Review the Big Q UbD

Have students complete the statement at the top of the page. These Key Concepts support their understanding of the chapter's Big Question. Have students return to the chapter opener question. What is different about how students view the image of the Macaw chick now that they have completed the chapter? Thinking about this will help them prepare for the *Apply the Big Q* activity in the Review and Assessment.

Partner Review

Have partners review definitions of vocabulary terms by using the Study Guide to quiz each other. Students could read the Key Concept statements and leave out words for their partner to fill in, or change a statement so that it is false and then ask their partner to correct it.

Class Activity: Concept Map

Students can develop a concept map to show how the information in the chapter is related. Have students brainstorm to identify the Key Concepts, vocabulary, details, and examples, then write each one on a self-sticking note and attach it at random on chart paper or on the board. Explain that the concept map will begin at the top with Key Concepts. Ask students to use the following questions to help them organize the information on the notes:

- What are three categories of environmental issues?
- Why are natural resources important?
- What are some ways to conserve natural resources?
- How and why has the human population grown over time?
- In what positive and negative ways can humans affect biodiversity?

My Science Coach allows students to complete the *Practice Test* online.

The Big Question allows students to complete the *Apply the Big Q* activity about how people use Earth's resources.

Vocab Flash Cards offer a way to review the chapter vocabulary words.

MY SCIENCE online.com **Resources and Living Things**

CHAPTER 3 Study Guide

People use both <u>renewable resources</u> and nonrenewable resources. Reducing resource use through <u>conservation</u> can help make resources last longer.

LESSON 1 Introduction to Environmental Issues

🔑 Environmental issues fall into three main categories: resource use, population growth, and pollution.

🔑 To balance opinions, decision makers weigh the costs and benefits of a proposal.

Vocabulary
- natural resource   • pollution
- point source   • nonpoint source
- environmental science

LESSON 2 Introduction to Natural Resources

🔑 Natural resources include organisms, water, sunlight, minerals, and oil.

🔑 Humans depend on Earth's natural resources for survival and for development.

Vocabulary
- renewable resource   • nonrenewable resource
- sustainable use   • ecological footprint
- conservation

LESSON 3 Human Population Growth

🔑 Over time, the human population has grown exponentially.

🔑 Advances in medicine and technology have improved human health and allowed for exponential human population growth.

Vocabulary
- exponential growth

LESSON 4 Forests and Fisheries

🔑 Forests can be renewable resources if new trees are planted to replace trees that are cut.

🔑 Managing fisheries for a sustainable yield includes setting fishing limits, changing fishing methods, developing aquaculture techniques, and finding new resources.

Vocabulary
- clear-cutting   • selective cutting   • sustainable yield
- fishery   • aquaculture

LESSON 5 Biodiversity

🔑 Biodiversity has both economic value and ecological value within an ecosystem.

🔑 Factors that affect biodiversity include climate, area, niche diversity, genetic diversity, and extinction.

🔑 Biodiversity can be negatively or positively affected by the actions of humans.

Vocabulary
- biodiversity   • keystone species   • gene   • extinction
- endangered species   • threatened species   • habitat destruction
- habitat fragmentation   • poaching   • captive breeding

ELL Support

4 Language Production

Divide the students into teams of four. Each member is given the number 1, 2, 3, or 4. Ask questions based on the Key Concept statements in the chapter. Groups work together to agree on a final answer. Call out a number and the corresponding member in each group answers the question.

Beginning
LOW/HIGH Allow students to answer with single words or short phrases.

Intermediate
LOW/HIGH Have students work cooperatively to answer the question aloud.

Advanced
LOW/HIGH Have students assist by acting as a coach for each team.

Review and Assessment

LESSON 1 Introduction to Environmental Issues

1. Coal and sunlight are examples of
   a. environmental sciences.
   b. pollution.
   c. natural resources.
   d. extinction.

2. _Pollution_ can take many forms, including chemical wastes, noise, heat, and light.

3. **Relate Cause and Effect** Fill in the blank circles with the other main categories of environmental issues. How are they related?

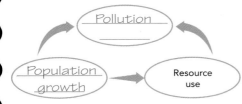

Sample: Growing populations use more resources and produce more pollution. Resource use can cause pollution.

4. **Write About It** Suppose your town is considering building a new coal-burning power plant. The benefits of the new facility include providing power and jobs for the town's growing population. What are some of the costs of this project? What do you think your town should do?
See TE rubric.

LESSON 2 Introduction to Natural Resources

5. Which of the following actions can increase an individual's ecological footprint?
   a. riding a bicycle more often
   b. reducing the use of plastic bags
   c. reusing materials before disposal
   d. turning on the air conditioner

6. Like oil, metals are an example of nonrenewable resources.

7. **Apply Concepts** When is water a renewable resource? When is it nonrenewable?
Sample: Water is renewable when it is replaced at the same rate or faster than it is used. It is nonrenewable when it is not replaced fast enough.

LESSON 3 Human Population Growth

8. Under which of the following conditions would the global population decrease?
   a. birthrate > death rate
   b. birthrate = death rate
   c. death rate > birthrate
   d. death rate = birthrate

9. _Exponential growth_, or growth at an ever-increasing rate, describes the pattern of human population growth.

10. **Infer** How would continued population growth affect Earth's natural resources?
Sample: Resources would become more and more scarce as the population grew. There would be fewer resources to go around.

119

Review and Assessment

Assess Understanding

Have students complete the answers to the Review and Assessment questions. Have a class discussion about what students find confusing. Write Key Concepts on the board to reinforce knowledge.

RTI Response to Intervention

3. If students need help with categorizing environmental issues, **then** have them use the sentence _Population growth_ increases _resource use_, which increases _pollution_.

7. If students have trouble distinguishing when water is a renewable and a nonrenewable resource, **then** have them review the definitions for each term.

10. If students cannot infer the effect of continued population growth on Earth's natural resources, **then** have them review and restate the key terms _sustainable use, ecological footprint,_ and _conservation_.

Alternate Assessment

L3 MAKE A MURAL Have students design and make a mural presenting the chapter content. Students can use drawn or scanned images, diagrams, and captions. Students should be sure to include the Key Concepts and the vocabulary terms from the chapter in the mural as well as address the Big Question.

CHAPTER 3

Write About It Assess student's writing using this rubric.				
SCORING RUBRIC	**SCORE 4**	**SCORE 3**	**SCORE 2**	**SCORE 1**
List costs of coal-burning power plant	Student accurately and precisely identifies two costs.	Student identifies two costs.	Student identifies one cost.	Student does not identify costs.
Make recommendation about a power plant	Student makes recommendation based on detailed analysis of costs and benefits.	Student makes recommendation based on adequate analysis of costs and benefits.	Student makes recommendation but does not analyze costs and benefits.	Student does not make recommendation.

Review and Assessment, Cont.

RTI Response to Intervention

14. **If** students have trouble comparing selective cutting and clear-cutting **then** review **Figure 2** in Lesson 4 with them.

17. **If** students need help assessing the impact of a species' extinction on humans **then** have them review the information under the red head Extinction of Species.

Apply the Big Q ? UbD

TRANSFER Students should be able to demonstrate understanding of the relationships between resources and living things by answering this question. See the scoring rubric below.

Connect to the Big Idea ? UbD

BIG IDEA Living things interact with the environment.

Send students back to the Big Ideas of Science at the beginning of their student edition. Have them read what they wrote about interactions of living things and their environment before they started the chapter. Lead a class discussion about how their thoughts have changed. If all chapters have been completed, have students fill in the bottom section for the Big Idea.

L3 WRITING IN SCIENCE Ask students to write a newspaper editorial persuading readers to be more conscious of the resources they use and how they interact with the environment.

LESSON 4 Forests and Fisheries

11. The practice of raising fish for food is called
  a. poaching.
  b. overfishing.
  c. captive breeding.
  d. aquaculture. ✓

12. A _sustainable yield_ is the amount of a resource that can be harvested regularly without reducing the future supply.

13. **Compare and Contrast** How does selective cutting compare with clear-cutting?
Sample: Clear-cutting removes all of the trees. Selective cutting removes only some trees. Clear-cutting is cheaper, but can be destructive. Both can provide habitats for certain species.

14. **Make Judgments** Do you think the government should encourage more aquaculture, the use of new fish species, or both? Explain your answer.
Sample: Both; aquaculture can provide fish to areas without access to them, but the farms can cause pollution and are expensive. Using new species could add to the supply of fish. This way, fewer farms would need to be built and pollution could be reduced. There would also be less pressure on the new species if some could be farmed too.

LESSON 5 Biodiversity

15. The most effective way to preserve biodiversity is through
  a. captive breeding.
  b. habitat destruction.
  c. habitat preservation. ✓
  d. habitat fragmentation.

16. _Extinction_ occurs when all members of a species disappear from Earth.

17. **Predict** How could the extinction of a species today affect your life in 20 years?
Sample: It could affect the larger ecosystem and other species. Those species might have been used for medicines or other products.

How do people use Earth's resources?

18. Humans depend on Earth's resources to survive. Name at least four resources that were used to produce the scene below.

Sample: the wood for the table, the land used to grow the food, the fuel used to deliver the food, the fuel used to provide electricity, the water to cook with and drink. See TE rubric.

? How do people use Earth's resources?
Assess student's response using this rubric.

SCORING RUBRIC	SCORE 4	SCORE 3	SCORE 2	SCORE 1
Identify resources used to produce meal	Student identifies four resources, explaining each as needed.	Student identifies four resources.	Students identifies three resources.	Student identifies one or no resource.

Standardized Test Prep

Multiple Choice

Circle the letter of the best answer.

1. Study the table below. Then choose the list that correctly ranks each country's ecological footprint per person, from smallest to largest.

Country	Average Ecological Footprint (gha/person)
United States	9.6
Germany	4.5
Mexico	2.6
China	1.6

   A China, Germany, Mexico, United States
   B United States, Mexico, Germany, China
   Ⓒ China, Mexico, Germany, United States
   D Mexico, China, United States, Germany

2. Which words best describe the growth patterns of the human population?
   A decreasing growth
   Ⓑ exponential growth
   C extended growth
   D incremental growth

3. In some areas, foresters plant one tree for every tree they cut. This activity is an example of
   Ⓐ a sustainable approach to a renewable resource.
   B an unsustainable approach to a renewable resource.
   C a sustainable approach to a nonrenewable resource.
   D an unsustainable approach to a nonrenewable resource.

4. How do conservation practices affect natural resources?
   Ⓐ They cause existing natural resources to last longer.
   B They increase Earth's natural resources.
   C They increase people's ecological footprint.
   D They cause natural resources to be depleted.

5. Which of the following terms describes a species that is in danger of becoming extinct in the near future?
   A captive species
   B keystone species
   C threatened species
   Ⓓ endangered species

Constructed Reponse

Use the chart below to help you answer Question 6. Write your answer on a separate sheet of paper.

Some Costs	Some Benefits
• Changes ecosystem	• Provides jobs
• Makes forest less attractive	• Provides wood

6. A city is considering whether or not to allow logging in a large forest nearby. Based on the costs and benefits of this decision, what do you think the city should do? Give at least three reasons to support your answer.

   See TE note.

121

Standardized Test Prep

Test-Taking Skills

INTERPRET A DATA TABLE Tell students that when they answer questions like Question 1, which involves interpreting a data table, they should ascertain precisely what the question is asking. To answer Question 1, students should remember to order countries' ecological footprints—from smallest to largest—as they read the answer choices.

Constructed Response

6. Accept student responses in favor of and against logging. Students should provide at least three reasons supporting their opinion. *(Sample answer: I think that the city should not allow logging in the forest. The logging will change the forest ecosystem. It may harm species by destroying their habitat. The organisms will have to move to new areas or die. The forest will also be less attractive. People will not have a place to hike or enjoy nature's beauty. The logging could also be dangerous to the loggers and injuries could occur. Also, once the trees are cut, it would take a long time for the trees to grow large or tall enough to harvest again so there would be no profit from the forest for a long time.)*

Additional Assessment Resources

Chapter Test
EXAMVIEW® Assessment Suite
Performance Assessment
Progress Monitoring Assessments
SuccessTracker™

ELL Support

5 Assess Understanding

Have ELLs complete the Alternate Assessment. Provide guidelines on the information it must cover, and a rubric for assessment.

Beginning

LOW/HIGH Allow students to work on the images for the mural.

Intermediate

LOW/HIGH Allow students to work on the diagrams for the mural.

Advanced

LOW/HIGH Allow students to work on the captions and text for the mural.

Remediate If students have trouble with....

QUESTION	SEE LESSON	STANDARDS
1	2	
2	3	
3	4	
4	1	
5	5	
6	4	

Science Matters

Think Like a Scientist

Have students read *Sustainable Seafood*. Point out that different kinds of fish and shellfish live in different parts of the ocean, much as different land animals live in different areas of land. For example, a kind of fish called Atlantic salmon lives primarily in the North Atlantic Ocean and cannot survive the warmer water temperatures of other areas. Because these fish live in a limited area, there are a limited number of them. If too many of them are caught, they will have trouble reproducing to replenish their population quickly.

Ask students to volunteer ideas about what might cause habitat loss for fish. Contribute to the discussion to suggest the causes that students don't, such as pollution, the building of dams, and changes in the way that humans use the land near the habitats.

Explain that bottom trawling is a method of fishing used to catch large numbers of fish. Fishing boats drag large heavy nets across the bottom of the sea floor and collect everything in their path. The nets destroy anything on the sea floor that is not collected and the habitat for the creatures that remain on the sea floor is destroyed. Organizations such as Greenpeace are trying to prevent the commercial fishing industry from being allowed to continue using this fishing method.

Ask: **What are some ways to make seafood more sustainable?** *(Sample: use environmentally friendly harvesting methods, set limits on fishing within a population, create more fish farms)* **What are the main arguments for and against bottom trawling?** *(for: allows fishermen to catch large numbers of fish; against: destroys marine habitats)*

SCIENCE MATTERS

Think Like a Scientist

SUSTAINABLE SEAFOOD

Fish and seafood are a tasty part of many foods all over the United States. Blackened Cajun shrimp, New England clam chowder, and smoked west-coast salmon are a few popular examples. But for how long? Overharvesting and habitat loss threaten many types of marine organisms. How do you know which types of seafood are sustainable? To identify sustainable seafood, ask yourself the following questions.

How healthy is the wild population? Some animals have been overharvested. Others are threatened by habitat loss.

What is the organism's life cycle? Some fish grow slowly. Some do not reproduce in large numbers. If these fish are overharvested, the population can take a long time to recover.

How are the fish harvested? Some fishing methods, such as bottom trawling, are much more damaging to the environment than others are.

What is the impact of farming? Sustainable fish farming can help save some wild populations. However, fish farms can also release waste and pollutants that harm the environment.

Research It Identify three types of fish or seafood that you can buy locally. Find out where each came from. Use a spreadsheet to record the answers to the questions above for each type of fish or seafood.

▲ Knowing the source of the seafood you eat can help you make decisions that support sustainable fishing practices.

Quick Facts

The National Park Service was created to preserve and maintain all the national parks in our country. Park Rangers work in national parks in urban, suburban, and rural areas. They have many important duties including fire protection, gathering scientific information, and enforcing laws related to protecting the land. Park Rangers also help people to enjoy the parks. They manage campsites within some parks and give information and guided tours to park visitors. Most rangers work outdoors, but they sometimes work in offices managing programs that are run within the park. More than half of all Park Rangers work in parks that are east of the Mississippi River. Being a Park Ranger can be a fun and rewarding job. Have students list some qualities that would make a person a good Park Ranger.

THE CONSERVATION PRESIDENT

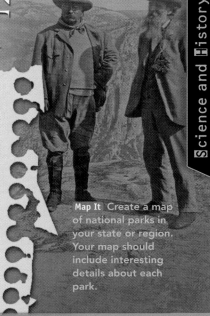

In 1901, if you wanted to go camping or hiking, you might run into a mine or a logging site. Although a lot of natural space existed in the United States when Theodore Roosevelt became president, the country had only five national parks. Years of uncontrolled mining, logging, and hunting threatened many of the country's natural areas. Roosevelt, at left in the photograph, was a passionate conservationist. He signed laws that protected over 93 million hectares of land in the United States. Today, the area of the United States that is protected as wilderness is greater than the area of France, Belgium, and the Netherlands combined!

Map It Create a map of national parks in your state or region. Your map should include interesting details about each park.

Science and History

Science and History

Have students read *The Conservation President*. Theodore Roosevelt was concerned with protecting the environment at a time when most people were not aware of the damages human activities could cause to it. In this 1903 photograph from Yosemite, Roosevelt is on the left and John Muir, founder of the Sierra Club, is on the right. Soon after Roosevelt's visit, Yosemite became a national park.

As students draw their maps, have them include information about what makes that park different from any other and activities one can participate in at that park, such as boating, hiking, or fishing.

Ask: **How could too much hunting harm the environment?** *(Species could be greatly reduced and unable to reproduce quickly.)* **Why are the laws Roosevelt signed important?** *(The laws keep land protected, so that there will always be areas of wilderness in our country.)*

Environmental Lawyer

As a child, Melissa Scanlan loved boating on the Fox River with her family. As she grew older, she learned that the river was polluted with industrial and agricultural chemicals. Scanlan went to law school and became an environmental lawyer. As a lawyer, she formed Midwest Environmental Advocates—a law firm that helps midwestern communities work with industries and the government to find solutions to local environmental problems. Scanlan says that seeing her work affect the world around her "is like dropping a pebble into water and seeing the rings echo out."

Debate It Research an environmental issue in your region. Choose a possible solution and stage a class debate. Make sure you support your opinion with facts and evidence from your research.

Environmental lawyer Melissa Scanlan finds inspiration from her childhood home in Wisconsin.

Careers

Careers

Have students read *Environmental Lawyers*. Explain that environmental lawyers solve disputes when two groups disagree over how to use land. Environmental lawyers help find solutions that satisfy both groups.

As students research their debate, encourage them to seek reasons to support their side, even if they disagree with their assigned position. Remind them to think like the group they represent in the debate.

Ask: **What is an example of a situation an environmental lawyer could help with?** *(Sample: a construction company wants to cut down a large number of trees to make space for a building)* **What solution could an environmental lawyer suggest?** *(Sample: build the building somewhere else or require to the construction company to plant trees somewhere else in the town)*

Land, Air, and Water Resources

Introduce the Big Q ? UbD

Have students look at the larger image and read the Engaging Question and description. Ask them to infer how reusing shipping containers and other objects can help our planet. Point out that the architect needed to think creatively to come up with the idea to reuse transportation containers. In other words, the architect needed to brainstorm without limiting himself or herself to ideas that are obvious. Ask: **Which resources at school might you and your classmates be able to use more wisely?** *(Sample response: Paper, water, packaging of food products, food)* **Which resources at home might you and other family members be able to use more wisely?** *(Sample response: Water, electricity, paper, food products and packaging, food, transportation)*

Untamed Science Video

MANATEE SURVIVAL Before viewing, invite students to suggest some ways in which humans affect the environments of animals. Then play the video. Lead a class discussion and make a list of questions that the video raises. You may wish to have students view the video again after they have completed the chapter to see if their questions have been answered.

To access the online resources for this chapter, search on or navigate to *Land, Air, and Water Resources.*

Untamed Science Video shows the effects humans have on the manatee's environment.

The Big Question allows students to answer the Engaging Question about using resources wisely.

MY SCIENCE online.com | Land, Air, and Water Resources

HOW IS THIS HOUSE SAVING OUR PLANET?

What can people do to use resources wisely?

Have you ever thought of ways to reuse something you would normally throw away? This home is made from the shipping containers you see transporting goods on ships and trucks. These containers would have been thrown away but an architect thought of a new way to use them.

Infer How can reusing shipping containers and other objects help our planet?

Sample: If recycled materials were used for building, resources such as trees would not have to be used as often.

> UNTAMED SCIENCE Watch the **Untamed Science** video to learn more about reusing resources.

124 Land, Air, and Water Resources

Professional Development Note | **From the Author**

Nine billion people live on our planet, and we continually use land, water, and air resources. These resources will run out unless we take care of them. How can we do this? By being sustainable. Sustainability is the capacity to maintain a certain process or state indefinitely. Sustainability has four prongs: economic, social, ecological, and technical. We are grappling with the fact that land, water, and air resources are limited. A government agency called the National Oceanic and Atmospheric Administration (NOAA) is responsible for monitoring these vital components, and it can help us learn how we can be sustainable and let our planet "live."

✏ *Don Buckley*

Land, Air, and Water Resources

CHAPTER 4

Chapter at a Glance

CHAPTER PACING: 10–15 periods or 5–7$\frac{1}{2}$ blocks

INTRODUCE THE CHAPTER: Engage students with the Engaging Question and the opening image. Activate prior knowledge and preteach vocabulary using the Getting Started pages.

Lesson 1: Conserving Land and Soil

Lesson 2: Waste Disposal and Recycling

Lesson 3: Air Pollution and Solutions

Lesson 4: Water Pollution and Solutions

Lesson 5: Ocean Resources

ASSESSMENT OPTIONS: Chapter Test, **EXAM**VIEW® Assessment Suite, Performance Assessment, Progress Monitoring Assessments, SuccessTracker™

Preference Navigator, in the online Planning tools, allows you to customize *Interactive Science* to your own teaching style. You can also edit lesson plans by selecting the Lesson Planner option.

Digital Teacher's Edition allows you to access your Teacher's Edition and Resource materials online.

my science online >

CHAPTER 4

Differentiated Instruction

L1 Using Visuals Help students understand that the photograph is taken on a slight upward angle of a building that stands approximately 10 or 11 meters high. Ask students whether they think the windows were part of the original containers, or whether they were added when the containers were reused, and why. *(Shipping containers are windowless; these windows were added during construction of the home.)*

L3 Container Shipping Challenge students to do research on the use of containers in shipping. Students might include information about standard sizes of containers used for domestic and international trade, as well as the types of goods that are typically shipped in containers.

125

Getting Started

Check Your Understanding

This activity assesses students' understanding of the water cycle. After students have shared their answers, point out that the word *cycle* refers to a continual process that has no beginning or end, like a wheel. Explain to students that *cycle* is derived from the Greek word *kuklos*, meaning "circle."

Preteach Vocabulary Skill

Explain to students that knowing Greek and Latin root words can make it easier to learn new vocabulary words. Have students look over the prefixes *bio-* and *aqua-* and their meanings in the table. Invite them to think about the color aqua. Then ask why that color might have been given that name *(Sample response: Aqua is the color of some seawater.)* Then ask students to explain what we mean when we refer to a person's "bio." *(A person's biography, the story of the person's life)*

L3 Challenge students to jot down other words that contain the prefix *bio-* and other words that use the prefix *aqua-*. *(Sample: biology, biome, biodiversity, biotic, biotechnology; aquamarine, aquarium, Aquarius, aquatic, aquifer)*

Check Your Understanding

1. **Background** Read the paragraph below and then answer the question.

> On a lazy summer day, Mia pours water on the hot sidewalk and imagines where the water will go as it travels through the **water cycle.** After the water **evaporates,** it may float through the **atmosphere** and fall as rain in faraway lands or the ocean.

The **water cycle** is the continuous process by which water moves from Earth's surface to the atmosphere and back.

Evaporation is the process by which molecules of liquid water absorb energy and change to a gas.

The **atmosphere** is the envelope of gases that surrounds the planet.

• What makes the water cycle a *cycle*?

The water moves in a circular pattern between Earth and the atmosphere.

> **MY READING WEB** If you had trouble answering the question above, visit **My Reading Web** and type in *Land, Air, and Water Resources.*

Vocabulary Skill

Prefixes Some words can be divided into parts. A root is the part of the word that carries the basic meaning. A prefix is a word part placed in front of the root to change the word's meaning. The prefixes below will help you understand some of the vocabulary in this chapter.

Prefix	Meaning	Example
bio-	life	biodegradable, *adj.* describes a material that can be broken down and recycled by bacteria and other decomposers
aqua-	water	aquaculture, *n.* the farming of saltwater and freshwater organisms

2. **Quick Check** In the definitions of the example words in the table, circle the part that includes the prefix meaning.

My Reading Web offers leveled readings related to chapter content.

Vocab Flash Cards offer extra practice with the chapter vocabulary words.

Digital Lesson
• Assign the *Check Your Understanding* activity online and have students submit their work to you.
• Assign the *Vocabulary Skill* activity online and have students submit their work to you.

my science online.com Land, Air, and Water Resources

CHAPTER 4

topsoil

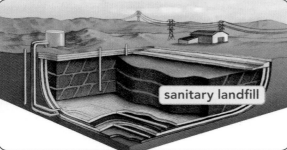

sanitary landfill

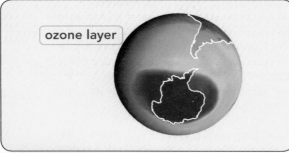

ozone layer

pesticide

Chapter Preview

> VOCAB FLASH CARDS For extra help with vocabulary, visit **Vocab Flash Cards** and type in **Land, Air, and Water Resources.**

127

Preview Vocabulary Terms

Have students create a personalized science glossary for the vocabulary terms in this chapter. In their glossaries, students should define each term and reference the pages in the chapter that define and explain the term. A list of Academic Vocabulary for each lesson can be found in the Support All Readers box at the start of the lesson.

L1 Have students look at the images on this page as you pronounce the vocabulary word. Have students repeat the word after you. Then read the definition. Use the sample sentence in italics to clarify the meaning of the term.

topsoil *(TAWP soyl)* The rich top layer of soil, a mixture of rock fragments, nutrients, water, air, and decaying animal and plant matter. *You can find the roots of grass and other plants in topsoil.*

sanitary landfill *(SAN ih tehr ee LAND fil)* An underground storage area for solid wastes designed to protect the surrounding area. *A sanitary landfill has many design features, including vent pipes and liners.*

ozone layer *(OH zohn LAY ur)* A layer of the upper atmosphere that protects people from the effects of too much ultraviolet radiation. *A hole in the ozone layer has formed over Antarctica.*

pesticide *(PES tih syd)* A poison used to kill insects or weeds. *A pesticide can pollute soil and water.*

E L L Support

Have students complete the **Preview Vocabulary Terms** activity either alone or in pairs. Before students begin creating their science glossaries, write each term and introduce it to students by pointing and saying it aloud.

Beginning
LOW Draw a picture for each vocabulary term in the glossary that helps associate the term with its definition.

HIGH Include English pronunciations for each term.

Intermediate
LOW/HIGH For each vocabulary term in the glossary, write a sentence.

Advanced
LOW/HIGH Analyze the terms by breaking them down into root words and affixes. Record the results of the analysis in the glossary.

Conserving Land and Soil

LESSON

1

What can people do to use resources wisely?

Lesson Pacing: 2–3 periods or 1–1½ blocks

🕐 **SHORT ON TIME?** To do this lesson in approximately half the time, do the Activate Prior Knowledge activity on page 128. A discussion of the key concepts on pages 128 and 131 will familiarize students with the lesson content. Have students do the Quick Labs. The rest of the lesson can be completed by students independently.

Preference Navigator, in the online Planning tools, allows you to customize *Interactive Science* to your own teaching style. You can also edit lesson plans by selecting the Lesson Planner option.

Digital Teacher's Edition allows you to access your Teacher's Edition and Resource materials online.

my science online.com

Lesson Vocabulary

- litter • topsoil • subsoil • bedrock • erosion
- nutrient depletion • fertilizer • desertification • drought
- land reclamation

 Content Refresher

The Dust Bowl and Conservation Districts Along with the Great Depression came the ecological disaster known as the Dust Bowl. A long, severe drought on the Great Plains, coupled with overgrazing and poor soil management, resulted in the windblown erosion of the region's soil. In 1935, Congress declared soil conservation a national priority in response to the Dust Bowl. Today there are about 3,000 conservation districts to help local citizens conserve land, water, forests, wildlife, and other natural resources. The National Association of Conservation Districts develops national conservation policies, influences lawmakers, and provides services to districts to help them serve their communities.

LESSON OBJECTIVES

🗝 Tell how people use land.
🗝 Describe why soil management is important.

Blended Path
Active learning using Student Edition, Inquiry Path, and Digital Path

ENGAGE AND EXPLORE

Teach this lesson using a variety of resources. Begin by reading **My Planet Diary** as a class. Have students share ideas about reasons to conserve land and soil. Then have students do the **Inquiry Warm-Up activity.** Students will learn how mining affects the land and what can be done to minimize its impact on the land. The **After the Inquiry Warm-Up worksheet** sets up a discussion about varying effects on the land of different methods of mining. Have volunteers share their answers to number 4 about the results of mining methods.

EXPLAIN AND ELABORATE

Teach Key Concepts by explaining that agriculture, mining, and development are three ways that people use the land. Have students do the first **Quick Lab** to explore land use.

Continue to **Teach Key Concepts** by explaining the causes of erosion, nutrient depletion, and desertification. **Lead a Discussion** about the structure of fertile soil using **Figure 2** and about the benefits of terracing using **Figure 3**. Use the **Support the Big Q** to discuss the role that land reclamation plays in using our resources wisely. Review the term *desertification* and have students do the **Apply It activity.** Have students do the **Quick Lab** to learn about erosion and how to prevent it.

Hand out the **Key Concept Summaries** as a review of each part of the lesson. Students can also use the online **Vocab Flash Cards** to review key terms.

EVALUATE

Have students take the **Lesson Quiz.** For an alternate assessment, see the **EXAM**VIEW® Assessment Suite, Progress Monitoring Assessments, or SuccessTracker™.

E L L Support

1 Content and Language
List the words *topsoil* and *bedrock* on the board. Explain that they are compound words, words made from two existing words. Explain that the two smaller words are clues to the meaning of the compound word. *(The upper layer of soil* and *the rock that is beneath all the layers of soil)*

Lab zone Inquiry Path
Hands-on learning in the Lab zone

ENGAGE AND EXPLORE

To teach this lesson with an emphasis on inquiry, begin with the **Inquiry Warm-Up activity.** Students will investigate how mining affects the land and what can be done to minimize its impact on the land. Discuss what happens to the land as mining is underway. Have the students do the **After the Inquiry Warm-Up worksheet.** Talk about what must be done to restore the land. Have volunteers share their answers to number 4 about effects on soil from digging.

EXPLAIN AND ELABORATE

Focus on the **Inquiry Skill** for the lesson. Point out that when you infer, you combine the evidence that you observe with your prior experience or knowledge to draw a conclusion. What conclusion can be drawn from the results in the **Inquiry Warm-Up activity?** *(Knowing where the minerals are located before beginning to mine for them lessens the impact of mining on the land.)* Have students do the **Quick Lab** and then share their results.

Conduct the **Teacher Demo.** Have students identify the various layers and compare them using the terms from **Figure 2.** Use the **Support the Big Q** to discuss the role that land reclamation plays in using our resources wisely. Review *desertification* before beginning the **Apply It activity.** Ask volunteers to share their findings. Have students do the **Quick Lab** to learn about erosion and how to prevent it. Students can use the online **Vocab Flash Cards** to review key terms.

EVALUATE

Have students take the **Lesson Quiz.** For an alternate assessment, see the **EXAM**VIEW® Assessment Suite, Progress Monitoring Assessments, or SuccessTracker™.

Digital Path
Online learning at **my science online**.com

ENGAGE AND EXPLORE

Teach this lesson using digital resources. Begin by having students explore real-world connections to land use at **My Planet Diary** online. Have them access the Chapter Resources to find the **Unlock the Big Question activity.** There they can answer the questions and refine their responses as they continue through the lesson. You can re-assign the activity and have students submit their work so you can track their progress.

EXPLAIN AND ELABORATE

Students reading above, at, or below the lexile measure of this lesson can access basic content readings at their level at **My Reading Web.** Have students use the online **Vocab Flash Cards** to preview key terms. Do the **Quick Lab** and then ask students to share their results.

Use the **Support the Big Q** to discuss the role that land reclamation plays in using our resources wisely. Review *desertification* before assigning the online **Apply It activity.** Ask volunteers to share their ideas for slowing or avoiding desertification in threatened areas. Have students submit their work to you. Have students do the **Quick Lab** to learn about erosion.

The **Key Concept Summaries** online allow students to read a summary and see an image associated with each part of the lesson. Online remediation is available at **My Science Coach.**

EVALUATE

Have students take the **Lesson Quiz.** For an alternate assessment, see the **EXAM**VIEW® Assessment Suite, Progress Monitoring Assessments, or SuccessTracker™.

2 Frontload the Lesson
Preview the lesson questions. Ask students about any words they do not understand. Explain specific meanings these words have in science.

3 Comprehensible Input
Have students study the visuals and their captions on page 130. Then, to support the key concepts of the lesson, have them complete this sentence: If you were to dig a deep hole in the ground, first you would dig through ____, then ____, and then ____ before coming to ____. *(Litter, topsoil, subsoil, bedrock)*

4 Language Production
Pair or group students with varied language abilities to complete labs collaboratively for language practice. Have each student copy the completed written lab for personal reference.

5 Assess Understanding
Divide the class into small groups. Have each student discuss a key concept from the lesson in his or her group. After the discussions, have students talk about the key concepts as a group.

LESSON 4.1

Conserving Land and Soil

Establish Learning Objectives

After this lesson, students will be able to:

🔑 Tell how people use land.

🔑 Describe why soil management is important.

Engage

Activate Prior Knowledge

MY PLANET DIARY Read *Land Inspiration* with the class. Point out that the word *ethic* means the principles that guide the conduct of a person or a group of people. Ask: **What can people do to protect land for future generations?** *(Students may suggest that people can treat the land respectfully and that government can pass laws to prevent misuse of land.)*

BIG IDEAS OF SCIENCE REFERENCE LIBRARY 📖
Have students look up the following topics: Farming, Soil.

Explore

Lab Resource: Inquiry Warm-Up 🔺

L1 HOW DOES MINING AFFECT THE LAND?
Students will use sand, sunflower seeds, and three everyday objects as mining tools to model the way mining affects land.

LESSON
1 Conserving Land and Soil

🔑 How Do People Use Land?

🔑 Why Is Soil Management Important?

my planet Diary
VOICES FROM HISTORY

Land Inspiration

Conservation is a state of harmony between men and land.
—Aldo Leopold

Aldo Leopold spent his life in beautiful landscapes. He was so inspired by what he saw that he sought to better understand it. Leopold realized that land and all it contains—living and nonliving—are connected. He believed people should use land in a way that protects it for all living things as well as for future generations. Leopold called his idea the "land ethic." He wrote several books on conservation using this philosophy, including his most famous book, *A Sand County Almanac.*

Communicate Discuss this question with a group of classmates. Write your answer below.

How do you think land should be used?

Sample: Land should be used to meet people's needs and to protect other living things that use it.

▷ **PLANET DIARY** Go to **Planet Diary** to learn more about conserving land and soil.

 Lab zone Do the Inquiry Warm-Up *How Does Mining Affect the Land?*

How Do People Use Land?

Less than a quarter of Earth's surface is dry, ice-free land. All people on Earth must share this limited amount of land to produce their food, build shelter, and obtain resources. As the American author Mark Twain once said about land, "They don't make it anymore."

People use land in many ways. 🔑 **Three uses that change the land are agriculture, mining, and development.** See **Figure 1.**

SUPPORT ALL READERS
Lexile Measure = 930L   Lexile Word Count = 1242

Prior Exposure to Content: Most students have encountered this topic in earlier grades

Academic Vocabulary: *cause, effect, infer*

Science Vocabulary: *erosion, desertification, land reclamation*

Concept Level: Generally appropriate for most students in this grade

Preteach With: My Planet Diary "Land Inspiration" and Figure 1 activity

Go to **My Reading Web** to access leveled readings that provide a foundation for the content.

my science online.com

Vocabulary
- litter • topsoil • subsoil • bedrock • erosion
- nutrient depletion • fertilizer • desertification
- drought • land reclamation

Skills
- ↻ Reading: Relate Cause and Effect
- △ Inquiry: Infer

Agriculture Land provides most of the food that people eat. Crops such as wheat require lots of fertile land, but less than a third of Earth's land can be farmed. The rest is too dry, too salty, or too mountainous. New farmland is created by clearing forests, draining wetlands, and irrigating deserts. Land can also be used to grow food for animals, to provide grazing for livestock, or to grow crops such as cotton.

Mining Mining is the removal of nonrenewable resources from the land. Resources just below the surface are strip mined. Strip mining removes a strip of land to obtain minerals. The strip is then replaced. Strip mining exposes soil, which can then be blown or washed away. The area may remain barren for years. Resources can also be removed from deeper underground by digging tunnels to bring the minerals to the surface.

Development People settled in areas that had good soil near fresh water. As populations grew, the settlements became towns and cities. People developed the land by constructing buildings, bridges, and roads. In the United States, an area half the size of New Jersey is developed each year.

FIGURE 1 ···

Land Use
The ways that people use land vary greatly. For example, about 93 percent of land in Nebraska is used for agriculture, while only 10 percent of land in Massachusetts is used for agriculture.

✎ **Describe** How is land used in your area?

<u>Sample: Most of my area is developed</u>
<u>and has few farms. There are no mines.</u>

Agriculture

Strip Mining

Development

Lab zone® Do the Quick Lab *Land Use.*

🔑 Assess Your Understanding
got**it?** ··

○ I get it! Now I know the ways people use and change land include <u>agriculture, mining,</u>
<u>and development.</u>

○ I need extra help with <u>See TE note.</u>

Go to **my science** ⓢ **coach** *online for help with this subject.*

129

ⒺⓁⓁ Support

1 Content and Language
Desertification and *reclamation* both use the suffix *-ation*, which means "the act or process of becoming." Have students identify and define the root of *desertification*. Discuss how the suffix shapes the word's meaning.

2 Frontload the Lesson
Use the section headings to help set the purpose for reading. Preview the

vocabulary by saying aloud each term as students point to the visuals.

3 Comprehensible Input
Use the visuals in **Figure 1** and a cause-and-effect graphic organizer to help students explain how humans' need for resources affects land use. Reread the page and ask students to underline the causes and circle the effects.

Explain ────────────

Introduce Vocabulary
Tell students that the word *soil* means "earth" or "firm land." The terms *topsoil* and *subsoil* identify specific layers of soil.

Teach Key Concepts 🔑
Explain that people change the land by using it in three ways. Ask: **How do people create new farmland?** *(They clear forests, drain wetlands, and irrigate deserts.)* **What negative effect does strip mining have on land?** *(Strip mining exposes soil and creates the possibility of erosion and barren land.)* **What kinds of human development can change land?** *(Constructing bridges, buildings, and roads)* Point out that 5 percent of U.S. land area, or 43,706,049 hectares, has been developed. This land area is larger than California, which is 40,393,196 hectares. Students may also find it interesting to know that U.S. roads and parking lots take up about 15,798,928 hectares. For comparison, the state of Georgia is 14,997,585 hectares.

Lab Resource: Quick Lab 🔲
L2 **LAND USE** Students will explore the various ways humans use land.

Evaluate ────────────

Assess Your Understanding
Have students evaluate their understanding by completing the appropriate sentence.

🆁🆃🅸 Response to Intervention
If students have trouble identifying the ways people use land, **then** have them review the three red heads in this section.

my science **coach** Have students go online for help in understanding the ways people use land.

My Planet Diary provides an opportunity for students to explore real-world connections to land use.

my science online.com | Land Use

Explain

Teach Key Concepts

Remind students that soil can take hundreds of years to form. Ask: **What happens when soil is exposed?** *(Erosion occurs more easily.)* **What farming practice contributes to nutrient depletion?** *(Planting the same crops in a field every year)* **How can farmers prevent this?** *(Apply fertilizers, leave fields unplanted periodically, and rotate the crops.)* **What are some causes of desertification?** *(Climate, overgrazing of grasslands, and cutting down trees)*

Relate Cause and Effect Tell students that a cause makes something happen. An effect is what happens. Relating cause and effect means recognizing that one event causes another.

Lead a Discussion

SOIL LAYERS Remind students that good soil is necessary for one of the uses of land—agriculture. Ask: **What does soil contain that plants need to grow?** *(Minerals and nutrients)* **What natural processes break up bedrock?** *(Freezing, thawing, acids in rainwater and chemicals released by organisms, and plant roots that wedge between rocks)* Ask students to identify the layer of soil where each of the following is most likely to be found: Rock fragments and a small amount of animal and plant matter *(Subsoil)*, water and nutrients absorbed by many plant roots *(Topsoil)*, dead leaves and grass *(Litter)*, rock *(Bedrock)*.

21st Century Learning

CREATIVITY Have students read *Soil* in the **Big Ideas of Science Reference Library** and create a diorama showing what they learned.

Why Is Soil Management Important?

To understand why soil management is important, you need to know about the structure and function of fertile soil. It can take hundreds of years to form just a few centimeters of new soil. Soil contains the minerals and nutrients that plants need to grow. Soil also absorbs, stores, and filters water. Bacteria, fungi, and other organisms in soil break down the wastes and remains of living things. See **Figure 2**.

FIGURE 2 ·····················
Structure of Fertile Soil
Fertile soil is made up of several layers, including litter, topsoil, and subsoil.

Identify Underline the organisms that make up or play a role in each soil layer.

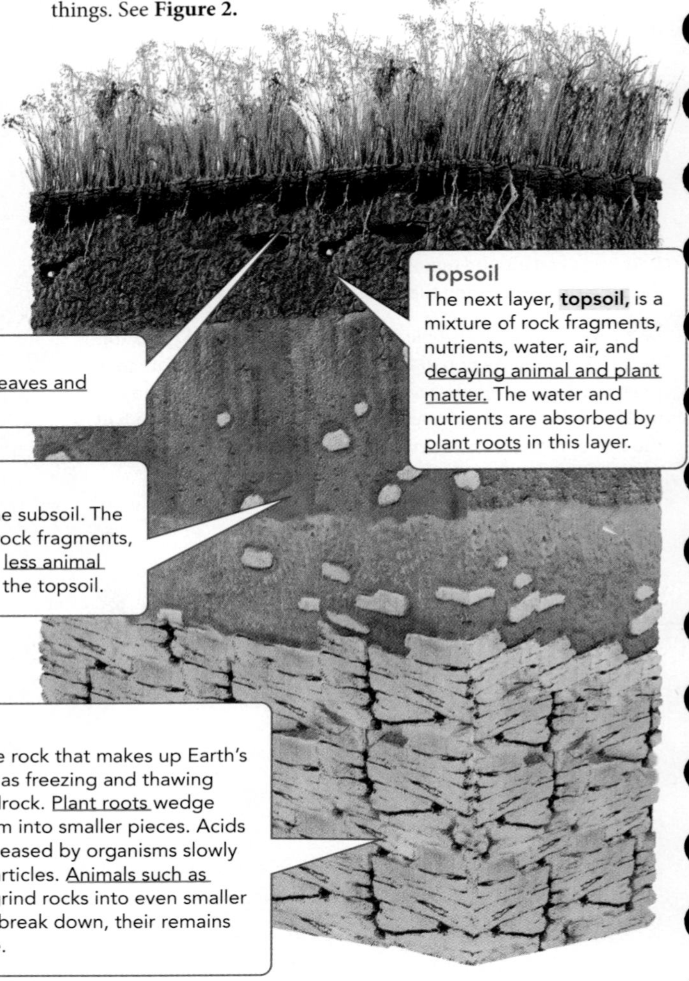

Litter
The top layer of <u>dead leaves and grass</u> is called **litter.**

Topsoil
The next layer, **topsoil,** is a mixture of rock fragments, nutrients, water, air, and <u>decaying animal and plant matter.</u> The water and nutrients are absorbed by <u>plant roots</u> in this layer.

Subsoil
Below the topsoil is the subsoil. The **subsoil** also contains rock fragments, water, and air, but has <u>less animal and plant matter</u> than the topsoil.

Bedrock
All soil begins as **bedrock,** the rock that makes up Earth's crust. Natural processes such as freezing and thawing gradually break apart the bedrock. <u>Plant roots</u> wedge between rocks and break them into smaller pieces. Acids in rainwater and chemicals released by organisms slowly break the rock into smaller particles. <u>Animals such as earthworms and moles</u> help grind rocks into even smaller particles. As <u>dead organisms</u> break down, their remains also contribute to the mixture.

130 Land, Air, and Water Resources

Professional Development Note **Teacher to Teacher**

Land, Water, and Air Resources In order to encourage involvement in the study of resources, I think it is important for students to look at their local resources. I had students bring in soil samples from around their neighborhoods. We established sample collection and data protocols. When we got samples to school, we tested for permeability, absorbency, texture, composition, etc. We also tested some samples for the ability to support life by trying to grow radish seeds in them. This activity lasted throughout the unit.

Joel Palmer, Ed.D.
Mesquite ISD
Mesquite, TX

Soil Use Problems Because rich topsoil takes so long to form, it is important to protect Earth's soil. 🔑 **Without soil, most life on land could not exist. Poor soil management can result in three problems: erosion, nutrient depletion, and desertification.** Fortunately, damaged soil can sometimes be restored.

Erosion Normally, plant roots hold soil in place. But when plants are removed during logging, mining, or farming, the soil is exposed and soil particles can easily move. The process by which <u>water, wind, or ice moves particles of rocks or soil is called</u> (erosion.) Terracing, one farming method that helps reduce erosion, is shown in **Figure 3**.

✏️ **Relate Cause and Effect** In the text, underline the causes and circle the effects of two soil use problems.

FIGURE 3 ·····················
Terracing
✏️ A terrace is a leveled section of a hill used to grow crops and prevent erosion. The flat surfaces allow crops to absorb water before the water flows downhill.

1. **Interpret Photos** Draw the path of water down the first hill and the terraced hill.

2. **Infer** Why do you think terracing helps prevent erosion?

The water will move slower and move fewer soil particles.

Nutrient Depletion Plants make their own food through photosynthesis. Plants also need nutrients such as the nitrogen, potassium, and phosphorus found in soil to grow. Decomposers supply these nutrients to the soil as they break down the wastes and remains of organisms. <u>But if a farmer plants the same crops in a field every year, the crops may use more nutrients than the decomposers can supply.</u> The soil becomes less fertile, a situation called (nutrient depletion.)

When soil becomes depleted, farmers usually apply **fertilizers,** which include nutrients that help crops grow better. Farmers may choose other methods of soil management, too. They may periodically leave fields unplanted. The unused parts of crops, such as cornstalks, can be left in fields to decompose, adding nutrients to the soil. Farmers also can alternate crops that use many nutrients with crops that use fewer nutrients.

131

Differentiated Instruction

L1 Comparing and Contrasting Soil Layers Have students create a Venn diagram that shows the similarities and differences between topsoil and subsoil. Encourage students to refer to **Figure 2** as they construct their diagram.

L3 Researching Organic Fertilizers Tell students that many farmers choose to use organic products and methods to grow their agricultural products. Invite students to research organic farming in order to make a brief oral presentation of the subject to their classmates.

Make Analogies

L1 VITAMINS FOR THE SOIL To help students understand the concept of using fertilizers to restore nitrogen, potassium, and phosphorus to depleted soil, compare such fertilizers to vitamins and nutrients that people sometimes add to their regular diet. Ask: **How would you compare people's use of fertilizers with people's use of vitamins?** *(Sample: People use fertilizers to restore nutrients to soil so that crops may grow better. People use vitamins to restore or boost the level of certain nutrients and other natural substances in their bodies.)*

Teach With Visuals

Have students look at **Figure 3.** Ask them if they have seen a house or public building with a terrace. Ask: **How is a terraced hillside like a terrace on a house?** *(Both have flat surfaces.)* **In addition to reducing erosion, how else is terracing helpful to farmers?** *(It provides flat areas for growing plants. When it rains, water falls on the flat areas and soaks into the soil instead of running off.)*

⚠️ **Infer** Explain to students that they must use what they learned about terracing and erosion along with prior knowledge in order to make an inference.

Elaborate

Teacher Demo 🔬

L2 OBSERVE SOIL LAYERS

Materials glass jars with screw-on lids, water, soil samples, hand lens

Time 20 minutes over 2 days

Review the layers of soil. Bring in about 500 mL of soil (removing any visible living organisms and leaving them at the location). Have groups of students put some soil in a jar, add water to cover it, screw on the lid, and then shake the jar gently to mix the soil and water. Remind students to wash their hands. Leave the jars undisturbed overnight and allow students to examine them the next day.

Ask: **What do you see in the jar now?** *(The largest and most dense particles will have settled in the bottom and finest particles will be at the top.)*

Explain

Teach With Visuals

Review the meaning of the term *desertification* and tell students to look at the map in the *Apply It* activity. Ask: **What areas of existing desert are shown on the map?** *(Southwestern U.S., the southern part of South America, the northern part of Africa, a small part of central Asia, and much of Australia)* **Which type of biome is most threatened by desertification? Why?** *(Grasslands; these areas tend to be dry, so wind erodes exposed soil.)*

Support the Big Q ? UbD

LAND RECLAMATION Review with students the ways human activities can damage land. Ask: **What is land reclamation?** *(The process of restoring land to a more productive state)* **What are two uses of reclaimed land?** *(Agriculture and habitats for wildlife)*

Elaborate

Apply It!

L1 Review the term *desertification* before beginning the activity. Ask: **Is there any place on the map where an area of red appears without an area of violet nearby?** *(Yes, in eastern South America, Central and East Asia, Southeastern Africa, and Central North America.)* **What can you infer about whether desertification is a threat only where there is existing desert?** *(It can be a threat also in areas where there is no existing desert.)*

▲ **Infer** Remind students that when they infer, they combine the evidence they observe with their prior experience or knowledge.

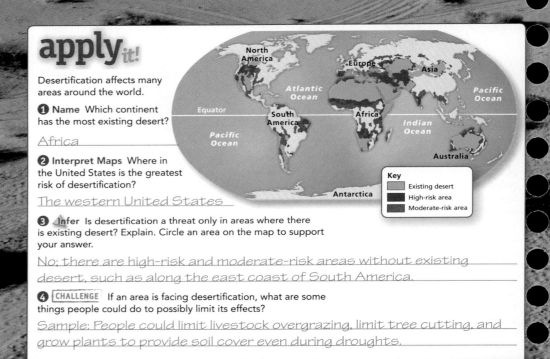

Desertification If the soil in a once-fertile area becomes depleted of moisture and nutrients, the area can become a desert. The advance of desertlike conditions into areas that previously were fertile is called **desertification** (dih zurt uh fih KAY shun).

One cause of desertification is climate. For example, a **drought** is a period when less rain than normal falls in an area. During droughts, crops fail. Without plant cover, the exposed soil easily blows away. Overgrazing of grasslands by cattle and sheep and cutting down trees for firewood can cause desertification, too.

Desertification is a serious problem. People cannot grow crops and graze livestock where desertification has occurred. As a result, people may face famine and starvation. Desertification is severe in central Africa. Millions of rural people there are moving to the cities because they can no longer support themselves on the land.

apply it!

Desertification affects many areas around the world.

❶ **Name** Which continent has the most existing desert?

Africa

❷ **Interpret Maps** Where in the United States is the greatest risk of desertification?

The western United States

❸ ▲ **Infer** Is desertification a threat only in areas where there is existing desert? Explain. Circle an area on the map to support your answer.

No; there are high-risk and moderate-risk areas without existing desert, such as along the east coast of South America.

❹ [CHALLENGE] If an area is facing desertification, what are some things people could do to possibly limit its effects?

Sample: People could limit livestock overgrazing, limit tree cutting, and grow plants to provide soil cover even during droughts.

Key
- Existing desert
- High-risk area
- Moderate-risk area

132 Land, Air, and Water Resources

Digital Lesson: Assign the *Apply It* activity online and have students submit their work to you.

my science online.com | **Soil Management**

Land Reclamation Fortunately, it is possible to replace land damaged by erosion or mining. The process of restoring an area of land to a more productive state is called **land reclamation.** In addition to restoring land for agriculture, land reclamation can restore habitats for wildlife. Many different types of land reclamation projects are currently underway all over the world. But it is generally more difficult and expensive to restore damaged land and soil than it is to protect those resources in the first place. In some cases, the land may not return to its original state.

FIGURE 4 ·······································
Land Reclamation
These pictures show land before and after it was mined.

✎ **Communicate** Below the pictures, write a story about what happened to the land.

Sample: Some trees were cut to make room for a mine. When the mining stopped, people replaced the soil and planted grass and trees. In time, the mine became a forest, but it is not the same as the original forest.

 Lab Do the Quick Lab
zone *Modeling Soil Conservation.*

🔑 Assess Your Understanding

1a. Review Subsoil has (less/more) plant and animal matter than topsoil.

b. Explain What can happen to soil if plants are removed?
Soil particles can move, eroding the area.

c. Apply Concepts What are some problems that could prevent people from supporting land reclamation?
Sample: The cost; the area might be needed for something other than wildlife habitat or farming.

got it? ·······································

○ **I get it!** Now I know that soil management is important because *people use soil in many ways, and poor management causes erosion, nutrient depletion, and desertification.*

○ **I need extra help with** *See TE note.*

Go to MY SCIENCE 🅢 COACH *online for help with this subject.*

133

21st Century Learning

CRITICAL THINKING Ask students to make a generalization about the relative appeal and value of land in its original state compared to land that has been restored through land reclamation. *(Sample: Land reclamation can help restore habitats and return land to a productive state. However, land in its original state may be more productive, appealing, and valuable than land that has been restored.)*

Lab Resource: Quick Lab

L1 **MODELING SOIL CONSERVATION** Students will explore the primary cause of erosion and a method used to prevent erosion.

Evaluate ──────────

Assess Your Understanding

After students answer the questions, have them evaluate their understanding by completing the appropriate sentence.

RTI Response to Intervention

1a. If students cannot contrast subsoil and topsoil, **then** have them review **Figure 2.**

b. If students need help with predicting the effect of plant removal from soil, **then** have them locate the highlighted term *erosion* and reread the paragraph that contains the term.

c. If students have trouble recognizing challenges to land reclamation, **then** have them look again at the material under the red head *Land Reclamation.*

MY SCIENCE 🅢 COACH Have students go online for help in understanding soil management.

Differentiated Instruction

L1 **Understanding Land Reclamation** Ask students to relate the text's description of erosion to their own direct experience. If students did the Inquiry Warm-Up activity at the beginning of the section, ask them what their mining sites looked like when they were finished. *(The site was full of holes and piles of soil.)* Have students recall their predictions about how easy or difficult it would be to restore the land.

L3 **The Dust Bowl and Beyond** Encourage pairs of students to do research on the history of desertification in the United States. Invite students to share their findings with the whole class in the form of an illustrated brochure or multimedia presentation.

Lab zone **After the Inquiry Warm-Up**

Conserving Land and Soil

Inquiry Warm-Up, *How Does Mining Affect the Land?*
In the Inquiry Warm-Up, you investigated how mining affects the land. Using what you learned from that activity, answer the questions below.

1. **DRAW CONCLUSIONS** How will restoring land to its original state after mining affect the final price of the mined resource? Explain.

   _____

   _____

   _____

   _____

2. **COMPARE AND CONTRAST** Which mining tool, pencil, tweezers, or spoon, had the least damaging effect on the sand and soil in your pan? Was it also the easiest to use?

   _____

   _____

3. **OBSERVE** Were you successful in finding a sunflower seed each time you dug a new hole? Explain.

   _____

   _____

4. **MAKE JUDGMENTS** Would knowing the exact locations of the sunflower seeds before digging have a greater or lesser damaging effect on the sand and soil in your pan than not knowing? Explain.

   _____

   _____

   _____

   _____

Assess Your Understanding

Conserving Land and Soil

How Do People Use Land?

got it? ··

○ **I get it!** Now I know the ways people use and change land include _____

_____

○ **I need extra help with** _____

_____

Why Is Soil Management Important?

1a. REVIEW Subsoil has (less/more) plant and animal matter than topsoil.

b. EXPLAIN What can happen to soil if plants are removed?

_____

_____

c. APPLY CONCEPTS What are some problems that could prevent people from supporting land reclamation?

_____

_____

got it? ··

○ **I get it!** Now I know that soil management is important because _____

_____

_____

○ **I need extra help with** _____

_____

Conserving Land and Soil

How Do People Use Land?

Less than a quarter of Earth's surface is dry, ice-free land. All people on Earth must share this limited amount of land to produce their food, build shelter, and obtain resources. **Three uses that change the land are agriculture, mining, and development.** Less than a third of Earth's land can be farmed.

People create new farmland by clearing forests, draining wetlands, and irrigating deserts. Mining is the removal of nonrenewable resources from the land. Strip mining exposes soil and causes erosion. People also develop land by building roads, bridges, and buildings.

Why Is Soil Management Important?

Soil contains the minerals and nutrients that plants need to grow. The structure of fertile soil contains layers including **litter, topsoil, subsoil,** and **bedrock.** Because it can take hundreds of years to form just a few centimeters of new soil, it is important to protect Earth's soil. **Without soil, most life on land could not exist.**

Poor soil management can result in three problems: erosion, nutrient depletion, and desertification. When plants are removed during logging, mining, or farming, the soil is exposed and soil particles can easily move. The process by which water, wind, or ice moves particles of rocks or soil is

called **erosion.** If a farmer plants a field with the same crops year after year, the soil becomes less fertile, a situation called **nutrient depletion.** When soil becomes depleted, farmers usually apply **fertilizers,** which include nutrients that help crops grow better. If soil in a once-fertile area becomes depleted of nutrients and moisture, it can become like a desert. The advance of desert-like conditions into areas that previously were fertile is called **desertification.** One cause of desertification is **drought,** a period when less rain than normal falls in an area. The process of restoring an area of land to a more productive state is called **land reclamation.**

On a separate sheet of paper, explain how agriculture changes the land and how farmers can contribute to good soil management.

Review and Reinforce

Conserving Land and Soil

Understanding Main Ideas
Answer the following questions on a separate sheet of paper.

1. Explain three ways that people use and change land.
2. Describe the structure of fertile soil.
3. Why is soil so important to human beings?
4. How do erosion, nutrient depletion, and desertification damage or destroy soil?

Building Vocabulary
Match each term with its definition by writing the letter of the correct definition in the right column on the line beside the term in the left column.

5. ___ litter

6. ___ topsoil

7. ___ subsoil

8. ___ bedrock

9. ___ erosion

10. ___ nutrient depletion

11. ___ fertilizer

12. ___ desertification

13. ___ drought

14. ___ land reclamation

a. material that includes nutrients that help crops grow better

b. layer of soil in which water and nutrients are absorbed by plant roots

c. a period when less rain than normal falls in an area

d. a process in which soil becomes less fertile

e. the rock that makes up Earth's crust

f. top layer of soil containing dead leaves and grass

g. restoring an area of land to a more productive state

h. layer of soil above bedrock

i. the advance of desert-like conditions into areas that were fertile

j. the process by which water, wind, or ice moves soil or particles of rocks

Enrich

Conserving Land and Soil

> The Copper Basin is a large area of land in southeastern Tennessee. The area gets its name from the copper mining that took place there about 150 years ago. The Copper Basin was once a deciduous forest ecosystem. Now, the area consists mostly of bare hills with deep gullies caused by erosion. What happened in the Copper Basin? Read the following passage. Then answer the questions that follow on a separate sheet of paper.

The Copper Basin

When people discovered copper ore in the Copper Basin, mining companies began to dig up and process this ore. Copper ore contains many unwanted materials mixed with the copper metal. To remove the unwanted materials, the mining companies would smelt the ore, or heat it in a furnace. The smelters looked like huge, open fire pits. To keep the smelters burning, all the surrounding trees were cut down and used as fuel.

The burning ore released sulfur dioxide gas. In the air, the sulfur dioxide reacted with water vapor to form sulfuric acid. The acid fell back to Earth in rain and soaked into the soil. The acid in the soil killed plants as they began to grow where the trees had been cut down.

Animals that depended on the trees and other forest plants for food and shelter left the area. And with no plant roots left to hold down the soil, runoff from rain eroded the land. In just a few years, the entire forest ecosystem in the Copper Basin was destroyed.

Beginning in the 1930s, government agencies tried to replant part of the Copper Basin, but the soil was still too acidic. Most of the plants died. Then, nearly 50 years later, land reclamation scientists tried again, using new planting methods. They were more successful, and plants began to repopulate parts of the Copper Basin. Their roots helped prevent further erosion. Dead leaves decomposed and enriched the soil. Small animals began returning to the area. But progress is slow. Scientists estimate that it will take at least 100 more years for a true forest ecosystem to return to the Copper Basin.

1. What type of ecosystem existed in the Copper Basin area before mining began?
2. Once mining began, why were there no plants roots to hold soil in place?
3. How did the soil become contaminated with sulfuric acid?
4. What does "land reclamation" mean?
5. What changes might occur in the area as new plants continue to grow?
6. Why do you think it will take so long for the original ecosystem to rebuild?

Lesson Quiz

Conserving Land and Soil

If the statement is true, write *true*. If the statement is false, change the underlined word or words to make the statement true.

1. _____ <u>Less than a quarter</u> of Earth's surface is dry, ice-free land.

2. _____ Because it can take <u>one year</u> to form just a few centimeters of new soil, it is important to protect Earth's soil.

3. _____ If a farmer plants a field with <u>different crops</u> each year, the soil becomes less fertile, a situation called nutrient depletion.

4. _____ Without <u>soil</u>, most life on land could not exist.

Fill in the blank to complete each statement.

5. The structure of fertile soil contains layers including litter, topsoil, _____, and bedrock.

6. Strip mining exposes soil and causes _____.

7. When soil becomes depleted, farmers usually apply fertilizers, which include _____ that help crops grow better.

8. One cause of desertification is _____, a period when less rain than normal falls in an area.

9. _____ is the layer of soil where the most water and nutrients are absorbed by plant roots.

10. The process of restoring an area of land to a more productive state is called _____.

Conserving Land and Soil

Answer Key

After the Inquiry Warm-Up

1. Sample: The resource will be more expensive because the cost of restoring the land must be added to its final price.

2. Accept all reasonable responses. Students may say: The tweezers made the least damage, but the spoon was the easiest to use.

3. Accept all reasonable answers. Students will likely say: No, I had to dig several holes to find each sunflower seed.

4. Sample: Knowing the locations would have a lesser damaging effect because less digging would be necessary.

Key Concept Summaries

Sample: To create new farmland, people change the land by clearing forests, draining wetlands, and irrigating deserts. For good soil management, it's important for farmers either to apply fertilizers to restore depleted nutrients or to plant different crops from year to year, allowing nutrients to be restored naturally.

Review and Reinforce

1. Sample: People use and change the land through agriculture. Forests are cleared, wetlands drained, and deserts irrigated to create new farmland. People also use and change the land by mining minerals and other resources from within the ground. Development, or the construction of buildings, bridges, and roads, also changes the land.

2. Fertile soil consists of four layers: litter, topsoil, subsoil, and bedrock.

3. Soil is vital to human beings, because most life on Earth could not exist without it. Soil contains the minerals and nutrients that plants need to grow. It also absorbs, stores, and filters water.

4. When plants are removed during logging, mining, or farming, erosion can occur as water, wind, or ice sweep soil away. Nutrient depletion can occur if the same crops are planted in a field every year, robbing the soil of nutrients. If soil is depleted of nutrients and moisture, desertification may happen. Plants die, soil blows away, and the area becomes a desert.

5. f   6. b   7. h   8. e

9. j   10. d   11. a   12. i

13. c   14. g

Enrich

1. a forest ecosystem

2. All the trees were cut down, and other plants were killed by the acid in the soil.

3. The open smelters released sulfur dioxide gas into the air. The gas reacted with water in the air to form sulfuric acid, which fell to Earth in rain and soaked into the soil.

4. restoring land to a more natural condition

5. Sample: (1) The plants' roots will hold the soil so it won't erode easily; (2) forest animals will begin returning to the area; and (3) dead leaves, animal wastes, and dead organisms will decompose and enrich the soil.

6. Sample: It takes a long time for trees to mature and for one type of plant to replace another type. The animals in a forest ecosystem will not return until the area has gone through earlier stages of regrowth and reached maturity. (Students might mention secondary succession.)

Lesson Quiz

1. true

2. hundreds of years

3. the same crop

4. true

5. subsoil

6. erosion

7. nutrients

8. drought

9. Topsoil

10. land reclamation

Place the outside corner, the corner away from the dotted line, in the corner of your copy machine to copy onto letter-size paper.

Waste Disposal and Recycling

 What can people do to use resources wisely?

Lesson Pacing: 2–3 periods or 1–1½ blocks

🕐 **SHORT ON TIME?** To do this lesson in approximately half the time, do the Activate Prior Knowledge activity on page 134. A discussion of the key concepts on pages 135, 138, and 141 will familiarize students with the lesson content. Have students do the Quick Labs. The rest of the lesson can be completed by students independently.

Preference Navigator, in the online Planning tools, allows you to customize *Interactive Science* to your own teaching style. You can also edit lesson plans by selecting the Lesson Planner option.

Digital Teacher's Edition allows you to access your Teacher's Edition and Resource online.

my science
online.com

Lesson Vocabulary

- municipal solid waste
- incineration
- pollutant
- leachate
- sanitary landfill
- recycling
- biodegradable
- hazardous waste

 Content Refresher
Professional Development Note

Municipal Solid Waste Disposal Reducing, reusing, recycling, and composting can considerably decrease the amount of solid waste to dispose of. However, what remains is an enormous burden to landfills. In 2005, U.S. residents and businesses produced more than 246 million tons of waste. That is about 2 kilograms of waste per person per day. To reduce waste volume, some local governments implemented a controlled incineration system to drastically reduce volume and convert water to steam for heating systems or electricity generation. These approved incinerators utilize scrubbers to reduce toxic emissions and can reduce the volume of waste up to 90 percent. Incineration has the added benefit of destroying harmful chemical compounds and disease-causing bacteria.

LESSON OBJECTIVES

- 🗁 Name three ways of solid waste disposal.
- 🗁 Identify ways people can help control the solid waste problem.
- 🗁 Explain how hazardous wastes can be safely disposed of.

Blended Path
Active learning using Student Edition, Inquiry Path, and Digital Path

ENGAGE AND EXPLORE

Teach this lesson using a variety of resources. Begin by reading **My Planet Diary** as a class. Have students share ideas about what kinds of trash they produce and how to produce less. Have students do the **Inquiry Warm-Up activity.** They will classify trash to determine common types. The **After the Inquiry Warm-Up worksheet** sets up a discussion about common materials in household trash and recycling possibilities. Have volunteers share their answers to number 4 about how recycling cuts down on household trash.

EXPLAIN AND ELABORATE

Teach Key Concepts by explaining that *municipal solid waste* is the waste produced by a city or town from homes, businesses, and schools. Have students practice the inquiry skill in the **Apply it activity.** Use **Figure 1** to explain the terms *pollutant* and *leachate*. **Lead a Discussion** about the advantages and disadvantages of incineration and sanitary landfills for solid waste disposal. Use the **Support the Big Q** to help students understand the similarities and differences of reuse and recycling.

Continue to **Teach Key Concepts** by exploring the four major categories of recycling: metal, glass, paper, and plastic. **Lead a Discussion** to help students categorize objects and products used in a typical day as "used once and disposed of" or "used many times."

Teach Key Concepts by explaining that landfills are not the only method of hazardous waste disposal. Other methods include incineration, storing wastes in deep rock layers, and using organisms to break down the wastes. **Lead a Discussion** about types of hazardous wastes, including radioactive material, flammable material, corrosive substances, and toxic substances. Hand out the **Key Concept Summaries** as a review of each part of the lesson. Students can also use the online **Vocab Flash Cards** to review key terms.

EVALUATE

Have students take the **Lesson Quiz.** For an alternate assessment, see the **EXAM**VIEW® Assessment Suite, Progress Monitoring Assessments, or SuccessTracker™.

ⒺⓁⓁ Support

1 Content and Language
Tell students to look at the parts of a word for a clue to its meaning. For example, show them *pollute* in *pollutant*. Explain that the word *pollutant* is related to *pollute*. Do the same with *recycle/recycling* and *hazard/hazardous*. Have students think about what they already know about the meaning of the base words to guess the meaning of the longer word.

DIFFERENTIATED INSTRUCTION KEY
L1 Struggling Students or Special Needs
L2 On-Level Students **L3** Advanced Students

Lab zone Inquiry Path
Hands-on learning in the Lab zone

ENGAGE AND EXPLORE

To teach this lesson with an emphasis on inquiry, begin with the **Inquiry Warm-Up activity.** Students will classify trash to determine the most common types. Have students do the **After the Inquiry Warm-Up worksheet.** Talk about the most common materials in household trash and the possibilities for recycling. Have volunteers share their answers to number 4 about how recycling would cut down on the amount of household trash.

EXPLAIN AND ELABORATE

Focus on the **Inquiry Skill** for the lesson. Point out that a graph can be used to compare pieces of information. Explain that the graph compares usage of three methods of municipal waste disposal. What conclusions can students make from categorizing trash in the **Inquiry Warm-Up activity?** (*There are two common types of household waste.*) Review *incineration, sanitary landfill*, and *recycling* before beginning the **Apply It activity.** Use the **Support the Big Q activity** to discuss how reuse and recycling are alike and different. Review the term *leachate* before doing the **Teacher Demo** to show how chemicals in discarded materials in landfills can pollute groundwater. Have students do the **Lab Investigation** to reinforce students' understandings of the importance of properly designed landfills.

Review the term *biodegradable* before doing the **Build Inquiry.** Have students predict which items are biodegradable. The next **Build Inquiry activity** allows students to determine how many trees would be required to produce a year's worth of a daily newspaper. Have the students do the **Quick Lab** and then share their findings about the recycling numbers of plastic products.

Have students do the last **Quick Lab** and share their findings about the decay of radioactive materials. Students can use the online **Vocab Flash Cards** to review key terms.

EVALUATE

Have students take the **Lesson Quiz.** For an alternate assessment, see the **EXAM**VIEW® Assessment Suite, Progress Monitoring Assessments, or SuccessTracker™.

Digital Path
Online learning at **my science online**.com

ENGAGE AND EXPLORE

Teach this lesson using digital resources. Begin by having students explore the interesting facts about the trash generated by people and real-world connections to waste disposal at **My Planet Diary** online. Have them access the Chapter Resources to find the **Unlock the Big Question activity.** There they can answer the questions and refine their responses as they continue through the lesson. You can re-assign the activity and have students submit their work so you can track their progress.

EXPLAIN AND ELABORATE

Students reading above, at, or below the lexile measure of this lesson can access basic content readings at their level at **My Reading Web.** Encourage students to use the online **Vocab Flash Cards** to preview key terms. Review *incineration, sanitary landfill*, and *recycling*. Assign the **Apply It activity** online and have students submit their work to you. **Support the Big Q** by discussing how reuse and recycling are alike and how they are different.

Use the **Interactive Art activity** online to encourage students to explore what objects can be made from recyclables. Have the students do the **Quick Lab** and then share their findings about the recycling numbers of plastic products.

Use **Figure 3** to help students understand the proper way to dispose of various wastes. Do the **Quick Lab** on half-life and have the students share their findings about the decay of radioactive materials. The **Key Concept Summaries** online allow students to read a summary and see an image associated with each part of the lesson. Online remediation is available at **My Science Coach.**

EVALUATE

Have students take the **Lesson Quiz.** For an alternate assessment, see the **EXAM**VIEW® Assessment Suite, Progress Monitoring Assessments, or SuccessTracker™.

2 Frontload the Lesson
Preview the lesson visuals, labels, and captions. Ask students what they know about *hazardous wastes*. Explain the specific meanings these words have in science.

3 Comprehensible Input
Ask pairs of students to look through the visuals in the lesson to find examples of hazardous wastes. Compare the findings of the pairs. Ask the students to use the name of a hazardous waste in a sentence.

4 Language Production
Pair or group students with varied language abilities to complete labs collaboratively for language practice. Have each student copy the completed written lab for personal reference.

5 Assess Understanding
Make true or false statements using lesson content and have students indicate if they agree or disagree by using a thumbs up or thumbs down gesture to check whole-class understanding.

LESSON 4.2

Waste Disposal and Recycling

Establish Learning Objectives

After this lesson, students will be able to:

🔑 Name three methods of solid waste disposal.

🔑 Identify ways people can help control the solid waste problem.

🔑 Explain how hazardous wastes can be safely disposed of.

Engage

Activate Prior Knowledge

MY PLANET DIARY Read *Trash Talk* with the class. Point out that every person in the room generates a variety of trash. Ask: **Where do you put trash in school?** *(Classroom trash cans, cafeteria trash cans, recycling bins)* **Where do you put trash at home?** *(Kitchen trash cans, wastepaper baskets, recycling bins)* **How many different types of trash do you produce in a day?** *(Sample: food, paper, packaging, discarded objects like old pens or elastic bands)*

BIG IDEAS OF SCIENCE REFERENCE LIBRARY 📖 Have students look up the following topics: Plastic, Recycling.

Explore

Lab Resource: Inquiry Warm-Up

L1 **WHAT'S IN THE TRASH?** Students will classify trash to determine the most common types.

---

2 Waste Disposal and Recycling

UNLOCK THE BIG ?

🔑 **What Are Three Solid Waste Disposal Methods?**

🔑 **What Are the Major Categories of Recycling?**

🔑 **How Are Hazardous Wastes Safely Disposed Of?**

my planet Diary

Trash Talk

Here are some interesting facts about trash:

- Every hour, people throw away 2.5 million plastic bottles.
- Recycling one aluminum can saves enough energy to run a TV for three hours.
- Americans create two kilograms of trash per day. That trash could fill 63,000 garbage trucks each day!
- In 2005 the U.S. government recorded the first-ever drop in the amount of trash produced from the previous year. Trash declined by 1.5 million metric tons from 2004 to 2005, partly due to an increase in recycling.

SCIENCE STATS

Communicate Discuss these questions with a group of classmates. Write your answers below.

1. Do you think the amount of trash we produce will increase or decrease in the future? Explain.

   Sample: decrease, because recycling has become more popular

2. What can you do to reduce the amount of trash you create?

   Sample: recycle more, reuse materials

▶ **PLANET DIARY** Go to **Planet Diary** to learn more about waste disposal and recycling.

Lab zone ▲ Do the Inquiry Warm-Up *What's in the Trash?*

SUPPORT ALL READERS

Lexile Measure = 960L   Lexile Word Count = 1444

Prior Exposure to Content: Most students have encountered this topic in earlier grades

Academic Vocabulary: *compare, contrast, graph*

Science Vocabulary: *incineration, pollutant, biodegradable*

Concept Level: Generally appropriate for most students in this grade

Preteach With: My Planet Diary "Trash Talk" and Figure 1 activity

Go to **My Reading Web** to access leveled readings that provide a foundation for the content.

my science online.com

Vocabulary
- municipal solid waste
- incineration
- pollutant
- leachate
- sanitary landfill
- recycling
- biodegradable
- hazardous waste

Skills
- Reading: Compare and Contrast
- Inquiry: Graph

What Are Three Solid Waste Disposal Methods?

People generate many types of waste, including empty packaging, paper, and food scraps. The wastes produced in homes, businesses, schools, and in the community are called **municipal solid waste.** Other sources of solid waste include construction debris, agricultural wastes, and industrial wastes. **Three methods of handling solid waste are burning, burying, and recycling.** Each method has its advantages and disadvantages.

Incineration The burning of solid waste is called **incineration** (in sin ur AY shun). The burning facilities, or incinerators, do not take up much space. They do not directly pollute groundwater. The heat produced by burning solid waste can be used to produce electricity. Incinerators supply electricity to many homes.

Unfortunately, incinerators do have drawbacks. Even the best incinerators create some air pollution. Although incinerators reduce the volume of waste by as much as 90 percent, some waste still remains and needs to be disposed of somewhere. Incinerators are also expensive to build.

apply it!

What happens to all the trash?

1 **Graph** Use the data in the table and the key to fill in the bar graph. The graph represents the methods of municipal waste disposal in the United States in 2007. Give the graph a title.

Disposal Method	Waste (Percent)
Incineration	13%
Landfills	54%
Recycling	33%

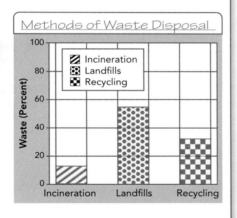

Methods of Waste Disposal

2 CHALLENGE Why do you think incineration is the least popular method of solid waste disposal?

<u>Incinerators create some air</u>
<u>pollution and some waste remains.</u>
<u>They are also expensive to build.</u>

135

Explain

Introduce Vocabulary
Explain to students that *municipal solid waste* refers to all of the wastes produced by a municipality, which is a city or town. This includes wastes from homes, business, and schools.

Teach Key Concepts
Explain to students that solid waste is an inevitable result of human activities. Since people can't avoid creating waste, they have focused research on how to dispose of it in the most responsible, healthful manner. Ask: **What three methods have people found for disposing of solid waste?** (Burning, burying, recycling) **What are some types of solid waste?** (Empty packaging, paper, food scraps, construction debris, agricultural and industrial wastes)

Lead a Discussion
HOUSEHOLD WASTE Point out that though all human beings generate solid household waste, people and communities handle waste in a variety of ways. Ask: **What kinds of things does your family throw away?** (Sample: Used paper, metal cans, glass jars, plastic milk jugs, and so on) **How does your family get rid of its trash?** (Trash may be collected in the students' community, or families may bring trash to a "dump" themselves. Some families may recycle part of their trash.)

Apply It!
L1 Relate the terms *incineration, landfills,* and *recycling* in the graph to the words *burning, burying,* and *recycling* in the section's Key Concept before beginning the activity.

Graph Have students examine the elements of the graph before they begin. They should note the presence of three terms along the bottom of the graph, the key containing the same three terms, and the increasing numbers and the label on the left side of the graph. Then have them relate the numbers and terms in the table to the elements in the graph.

My Planet Diary provides an opportunity for students to explore real-world connections to waste disposal.

Digital Lesson: Assign the *Apply It* activity online and have students submit their work to you.

LESSON 4.2

Explain

Teach With Visuals

Tell students to look at **Figure 1**. Remind them why sanitary landfills were developed. Ask different volunteers to read the labels aloud. Ask: **How is this landfill designed to reduce health risks?** *(Vent pipes release gases that might cause an explosion. Wells are monitored for wastes polluting groundwater. Leachate forms at the bottom rather than running off into surrounding water. Liners keep liquids from leaking into the soil.)* **What can people do to further decrease the risk of pollution from landfills?** *(Reduce the amount of landfill waste that could be poisonous, such as pesticides.)* Remind students that even well-designed landfills do not prevent all leakage.

Lead a Discussion

DISPOSAL OF SOLID WASTES Have students brainstorm and name items they throw away that might end up in a landfill. Explain that solid waste can be disposed of by incineration or by burying it in landfills. Ask: **What are the advantages of incineration?** *(Incinerators take up little space, do not pollute groundwater, and produce heat that can be used to generate electricity.)* **What are the disadvantages of incineration?** *(It releases pollution, does not completely destroy the solid waste, and incinerators are expensive to build.)* **What are the advantages of sanitary landfills over open dumps?** *(They prevent leachate from contaminating groundwater, contain wastes more safely, and are not as unsightly.)* **What are the disadvantages of sanitary landfills?** *(They still can pollute groundwater, and the uses of capped landfills are limited.)*

Compare and Contrast Tell students that when they compare and contrast, they examine the similarities and differences between things.

Support the Big Q ? UbD

THE THREE R'S Ask students to give examples of reuse and recycling. Ask: **How are reuse and recycling similar?** *(They do not use raw materials from Earth.)* **How are they different?** *(Reuse does not change the object. Recycling breaks down the object and forms the material into new objects.)*

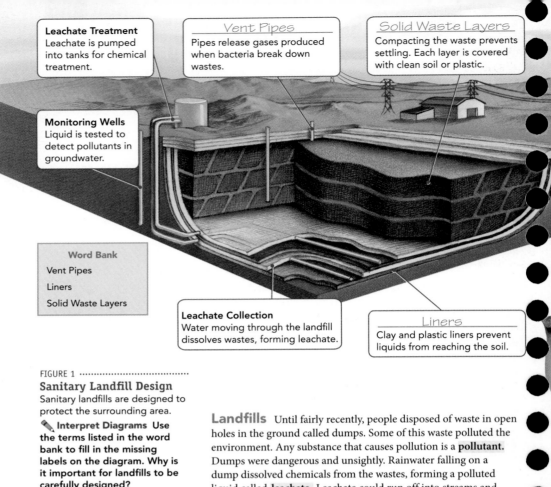

Leachate Treatment
Leachate is pumped into tanks for chemical treatment.

Vent Pipes
Pipes release gases produced when bacteria break down wastes.

Solid Waste Layers
Compacting the waste prevents settling. Each layer is covered with clean soil or plastic.

Monitoring Wells
Liquid is tested to detect pollutants in groundwater.

Word Bank
Vent Pipes
Liners
Solid Waste Layers

Leachate Collection
Water moving through the landfill dissolves wastes, forming leachate.

Liners
Clay and plastic liners prevent liquids from reaching the soil.

FIGURE 1 ....
Sanitary Landfill Design
Sanitary landfills are designed to protect the surrounding area.

✎ **Interpret Diagrams** Use the terms listed in the word bank to fill in the missing labels on the diagram. Why is it important for landfills to be carefully designed?

Leachate could
pollute groundwater.
_____
_____
_____

Landfills Until fairly recently, people disposed of waste in open holes in the ground called dumps. Some of this waste polluted the environment. Any substance that causes pollution is a **pollutant.** Dumps were dangerous and unsightly. Rainwater falling on a dump dissolved chemicals from the wastes, forming a polluted liquid called **leachate.** Leachate could run off into streams and lakes, or trickle down into the groundwater.

In 1976, the government banned open dumps. Now much solid waste is buried in landfills that are built to hold the wastes more safely. A **sanitary landfill** holds municipal solid waste, construction debris, and some types of agricultural and industrial waste. **Figure 1** shows the parts of a well-designed sanitary landfill. Once a landfill is full, it is covered with a clay cap to keep rainwater from entering the waste.

Even well-designed landfills can pollute groundwater. Capped landfills can be reused as parks and sites for sports arenas. They cannot be used for housing or agriculture.

136 Land, Air, and Water Resources

Recycling You may have heard of the "three R's"—reduce, reuse, and recycle. *Reduce* refers to creating less waste from the beginning, such as using cloth shopping bags rather than disposable ones. *Reuse* refers to finding another use for an object rather than discarding it, such as refilling reusable bottles with drinking water instead of buying new bottled water.

The process of reclaiming raw materials and reusing them to create new products is called **recycling.** You can recycle at home and encourage others to recycle. You can buy products made from recycled materials. Your purchase makes it more profitable for companies to use recycled materials in products.

Another way to reduce solid waste is to start a compost pile. The moist, dark conditions in a compost pile allow natural decomposers to break down grass clippings, leaves, and some food wastes. Compost is an excellent natural fertilizer for plants.

✎ Compare and Contrast
In the table below, write one pro and one con for each of the three solid waste disposal methods.

	Incineration	Sanitary Landfills	Recycling
Pro	Incinerators take up little space.	Sanitary landfills can become parks after they are capped.	Materials are used again and not thrown out.
Con	Incinerators are expensive to build.	Landfills can pollute groundwater.	Not everyone recycles.

Lab zone Do the Lab Investigation *Waste, Away!*

🔑 Assess Your Understanding

1a. Define What is incineration?
The burning of solid waste

b. Design a Solution What could be some possible uses for the space over a landfill once it is capped? Sample: ball fields, playgrounds, skating rinks

c. Make Judgments Which solid waste disposal method do you think is best? Why?
Sample: recycling, because materials are reused

got it?

○ I get it! Now I know solid waste can be disposed of through incineration, sanitary landfills, and recycling.

○ I need extra help with See TE note.

Go to MY SCIENCE **COACH** *online for help with this subject.*

137

Differentiated Instruction

L1 Explaining a Position Call on students at random to give concise oral explanations of why metal, plastic, glass, and paper should be recycled instead of being discarded in landfills.

L3 Debating Methods of Waste Disposal Have three pairs or groups of students do further research about the benefits and drawbacks of each method of solid waste disposal. Then have students stage a debate in which they present and defend the position that their method is superior to the other two methods.

L3 Researching Packaging Design Point out to students that some large American corporations, such as many fast-food restaurants, have redesigned their packaging to reduce the amount of solid waste. Students might prepare a brief oral report in which they share their findings.

Elaborate

Teacher Demo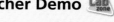

L1 MAKE A MODEL OF A LANDFILL

Materials beaker, coffee filter, food coloring, jar, rubber band, soil, water

Time 10 minutes

Review the meaning of *leachate*. Put a coffee filter over the mouth of a jar, letting it hang into the jar, and secure it in place with a rubber band. Fill the filter about halfway with soil. Put several drops of food coloring on the soil, and then pour water into the jar. Let water collect in the jar. Ask: **What do you see in the jar?** *(Colored water)* **Where did the color come from?** *(The food coloring)* **What does the food coloring represent in this landfill model?** *(Chemicals in the soil)* **In a real landfill, where do chemicals come from?** *(The wastes in the landfill)*

Lab Resource: Lab Investigation

L2 WASTE, AWAY! Students will observe how well different models of landfills protect groundwater from leachate, and they will make models of a sanitary landfill, a poorly designed landfill, and an open dump.

Evaluate

Assess Your Understanding

After students answer the questions, have them evaluate their understanding by completing the appropriate sentence.

RTI Response to Intervention

1a. If students cannot define *incineration*, **then** have them locate the highlighted term *incineration* and reread the definition.

b. If students have trouble identifying uses of land, **then** have them brainstorm ideas as they look again at **Figure 1**.

c. If students need help with evaluating disposal methods, **then** have them review the chart they completed on this page.

MY SCIENCE **COACH** Have students go online for help in understanding waste disposal.

Explain

Teach Key Concepts 🔑

Point out to students that the most commonly recycled materials are ones for which there are practical uses. Ask: **What four materials are recycled most commonly?** *(Metal, glass, paper, plastic)* **What are some items that are not biodegradable or that degrade very slowly?** *(Plastic, metal, glass)* **What are the benefits of recycling aluminum and other metals?** *(It takes less energy to recycle than to mine the raw materials and process the ore. It also saves money and causes less pollution.)* **What are plastic products that can be recycled?** *(Milk jugs, detergent containers, and soda bottles)*

Lead a Discussion

REUSED OR DISCARDED Have students identify the many objects and products that they use in the course of a day, from a toothbrush to carton of orange juice. Ask: **Which objects and products get used only once?** *(Sample: small bottle of water or soda, sheet of paper)* **Which get used many times?** *(Sample: toothbrush, silverware, clothing)* **How do various products get disposed of?** *(Sample: household trash, recycling bin, compost pile)*

Elaborate

Build Inquiry 🧪

L3 **WHAT WILL DECOMPOSE?**

Materials common materials, such as "biodegradable" packaging, paper, cardboard, plastic wrap, wax paper, aluminum foil, plastic gloves, trowel

Time 15 minutes on two different days

Have small groups of students select an item to bury on the school grounds. Advise each group to select an item made of a different material. Ask students to predict whether their material will be biodegradable. At the end of their work on this chapter, have the groups dig up their items to see which materials began to decompose.

CAUTION: Request permission from school officials to do this activity before you begin. Do not allow students to bury food. Have students wear plastic gloves when handling materials and soil and wash their hands afterward. Students who are allergic to molds should not participate.

Ask: **Why do certain items appear not to have begun decomposing?** *(Sample response: The materials in the item may take longer to break down or it might not be biodegradable.)*

What Are the Major Categories of Recycling?

Recycling reduces the volume of solid waste by reusing materials. Recycling uses energy, but it also saves the energy that would be needed to obtain, transport, and process raw materials. Recycling is also cheaper than making new materials. Additionally, recycling conserves nonrenewable resources and limits the environmental damage caused by mining for raw materials.

Materials that can be broken down and recycled by bacteria and other decomposers are **biodegradable** (by oh dih GRAY duh bul). Many products people use today are not biodegradable, such as plastic containers, metal cans, rubber tires, and glass jars. Instead, people have developed different ways to recycle the raw materials in these products.

A wide range of materials can be recycled. 🔑 **Most recycling focuses on four major categories of products: metal, glass, paper, and plastic.**

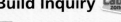

Vocabulary Prefixes The prefix *bio-* means "life." A material is biodegradable if it can be broken down and recycled by living things such as

<u>bacteria and other</u>
<u>decomposers.</u>

Material	Recycling Process	Products Made From Recycling
Metal	Metals are melted in furnaces and rolled into sheets.	Cars, cans, bicycles, jewelry, office supplies, house siding
Glass	Glass pieces are melted in furnaces and cast into new glass.	Bottles, floor tiles, countertops, jewelry, jars
Paper	Paper is shredded and mixed with water to form pulp. The pulp is washed, dried, and rolled into new sheets.	Toilet paper, notebook paper, paper cups, paper plates, napkins, envelopes
Plastic	Plastic containers are chopped, washed, and melted. The molten plastic is turned into pellets that can be heated and molded.	Picnic tables, park benches, speed bumps, recycling bins, playground equipment, deck lumber, fleece (see girl's jacket at left)

Is recycling worthwhile? Besides conserving resources, recycling saves energy. Making aluminum products from recycled aluminum rather than from raw materials uses about 90 percent less energy overall. For certain materials, recycling is usually worthwhile. However, recycling is not a complete answer to the solid waste problem. For some cities, recycling is not cost-effective. Scientists have not found good ways to recycle some materials, such as plastic-coated paper and plastic foam. Some recycled products, such as low-quality recycled newspaper, have few uses. All recycling processes require energy and create pollution. The value of recycling must be judged on a case-by-case basis.

138 Land, Air, and Water Resources

Interactive Art allows students to determine what objects can be made from recyclables.

my science online.com   **Recycling**

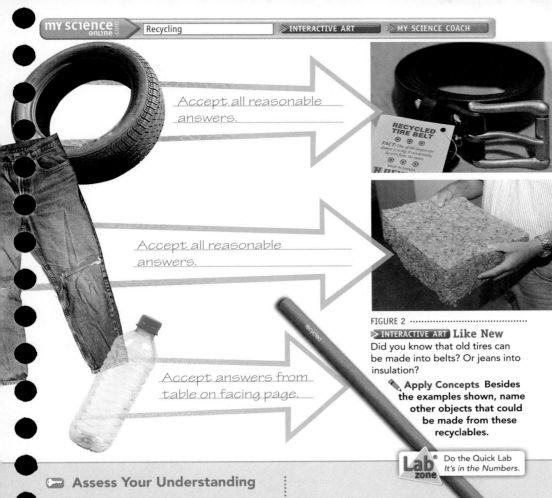

Accept all reasonable answers.

Accept all reasonable answers.

Accept answers from table on facing page.

FIGURE 2 ....

> INTERACTIVE ART **Like New**
Did you know that old tires can be made into belts? Or jeans into insulation?

✏ **Apply Concepts** Besides the examples shown, name other objects that could be made from these recyclables.

Lab zone Do the Quick Lab *It's in the Numbers.*

🔑 Assess Your Understanding

2a. Explain How does recycling save energy?
Less energy is used when recycling than when mining, transporting, or processing raw materials.

b. Solve Problems How could your community solve its solid waste problem?
Increase recycling and awareness, build sanitary landfills that limit water pollution, and use incinerators when useful.

got it?

○ **I get it!** Now I know recyclable materials are categorized as metal, glass, paper, and plastic.

○ **I need extra help with** See TE note.

Go to **my science COACH** *online for help with this subject.*

139

Build Inquiry **Lab zone**

L2 CALCULATE TREES TO MAKE NEWSPAPER

Materials calculator (optional), metric ruler, newspapers

Time 10 minutes

Show students a stack containing one week of daily newspapers that you have collected. Ask them to estimate how many newspapers they think one tree can make. Explain that one tree 10.5 to 12 m tall produces a stack of newspapers 1.2 m high. Have a volunteer measure the height of the stack.

Ask: **In how many weeks would I use up one tree by reading the newspaper?** *(120 cm divided by the height of the stack)* **How many trees would I use up in a year?** *(52 divided by weeks to use one tree)*

Lab Resource: Quick Lab **Lab zone**

L2 IT'S IN THE NUMBERS Students will explore, analyze, and classify plastic products according to their recycling numbers.

Evaluate

Assess Your Understanding

After students answer the questions, have them evaluate their understanding by completing the appropriate sentence.

R T I Response to Intervention

2a. If students cannot explain energy savings, **then** have them reread the last paragraph under *What Are the Major Categories of Recycling?*

b. If students need help with explaining a solution, **then** have them identify specific facts about how their community handles solid waste and review the information on three disposal methods in light of community needs.

my science COACH Have students go online for help in understanding recycling.

Differentiated Instruction

L1 Reviewing Methods of Solid Waste Disposal Help students summarize what they have learned about solid waste disposal methods by making a compare/contrast chart showing the benefits and drawbacks of incineration, sanitary landfills, and recycling.

L3 Converting Used Items Ask students to look around their homes for items that are typically used once and then discarded. Challenge students to think of ways to convert the items into items that would be useful at home or in school. Encourage students who are artistically inclined to create works of art. *(Examples: A used greeting card can be cut to make gift tags. Items can be turned into art or jewelry.)*

Explain

Teach Key Concepts 🔑

Explain to students that the use of specially designed landfills is not the only method of hazardous waste disposal today. Ask: **What other methods are sometimes used for hazardous waste disposal?** *(Incineration, storing them in deep rock layers, using organisms to break down the wastes)* Have students brainstorm ways to reduce the use of hazardous materials, such as using rechargeable batteries, and buying nontoxic arts and crafts supplies.

Teach With Visuals

Have students look at each of the items pictured in **Figure 3.** Discuss each type of waste and its proper disposal. Students may disagree on how to dispose of some items. For example, some students may say that an old cell phone should go in the recycling container, rather than in the hazardous waste container. Point out that some materials in cell phones can be recycled, but it is a specialized process. A cell phone should not be put in a collection for paper, plastics, and other common recyclables. Some students may say to throw a pizza box in the trash, while others say it can be recycled. Point out to students that it is important to make sure recyclable items are as clean as possible when you dispose of them. For example, it is best to remove any remaining food from pizza boxes and yogurt containers before recycling them.

How Are Hazardous Wastes Safely Disposed Of?

Many people picture hazardous wastes as bubbling chemicals or oozing slime. Any material that can be harmful to human health or the environment if it is not properly disposed of is a **hazardous waste.**

Types of Hazardous Wastes Toxic wastes can damage the health of humans and other organisms. Explosive wastes can react very quickly when exposed to air or water, or explode when dropped. Flammable wastes easily catch fire. Corrosive wastes can dissolve many materials. Everyday hazardous wastes include electronic devices, batteries, and paint.

Other wastes that require special disposal are radioactive wastes. Radioactive wastes give off radiation that can cause cancer and other diseases. Some radioactive waste can remain dangerous for millions of years.

Health Effects A person can be exposed to hazardous wastes by breathing, eating, drinking, or touching them. Even short-term exposure to hazardous wastes can cause problems such as skin irritation or breathing difficulties. Long-term exposure can cause diseases such as cancer, damage to body organs, or death.

FIGURE 3 ·····································
Sort It Out!
Wastes can be thrown away, recycled, or disposed of as hazardous waste.

✎ **Summarize** Draw a line from each object to its appropriate disposal container.

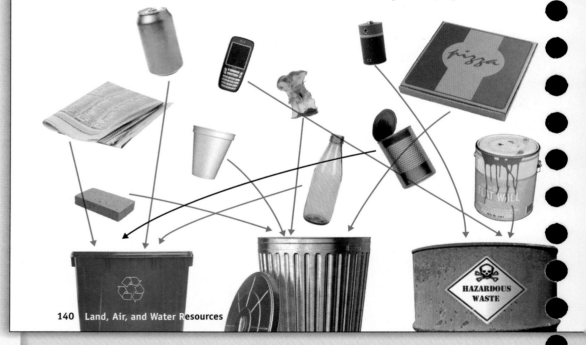

Disposal Methods It is difficult to safely dispose of hazardous wastes. Hazardous wastes are most often disposed of in carefully designed landfills. The landfills are lined and covered with clay and plastic. These materials prevent chemicals from leaking into the soil and groundwater. **Hazardous wastes that are not disposed of in carefully designed landfills may be incinerated or broken down by organisms. Liquid wastes may be stored in deep rock layers.**

Scientists are still searching for methods that will provide safe and permanent disposal of radioactive wastes. Some wastes are currently stored in vaults dug hundreds of meters underground or in concrete and steel containers above ground.

Disposal Sites It is a challenge to decide where to build hazardous waste disposal facilities. In general, people would prefer to have a single large facility located in an area where few people live. However, it may be safer, cheaper, and easier to transport wastes to small local facilities instead.

Reducing Hazardous Waste The best way to manage hazardous wastes is to produce less of them in the first place. Industries are eager to develop safe alternatives to harmful chemicals. At home, you can find substitutes for some hazardous household chemicals. For example, you could use citronella candles instead of insect spray to repel insects.

FIGURE 4 ·······

Hazardous Wastes

Hazardous waste can be harmful if improperly handled.

✎ **Review** What is the best way to manage hazardous wastes?

○ Store waste in small facilities.

◉ Produce less waste to start.

○ Incinerate waste.

 Do the Quick Lab Half-Life.

🔑 **Assess Your Understanding**

3a. Name What are some negative health effects of exposure to hazardous wastes?
Skin irritation, difficulty
breathing, cancer, damage to
body organs, death

b. Make Judgments Do you think hazardous wastes should be disposed of at one large central facility? Explain.
Accept all reasonable answers.
Students should justify their
answers with evidence.

got it? ·······

○ **I get it!** Now I know that hazardous wastes are disposed of by _putting them in_
landfills or in rock layers, by incinerating them, or by using organisms
to break waste down.

○ **I need extra help with** _See TE note._

Go to my science 💬 **coach** *online for help with this subject.*

141

Differentiated Instruction

L1 Hidden Hazards Help students understand that not all hazardous wastes can be seen directly or easily. For example, the outside parts of a battery or a fluorescent light bulb hide the hazardous materials—potassium hydroxide and mercury—that exist within the objects. Lead a discussion about other objects that are not *obviously* hazardous.

L3 Picturing Hazardous Wastes Encourage students to look for photographs of the various types of hazardous waste. Students might make photocopies of these images in order to put together an annotated photo gallery. Have students find images that represent toxic, explosive, flammable, corrosive, and radioactive wastes. Encourage students to find the symbols used to mark these kinds of wastes.

LESSON 4.2

Lead a Discussion

TYPES OF HAZARDOUS MATERIALS Tell students that hazardous wastes are sometimes not easy to identify. Explain that radioactive material is a material that contains unstable atoms and gives off radiation that can cause health problems. Ask: **What is a flammable material?** *(A material that can catch fire easily)* **How do corrosive substances affect materials?** *(They dissolve the materials.)* **What effect do toxic substances have on the body?** *(They act as poisons to harm the body.)* **How should hazardous wastes be disposed of?** *(In carefully designed landfills, by incineration, by being broken down by organisms, or by storage in deep rock layers)*

Elaborate ———

Lab Resource: Quick Lab

L2 HALF-LIFE Students will explore the decay of radioactive materials.

Evaluate ———

Assess Your Understanding

After students answer the questions, have them evaluate their understanding by completing the appropriate sentence.

RTI Response to Intervention

3a. If students have trouble identifying negative health effects, **then** have them look again at the red heads *Types of Hazardous Wastes* and *Health Effects.*

b. If students cannot make a judgment about hazardous waste disposal, **then** have them review the information under the red head *Disposal Methods.*

my science 💬 **coach** Have students go online for help in understanding the various methods of disposing of hazardous wastes.

Lab zone **After the Inquiry Warm-Up**

Waste Disposal and Recycling

> **Inquiry Warm-Up, *What's in the Trash?***
> In the Inquiry Warm-Up, you investigated the most common materials in household trash. Using what you learned from that activity, answer the questions below.

1. **INTERPRET DATA** How many times more paper items than metal items did you have in your trash bag?

   _____

2. **INTERPRET DATA** How many categories of trash did you show on your graph?

   _____

3. **USE PRIOR KNOWLEDGE** Are any materials in the trash recyclable? Explain.

   _____

   _____

4. **APPLY CONCEPTS** Would recycling cut down on the amount of household trash? Explain.

   _____

   _____

   _____

   _____

Assess Your Understanding

Waste Disposal and Recycling

What Are Three Solid Waste Disposal Methods?

1a. DEFINE What is incineration? _____

_____

b. DESIGN A SOLUTION What could be some possible uses for the space over a landfill once it is capped? _____

_____

c. MAKE JUDGMENTS Which solid waste disposal method do you think is best? Why? _____

_____

got it? ··

○ **I get it!** Now I know solid waste can be disposed of by _____

_____

○ **I need extra help with** _____

_____

What Are the Major Categories of Recycling?

2a. EXPLAIN How does recycling save energy? _____

_____

b. SOLVE PROBLEMS How could your community solve its solid waste problem? _____

_____

got it? ··

○ **I get it!** Now I know recyclable materials are categorized as _____

_____

○ **I need extra help with** _____

_____

Assess Your Understanding

Waste Disposal and Recycling

| How Are Hazardous Wastes Safely Disposed Of? |

3a. NAME What are some negative health effects of exposure to

hazardous waste? _____

_____

_____

b. MAKE JUDGMENTS Do you think hazardous wastes should be disposed

of at one large central facility? Explain. _____

_____

_____

_____

got_{it}?..

○ **I get it!** Now I know that hazardous wastes are disposed of by _____

_____

_____

○ **I need extra help with** _____

_____

Key Concept Summaries

Waste Disposal and Recycling

What Are Three Solid Waste Disposal Methods?

The wastes produced in homes, businesses, schools, and in the community—such as paper, food scraps, empty packaging, construction debris, agricultural wastes, and industrial wastes—are called **municipal solid waste. Three methods of handling solid waste are burning, burying, and recycling.** The burning of solid waste is called **incineration.** Any substance that causes pollution is a **pollutant.** Until a few decades ago, people buried waste in open dumps. Some of this waste polluted the environment. Rainwater falling on a dump dissolved chemicals from the wastes, forming a liquid called **leachate** that could pollute rivers, streams, and groundwater.

Now much solid waste is buried safely in landfills. A **sanitary landfill** is specially designed to safely hold municipal solid waste, construction debris, and some types of agricultural and industrial waste.

We can all decrease the amount of waste we produce by following the "three R's"—reduce, reuse, and recycle. We can reduce by using less and creating less waste in the first place. We reuse objects and materials when we find another use instead of discarding them. **Recycling** is the process of reclaiming raw materials and reusing them to create new products.

What Are the Major Categories of Recycling?

Recycling reduces the volume of solid waste by reusing materials. Materials that can be broken down by bacteria and other decomposers are **biodegradable. Most recycling focuses on four major categories** **of products: metal, glass, paper, and plastic.** Recycling conserves resources and saves energy, yet it does not solve the solid waste problem.

How Are Hazardous Wastes Safely Disposed Of?

Any material that can be harmful to human health or the environment if it is not properly disposed of is a **hazardous waste.** Hazardous wastes include those that are toxic, explosive, flammable, corrosive, and radioactive. **Hazardous wastes that are not disposed of in carefully designed landfills may be incinerated or broken down by organisms. Liquid wastes may be stored in deep rock layers.**

On a separate sheet of paper, explain how people can use the "three R's" to decrease the amount of waste we produce.

Place the outside corner, the corner away from the dotted line, in the corner of your copy machine to copy onto letter-size paper.

Waste Disposal and Recycling

Understanding Main Ideas
Answer the following questions on a separate sheet of paper.

1. What are three methods for the disposal of solid waste?
2. What are three advantages and three disadvantages of incinerators?
3. What is leachate and what major problem does it cause?
4. What are the four major categories of materials that can be recycled?
5. How can exposure to hazardous wastes affect human health?
6. Identify four methods for disposing of hazardous wastes.

Building Vocabulary
Write a definition for each of these terms on the lines below.

7. biodegradable

_____

_____

8. pollutant

_____

_____

9. sanitary landfill

_____

_____

10. municipal solid waste

_____

_____

Waste Disposal and Recycling

The table below shows how the types of wastes discarded by households in the United States changed between 1960 and 2000. The table shows the amounts as percents of the total wastes discarded. These percents include all materials discarded, whether they were recycled, incinerated, or sent to a landfill. On a separate sheet of paper, use the data to answer the questions that follow the table.

How Wastes Changed

Household Discards from 1960 to 2000

Types of Wastes	Percent of Total Wastes				
	1960	**1970**	**1980**	**1990**	**2000**
Paper and Cardboard	34.0	36.6	36.4	38.6	37.4
Glass	7.6	10.5	10.0	6.4	5.5
Metals	12.3	11.4	10.2	8.1	7.8
Plastics	0.4	2.4	4.5	8.3	10.7
Food Waste	13.8	10.6	8.6	10.1	11.2
Yard Waste	22.7	19.2	18.1	17.1	12.0
Other Wastes	9.2	9.3	12.2	11.4	15.4

1. Use the data in the table to make a line graph on a sheet of graph paper. Plot the percentages on the vertical axis. Plot the years on the horizontal axis. Draw a separate line for each type of waste. Use a different color for each line. Include a key to identify the color-coding you used.
2. Which types of wastes increased as a percentage form 1960 to 2000?
3. Which types of wastes decreased as a percentage during that period?
4. Which type of waste increased the most between 1960 and 2000? Is this change related to other changes in the data? Explain your answer.
5. How might you expect the data for 2000 to be different if it included only the materials sent to landfills? Explain your answer.

Lesson Quiz

Waste Disposal and Recycling

Fill in the blank to complete each statement.

1. _____ solid waste includes empty packaging, paper, food scraps, agricultural and industrial waste, and construction debris.

2. The burning of solid waste is called _____.

3. One safe way to handle solid waste is to bury it in _____.

4. _____ is reclaiming and reusing raw materials to create new products.

If the statement is true, write *true*. If the statement is false, change the underlined word or words make the statement true.

5. _____ Materials that can be broken down and recycled by bacteria and other decomposers are <u>biodegradable</u>.

6. _____ <u>Recycling</u> conserves resources and saves energy.

7. _____ <u>Solid waste</u> is any material that can be harmful to human health or to the environment.

8. _____ When rainwater filters down through a dump and dissolves chemicals in the waste, the polluted result is called <u>run-off</u>.

9. _____ Most recycling focuses on four major categories of products: metal, glass, paper, and <u>rubber</u>.

10. _____ A person can be exposed to <u>hazardous wastes</u> by breathing, eating, drinking, or touching them.

Waste Disposal and Recycling

Answer Key

After the Inquiry Warm-Up

1. four times as much

2. 7

3. Sample: Yes. Paper, yard and food waste, metal, glass, and plastic can all be recycled.

4. Sample: Yes, recycling many of the materials would cut down on the amount of material that needs to be thrown away.

Key Concept Summaries

People can reduce by using less and creating less waste in the first place. Instead of discarding used objects and materials, they can reuse them by finding another use for them. Recycling reduces waste by reclaiming raw materials from waste and reusing them to create new products.

Review and Reinforce

1. burning (or incineration), burying, and recycling

2. Advantages: take up less space than landfills, do not pollute groundwater, can generate electricity

   Disadvantages: cause some air pollution, some waste remains, more expensive to build than sanitary landfills

3. Leachate is polluted water that contains dissolved chemicals from the waste it has seeped through. It can run off into streams and lakes or trickle down into groundwater and pollute water supplies.

4. metal, glass, paper, and plastic

5. Short-term exposure may cause health problems such as skin irritation or breathing difficulties. Long-term exposure may cause diseases such as cancer, damage to body organs, or death.

6. Hazardous wastes can be placed in carefully designed landfills, incinerated, or broken down by organisms. Liquid wastes may be stored in deep rock layers.

7. can be broken down and recycled by bacteria and other decomposers

8. any substance that causes pollution

9. a landfill specially designed to hold solid waste safely

10. wastes produced in homes, businesses, schools, and in a community

Enrich

1. The graph should show that paper and cardboard increased slightly, glass, metals, and yard waste decreased, and plastics increased. Food wastes decreased, then increased.

2. plastics, paper

3. glass, metals, yard wastes

4. Plastics increased the most. At the same time, glass and metals decreased. Sample response: During this time, plastics were used for more containers, replacing glass in many uses.

5. Sample: Paper, glass, metals, and plastics would all have lower percentages. These materials are easily recycled, which means less of them ends up in landfills.

Lesson Quiz

1. Municipal
2. incineration
3. sanitary landfills
4. Recycling
5. true
6. true
7. Hazardous waste
8. leachate
9. plastic
10. true

Air Pollution and Solutions

What can people do to use resources wisely?

Lesson Pacing: 2–3 periods or 1–1½ blocks

⏱ **SHORT ON TIME?** To do this lesson in approximately half the time, do the Activate Prior Knowledge activity on page 142. A discussion of the key concepts on pages 143, 146, 148, and 150 will familiarize students with the lesson content. Have students do the Quick Labs. The rest of the lesson can be completed by students independently.

Preference Navigator, in the online Planning tools, allows you to customize *Interactive Science* to your own teaching style. You can also edit lesson plans by selecting the Lesson Planner option.

Digital Teacher's Edition allows you to access your Teacher's Edition and Resource materials online.

Lesson Vocabulary

- emissions
- photochemical smog
- ozone
- temperature inversion
- acid rain
- radon
- ozone layer
- chlorofluorocarbon

Professional Development Note

Content Refresher

Acid Rain Acid rain is a general term to describe precipitation that has a pH lower than 5.6, which is normal rain. Pure water has a pH of 7. The Environmental Protection Agency (EPA) uses the term *acid deposition*. Acid deposition has two types, wet and dry. Wet deposition refers to acidic rain, fog, and snow. This acidic precipitation flows over the ground and affects plants, animals, and structures. Dry deposition refers to acidic gases and particles. Half of the acidity in the atmosphere falls back to Earth through dry deposition and is blown onto cars, buildings, homes, and trees. Often, dry deposition is washed off these surfaces by rain, making the combination more acidic than the acid rain alone.

LESSON OBJECTIVES

☞ Identify the causes of indoor and outdoor air pollution.
☞ Explain the importance of the ozone layer and how it has been damaged.
☞ Explain the key to reducing air pollution.

Blended Path
Active learning using Student Edition, Inquiry Path, and Digital Path

ENGAGE AND EXPLORE

Teach this lesson using a variety of resources. Begin by reading **My Planet Diary** as a class. Have students share ideas about how they can raise awareness about reducing air pollution. Then have students do the **Inquiry Warm-Up activity.** Discuss how quickly and how far the scent spread. The **After the Inquiry Warm-Up worksheet** asks students to predict what happens if variables of the activity were changed. Have volunteers share their answers to number 4 about designing a new experiment to test other scents.

EXPLAIN AND ELABORATE

Teach Key Concepts to identify the major causes of outdoor and indoor air pollution. **Lead a Discussion** about specific examples of air pollution that students have encountered. **Lead a Discussion** about the causes of smog and the causes and effects of acid rain. Then have students do the **Apply It activity** about limiting emissions that lead to acid rain. Continue to **Teach Key Concepts** by reminding students that air pollution exists indoors and outdoors.

Lead a Discussion about the ozone layer. Use **Figure 5** to explain how the ozone cycle prevents harmful ultraviolet radiation from reaching Earth's surface. **Teach Key Concepts** to explain the importance of the ozone layer and how it has been damaged. Use **Figure 6** to discuss what scientific inquiry has revealed about the ozone hole caused by chlorofluorocarbons.

Continue to **Teach Key Concepts** by discussing how to reduce air pollution and what students can do to reduce air pollution. Use the **Support the Big Q activity** to help students understand how they can make changes in their everyday activities and reduce air pollution. Hand out the **Key Concept Summaries** as a review of the lesson. Students can use the online **Vocab Flash Cards** to review key terms.

EVALUATE

Have students take the **Lesson Quiz.** For an alternate assessment, see the **EXAM**VIEW® Assessment Suite, Progress Monitoring Assessments, or SuccessTracker™.

E L L Support

1 Content and Language

Have students copy the vocabulary words in a journal. Then ask them to find the first time the words are used in the chapter. Have them copy the definition of each vocabulary word into their journals.

DIFFERENTIATED INSTRUCTION KEY
L1 Struggling Students or Special Needs
L2 On-Level Students **L3** Advanced Students

LESSON PLANNER 4.3

Lab zone Inquiry Path
Hands-on learning in the Lab zone

ENGAGE AND EXPLORE

To teach this lesson with an emphasis on inquiry, begin with the **Inquiry Warm-Up activity.** Students will try to detect a scent and then describe the way in which the scent spreads throughout the room. Have students do the **After the Inquiry Warm-Up worksheet.** Discuss their prediction about what would happen if certain variables of the activity were changed. Have volunteers share their answers to number 4 about designing a new experiment to compare the direction and speed at which other scents spread.

EXPLAIN AND ELABORATE

Focus on the **Inquiry Skill** for the lesson. Point out that when you communicate, you are share ideas with others through writing and speaking. What role did communication play in the **Inquiry Warm-Up activity?** *(The accuracy of communicating the arrival of the scent determined the outcome of the experiment)* Assign the **Build Inquiry activity.** Ask students to predict the effects of air pollutants on the nylon fabric. Review the cause, forms, and effects of acid rain and have students do the **Apply It activity.**

Build Inquiry to help students identify indoor pollutants. Assign the **Quick Lab activity** and then have students share their results about the levels of acid rain in your area.

Continue to **Build Inquiry** by challenging students to create a model of the ozone cycle. Have students present their models to the class. Assign the **Quick Lab** on creating models of oxygen and ozone molecules.

Use the **Support the Big Q activity** to help students understand how they can make changes in their everyday activities and reduce air pollution. Assign the **Quick Lab** and the ask students to discuss the solid particles they found in indoor air and outdoor air. Students can use the online **Vocab Flash Cards** to review key terms.

EVALUATE

Have students take the **Lesson Quiz.** For an alternate assessment, see the **EXAM**VIEW® Assessment Suite, Progress Monitoring Assessments, or SuccessTracker™.

Digital Path
Online learning at **my science online**.com

ENGAGE AND EXPLORE

Teach this lesson using digital resources. Begin by having students explore real-world connections to air pollution at **My Planet Diary** online. Have them access the Chapter Resources to find the **Unlock the Big Question activity.** There they can answer the questions and refine their responses as they continue through the lesson. You can re-assign the activity and have students submit their work so you can track their progress.

EXPLAIN AND ELABORATE

Students reading above, at, or below the lexile measure of this lesson can access basic content readings at their level at **My Reading Web.** Have students use the online **Vocab Flash Cards** to preview key terms. Review the cause, forms, and effects of acid rain before assigning the **Apply It activity.** Assign the **Quick Lab** and have students submit their work to you.

Assign the **Quick Lab activity** on creating models of oxygen and ozone molecules and have students share their results.

Use the **Support the Big Q activity** to help students understand how they can make changes in their everyday activities and reduce air pollution. The **Interactive Art activity online** allows students to find sources of air pollution and possible mitigations. Assign the **Quick Lab** and then ask students to discuss the solid particles they found in indoor air and outdoor air. The **Key Concept Summaries** online allow students to read a summary and see an image associated with each part of the lesson. Online remediation is available at **My Science Coach.**

EVALUATE

Have students take the **Lesson Quiz.** For an alternate assessment, see the **EXAM**VIEW® Assessment Suite, Progress Monitoring Assessments, or SuccessTracker™.

2 Frontload the Lesson
Read the caption on page 148 aloud. Have students study the visuals. Pair students and ask them to prepare demonstrations of what happens to the ozone hole from one visual to the next. *(One student might read the years aloud while the other acts out the growth of the ozone hole.)*

3 Comprehensible Input
Have students study the visual on page 144. Discuss the labels. Ask students to complete these sentences. The warm air is above the _____ air. The warm air keeps the _____ close to the ground. Have them make up other sentence pairs describing the visual.

4 Language Production
Pair or group students with varied language abilities to complete labs collaboratively for language practice. Have each student copy the completed written lab for personal reference.

5 Assess Understanding
Divide the class into small groups. Have each student identify a key concept from the lesson to discuss in his or her group. After the discussions, have students talk about the key concepts as a group.

Air Pollution and Solutions

Establish Learning Objectives

After this lesson, students will be able to:

🔑 Identify the causes of indoor and outdoor air pollution.

🔑 Explain the importance of the ozone layer and how it has been damaged.

🔑 Explain the key to reducing air pollution.

Engage

Activate Prior Knowledge

MY PLANET DIARY Read *Drawing for a Difference* with the class. Help students appreciate that each person in every community can have an effect on raising awareness about air pollution, as well as on reducing pollution. Ask: **What causes air pollution in your community?** *(Sample: motor vehicles)* **What could students do to encourage people to limit this kind of air pollution?** *(Students might mention posters, murals, blogs, or Web sites.)*

BIG IDEAS OF SCIENCE REFERENCE LIBRARY 📖 Have students look up the following topic: Acid Rain, Air Pollution.

Explore

Lab Resource: Inquiry Warm-Up 🔬

L1 **HOW DOES THE SCENT SPREAD?** Students will try to detect a scent and then describe the way in which the scent spreads throughout the room.

LESSON **3** **Air Pollution and Solutions**

UNLOCK THE BIG **?**

🔑 What Causes Outdoor and Indoor Air Pollution?

🔑 What Causes Damage to the Ozone Layer?

🔑 How Can Air Pollution Be Reduced?

my pLaneT DiaRY

PROFILE

Drawing for a Difference

Some people may think that kids can't help the environment. Kids in the San Joaquin Valley of California know better! Each year, students enter their drawings into a contest for a Clean Air Kids Calendar sponsored by the San Joaquin Valley Air Pollution Control District. Lisa Huang (bottom right drawing) and Saira Delgada (bottom left drawing) are two middle school students whose work was chosen to be a part of the 2008 calendar. Their drawings show people why healthy air is important. Every time people looked at the calendar, the drawings reminded them of the simple ways they can help the planet.

Communicate Discuss the question with a group of classmates. Then, write your answer below.

How could you raise awareness about air pollution in your community?

Sample: Put posters and flyers in local businesses, launch an e-mail campaign, or give talks at local schools.

▶ PLANET DIARY Go to **Planet Diary** to learn more about air pollution and solutions.

🔬 Do the Inquiry Warm-Up *How Does the Scent Spread?*

SUPPORT ALL READERS

Lexile Measure = 980L   Lexile Word Count = 2216

Prior Exposure to Content: Most students have encountered this topic in earlier grades

Academic Vocabulary: *communicate*

Science Vocabulary: *emissions, ozone, radon, chloroflourocarbon*

Concept Level: Generally appropriate for most students in this grade

Preteach With: My Planet Diary "Drawing for a Difference" and Figure 2 activity

Go to **My Reading Web** to access leveled readings that provide a foundation for the content.

my science online .com

Vocabulary
- emissions
- photochemical smog
- ozone
- temperature inversion
- acid rain
- radon
- ozone layer
- chlorofluorocarbon

Skills
- ⟳ Reading: Relate Text and Visuals
- △ Inquiry: Communicate

What Causes Outdoor and Indoor Air Pollution?

You can't usually see it, taste it, or smell it, but you are surrounded by air. Air is a mixture of nitrogen, oxygen, carbon dioxide, water vapor, and other gases. Almost all living things depend on these gases to survive. Recall that these gases cycle between living things and the atmosphere. These cycles guarantee that the air supply will not run out, but they don't guarantee that the air will be clean.

Outdoor Air Pollution What causes air pollution? Until the mid-1900s in the United States, factories and power plants that burned coal produced most of the pollutants, or **emissions,** that were released into the air. 🔑 **Today, a large source of emissions resulting in air pollution outdoors comes from motor vehicles such as cars and trucks.** There are also some natural causes of air pollution. <u>Methane released from animals such as cows also sends pollutants into the atmosphere.</u>

Air pollution sources can be grouped as point or nonpoint sources. A point source is a specific source of pollution that is easy to identify, such as a smokestack. A nonpoint source is a source that is widely spread and cannot be tied to a specific origin, such as vehicle emissions. So the pollution cannot be traced to any specific vehicle.

FIGURE 1 ·····················
Volcanoes and Air Pollution
Not all air pollution is caused by people. Gases released by volcanic eruptions can also harm the atmosphere.
✎ **Infer** In the text, underline one natural source of air pollution. Name at least one other natural source of air pollution.

Sample: large forest fires, dust storms

143

Explain

Introduce Vocabulary

Tell students that *ozone* and the *ozone layer* affect human beings in dramatically different ways. Point out that *ozone* is a toxic chemical found in smog, whereas the *ozone layer* is a layer of the upper atmosphere that protects people from the effects of too much ultraviolet radiation.

Teach Key Concepts 🔑

Explain to students that there are two main sources of air pollution: point and nonpoint. However, one source is the primary cause of air pollution. Ask: **What is the nonpoint source of a large part of our planet's outdoor air pollution?** *(Exhaust from motor vehicles)* **In previous centuries, what point sources were the leading cause of outdoor air pollution?** *(Factories and power plants)*

Lead a Discussion

Encourage students to describe specific examples of air pollution that they have seen in person or in pictures, such as smog hanging over a city, smoke coming from factory smokestacks, and grime settling on cars parked outdoors. Ask: **Which of these types of air pollution do you think we could control?** *(You may wish to accept all responses at this time.)*

My Planet Diary provides an opportunity for students to explore real-world connections to air pollution.

my science online | Air Pollution

ⒺⓁⓁ Support

1 Content and Language
In the last paragraphs on pages 148 and 149, the phrase *as a result* is used. Explain to students that this phrase often signals a cause-and-effect relationship between ideas or events.

2 Frontload the Lesson
Review the term *cycle*. Ask students to explain cycles they've learned about (i.e., water cycle, carbon cycle, oxygen cycle). Explain to students that the

term *cycle* is used in science to describe processes that repeat continuously.

3 Comprehensible Input
Some students may not be familiar with the role that Congress can enact legislation to limit behaviors by businesses. Explain that when someone is asked to *testify* before Congress, it is because he or she is an expert on a topic for which Congress is considering making laws.

Explain

Lead a Discussion

CAUSES OF SMOG Encourage students to offer descriptions of smog. Help students understand that smog usually appears as a brownish haze in the air. Ask: **What gases are the sources of smog?** *(Hydrocarbons and nitrogen oxides emitted by automobiles and trucks.)* **How do these gases form smog?** *(They react with sunlight to form ozone.)* **What other factor must be present for smog to form?** *(Temperature inversion)* **Why are most smog alerts issued in summer?** *(The gases react with sunlight, which is more intense in summer.)* Point out that ozone is harmful when it is close to Earth's surface. Ozone in the upper atmosphere filters ultraviolet radiation.

Lead a Discussion

CAUSES AND EFFECTS OF ACID RAIN Remind students that an acid is a substance that has a pH lower than 7.0. Tell students that each whole pH value below 7 is ten times more acidic than the next higher value. Normal rain has a pH of 5.5. The most acidic rain in the U.S. has a pH of about 4.3. Ask: **How much more acidic is acid rain than normal rain?** *(About ten times)* **How is acid rain formed?** *(Nitrogen oxides and sulfur oxides react with water vapor to form nitric acid and sulfuric acid, which fall to Earth as precipitation.)* **How does acid rain affect living things?** *(It damages trees and other plants, and can kill fish and other aquatic organisms.)*

Address Misconceptions

L2 **ACID RAIN** Students may not realize that rainwater is naturally acidic. Explain to students that when water and carbon dioxide in the atmosphere react, a weak acid, called carbonic acid, is produced. Carbonic acid can easily weather and erode rocks such as marble and limestone. Ask: **When human activities cause acid rain, what happens to the rate at which rocks erode?** *(By increasing acid rain, human activities actually cause the rate at which rocks erode to increase.)*

Cool air

Warm air

Polluted air

FIGURE 2 ······························

Temperature Inversion
Normally, pollutants rise into the atmosphere and blow away. During a temperature inversion, warm air traps the pollution close to the ground.

✎ **Interpret Photos** On the photo above, label the warm air, cool air, and polluted air.

Smog Have you ever heard a weather forecaster talk about a "smog alert"? A smog alert is a warning about a type of air pollution called photochemical smog. **Photochemical smog** is a thick, brownish haze formed when certain gases in the air react with sunlight. When the smog level is high, it settles as a haze over a city. Smog can cause breathing problems and eye and throat irritation. Exercising outdoors can make these problems worse.

The major sources of smog are the gases emitted by cars and trucks. Burning gasoline in a car engine releases gases into the air. These gases include hydrocarbons (compounds containing hydrogen and carbon) and nitrogen oxides. The gases react in the sunlight and produce a form of oxygen called **ozone.** Ozone, which is toxic, is the major chemical found in smog. Ozone can cause lung infections and damage the body's defenses against infection.

Normally, air close to the ground is heated by Earth's surface. As the air warms, it rises into the cooler air above it. Any pollutants in the air are carried higher into the atmosphere and are blown away from the place where they were produced.

Certain weather conditions can cause a condition known as a temperature inversion. During a **temperature inversion,** as shown in **Figure 2,** a layer of warm air prevents the rising air from escaping. The polluted air is trapped and held close to Earth's surface. The smog becomes more concentrated and dangerous.

144 Land, Air, and Water Resources

Digital Lesson: Assign the *Apply* It activity online and have students submit their work to you.

MY SCIENCE online.com ❭ **Air Pollution**

Acid Rain Precipitation that is more acidic than normal because of air pollution is called **acid rain.** Acid rain can also take the form of snow, sleet, or fog. <u>Acid rain is caused by the emissions from power plants and factories that burn coal and oil.</u> These fuels produce nitrogen oxides and sulfur oxides when they are burned. The gases that are released react with water vapor in the air, forming nitric acid and sulfuric acid. The acids dissolve in precipitation and return to Earth's surface.

As you can imagine, acid falling from the sky has some negative effects. When acid rain falls into a pond or lake, it changes the conditions there. Many fish, particularly their eggs, cannot survive in more acidic water. When acid rain falls on plants, it can damage their leaves and stems. Acid rain that falls on the ground can also damage plants by affecting the nutrient levels in the soil. Whole forests have been destroyed by acid rain. Fortunately, some of the effects of acid rain are reversible. Badly damaged lakes have been restored by adding lime or other substances that neutralize the acid.

Acid rain doesn't just affect living things. The acid reacts with stone and metal in buildings and statues. Statues and stonework damaged by acid rain may look as if they are melting, as seen in **Figure 3.** Automobiles rust more quickly in areas with acid rain. These effects are not reversible and the damage can be costly.

FIGURE 3 ....

Acid Rain
Acid rain harms plants, animals, buildings, and statues.

✎ **Review** In the text, underline the cause of acid rain.

apply it!

You are a scientist called to testify before Congress about acid rain. The government is proposing putting limits on emissions that lead to acid rain.

❶ Communicate Some of the members of Congress do not think acid rain causes real damage. What do you tell them?

Sample: Acid rain damages plants, buildings, cars, and statues.
It can also kill fish and their eggs.

❷ Explain Is rain the only form of precipitation you would identify as being potentially acidic? Explain.

No, acidic precipitation also includes snow, sleet, and fog.

❸ CHALLENGE What could you tell a company that was unwilling to reduce its emissions because the initial cost was high?

Sample: The initial cost may be high, but in the long run people may be
willing to do more business with you if they know you are helping the
environment.

145

Elaborate

Build Inquiry Lab

L2 OBSERVE EFFECTS OF AIR POLLUTANTS

Materials hand lens, foam cup, piece of nylon-stocking fabric, scissors, tape

Time 10–15 minutes for setup, plus follow-up observations

Ask students if they think the air they are breathing today is clean. *(Unless pollution is obvious, most students will say yes.)* Have students examine the fabric with a hand lens. Ask them to pull and twist the fabric to test its strength and flexibility and to make notes about their observations. Then have each student cut out the bottom of the cup and tape a piece of stocking over the opening. Have students hang the cups outdoors where they will be exposed to air and rain. After a week, have students observe the fabric for strength, flexibility, and broken fibers or other signs of damage.

Ask: **Do you agree with your original answer?** *(Most students will think that the air is polluted because of the negative effects on the nylon.)*

Point out that air pollution can affect the nylon but sunlight also has a negative effect on it.

Apply It!

L1 Review the cause, forms, and effects of acid rain discussed on this page before beginning the activity. Remind students that acid rain affects plants, bodies of water, as well as stone and metal.

◢ **Communicate** Remind students that communications of this sort should be clear, concise, and respectful of the audience.

Differentiated Instruction

L1 Illustrate a Temperature Inversion Invite students to draw a diagram that illustrates how air pollution is blown away during normal atmospheric conditions. In a second diagram, ask students to show how pollution is trapped near the ground when a certain set of weather conditions creates a temperature inversion.

L3 Charting the History of Pollution Have students research the history of air pollution and create an illustrated timeline that notes the appearance of significant pollutants, such as the burning of coal beginning in the late 1700s, and the development of automobiles at the start of the 20th century. Students may wish to work together to produce a timeline that can be displayed in the classroom.

Explain

Teach Key Concepts

Students may think of air pollution as something that exists only outdoors. Explain that people can be affected by air pollution indoors as well as outdoors. Ask: **What kinds of substances can cause indoor air pollution?** (*Dust, animal hair, cleaning supplies, toxic chemicals such as carbon monoxide and radon*) **In what respect might indoor air pollution be harder for people to avoid than outdoor air pollution?** (*Sample: Much outdoor air pollution rises into the atmosphere and blows away, whereas indoor air pollution is trapped inside.*)

Elaborate

Build Inquiry **Lab** zone

L2 IDENTIFY INDOOR POLLUTANTS

Materials containers of products that give off toxic fumes

Time 10 minutes

Review the names of products that can cause indoor air pollution. Tell students that many product labels have information about safe handling and use. Display the products, and have volunteers read aloud the cautionary statements on the labels. CAUTION: *Instruct students not to open any container.* Ask: **How can these products be used safely?** (*Usually outside or in well-ventilated areas*)

Lab Resource: Quick Lab **Lab** zone

L2 How Acid Is Your Rain? Students will test and compare the acid levels of lemon juice (citric acid) and of rain in your geographical area.

Evaluate

Assess Your Understanding

After students answer the questions, have them evaluate their understanding by completing the appropriate sentence.

RTI Response to Intervention

1a. If students cannot define *photochemical smog,* **then** have them skim the section to locate the highlighted term *photochemical smog* and reread the paragraph in which it is found.

b. If students have difficulty evaluating pollution regulation, **then** have them review the information about the effects of such pollution.

MY SCIENCE COACH Have students go online for help in understanding air pollution.

FIGURE 4

Indoor Air Pollution
Indoor air pollution has many sources. **Identify** Circle the sources of indoor air pollution in this room.

Indoor Air Pollution You might think that you can avoid air pollution by staying inside. The air inside buildings can be polluted, too. Some substances that cause indoor air pollution, such as dust and pet hair, bother only those people who are sensitive to them. Other indoor air pollutants, such as toxic chemicals, can affect anyone. Glues and cleaning supplies may give off toxic fumes. Cigarette smoke, even from another person's cigarette, can damage the lungs and heart. **Figure 4** shows some sources of air pollution that can be found in homes.

Carbon Monoxide One particularly dangerous indoor air pollutant is carbon monoxide. Carbon monoxide is a colorless and odorless gas that forms when fuels are not completely burned. When carbon monoxide builds up in an enclosed space, like a house, it can be deadly. Any home heated by wood, coal, oil, or gas needs a carbon monoxide detector.

Radon Another indoor air pollutant that is difficult to detect is radon. **Radon** is a colorless, odorless gas that is radioactive. It is formed naturally by certain rocks underground. Radon can enter homes through cracks in basement walls or floors. Breathing radon gas over many years may cause lung cancer and other health problems. Homeowners can install ventilation systems to prevent radon from building up in their homes.

Lab zone Do the Quick Lab *How Acid Is Your Rain?*

Assess Your Understanding

1a. Name (Photochemical smog/Methane) is a thick, brownish haze formed when gases in the air are exposed to sunlight.

b. Make Judgments Do you think the government should regulate sources of air pollution such as factory and car emissions? Explain.
<u>Accept all reasonable answers.</u>
<u>Students should justify</u>
<u>answers with evidence.</u>

got it?

○ I get it! Now I know outdoor air pollution is caused by <u>car and factory</u> <u>emissions</u>

and indoor air pollution is caused by <u>dust,</u> <u>pet hair, and chemicals.</u>

○ I need extra help with_____
<u>See TE note.</u>

Go to **MY SCIENCE COACH** *online for help with this subject.*

What Causes Damage to the Ozone Layer?

If you have ever had a sunburn, you have experienced the painful effects of the sun's ultraviolet radiation. But did you know that sunburns would be even worse without the protection of the ozone layer? The **ozone layer** is a layer of the upper atmosphere about 15 to 30 kilometers above Earth's surface. The amount of ozone in this layer is very small. Yet even this small amount of ozone in the ozone layer protects people from the effects of too much ultraviolet radiation. These effects include sunburn, eye diseases, and skin cancer.

Because you read earlier that ozone is a pollutant, the fact that ozone can be helpful may sound confusing. The difference between ozone as a pollutant and ozone as a helpful gas is its location in the atmosphere. Ozone close to Earth's surface in the form of smog is harmful. Ozone higher in the atmosphere, where people cannot breathe it, protects us from too much ultraviolet radiation.

The Source of Ozone Ozone is constantly being made and destroyed. See **Figure 5**. When sunlight strikes an ozone molecule, the energy of the ultraviolet radiation is partly absorbed. This energy causes the ozone molecule to break apart into an oxygen molecule and an oxygen atom. The oxygen atom soon collides with another oxygen molecule. They react to form a new ozone molecule. Each time this cycle occurs, some energy is absorbed. That energy does not reach Earth's surface.

FIGURE 5 ·······························

Ozone Cycle
The ozone cycle prevents harmful ultraviolet radiation from reaching Earth's surface.

✎ **Sequence** Explain the ozone cycle in your own words.

Sample: An ozone molecule absorbs UV radiation from the sun. This energy breaks the ozone apart into an oxygen atom and oxygen molecule. These then react with other oxygen atoms and molecules to form new ozone molecules.

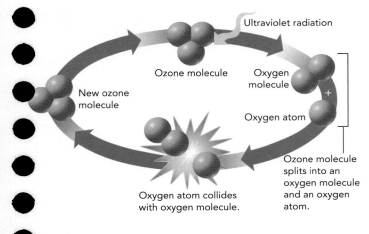

Ultraviolet radiation

Ozone molecule | Oxygen molecule

New ozone molecule

Oxygen atom

Oxygen atom collides with oxygen molecule.

Ozone molecule splits into an oxygen molecule and an oxygen atom.

147

Explain

Lead a Discussion

THE OZONE LAYER Remind students that ozone is a form of oxygen that is produced when gases react in sunlight. It is toxic and helps to form smog near Earth's surface. Ask: **How can ozone be both harmful and beneficial?** *(It is harmful when it is close to Earth's surface where people can breathe it. It is beneficial when it is higher in the atmosphere and helps to absorb ultraviolet light.)* **How does ozone protect us from ultraviolet radiation?** *(It absorbs ultraviolet radiation so that it does not reach Earth's surface.)*

Teach With Visuals

Tell students to look at **Figure 5**. Ask: **What happens when the free oxygen atom collides with an oxygen molecule?** *(It forms a new ozone molecule.)* **During the ozone cycle, what event limits the number of ozone molecules?** *(Energy from ultraviolent radiation breaks ozone apart into an oxygen molecule and an oxygen atom.)*

Differentiated Instruction

L1 Writing Labels Pair special needs students with more able students. Distribute photocopies of **Figure 4**. Suggest that students add a label to identify each source of indoor pollution shown. Then have students add other sources of air pollution to the drawing (indoors or outdoors) and add labels for those.

L3 Researching Word Parts Invite students to research the word parts that indicate the differences in meaning between the terms *carbon dioxide* and *carbon monoxide*. Invite students to present their findings to the class. Students should explain that *di-* means "two" and that *mono-* means "one." Carbon dioxide has two atoms of oxygen, and carbon monoxide has one atom of oxygen. Students might wish to draw a diagram of each molecule to clarify the difference in the number of atoms in each molecule.

Explain

Teach Key Concepts

Remind students that the ozone layer protects human beings and other living things by limiting the amount of ultraviolet radiation that reaches Earth's surface. Ask: **What has damaged the ozone layer?** *(The use of CFCs)* **What are CFCs?** *(A group of human-made gases used in many household products)* **What effect have CFCs had on the ozone layer?** *(In the upper atmosphere, CFCs have interrupted the ozone cycle, allowing more ultraviolet light to reach Earth's surface.)* Tell students that the dramatic ozone "hole" exists only over Antarctica, but currently the ozone layer over the United States is depleted by about 6 percent.

Teach With Visuals

Tell students to look at **Figure 6.** Point out that after nearly a decade of hypothesizing, scientists confirmed the presence of the ozone hole in 1986. Ask: **What do you see in Figure 6 that reinforces the contrast between what scientists saw and thought about the ozone layer in the 1970s and in 1986?** *(Sample response: The area of blue is dramatically larger and more clearly defined in 1986 than in 1979.)*

Relate Text and Visuals Tell students that learning to relate text and visuals will help them better understand the content of the lessons in this book.

Elaborate

Build Inquiry

L2 MODEL THE EFFECTS OF CFCS ON OZONE

Materials craft supplies

Time 15 minutes

Review the ozone cycle shown in **Figure 5.** Explain that when sunlight hits a CFC molecule, it releases a chlorine atom. This atom hits an ozone molecule and interrupts the normal cycle. Chlorine breaks up the ozone molecule, and it becomes regular oxygen—it never re-forms into ozone. Challenge pairs of students to create a model to demonstrate the ozone cycle and its interruption by CFCs, and then present their models to the class.

Ask: **Why is more oxygen not helpful in blocking ultraviolet radiation?** *(Because the oxygen molecule is not the right size and shape to absorb the sun's harmful rays)* Tell students that one chlorine atom can break apart 100,000 ozone molecules.

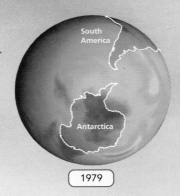 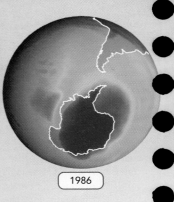

1979   1986

FIGURE 6
Ozone Hole
The ozone hole (shown in blue) is over Antarctica. The hole has grown over time, but it varies seasonally and from year to year.

The Ozone Hole In the late 1970s, scientists observed from satellite images that the ozone layer over Antarctica was growing thinner each spring. The amount of ozone in the ozone layer was decreasing. This caused an area of severe ozone depletion, or an ozone hole. In **Figure 6,** you can see the size of the ozone hole in five selected years.

What is to blame for the ozone hole? **Scientists determined that the major cause of the ozone hole is a group of gases called CFCs.** CFCs, or **chlorofluorocarbons**, are human-made gases that contain chlorine and fluorine. CFCs had been used in air conditioners, aerosol spray cans, and other household products. CFCs reach high into the atmosphere, and react with ozone molecules. The CFCs block the cycle in which ozone molecules absorb ultraviolet radiation. As a result, more ultraviolet light reaches Earth's surface.

FIGURE 7
Ozone and Ultraviolet Radiation
The amount of ozone in the atmosphere and the amount of UV radiation reaching Earth are linked.

1. **Read Graphs** Label the curve on the graph representing ozone and the curve representing UV radiation.
2. **Summarize** Explain the graph in your own words.

<u>Sample: CFCs cause the amount of ozone in the atmosphere to decrease. Then, the amount of UV radiation that reaches Earth's surface increases.</u>

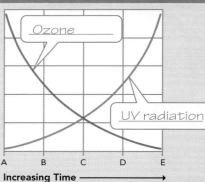

Ozone and UV Radiation Resulting From CFCs

Ozone

UV radiation

A   B   C   D   E

Increasing Time ⟶

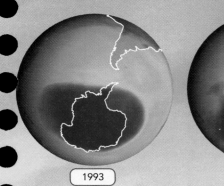

1993   2000   2004

What's Being Done In 1990, many nations signed an agreement to eventually ban the use of ozone-depleting substances, including CFCs. Most uses of CFCs were banned in 2000. Some uses of CFCs are still allowed, but compared to the 1970s, few CFCs now enter the atmosphere. Unfortunately, CFC molecules remain in the atmosphere for a long time. Scientists predict that if the ban on ozone-depleting substances is maintained, the ozone layer will gradually recover.

When scientists discovered that CFCs were harming the atmosphere, they immediately began to search for substitutes. Refrigerators and air conditioners were redesigned to use less-harmful substances. Most spray cans were either replaced by pump sprays or redesigned to use other gases. Researchers developed new ways to make products such as plastic foam without using CFCs. As a result of this research and the development of CFC substitutes, far less CFCs now enter the atmosphere.

Relate Text and Visuals Based on the photos, describe what happened to the hole in the ozone layer before CFCs were banned. What do you think could happen if the ban is maintained and enforced?

The ozone hole has
grown over time. The
hole may get smaller
if there are fewer
CFCs damaging the
atmosphere.

Lab zone® Do the Quick Lab _Analyzing Ozone._

🔑 **Assess Your Understanding**

2a. Explain How can ozone be both a pollutant and something beneficial to Earth?

Ozone as smog close to Earth
is harmful, but ozone higher in
the atmosphere blocks harmful
ultraviolet rays.

b. Solve Problems What can countries do to help the ozone layer recover?

Maintain and enforce the ban
on products that contain CFCs
and use alternatives to CFCs
in products.

got it?

○ **I get it!** Now I know the ozone layer was damaged by _CFCs that were used in_ _many household products._

○ **I need extra help with** _See TE note._

Go to **my science COACH** online for help with this subject.

149

COMMUNICATION Have students group into pairs; challenge them to list events and conditions relating to CFCs and the ozone layer that occurred prior to 1970 and through 2000. *(Before the 1970s, there was extensive use of CFCs worldwide. In the 1970s, scientists detected a hole in the ozone layer. In 1990, many nations signed an agreement to ban the use of CFCs eventually. In 2000, most uses of CFCs were banned.)* Point out to students that 93 nations agreed to ban the use of ozone-depleting substances. The 1990 agreement is an example of nations coming together to solve a global environmental problem. Another key example of nations working together is the Kyoto Protocol, which went into effect in 2005. As of 2009, 184 nations have agreed to adhere to the Kyoto Protocol that targets the reduction of greenhouse gas emissions. Ask: **What are some other issues that global nations could work together to solve?** *(Students may mention other types of pollution, protecting ecosystems and biodiversity, world hunger, and disease.)*

Lab Resource: Quick Lab **Lab zone**

L2 ANALYZING OZONE Students will explore ozone and the ozone cycle.

Evaluate ——————

Assess Your Understanding

After students answer the questions, have them evaluate their understanding by completing the appropriate sentence.

RTI Response to Intervention

2a. If students cannot explain the effects of ozone, **then** have them read the second paragraph of this section.

b. If students need help with suggesting ways to help the ozone layer, **then** have them reread the material under the red head *What's Being Done*.

my science COACH Have students go online for help in understanding the cause of damage to the ozone layer.

Differentiated Instruction

L3 Researching Ozone Depletion Potential Have students research the Ozone Depletion Potential (ODP), a number that refers to the amount of ozone depletion caused by a substance. Tell them to plan and present an oral report that includes how the number is determined and a list of common products and their ODPs. *(It is compared to the impact of a similar mass of CFC-11.)*

L1 Naming Geographical Locations Invite students to review the illustrations in **Figure 6** that show the widening ozone hole. Then have students use a globe or a world atlas to find the continents and name the countries that are affected by the growing ozone hole.

Explain

Teach Key Concepts 🗝

Explain to students that solving the problem of air pollution requires people to identify exactly what causes it. Ask: **What causes outdoor air pollution?** *(Emissions)* **What is the best way to reduce air pollution?** *(Control the amount of emissions going into the air.)* **What are the main sources of emissions?** *(Factories and vehicles)*

Support the Big Q ❓ UbD

PROTECTING AIR QUALITY Remind students that when they ride in a car or use electricity, they are contributing to air pollution. Ask: **How can you reduce pollution caused by vehicles?** *(Walk or ride a bicycle instead of being driven somewhere)* **How does using electricity contribute emissions?** *(Many power plants burn fuels to produce electricity.)* **How can you reduce the pollution caused when electricity is generated?** *(Use less electricity.)*

Make Analogies

L1 **COLLECTIVE ACTION** Students may have trouble understanding how an individual's actions can make a positive difference in reducing air pollution. Tell students to imagine a penny drive organized at school. Ask how much money a "typical" individual might contribute. *(Students may indicate 40 or 50 cents.)* How does the individual's contribution relate to the success of the penny drive as a whole? *(If each student contributes 40 or 50 cents, the total amount collected will be impressive.)* How is each individual's action to reduce air pollution like the penny drive? *(Even though individuals may save a small amount of electricity, when added, the total amount will be impressive.)* Ask: **In addition to turning off devices that use electricity, as well as walking and riding bikes instead of riding in cars, what can an individual do to further reduce air pollution?** *(Sample: Encourage other individuals to make similar choices.)*

How Can Air Pollution Be Reduced?

Air pollution can be reduced if we examine the sources. 🗝 **The key to reducing air pollution is to control emissions.** In the United States, laws such as the Clean Air Act regulate the amount of certain pollutants that can be released into the air. Laws also encourage the development of new technology that reduces air pollution. Reducing emissions also requires your efforts.

Controlling Emissions From Factories At one time, industries dealt with emissions by building tall smokestacks. The stacks released wastes high into the air where they could blow away, but the pollutants still ended up somewhere. Now factories remove pollutants from their emissions with devices known as scrubbers that release water droplets. Pollutants dissolve in the water and fall into a container. The use of scrubbers explains why "smoke" from factories is white—it's not smoke, it's steam.

Controlling Emissions From Vehicles Cars and trucks now contain pollution-control devices. A catalytic converter is a part of the exhaust system that reduces emissions of carbon monoxide, hydrocarbons, and nitrogen oxides. This device causes the gases to react, forming less-harmful carbon dioxide and water. Laws can ensure that people use pollution-control devices. For example, in many states, cars must pass emissions tests to be allowed on the road.

What You Can Do You may not think there is much you can do to reduce air pollution. However, even small changes in your behavior can make a big difference.

You can help reduce air pollution by reducing certain types of energy use. Much air pollution is a result of burning fuels to provide electricity and transportation. Using less energy conserves fuel resources and reduces emissions. Turning off lights, computers, and televisions in empty rooms uses less energy and reduces emissions. When you take public transportation, carpool, walk, or ride a bicycle, there are fewer cars on the road. This means there are less emissions that contribute to air pollution.

FIGURE 8 ·······························
> INTERACTIVE ART
Your Solutions
✎ Communicate With a partner, list ways you can reduce air pollution in your everyday life.

Sample: Ride a bike or walk instead of being driven and use less electricity by turning off lights, computers, and TVs when not in use.

150 Land, Air, and Water Resources

Interactive Art: allows students to find sources of air pollution and possible mitigations.

my science online.com | **Air Pollution Solutions**

Apples are grown in an orchard in Chile.

Trucks carry apples from the orchard to the airport.

Airplanes carry the apples from Chile to the United States.

Food Mart

More trucks bring the apples from the airport to shipping centers and grocery stores around the country.

FIGURE 9 ⋯⋯⋯⋯⋯⋯⋯⋯⋯⋯⋯⋯⋯⋯⋯⋯⋯⋯⋯

Where Does an Apple Really Come From?
Many things in our everyday lives, even where food comes from, can contribute to air pollution. ✎ **Analyze Costs and Benefits** Read the comic strip above. Then, fill in the boxes with pros and cons of buying apples that were grown locally instead of those grown in another country.

Pros

Sample: Less air pollution; supports local business

Cons

Sample: Could be more expensive; fruit may not be available locally or year-round.

Do the Quick Lab
It's in the Air.

🔑 **Assess Your Understanding**
got it? ⋯⋯⋯⋯⋯⋯⋯⋯⋯⋯⋯⋯⋯⋯⋯⋯⋯

○ I get it! Now I know the key to reducing air pollution is controlling emissions from factories and vehicles.

○ I need extra help with See TE note.

Go to my science COACH online for help with this subject.

151

Elaborate ——————————

21st Century Learning

ACCOUNTABILITY Have students read *Air Pollution* in the **Big Ideas of Science Reference Library.** Ask them to find out if a green building project is under way in their local area. Have students prepare and write down three questions about how the project will affect the community. They can call, email, or have an adult accompany them to talk to a city or town representative, homeowner, architect, or builder.

Lab Resource: Quick Lab

L1 IT'S IN THE AIR Students will collect and compare samples of solid particles from indoor air and outdoor air.

Evaluate ——————————

Assess Your Understanding

Have students evaluate their understanding by completing the appropriate sentence.

If students have trouble identifying ways to reduce air pollution, **then** have them review the material under the first two red heads in this section.

my science COACH Online remediation to assist students in understanding air pollution.

Differentiated Instruction

L1 Picturing Ways to Improve Air Quality Help students summarize what they have learned about what individuals—adults as well as children—can do during their daily lives to reduce air pollution. Have students draw pictures or create collages to show specific actions individuals can take, such as riding a bicycle, shutting off a computer, or spreading the word to other people.

L3 Respiratory Health Encourage students to do research to learn why some respiratory problems, such as asthma, bronchitis, and emphysema, are caused or worsened by breathing polluted air. Encourage students to make posters that include a labeled diagram of the respiratory system and a brief description of how the system is affected.

Lab zone **After the Inquiry Warm-Up**

Air Pollution and Solutions

Inquiry Warm-Up, *How Does the Scent Spread?*

In the Inquiry Warm-Up, you investigated how scents spread through air. Using what you learned from that activity, answer the questions below.

1. **PREDICT** Would the scent travel faster or slower if a fan were used to circulate the air in the classroom? Explain.

   _____

   _____

2. **PREDICT** How would a second person spraying perfume on the opposite side of the classroom affect the results? Explain.

   _____

   _____

3. **CONTROL VARIABLES** How would having all the students stand closely together, as opposed to evenly spaced throughout the classroom, affect the results? Explain.

   _____

   _____

4. **DESIGN EXPERIMENTS** Assume your class wants to compare and contrast the direction and speed at which another scent spreads. What part of the experiment, if any, would you recommend changing for the second trial? Explain.

   _____

   _____

   _____

   _____

Place the outside corner, the corner away from the dotted line, in the corner of your copy machine to copy onto letter-size paper.

Name _____ Date _____ Class _____

Air Pollution and Solutions

> **What Causes Outdoor and Indoor Air Pollution?**

1a. **NAME** (Photochemical smog/Ozone) is a thick, brownish haze formed when gases in the air are exposed to sunlight.

b. **MAKE JUDGMENTS** Do you think the government should regulate sources of air pollution such as factory and car emissions? Explain. _____

_____

_____

got it? ....

○ **I get it!** Now I know outdoor air pollution is caused by _____

_____

and indoor air pollution is caused by _____

_____

○ **I need extra help with** _____

_____

Assess Your Understanding

Air Pollution and Solutions

What Causes Damage to the Ozone Layer?

2a. EXPLAIN How can ozone be both a pollutant and something beneficial
to the Earth? _____

_____

_____

b. SOLVE PROBLEMS What can countries do to help the ozone layer
recover? _____

_____

_____

gotit? ···

○ **I get it!** Now I know the ozone layer was damaged by _____

_____

○ **I need extra help with** _____

_____

How Can Air Pollution Be Reduced?

gotit? ···

○ **I get it!** Now I know the key to reducing air pollution is _____

_____

○ **I need extra help with** _____

_____

Key Concept Summaries

Air Pollution and Solutions

What Causes Outdoor and Indoor Air Pollution?

Air is a mixture of gases that cycle between living things and the atmosphere. **Emissions** are pollutants released into the air. **Today, a large source of emissions resulting in air pollution outdoors comes from motor vehicles such as cars and trucks.** In addition, factories, power plants, and natural sources cause air pollution.

Photochemical smog is a thick, brownish haze formed when certain gases in the air react with sunlight. It can cause breathing problems and eye and throat irritation. The major sources of smog are the gases emitted by cars and trucks, which react in the sunlight and produce **ozone,** a toxic form of oxygen.

Weather conditions can cause a **temperature inversion,** in which a layer of warm air prevents rising air from escaping. Polluted air is then held close to Earth's surface. Precipitation that is more acidic than normal because of air pollution is called **acid rain.** Acid rain damages plants, waterways, and metals and stones. Even indoor air can be polluted. **Some substances that cause indoor air pollution, such as dust and pet hair, bother only those people who are sensitive to them. Other indoor air pollutants, such as toxic chemicals, can affect anyone. Radon** is a colorless, odorless gas that is radioactive.

What Causes Damage to the Ozone Layer?

The **ozone layer** is a layer of the upper atmosphere about 30 kilometers above Earth's surface. It protects people from the effects of too much ultraviolet radiation. Ozone is constantly being made and destroyed as part of the ozone cycle. The amount of ozone in the ozone layer is decreasing, creating an ozone hole. **Scientists determined that the major cause of the ozone hole is a group of gases called CFCs. CFCs were used in many household products.** Most uses of CFCs were banned in 2000.

How Can Air Pollution Be Reduced?

The key to reducing air pollution is to control emissions. Factories and vehicles use devices and systems to reduce emissions. Individuals can reduce air pollution by using electricity and motor vehicles less.

On a separate sheet of paper, explain how emissions cause outdoor air pollution.

Review and Reinforce

Air Pollution and Solutions

Understanding Main Ideas

Answer the following questions on a separate sheet of paper.

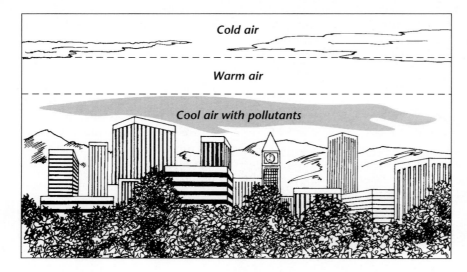

Cold air

Warm air

Cool air with pollutants

1. What condition is shown in the figure above? Why is this condition dangerous to people?
2. How is photochemical smog formed?
3. How is acid rain formed?
4. What are two effects of acid rain?
5. Why is carbon monoxide such a dangerous form of indoor air pollution?
6. How does walking instead of driving a car help reduce air pollution?

Building Vocabulary

On a separate sheet of paper, write a definition for each of these terms.

7. emissions
8. photochemical smog
9. acid rain
10. radon

Air Pollution and Solutions

Ozone is a gas that can be found in both the upper layer of Earth's atmosphere as well as at ground level. Read the passage and study the table about ozone at ground level. Then use a separate sheet of paper to answer the questions that follow the table.

Ozone

At ground level, ozone is formed from pollutants released by motor vehicles. It is toxic and is a major component of smog. Ozone can increase a person's susceptibility to lung infections and damage the body's defenses against infection. The following scale, the Air Quality Index (AQI), was created by the Environmental Protection Agency (EPA) in order to report ground levels of ozone and other air pollutants. Each day, local air quality is rated according to the scale and is reported in local newspapers or on local news and weather reports.

Index Values	Descriptions	Cautionary Statements for Ozone
0 to 50	Good	None
51 to 100	Moderate	Unusually sensitive people should consider limiting prolonged outdoor exertion.
101 to 150	Unhealthy for Sensitive Groups	Active children and adults, and people with respiratory diseases, such as asthma, should limit prolonged outdoor exertion.
151 to 200	Unhealthy	Active children and adults, and people with respiratory diseases, such as asthma, should avoid prolonged outdoor exertion. Everyone else, especially children, should limit prolonged outdoor exertion.
201 to 300	Very Unhealthy	Active children and adults, and people with respiratory diseases, such as asthma, should avoid all outdoor exertion. Everyone else, especially children, should limit outdoor exertion.

1. How is ozone harmful to humans?
2. What does it mean if the AQI value for a particular day is 125?
3. Suppose the AQI value for a particular day is 167. What precautions should a person with asthma take on this day?
4. Suppose you are an active adult with no sensitivities or respiratory disease. At what AQI value would you want to limit prolonged outdoor exertion?

Lesson Quiz

Air Pollution and Solutions

If the statement is true, write *true*. If the statement is false, change the underlined word or words make the statement true.

1. _____ A large percentage of emissions resulting in air pollution today comes from <u>motor vehicles</u>.

2. _____ <u>Radon</u> is a thick, brownish haze formed when certain gases in the air react with sunlight.

3. _____ In a(n) <u>ozone layer</u>, a layer of warm air prevents rising air from escaping and traps pollutants near Earth's surface.

4. _____ The key to reducing air pollution is to control <u>emissions</u>.

5. _____ <u>Carbon monoxide</u> damages plants, waterways, and metals and stones.

6. _____ CFCs once used in many household products contributed to the creation of a(n) <u>ozone hole</u>.

Fill in the blank to complete each statement.

7. _____ are pollutants released into the air.

8. Some substances that cause _____ air pollution, such as dust and pet hair, bother only those people who are sensitive to them.

9. The _____ protects people from the effects of too much ultraviolet radiation.

10. Individuals can reduce air pollution by using electricity and motor vehicles _____.

Air Pollution and Solutions

Answer Key

After the Inquiry Warm-Up

1. The scent would travel faster since the fan is moving the air around the room faster than if no fan were used.

2. Accept all reasonable responses. Students may say: A second source of scent would make it more difficult to know from which direction the scent was spreading and speed at which it was spreading.

3. Accept all reasonable responses. Sample: Most students smell the scent at the same time, making it difficult to measure the direction and speed of the scent's movement.

4. Accept all reasonable responses. Student may say: Nothing. In order to compare and contrast test results, all the variables except the one being tested must remain the same between trials. Otherwise, you're not sure where or how the difference in results comes about.

Key Concept Summaries

Sample: A major source of emissions is motor vehicles, but many factories and power plants also produce harmful emissions. When the exhausts from motor vehicles are exposed to sunlight, they react and form a thick, brown haze called photochemical smog. Emissions from factories and power plants can combine with moisture in the air to form acid rain.

Review and Reinforce

1. The figure shows a temperature inversion, when polluted air is trapped close to Earth's surface and becomes more concentrated. The polluted air can cause lung problems and harm the body's defenses against infection.

2. Gases are released into the air when gasoline in an automobile engine is burned. The gases react in sunlight and produce ozone, the major chemical found in photochemical smog.

3. When coal and oil are burned, they produce nitrogen oxides and sulfur oxides. These gases react with water vapor in the air to form nitric acid and sulfuric acid. The acids return to Earth's surface dissolved in precipitation.

4. Acid rain harms organisms and corrodes stone and metal.

5. Carbon monoxide is colorless and odorless, so it is difficult to detect. Carbon monoxide can cause death.

6. One less car on the road means fewer emissions that contribute to air pollution.

7. particles and gases that are released into the air

8. a thick, brownish haze formed when certain gases in the air react with sunlight

9. precipitation that is more acidic than usual because of air pollution

10. a colorless, odorless, radioactive gas

Enrich

1. Ozone is toxic and a major component of smog. Ozone can make lung infections more likely and damage the body's defenses against infection.

2. This level is unhealthy for sensitive groups. Active children and adults, and people with respiratory disease, such as asthma, should limit prolonged outdoor exertion.

3. Avoid prolonged outdoor exertion.

4. Limit prolonged outdoor exertion when the AQI value is greater than 100.

Lesson Quiz

1. true	2. Photochemical smog	3. temperature inversion
4. true	5. Acid rain	6. true
7. Emissions	8. indoor	9. ozone layer
10. less		

Water Pollution and Solutions

4 What can people do to use resources wisely?

Lesson Pacing: 2–3 periods or 1–1½ blocks

⏱ **SHORT ON TIME?** To do this lesson in approximately half the time, do the Activate Prior Knowledge activity on page 152. A discussion of the key concepts on pages 153, 154, and 156 will familiarize students with the lesson content. Use the Explore the big Q to help students identify six pollution sources. Do the Quick Labs and have students do the Real-World Inquiry online. The rest of the lesson can be completed by students independently.

Preference Navigator, in the online Planning tools, allows you to customize *Interactive Science* to your own teaching style. You can also edit lesson plans by selecting the Lesson Planner option.

Digital Teacher's Edition allows you to access your Teacher's Edition and Resource materials online.

my science online.com

Lesson Vocabulary

• groundwater   • pesticide   • sewage   • sediment

 Content Refresher

Professional Development Note

Nonpoint Source Pollution Nonpoint source pollution is a pollution source you can't "point to" directly. Effluent pouring from a factory pipe into a river is a point source because it comes from a specific point.

Nonpoint source pollution is the leading cause of water pollution in the United States. It comes from scattered sources in the environment. As water moves across and through the land it picks up pollutants and carries them into waterways and groundwater. These pollutants include fertilizers and pesticides from agriculture, oil and toxic chemicals from urban runoff, sediment from construction sites and eroding stream banks, bacteria and nutrients from livestock, and atmospheric particles.

Nonpoint source pollution is difficult to control because there is no one source against which to levy a fine, enforce regulations, or mandate a cleanup. It is, in fact, the responsibility of individuals to be aware of their own contributions to nonpoint source pollution. Every person can contribute to the problem without even realizing it. Most people wouldn't pour oil from their car into the sewer, but the person whose car drips oil on the driveway contributes to nonpoint source pollution.

LESSON OBJECTIVES

⌦ Explain why fresh water is a limited resource.
⌦ Identify the major sources of water pollution.
⌦ Describe how water pollution can be reduced.

ENGAGE AND EXPLORE

Teach this lesson using a variety of resources. Begin by reading **My Planet Diary** as a class. Have students identify waterways in your area that are not safe for recreation or fishing. Then have students do the **Inquiry Warm-Up activity.** Students will investigate how pollutants in water affect the passage of light through the water. Have students do the **After the Inquiry Warm-Up worksheet.** Ask volunteers to share their observations to number 4 about the clarity of the mixture.

EXPLAIN AND ELABORATE

Teach Key Concepts by explaining that fresh water is a limited resource because most of Earth's surface water is salt water and not suitable for drinking or watering plants and crops.

Review the terms *pesticide, sewage,* and *sediment.* Continue to **Teach Key Concepts** by explaining that most water pollution is the result of human activities, such as wastes from agriculture, households, industry, and mining. Using **Figure 2,** ask students to identify the potential sources of water pollution.

Teach Key Concepts by explaining that everyone is responsible for water quality and that there are three keys to keeping water clean: effective cleanup of oil and gasoline spills, proper sewage treatment, and reduction of pollutants. **Lead a Discussion** about what individuals and communities can do to properly dispose of hazardous materials and thereby improve water quality. Review the term *groundwater* before beginning the **Apply It activity.** Use the **Explore the Big Q activity** to have students identify the potential sources of air pollution and water pollution. Then **Answer the Big Q** to discuss how people can use resources wisely.

Hand out the **Key Concept Summaries** as a review of each part of the lesson. Students can also use the online **Vocab Flash Cards** to review key terms.

EVALUATE

Have students take the **Lesson Quiz.** For an alternate assessment, see the **EXAM**VIEW® Assessment Suite, Progress Monitoring Assessments, or SuccessTracker™.

E L L Support

1 Content and Language

Review the definitions of the vocabulary words: *groundwater, pesticide,* and *sewage.* Then ask a volunteer to use all words to complete this sentence: _____ can be polluted by _____ and _____ .

Lab zone Inquiry Path
Hands-on learning in the Lab zone

ENGAGE AND EXPLORE

To teach this lesson with an emphasis on inquiry, begin with the **Inquiry Warm-Up activity.** Students will investigate how pollutants change water by observing how water changes when milk is added to it. Have students do the **After the Inquiry Warm-Up worksheet.** Talk about the effects of pollutants on water. Have volunteers share their answers to number 4 about the distribution of pollutants in water.

EXPLAIN AND ELABORATE

Focus on the **Inquiry Skill** for the lesson. Reminds students that when they design experiments, they seek to test a hypothesis. Have students state a hypothesis for the experiment in the **Inquiry Warm-up activity.** *(Sample: By adding milk to water the mixture will become cloudy and reduce the clarity of the water.)* Have students do the first **Quick Lab** to model distribution of Earth's water and then share their results.

Assign the next **Quick Lab** on cleaning up oil spills. Students will model the difficult process of removing oil from water.

Review the term *groundwater* before beginning the **Apply It activity.** Ask volunteers to share their pros and cons of using bacteria to clean up oil spills. Use the aerial photograph in **Figure 4** to **Explore the Big Q.** Have students identify the potential sources of air pollution and water pollution. Do the **Teacher Demo** to model an oil spill clean-up. Discuss the implications of a much larger spill. Do the **Real-World Inquiry** which allows students to explore the effects of water pollution on frog populations. Have students do the **Quick Lab** to model the way fresh water is purified in the water cycle. **Answer the Big Q** by leading a discussion about how people can use resources wisely. Students can use the online **Vocab Flash Cards** to review key terms.

EVALUATE

Have students take the **Lesson Quiz.** For an alternate assessment, see the **EXAM**VIEW® Assessment Suite, Progress Monitoring Assessments, or SuccessTracker™.

Digital Path
Online learning at my science online.com

ENGAGE AND EXPLORE

To teach this lesson using digital resources, begin by having students learn more about water pollution and solutions as well as explore real-world connections to water resources at **My Planet Diary** online. Have them access the Chapter Resources to find the **Unlock the Big Question activity.** There they can answer the questions and refine their responses as they continue through the lesson. You can re-assign the activity and have students submit their work so you can track their progress.

EXPLAIN AND ELABORATE

Students reading above, at, or below the lexile measure of this lesson can access basic content readings at their level at **My Reading Web.** Encourage students to use the online **Vocab Flash Cards** to preview key terms. Do the **Quick Lab** and then ask students to discuss how water is distributed on Earth. Review clean-up of oil and gasoline spills before assigning the **Apply It activity** online. Have students submit their work to you.

Have students do the **Quick Lab.** Ask volunteers to share what they learned from the model of an oil spill clean-up. Then, assign the **Apply It activity** online. Have students submit their work to you.

Use the aerial photograph in **Figure 4** to **Explore the Big Q.** Have students identify the potential sources of air pollution and water pollution. Do the **Quick Lab** to have students model how fresh water is purified through the water cycle. **Answer the Big Q** by leading a discussion about how people can use resources wisely. The **Key Concept Summaries** online allow students to read a summary and see an image associated with each part of the lesson. Online remediation is available at **My Science Coach.**

EVALUATE

Have students take the **Lesson Quiz.** For an alternate assessment, see the **EXAM**VIEW® Assessment Suite, Progress Monitoring Assessments, or SuccessTracker™.

2 Frontload the Lesson
Preview the lesson questions. Ask students if there are any words they do not understand. Explain the specific meanings these words have in this science lesson.

3 Comprehensible Input
Have students look at the questions in the blue heads and the visuals on pages 152–154 and 156. Have them predict how the questions and the visuals are related. Have them check their predictions as they read the lesson.

4 Language Production
Pair or group students with varied language abilities to complete labs collaboratively for language practice. Have each student copy the completed written lab for personal reference.

5 Assess Understanding
Have students keep a content area log. Use a two-column format with the headings "What I Understand" and "What I Don't Understand." Follow up so that students can move items from the "Don't Understand" to the "Understand" column.

LESSON 4.4

Water Pollution and Solutions

Establish Learning Objectives

After this lesson, students will be able to:

 Explain why fresh water is a limited resource.

 Identify the major sources of water pollution.

 Describe how water pollution can be reduced.

Engage

Activate Prior Knowledge

MY PLANET DIARY Read *A Flood of Sludge* with the class. Point out that pollution can affect all types of waterways, including streams and lakes, as well as bays, tidal inlets, and other salt water sources. Ask: **Do people avoid swimming or fishing in certain waterways in your community because of water pollution?** *(Students may indicate that some waterways are not used for recreation or fishing.)*

BIG IDEAS OF SCIENCE REFERENCE LIBRARY 📖 Have students look up the following topic: Oil Spills.

Explore

Lab Resource: Inquiry Warm-Up 🧪

L1 **HOW DOES THE WATER CHANGE?** Students will observe how water changes when milk is added to it.

LESSON 4

Water Pollution and Solutions

 UNLOCK THE BIG ?

 Why Is Fresh Water a Limited Resource?

 What Are the Major Sources of Water Pollution?

 How Can Water Pollution Be Reduced?

my planet diary

DISASTERS

A Flood of Sludge

In December 2008, over 4.5 billion liters of polluted water flooded the area around Kingston, Tennessee. A nearby coal-powered electric plant produced polluted water containing arsenic, lead, and other toxic chemicals. The toxic chemicals and coal ash mixed with water in a holding pond to form a thick sludge. When the dam holding back the pond broke, the water poured into rivers. The sludge water spilled over the land, damaging trees, homes, and other buildings. Local residents feared the flood would be dangerous to their health as well.

Communicate Discuss the question with a group of classmates. Then write your answer below.

Is water pollution a problem in your community? Why or why not?

Sample: Yes; there is a polluted river where it is often unsafe to swim.

▶ **PLANET DIARY** Go to **Planet Diary** to learn more about water pollution and solutions.

🧪 **Lab zone** Do the Inquiry Warm-Up *How Does the Water Change?*

Why Is Fresh Water a Limited Resource?

Most of Earth's surface is covered by some form of water. Oceans cover nearly three fourths of Earth's surface. Around the poles are vast sheets of ice. From space you cannot even see many parts of Earth because they are hidden behind clouds of tiny water droplets. There seems to be so much water—it's hard to believe that it is a scarce resource in much of the world.

152 Land, Air, and Water Resources

SUPPORT ALL READERS

Lexile Measure = 960L   Lexile Word Count = 1400

Prior Exposure to Content: Many students may have misconceptions on this topic

Academic Vocabulary: *outline*

Science Vocabulary: *pesticide, sediment*

Concept Level: Generally appropriate for most students in this grade

Preteach With: My Planet Diary "A Flood of Sludge"

Go to **My Reading Web** to access leveled readings that provide a foundation for the content.

my science online.com

Vocabulary
- groundwater • pesticide • sewage • sediment

Skills
- Reading: Outline
- Inquiry: Design Experiments

How can water be scarce when there is so much of it on Earth's surface? **Water is scarce on Earth because most of it—about 97 percent—is salt water.** Salt water cannot be used for drinking or watering crops. Also, about three quarters of the fresh water on Earth is ice. Most liquid fresh water is **groundwater,** water stored in soil and rock beneath Earth's surface. People use groundwater for drinking, but it is not always found near where people live. Cities in dry areas may draw their drinking water from hundreds of kilometers away.

Renewing the Supply Fortunately, Earth's fresh water is renewable. Remember that water continually moves between the atmosphere and Earth's surface in the water cycle. Even though fresh water is renewable, there is not always enough of it in a given place at a given time.

Water Shortages Water shortages occur when people use water faster than the water cycle can replace it. This is likely to happen during a drought when an area gets less rain. Many places never receive enough rain to meet their needs and use other methods to get water. Desert cities in Saudi Arabia get more than half of their fresh water by removing salt from ocean water, which is very expensive.

FIGURE 1 ....
Water
Most of Earth's surface is covered with water, but fresh water is still a limited resource.

✏ **Identify** Reread the text. Then, underline the reasons why fresh water is scarce.

Lab zone® Do the Quick Lab *Where's the Water?*

Assess Your Understanding
got it? ....

○ I get it! Now I know that fresh water is limited on Earth because <u>97 percent of the water</u> <u>is salt water that cannot be used for drinking or for watering crops.</u>

○ I need extra help with <u>See TE note.</u>

Go to my science COACH *online for help with this subject.*

153

Explain

Introduce Vocabulary
Point out that the word *groundwater* is a compound word. Students would be able to infer that it describes water that is in the ground.

Teach Key Concepts
Explain to students that Earth's salt water is abundant and although Earth's fresh water is a limited resource, it is renewable. Ask: **Where is salt water found on Earth?** *(Oceans and seas, some lakes)* **What uses are not appropriate for salt water?** *(Drinking, watering plants and crops)* **What percent of Earth's water is fresh water?** *(3 percent of the total surface water)* **In what form is most of this water?** *(Ice)*

Lab Resource: Quick Lab
L1 **WHERE'S THE WATER?** Students will explore the distribution of Earth's water.

Evaluate

Assess Your Understanding
Have students evaluate their understanding by completing the appropriate sentence.

RTI Response to Intervention
If students cannot explain why fresh water is a limited resource, **then** have them reread the first two paragraphs of the section.

my science COACH Have students go online for help in understanding the reasons why fresh water is a limited resource.

My Planet Diary provides an opportunity for students to explore real-world connections to water resources.

my science online | Limited Water

Explain

Teach Key Concepts 🔑

Explain to students that some pollutants make water merely unpleasant, whereas other pollutants make water unhealthy. Ask: **What is the cause of most water pollution?** *(Human activities)* **What are four activities whose waste can pollute water?** *(Agriculture, industry, mining, and human households)* **What kinds of pollution does agriculture add to water?** *(Pesticides, fertilizers, and animal wastes)* **What is the name given to wastes that households wash down sinks, showers, and toilets?** *(Sewage)* **What are some forms of pollution caused by industry and mining?** *(Chemicals, metal wastes, and heat)* Explain that when agricultural wastes cause algae to grow, the algae block light from penetrating into the pond. The lack of light hinders the growth of plants that live in the water.

⤵ **Outline** When students outline, they list topics and subtopics in a formal structure. Tell students that making an outline can help them see the relationship between main ideas and supporting ideas.

Teach With Visuals

Tell students to look at **Figure 2.** Ask: **What two sources of pollution shown are chemicals the farmer will add to the soil?** *(Pesticides and fertilizer)* Explain how pesticides build up in the food chain. As organisms take in pollutants, they eliminate some pesticides, but the remainder is stored in body tissue to be consumed by the next animal in the food chain.

What Are the Major Sources of Water Pollution?

Since fresh water is scarce, water pollution can be devastating. Some pollutants, such as iron and copper, make water unpleasant to drink or wash in. Other pollutants, such as mercury or benzene, can cause sickness or even death.

🔑 **Most water pollution is the result of human activities. Wastes produced by agriculture, households, industry, mining, and other human activities can end up in water.** Water pollutants can be point or nonpoint pollution sources, classified by how they enter the water. A pipe gushing wastewater directly into a river or stream is an example of a point source. The pipe is a specific pollution source that can be easily identified. Nonpoint pollution sources include farm, street, and construction site runoff. The exact pollution source is hard to trace and identify.

Agricultural Wastes Animal wastes, fertilizers, and pesticides are also sources of pollution. **Pesticides** are chemicals that kill crop-destroying organisms. Rain washes animal wastes, fertilizers, and pesticides into ponds, causing algae to grow. The algae block light and deplete the oxygen in the pond.

Household Sewage The water and human wastes that are washed down sinks, showers, and toilets are called **sewage.** If sewage is not treated to kill disease-causing organisms, the organisms quickly multiply. People can become ill if they drink or swim in water containing these organisms.

FIGURE 2 ··
Farm Pollution
This scene may show common things found on a farm, but even common things can lead to water pollution.

✎ **Relate Text and Visuals**
Circle the potential sources of water pollution in this scene.

154 Land, Air, and Water Resources

Industry and Mining Wastes Some plants, mills, factories, and mines produce wastes that can pollute water. Chemicals and metal wastes can harm organisms that live in bodies of water. Animals that drink from polluted bodies of water or eat the organisms that live in the water can also become ill.

Sediments Water that causes erosion picks up **sediments,** or particles of rock and sand. Sediments can cover up the food sources, nests, and eggs of organisms in bodies of water. Sediments also block sunlight, preventing plants from growing.

Heat Heat can also have a negative effect on a body of water. Some factories and power plants release water that has been used to cool machinery. This heated water can kill organisms living in the body of water into which it is released. This type of pollution is also known as thermal pollution.

Oil and Gasoline An oil spill is a very dramatic form of water pollution. It can take many years for an area to recover from an oil spill because the oil floats on water and is difficult to collect. Another water pollution problem is caused by oil and gasoline that leak out of damaged underground storage tanks. The pollution can be carried far away from a leaking tank by groundwater.

⊙ **Outline** Look back in the text and fill in the graphic organizer below to outline causes of water pollution.

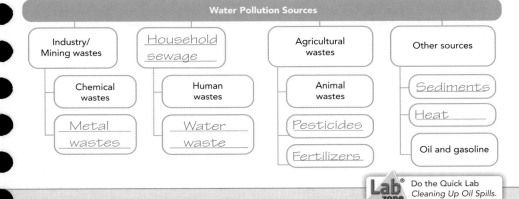

Water Pollution Sources

- Industry/ Mining wastes
  - Chemical wastes
  - *Metal wastes*
- *Household sewage*
  - Human wastes
  - *Water waste*
- Agricultural wastes
  - Animal wastes
  - *Pesticides*
  - *Fertilizers*
- Other sources
  - *Sediments*
  - *Heat*
  - Oil and gasoline

Lab zone Do the Quick Lab *Cleaning Up Oil Spills.*

⊂ **Assess Your Understanding**

got it? ....

○ **I get it!** Now I know that the major sources of water pollution include *wastes produced by agriculture, households, industry, mining, and other human activities.*

○ **I need extra help with** *See TE note.*

Go to my science coach *online for help with this subject.*

155

Differentiated Instruction

L1 Classifying Water Terms Students may be confused by various terms and descriptions in this section. Have pairs of students create web diagrams containing two ovals labeling one *Fresh Water* and the other *Salt Water.* Students can write the terms *water, ice, liquid fresh water, drinking water,* and *groundwater* on lines connected to the appropriate oval. The term water should appear twice.

L3 Thermal Pollution Urge students to learn more about how excessive heat can be a form of pollution in a body of water. Students might research which types of industries or mechanical processes are most likely to cause thermal pollution. Invite students to illustrate their findings to show how organisms in water can be harmed by thermal pollution.

Address Misconceptions

L1 POLLUTION FROM MOTOR OIL CHANGES Many students may think that spills from tankers cause most of the water pollution from oil. Tell students that oil is also released into the environment from households. Some people who change their own motor oil pour the used oil down a drain or into the garbage. Underground tanks of home heating oil may leak into the soil. Although these are small releases, they total more than the amount of oil released by tanker spills. The used oil from one oil change has the potential to pollute 4 million liters of groundwater. Ask: **How should motor oil be safely disposed of?** *(It should be taken to a recycling center.)*

Elaborate

21st Century Learning

COMMUNICATION Have students think about how each of the six sources of water pollution identified in this section could apply to bodies of water in their community or region. Call on volunteers to offer ideas about which sources are present in their area. Students' examples will give local or regional context to pollutants with sources in industry, agriculture, sediments, heat, oil and gasoline spills, and household sewage. Ask students to explain why they think some sources of pollution may be more dangerous to their community.

Lab Resource: Quick Lab

L2 CLEANING UP OIL SPILLS Students will model the difficult process of removing oil from water.

Evaluate

Assess Your Understanding

Have students evaluate their understanding by completing the appropriate sentence.

RTI Response to Intervention

If students need help with identifying sources of water pollution, **then** have them review the six red heads in this section.

my science coach Have students go online for help in understanding the sources of water pollution.

LESSON 4.4

Explain

Teach Key Concepts 🔑

Explain to students that keeping water clean requires action by individuals, industries and agriculture, as well as federal, state, county, and local governments. Ask: **What are three keys to keeping water clean?** *(Effective cleanup of oil and gasoline spills, proper sewage treatment, reduction of pollutants)* **Which of these keys is especially important for individual citizens to address in their own lives?** *(Reduction of pollutants)* **How are disease-causing organisms kept out of drinking water?** *(Wastewater is treated to kill the organisms.)* **What can industries do to keep water clean?** *(Recycle or reduce their wastes, or produce less harmful waste.)* **Why can't bacteria that break down oil take care of large oil spills?** *(There is too much oil for them to break down.)*

Lead a Discussion

REDUCE WATER POLLUTION Remind students that everyone is responsible for water quality. Ask: **What can an individual do to help prevent water pollution?** *(Never pour hazardous chemicals down the drain)* **Does your community have a hazardous-materials collection program?** *(Students may have heard of special days when hazardous materials may be taken to a collection place for proper disposal.)* Work with students to help them identify places (through the phone directory, the Internet, or state environmental agency) where their families can drop off hazardous materials. Environmental agencies can provide information about hazardous household materials that should not be disposed of down the drain or in the regular trash.

How Can Water Pollution Be Reduced?

By working together, governments, industries, and individuals can improve water quality. Federal and state laws in the United States regulate the use of certain substances that can pollute water.

🔑 **The keys to keeping water clean are effective cleanup of oil and gasoline spills, proper sewage treatment, and reduction of pollutants.** There are also some important ways that people can reduce water pollution at home.

Cleaning Up Oil and Gasoline Spills Nature can handle oil in small amounts. A natural cleaning process slowly takes place after oil spills. Certain bacteria living in the ocean feed on the oil. Of course, oil can cause much damage to an area in the time it takes the bacteria to work, so people often help clean up large spills. The hard work of many scientists and volunteers can minimize environmental damage from large spills.

Gasoline or oil that leaks from an underground tank is hard to clean up. If the pollution has not spread far, the soil around the tank can be removed. But pollution that reaches groundwater may be carried far away. Groundwater can be pumped to the surface, treated, and then returned underground. This can take many years.

Sewage Treatment Most communities treat wastewater before returning it to the environment. Treatment plants handle the waste in several steps. During primary treatment, wastewater is filtered to remove solid materials. Then it is held in tanks where heavy particles settle out. During secondary treatment, bacteria break down the wastes. Sometimes the water is then treated with chlorine to kill disease-causing organisms. See **Figure 3.**

FIGURE 3 ···································

Wastewater Treatment
There are several steps to proper sewage treatment.

✎ **Sequence** Put the steps of proper sewage treatment in order by writing the numbers one through four in the circles.

③ Bacteria break down wastes.

① Water is filtered to remove solids.

④ Water is treated with chlorine.

② Heavy particles settle in tank.

Digital Lesson: Assign the *Apply* It activity online and have students submit their work to you.

mY SCIENCE online.com ▶ | **Water Pollution Solutions** |

Reducing Pollutants Instead of releasing wastes into the environment, industries can recycle their wastes. Once such programs are underway, companies often find they save money as well as reduce pollution. Other companies change their processes to produce less waste or less-harmful waste by using fruit acids as cleaning agents instead of toxic chemicals.

What You Can Do It is easy to prevent water pollution at home. Some common household water pollutants are paints and paint thinner, motor oil, and garden chemicals. You can avoid causing water pollution by never pouring these chemicals down the drain. Instead, save these materials for your community's next hazardous waste collection day.

know?

The Exxon *Valdez* oil tanker spilled 40.9 million liters of oil into the Pacific Ocean on March 24, 1989. The oil eventually covered 28,000 square kilometers of ocean!

apply it!

Bacteria can be used to clean up oil spills. Some companies specialize in creating bacteria for cleaning up oil.

❶ **Analyze Costs and Benefits** Fill in the boxes with some pros and cons of using bacteria to clean oil spills.

Pros	Cons
Sample: Natural process; it could be cheaper than using people to clean oil spills.	Sample: Designing bacteria could be expensive; too many bacteria could harm the ecosystem.

❷ **Design Experiments** If you were creating bacteria for cleaning oil spills, what characteristics would you want to test the bacteria for? How much oil the bacteria could digest and how quickly the bacteria could digest it

157

Elaborate

Apply It!

L1 Review the first paragraph under the red head *Cleaning Up Oil and Gasoline Spills* before beginning the activity. Encourage students to reflect on what they already know about bacteria.

▲ **Design Experiments** Reminds students that when they design experiments, they seek to test a hypothesis. Ask: **What could be the manipulated variable in your experiment?** (*A particular type of bacteria*)

LESSON 4.4

Differentiated Instruction

L1 Identify Main Ideas Have students write a main idea sentence for each red head in this section. For example, for *Sewage Treatment*, a main idea sentence might be: A typical sewage treatment plant uses several steps to clean water before returning it to the environment.

L3 Historic Oil Spill Invite students to do additional research on one of the worst environmental disasters in U.S. history, the *Exxon Valdez* oil spill in 1989. Students might create a multimedia presentation showing their findings or make an oral presentation.

Elaborate

Explore the Big Q

Direct students' attention to the aerial photograph. Have students look carefully at the details in the photograph, as well as reading the key of six pollution sources. Point out that the location pictured contains a large body of water with a port, a river, farmland, and mountains, as well as industrial, residential, and commercial areas. Ask: **Which of the labeled sources contributes to air pollution?** *(The smokestack in location "D")* **What is a term sometimes used to identify an area like source "B"?** *(A dump or landfill)* **Which sources could cause water pollution?** *(A, B, C, E, F)*

Teacher Demo

L2 MODELING OIL SPILL CLEAN-UP

Materials shallow pan, small yogurt container, sand or soil, tap water, scissors, spoon or scoop, small paper bag

Time 5 minutes

Place the small yogurt container in the shallow pan, filling the pan with sand or soil around the small container. Pour water into the yogurt container until it is almost full. Tell students that the water represents oil, the yogurt container represents an oil tank, and the sand or soil is the ground around the tank.

Model an oil leak by slicing a hole in one side of the yogurt container, so that water seeps out into the soil. Show students the limited area where the soil is wet and the greater area where it is untainted by oil. Then use the spoon or scoop to remove the "contaminated" soil to a secure receptacle, the paper bag.

Ask: **What about this oil spill made it possible to do a thorough clean-up?** *(The spill was relatively small and involved a small amount of soil.)*

Pollution and Solutions

EXPLORE THE BIG Q

What can people do to use resources wisely?

FIGURE 4

> **REAL-WORLD INQUIRY** All living things depend on land, air, and water. Conserving these resources for the future is important. Part of resource conservation is identifying and limiting sources of pollution.

✎ **Interpret Photos** On the photograph, write the letter from the key into the circle that best identifies the source of pollution.

Land
Describe at least one thing your community could do to reduce pollution on land.

Sample: Be sure that landfills are carefully built, produce less solid waste by increasing recycling, and educate people about recycling.

Key of Pollution Sources
A. Sediments
B. Municipal solid waste
C. Runoff from development
D. Emissions
E. Oil and gasoline
F. Agricultural wastes

158 Land, Air, and Water Resources

Real-World Inquiry allows students to explore the effects of water pollution on frog populations.

my science online.com | **Water Pollution Solutions**

Air
Describe at least one thing your community could do to reduce air pollution.

Sample: Encourage people to take public transportation or require all factories to use scrubbers.

Water
Describe at least one thing your community could do to reduce water pollution.

Sample: Educate people about what they should not dump down drains, stop factories from dumping waste into water, or launch a campaign for people to use less water.

 **Do the Quick Lab** Getting Clean.

🔖 Assess Your Understanding

1a. Define What are sediments?

Particles of rock and sand

b. Explain How can bacteria help clean an oil spill in the ocean?

Sample: The bacteria clean the oil spill by feeding on the oil.

c. ANSWER THE BIG ? What can people do to use resources wisely?

Sample: Avoid and minimize pollution; conserve resources by limiting use.

d. CHALLENGE Why might a company not want to recycle the waste they produce even if it would reduce water pollution?

Sample: The equipment needed to recycle the waste could be expensive and the company may not be able to afford it.

got it? ....

○ **I get it!** Now I know that water pollution can be reduced by _treating sewage, reducing pollutants, and cleaning gas and oil spills._

○ **I need extra help with** _See TE note._

_Go to_ **MY SCIENCE COACH** _online for help with this subject._

159

Lab Resource: Quick Lab 🔖

L1 GETTING CLEAN Students will model the way that fresh water is purified in the water cycle.

Evaluate

Assess Your Understanding
After students answer the questions, have them evaluate their understanding by completing the appropriate sentence.

Answer the Big Q ? UbD

To help students focus on the Big Question, lead a class discussion about how people can use resources wisely.

R T I Response to Intervention

1a. If students cannot define *sediments*, **then** have them locate the highlighted term and read its definition.

b. If students have trouble explaining the action of bacteria on an oil spill, **then** have them read the first paragraph under the red head *Cleaning Up Oil and Gasoline Spills*.

c. If students need help with explaining how to use resources wisely, **then** have them look over the information under the red heads *Reducing Pollutants* and *What You Can Do*.

d. If students cannot explain the reluctance to recycle, **then** have them consider the financial burdens recycling might place on the company.

MY SCIENCE COACH Have students go online for help in understanding how to reduce water pollution.

Differentiated Instruction

L1 Photographic Details Have pairs or small groups of students work together to decode a variety of details shown in the photograph. Using terms such as *bridge, farmland, skyscrapers, river, tanker,* and *housing development* will help students infer sources of pollution.

L3 Research Air Quality Index Have students do research on the "air quality index" that meteorologists use to inform people about the presence of pollutants in the air in a certain region. Students can prepare a brief oral or multimedia presentation, perhaps in a format similar to that used by broadcast meteorologists.

Lab zone **After the Inquiry Warm-Up**

Water Pollution and Solutions

Inquiry Warm-Up, *How Does the Water Change?*
In the Inquiry Warm-Up, you investigated how pollutants change water. Using what you learned from that activity, answer the questions below.

1. **APPLY PRIOR KNOWLEDGE** How does less light passing through a body of water affect plants that live in the water? Explain.

_____

_____

_____

_____

2. **PREDICT** Would adding more water to the cup make the water–milk mixture clearer or more cloudy? Explain.

_____

_____

3. **INFER** Do you think adding a clear pollutant, such as rubbing alcohol, to water would make it cloudy?

_____

_____

4. **DRAW CONCLUSIONS** What difference in your observations would you expect if in the experiment, you did not stir the milk after adding it to the water? Explain.

_____

_____

Assess Your Understanding

Water Pollution and Solutions

> **Why Is Fresh Water a Limited Resource?**

got_it? ....

○ **I get it!** Now I know that fresh water is limited on Earth because _____

_____

○ **I need extra help with** _____

_____

> **What Are the Major Sources of Water Pollution?**

got_it? ....

○ **I get it!** Now I know that the major sources of water pollution include _____

_____

○ **I need extra help with** _____

_____

Assess Your Understanding

Water Pollution and Solutions

How Can Water Pollution Be Reduced?

1a. DEFINE What are sediments? _____

_____

b. EXPLAIN How can bacteria help clean an oil spill in the ocean? _____

_____

c. ANSWER (?) What can people do to use resources wisely? _____

_____

_____

d. CHALLENGE Why might a company not want to recycle the waste

they produce even if it would reduce water pollution? _____

_____

_____

got it? ···

○ **I get it!** Now I know that water pollution can be reduced by _____

_____

○ **I need extra help with** _____

_____

Key Concept Summaries

Water Pollution and Solutions

Why Is Fresh Water a Limited Resource?

Oceans cover nearly three fourths of the Earth's surface. Yet **water is scarce on Earth because most of it—about 97 percent—is salt water.** Salt water cannot be used for drinking or watering crops. And about three quarters of the planet's fresh water is ice. For drinking water, people use fresh liquid water and **groundwater,** which is water stored in soil and rock beneath Earth's surface. Water is renewable: It cycles between the atmosphere and Earth's surface. Water shortages occur when people in an area use water faster than the water cycle can replace it.

What Are the Major Sources of Water Pollution?

Since fresh water is scarce, water pollution can be devastating. **Most water pollution is the result of human activities. Wastes produced by agriculture, households, industry, mining, and other human activities can end up in water.** Agricultural wastes include animal wastes, fertilizers, and **pesticides,** chemicals that kill crop-destroying organisms. The water and human wastes that are washed down sinks, showers, and toilets are called **sewage.** Sewage must be treated to kill disease-causing organisms. Water that causes erosion picks up **sediments,** or particles of rock and sand. In bodies of water, sediments can prevent plants from growing by blocking sunlight. Industries and mines produce chemicals and metal wastes that pollute water. Some factories and power plants also produce thermal pollution, releasing heated water that can kill organisms living in bodies of water. Spills and leaks of oil and gasoline can cause catastrophic damage to living things in water.

How Can Water Pollution Be Reduced?

By working together, governments, industries, and individuals can improve water quality. **The keys to keeping water clean are effective cleanup of oil and gasoline spills, proper sewage treatment, and reduction of pollutants.** While natural bacteria can clean up small amounts of oil in bodies of water, it is necessary for people to help clean up large spills. In most communities, wastewater and sewage are treated before they are returned to the environment. Many industrial companies are trying to reduce the amount of waste they produce, as well as to recycle wastes. Individuals can take steps at home to avoid creating water pollution.

On a separate sheet of paper, explain several threats to our planet's supply of fresh water.

Review and Reinforce

Water Pollution and Solutions

Understanding Main Ideas
Answer the following questions on a separate sheet of paper.

Water on Earth

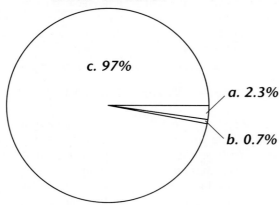

1. Which section of the circle graph above represents Earth's salt water? Which section represents ice? Which section represents usable fresh water?
2. How does the water cycle purify Earth's water?
3. What is sewage? Why is it important to treat sewage?
4. How can farm chemicals pollute water? Why is it hard to keep these chemicals from getting into nearby water?
5. What are the keys to keeping water clean?

Building Vocabulary
Write the correct term to complete each sentence below.

6. Water that is stored in layers of soil and rock beneath Earth's surface is called _____.

7. The water and human wastes that are washed down sinks, toilets, and showers are called _____.

8. Chemicals that kill crop-destroying organisms are known as _____.

9. Water that causes erosion picks up _____, or particles of rock and sand.

Water Pollution and Solutions

In addition to primary and secondary treatment, many sewage plants use tertiary treatment to clean wastewater. (*Tertiary* means "third.") The chart below shows which materials are removed in each treatment step. The thickness of the black bar shows how much of each substance remains in the water. Use the chart to answer the following questions on a separate piece of paper.

Sewage Treatment

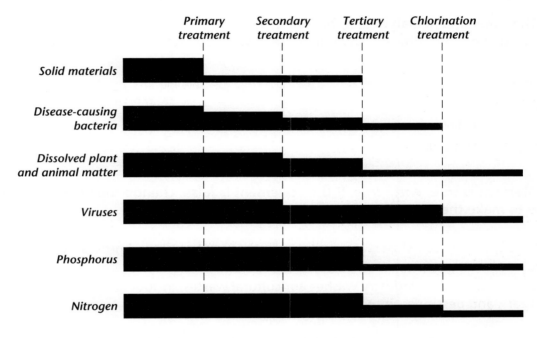

1. Which materials are mostly removed by primary treatment?
2. Which materials are partly removed by secondary treatment?
3. Which materials does tertiary treatment help remove?
4. If a sewage plant did not use tertiary treatment, which material(s) would not be removed at all?
5. Which materials are completely removed before the treated water is released into the environment after chlorination treatment?
6. Phosphorus and nitrogen are nutrients that help algae and plants grow. Why is it important to reduce these materials before treated water is released?

Name _____ Date _____ Class _____

Water Pollution and Solutions

Write the letter of the correct answer on the line at the left.

1. ___ About 97% of the water on Earth is

A fresh water

B groundwater

C salt water

D ice

2. ___ Chemicals that kill crop-destroying organisms are called

A sediments

B fertilizers

C acid rain

D pesticides

3. ___ The water and human wastes that are washed down sinks, showers, and toilets are called

A the water cycle

B sewage

C thermal pollution

D point pollution sources

4. ___ Water that causes erosion picks up

A sediments

B sewage

C pollutants

D algae

If the statement is true, write _true_. If the statement is false, change the underlined word or words to make the statement true.

5. _____ Most water pollution is the result of <u>natural processes</u>.

6. _____ <u>Industry</u> washes agricultural wastes, including animal wastes, fertilizers, and pesticides, into ponds, causing algae to grow.

7. _____ Wastes produced by agriculture, households, industry, mining, and other human activities can end up in <u>water</u>.

8. _____ <u>Fresh liquid water</u> is stored in soil and rock beneath Earth's surface.

9. _____ <u>Keeping water clean</u> requires effective cleanup of oil and gasoline spills, proper sewage treatment, and reduction of pollutants.

10. _____ Most communities treat <u>groundwater</u> before returning it to the environment.

Water Pollution and Solutions

Answer Key

After the Inquiry Warm-Up

1. Accept all reasonable responses. Students may say: Plants need sunlight to live and grow. If less light passes through the water, then plants in the water will find it harder to survive.

2. Adding more water would dilute the solution, making the mixture clearer.

3. No, the water-alcohol mixture would likely be clear.

4. Accept all reasonable responses. Students may say: The clarity of the mixture will change more slowly if the milk is not stirred after adding it to the water. The milk and water may not mix well.

Key Concept Summaries

Major threats to Earth's supply of fresh water include wastes produced by agriculture (animal wastes, pesticides, and fertilizers), households (sewage), industry and mining (chemicals and metals), sediments, heat, and oil and gasoline.

Review and Reinforce

1. Salt water: c; Ice: a; Usable fresh water: b

2. When water evaporates from Earth's surface, any harmful substances that were dissolved in the water are left behind. The water vapor in the air is pure fresh water.

3. Sewage is the water and human wastes that are washed down sinks, toilets, and showers. Sewage contains disease-causing organisms. If sewage is not treated and it mixes with water used for drinking or swimming, the organisms can make people very sick.

4. Farm chemicals can be washed into bodies of water by rain. This is hard to prevent because farm chemicals are usually spread over a large, open area.

5. proper sewage treatment; reduction of pollutants; effective cleanup of oil and gasoline spills

6. groundwater

7. sewage

8. pesticides

9. sediments

Enrich

1. Solid materials

2. Disease-causing bacteria, dissolved plant and animal matter, and viruses

3. Solid materials, disease-causing bacteria, dissolved plant and animal matter, phosphorus, and nitrogen

4. Phosphorus (nitrogen would still be partly removed by chlorination)

5. Solid materials and disease-causing bacteria

6. If they are not reduced, they can cause overgrowth of algae in the rivers or lakes into which the treated water is released.

Lesson Quiz

1. C	2. D
3. B	4. A
5. human activities	6. Rain
7. true	8. Groundwater
9. true	10. sewage

Ocean Resources

5 What can people do to use resources wisely?

Lesson Pacing: 1–2 periods or $\frac{1}{2}$–1 block

🕐 **SHORT ON TIME?** To do this lesson in approximately half the time, do the Activate Prior Knowledge activity on page 160. A discussion of the key concepts on pages 161, 163, and 166 will familiarize students with the lesson content. Have students do the Quick Labs. The rest of the lesson can be completed by students independently.

Preference Navigator, in the online Planning tools, allows you to customize *Interactive Science* to your own teaching style. You can also edit lesson plans by selecting the Lesson Planner option.

Digital Teacher's Edition allows you to access your Teacher's Edition and Resource materials online.

Lesson Vocabulary
- nodule
- upwelling

Content Refresher

The Impact of Overfishing The world's fisheries are being overfished at an accelerating rate. A United Nations study has concluded that most of the world's fisheries are already being exploited and have begun to be depleted. In addition to threatening the biodiversity of fish, overfishing impacts the well-being of hundreds of millions of people. Approximately 200 million people, mostly in developing nations, depend on fishing for their livelihood, while 20 percent of the world's population relies on fish as their primary source of protein.

LESSON OBJECTIVES

- Identify the ocean's living and nonliving resources.
- Identify sources of ocean pollution.

Blended Path
Active learning using Student Edition, Inquiry Path, and Digital Path

ENGAGE AND EXPLORE

Teach this lesson using a variety of resources. Begin by reading **My Planet Diary** as a class. Have students share ideas about how to restore healthy fish populations. Then do the **Inquiry Warm-Up activity.** Students will classify a variety of household products as derived from ocean resources or not. The **After the Inquiry Warm-Up worksheet** sets up a discussion about the potential effects of ocean pollution on the availability or price of foods and products that include ingredients from the ocean. Have volunteers share their answers to number 4 about how pollution in the ocean may affect availability and the price of ocean-sourced products.

EXPLAIN AND ELABORATE

Teach Key Concepts by exploring the variety of seafood that students are familiar to students. Review the terms *fisheries* and *harvest* before beginning the **Apply It activity.** Continue to **Teach Key Concepts** by explaining that people also use nonliving resources from the ocean. **Lead a Discussion** about the living and nonliving resources from the ocean that students and their families use. Use **Figure 1** to determine how both the living and nonliving resources from the ocean are distributed around the world. **Lead a Discussion** to explore how upwelling water affects the algae population and how fluctuations in the algae population affect fish populations and the fishing industry.

Teach Key Concepts by explaining that while some natural occurrences pollute the ocean, the primary cause of ocean pollution is human activity (runoff of chemicals used in agriculture and industry, releasing sewage, spilling oil or gas). **Support the Big Q** by discussing the ownership of the ocean and the need for great cooperation from all nations to protect the ocean's health.

Hand out the **Key Concept Summaries** as a review of each part of the lesson. Students can also use the online **Vocab Flash Cards** to review key terms.

EVALUATE

Have students take the **Lesson Quiz.** For an alternate assessment, see the **EXAM**VIEW® Assessment Suite, Progress Monitoring Assessments, or SuccessTracker™.

E L L Support

1 Content and Language
Explain to students that *interpret,* in the lesson, means "to explain the meaning of," and *data* means "individual facts, figures, and other items of information." Ask students to give a definition of *interpreting data* in their own words.

DIFFERENTIATED INSTRUCTION KEY
L1 Struggling Students or Special Needs
L2 On-Level Students **L3** Advanced Students

LESSON PLANNER 4.5

Lab zone Inquiry Path
Hands-on learning in the Lab zone

Digital Path
Online learning at **my science online**.com

ENGAGE AND EXPLORE

To teach this lesson with an emphasis on inquiry, begin with the **Inquiry Warm-Up activity.** Discuss the importance of food and product ingredients from the ocean to our everyday life. Have students do the **After the Inquiry Warm-Up worksheet** and discuss the potential effects of ocean pollution. Have volunteers share their answers to number 4 about how pollution might affect the availability or price of foods and products that include ingredients from the ocean.

EXPLAIN AND ELABORATE

Focus on the **Inquiry Skill** for the lesson. Explain that when you interpret data you should read symbols and labels to inform your observations about information. What interpretations can be made from the classifications in the **Inquiry Warm-Up activity?** *(Our lives could be affected if resources from the ocean are not available.)* Review *fisheries* and *harvest* before beginning the **Apply It activity.**

Set up the **Teacher Demo.** After students have used the stereomicroscope to observe the tiny shells produced by diatomite algae, discuss possible uses for the shells. Have students do the **Quick Lab** to explore making an Asian dessert out of ingredients including algae. Have students share their results.

Use the **Support the Big Q** to discuss ownership of the ocean and the need for great cooperation from all nations to protect the ocean's health. Do the **Quick Lab** to have students examine objects that often pollute the ocean and analyze their negative effects. Students can use the online **Vocab Flash Cards** to review key terms.

EVALUATE

Have students take the **Lesson Quiz.** For an alternate assessment, see the **EXAM**VIEW® Assessment Suite, Progress Monitoring Assessments, or SuccessTracker™.

ENGAGE AND EXPLORE

Teach this lesson using digital resources. Begin by having students learn more about ocean resources and explore real-world connections to ocean resources at **My Planet Diary** online. Have them access the Chapter Resources to find the **Unlock the Big Question activity.** There they can answer the questions and refine their responses as they continue through the lesson. You can re-assign the activity and have students submit their work so you can track their progress.

EXPLAIN AND ELABORATE

Students reading above, at, or below the lexile measure of this lesson can access basic content readings at their level at **My Reading Web.** Have students use the online **Vocab Flash Cards** to preview key terms. Review *fisheries* and *harvest* before assigning the **Apply It activity** online. Have students submit their work to you.

Use the **Art in Motion activity** online to show the distribution among nations of fisheries, oil and gas deposits, and mineral resources. Have students do the **Quick Lab** to explore making an Asian dessert out of ingredients including algae. Have students share their results.

Support the Big Q by discussing ownership of the ocean and the need for great cooperation from all nations to protect the ocean's health. Assign the **Do the Math activity** online and have students submit their work to you. Do the **Quick Lab** to have students examine objects that often pollute the ocean. Have students share their results. The **Key Concept Summaries** online allow students to read a summary and see an image associated with each part of the lesson. Online remediation is available at **My Science Coach.**

EVALUATE

Have students take the **Lesson Quiz.** For an alternate assessment, see the **EXAM**VIEW® Assessment Suite, Progress Monitoring Assessments, or SuccessTracker™.

---

2 Frontload the Lesson
Preview by looking at the data in the **Apply It activity** on page 161 and the visual on page 162. Help students locate the Key for each visual. Discuss how using the Key helps interpret the data in the visuals.

3 Comprehensible Input
Have students study the visual and read the caption of *upwelling* on page 165. Have them write a description of the diagram in their own words.

4 Language Production
Pair or group students with varied language abilities to collaborate to complete the labs. Have each student copy the completed written lab for personal reference.

5 Assess Understanding
Ask students to make notes about key concepts from the lesson and prepare an oral presentation of the concepts. Encourage students to use the visuals in the lesson to support their presentations.

LESSON 4.5

Ocean Resources

Establish Learning Objectives

After this lesson, students will be able to:

🗝 Identify the ocean's living and nonliving resources.

🗝 Identify sources of ocean pollution.

Engage

Activate Prior Knowledge

MY PLANET DIARY Read *Are There Plenty of Fish in the Sea?* with the class. Explain that people may have misguided perceptions about the availability of fish partly because the planet's oceans are so vast. Point out that the oceans cannot support a limitless, infinite supply of fish—or any other organism— despite their impressive size. Ask: **What has caused there to be fewer cod in the ocean off the eastern coast of North America?** *(Overfishing)*

BIG IDEAS OF SCIENCE REFERENCE LIBRARY 📖 Have students look up the following topics: Farming, Seaweed.

Explore

Lab Resource: Inquiry Warm-Up 🔬

L1 **IS IT FROM THE OCEAN?** Students will classify a variety of household products as derived from ocean resources or not.

---

5 Ocean Resources

🗝 **What Are the Ocean's Living and Nonliving Resources?**

🗝 **What Are the Sources of Ocean Pollution?**

my planet diary

Are There Plenty of Fish in the Sea?

Huge schools of codfish used to swim off the eastern coast of North America. Sailors reported that sailing through crowded schools of cod slowed the boats down!

For more than 400 years, the seemingly endless cod supply supported a thriving fishing industry. But starting in the early 1900s, it became clear that the cod population was decreasing. Cod prices rose. There was more competition to catch fewer fish. In 1992, the Canadian government closed its cod fishery. Today, cod and many other fish species are struggling to return to healthy population sizes.

MISCONCEPTIONS

Communicate Discuss the question with a group of classmates. Write your answer below.

What do you think needs to happen for fish populations to reach healthy population sizes?

Set limits on fishing so fish can grow in numbers.

_____

_____

_____

▶ **PLANET DIARY** Go to **Planet Diary** to learn more about ocean resources.

 Do the Inquiry Warm-Up *Is It From the Ocean?*

160 Land, Air, and Water Resources

SUPPORT ALL READERS

Lexile Measure = 930L   Lexile Word Count = 1471

Prior Exposure to Content: Many students may have misconceptions on this topic

Academic Vocabulary: *interpret, main idea*

Science Vocabulary: *evaporation, condensation, precipitation*

Concept Level: Generally appropriate for most students in this grade

Preteach With: My Planet Diary "Are There Plenty of Fish in the Sea" and Figure 1 activity

Go to **My Reading Web** to access leveled readings that provide a foundation for the content.

my science online

Vocabulary
- nodule
- upwelling

Skills
- 🔁 Reading: Identify the Main Idea
- 🔺 Inquiry: Interpret Data

What Are the Ocean's Living and Nonliving Resources?

The ocean holds a variety of resources you often use, from edible fish and seaweeds to plants used in medicine to oil for vehicles.

Living Resources How many kinds of seafood have you eaten? 🗝 **People depend on ocean organisms for food. Ocean organisms also provide materials that are used in products such as detergents and paints.**

Harvesting Fish Many kinds of fishes are caught to be eaten. Anchovies, pollock, mackerel, herring, and tuna make up most of the worldwide catch. Nearly all fishes are harvested from coastal waters or areas with nutrients and plankton on which the fish feed.

If used wisely, fisheries naturally renew themselves each year. New fish hatch, replacing those that are caught, but only as long as the fishery is not overfished. Better technology has enabled people to quickly catch large numbers of fish. The fish can be caught faster than they can reproduce. When fish reproduction decreases, there are fewer fish each season. Eventually, the fish in the fishery may become very scarce.

apply it!

Imagine you are a fisheries scientist asked to evaluate a new harvesting strategy, pictured right. During each annual harvest, 40,000 fish are caught. Some people think the current population could support a larger harvest for 50 years into the future.

❶ **Make Judgments** Should the harvest be increased? Why?

No; the population is not replacing itself after harvest. The population only grew by 10,000 fish after the first harvest of 40,000.

❷ CHALLENGE Why is it important to carefully monitor fish populations before, during, and after setting harvest limits?

The population can change. The limit used in one year might be too high in the next.

10,000 fish

Population before first harvest

Population after first harvest

Population after second harvest

161

ELL Support

1 Content and Language
Help students understand complex words such as *desalination* by breaking the word into its parts. Circle the root word *sal* and underline the prefix *de-* and the suffix *-ation*. Explain that the prefix *de-* denotes removal or reversal, the Latin root *sal* refers to salt, and the suffix *-ation* denotes a process.

2 Frontload the Lesson
Preview the lesson by calling students'

attention to the titles, visuals, labels, captions, and features. Ask students what they think this text is about.

3 Comprehensible Input
Drawing visuals can simplify text passages that carry a heavy language load. The paragraph on how fuels are created contains a number of academic words that may be new or difficult for students. Draw a visual to help support the explanation of this process.

Explain

Introduce Vocabulary
Tell students that the word *nodule* has several related meanings. In addition to "a small round lump of a mineral," the term can also mean "a small abnormal knobby growth on the body" or "a swelling on a root."

Teach Key Concepts 🗝
Explain to students that people use organisms in the ocean for food and for a variety of products. Ask: **What kinds of fish have you eaten?** *(Students may indicate tuna and a variety of other types of seafood.)* **How many other examples of seafood can you name?** *(Sample: Salmon, swordfish, bluefish, cod, grouper)* **Under what conditions is a fishery a renewable resource?** *(If new fish are hatched and the fishery is not overfished, the fishery is a renewable resource.)*

Apply It!
L1 Review the terms *fisheries* and *harvest* before beginning the activity. Explain that a *fishery* is a place where fish are raised and that a *harvest* is the process of gathering a crop such as plants or fish. Ask: **How does the fish population before the first harvest compare with the fish population after the first harvest?** *(The population is smaller after the first harvest.)* **How does the population after the first harvest compare with the population after the second harvest?** *(The population is smaller after the second harvest.)*

My Planet Diary provides an opportunity for students to explore real-world connections to ocean resources.

Digital Lesson Assign the *Apply It* activity online and have students submit their work to you.

Explain

Teach Key Concepts 🗝

Explain to students that in addition to living resources, there are many nonliving resources that people use from the ocean. Ask: **Do you think that it is easier or more difficult to get water, fuel, and minerals from the ocean compared to the land?** *(It is more difficult.)* **Then why do people get these resources from the oceans?** *(Supplies on land are limited or not available in a particular region.)* **Where on Earth might people want to desalinate ocean water?** *(Desert and other arid regions)*

Lead a Discussion

Invite students to think about how they and their families use one or more products that comes from the ocean. Ask: **What kinds of foods do people obtain from the ocean?** *(Students should name a variety of fishes, shellfish, and other marine organisms such as seaweeds.)* **Besides food, what other ocean resources do people use?** *(Accept all reasonable responses.)*

🔄 **Identify the Main Idea** Tell students that the most important—or biggest—idea in a paragraph or section of text is the main idea. Sometimes main ideas are stated directly, and sometimes the reader must identify the main idea.

Teach With Visuals

Tell students to look at **Figure 1.** Ask: **Where are most major fisheries located?** *(Near coastlines)* **Which continents have the fewest fisheries, and which have the most?** *(Africa, Australia; North America, South America)* **Which continents have the fewest oil and gas deposits?** *(Africa, South America, Australia)*

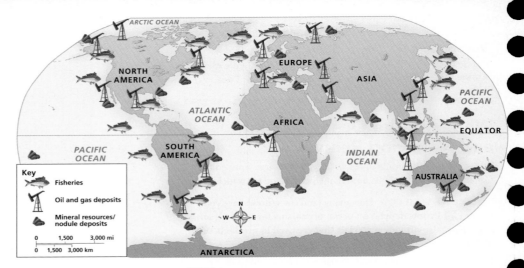

Key
- Fisheries
- Oil and gas deposits
- Mineral resources/ nodule deposits

| 0 | 1,500 | 3,000 mi |
| 0 | 1,500 | 3,000 km |

FIGURE 1 ·····

▷ ART IN MOTION Ocean Resources

As you can see on the map, ocean resources are not evenly distributed among nations. ✎ **Interpret Maps** What problems do you think could arise from this distribution?

<u>Sample: Some countries would have many resources while other countries would have none and have to pay for resources.</u>

🔄 **Identify the Main Idea** Why is aquaculture important in areas without ocean resources?

<u>Aquaculture can provide fish for people to eat in areas where there is no ocean to support fish.</u>

Aquaculture As fish stocks decrease, aquaculture, or the farming of saltwater and freshwater organisms, is likely to become more common. Aquaculture has been practiced in some Asian countries for centuries.

Aquaculture involves creating an environment for the organisms. To help the organisms thrive, nutrient levels, water temperature, light, and other factors must be controlled. Oysters, abalone, and shrimp have successfully been farmed in artificial saltwater ponds and protected bays. Even landlocked regions can produce seafood using aquaculture. For example, salmon are now being raised in Nebraska fields that once were cattle ranches.

Other Ocean Products People harvest ocean organisms for many purposes besides food. Algae are an ingredient in many household products. Their gelatin-like texture make an ideal base for detergents, shampoos, cosmetics, paints, and even ice cream! Sediments containing the hard pieces of algae are used for abrasives and polishes. Many researchers think that other marine organisms may be important sources of chemicals for medicines in the future.

162   Land, Air, and Water Resources

Art in Motion demonstrates how fisheries, oil and gas deposits, and mineral resources are distributed among nations.

my science online .com   **Ocean Resources**

Nonliving Resources The ocean also contains valuable nonliving resources. ⚷ **Some nonliving ocean resources include water, fuels, and minerals.**

Water Fresh water can be extracted from ocean water using a process called desalination. See **Figure 2**. Desalination provides fresh water for many dry areas, islands, ships, and submarines. However, the process also requires a large amount of energy to heat water for removing the salt.

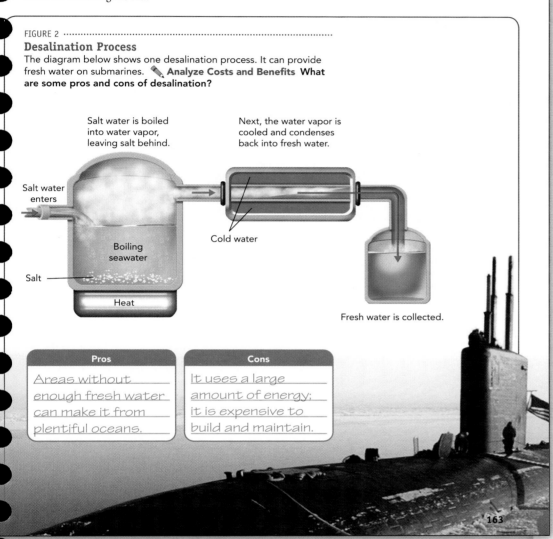

FIGURE 2 ···

Desalination Process
The diagram below shows one desalination process. It can provide fresh water on submarines. ✎ **Analyze Costs and Benefits** What are some pros and cons of desalination?

Salt water is boiled into water vapor, leaving salt behind.

Next, the water vapor is cooled and condenses back into fresh water.

Salt water enters

Cold water

Boiling seawater

Salt

Heat

Fresh water is collected.

Pros	Cons
Areas without enough fresh water can make it from plentiful oceans.	It uses a large amount of energy; it is expensive to build and maintain.

163

Elaborate

21st Century Learning

CRITICAL THINKING Ask students to make a generalization about the likely future of aquaculture. *(Sample: Aquaculture will probably grow in importance if fish stocks continue to decrease.)*

Teacher Demo 🔬

L1 INEDIBLE OCEAN RESOURCES

Materials diatomite, microscope slide, stereomicroscope, microscope lamp

Time 15 minutes

Remind students that ocean organisms provide many types of resources, not just food. Place a small sample of diatomite under a stereomicroscope and allow students to observe. Students will see the tiny shells produced by these algae.

Ask: **How could these shells be useful?** *(The shells are used in abrasives, polishes, and to kill insects.)*

Differentiated Instruction

L1 Define Algae Encourage students to use a glossary or dictionary to read the definition of algae. After they have familiarized themselves with the definition, have them reread the paragraph about "Other Ocean Products." Have them write a sentence using the word algae that describes the type of organisms in the definition.

L3 Research Aquaculture
Aquaculture is an important and expanding industry. Oysters are farmed for food and for pearls. Other farmed organisms include clams, fish, and algae. Encourage students to learn more about marine aquaculture and report to the class.

Elaborate

Address Misconceptions

L1 **UNLIMITED RESOURCES** Tell students that some resources, such as sunlight, will be available for billions of years, but that other resources are available in limited supply. Some students may have the misconception that the ocean has an unlimited supply of resources. Help students understand that organisms can be harvested faster than they can reproduce. Even resources such as oil and minerals are present in limited supply. Ask: **How might society prevent shortages of ocean resources from occurring and how might society adapt if shortages do occur?** *(Accept all responses. Sample: To prevent shortages, society can have nations' governments work together to regulate industries that limit uses of ocean resources so that they can be replenished.)*

Lead a Discussion

FUTURE ENERGY SOURCE In marine sediments on the ocean floor lie another potential fuel source—methane hydrates. A methane hydrate is a crystalline solid consisting of methane molecules that are surrounded by an ice-like cage of water molecules. Hydrates form in the deep ocean floor at very low temperatures and very high pressures. Since methane is the primary component of natural gas, methane hydrate deposits could potentially be a future energy source. Some estimates state that the amount of energy stored in methane hydrate deposits could be more than twice the global reserves of gas, oil, and coal deposits combined. Ask: **Do you think obtaining methane hydrates from beneath the ocean floor is easy to do?** *(Students may say that it is difficult to obtain methane hydrates due to the depth, temperature, and pressure on the ocean floor.)*

Lead a Discussion

NUTRIENTS FOR ALGAE Remind students that plants need nutrients to grow. Tell them the algae that live in the ocean also need nutrients. Help students understand that nutrients are compounds such as nitrates that are dissolved in the water. Ask: **If algae need nutrients to grow and reproduce, how do you think upwelling water affects algae populations in the ocean?** *(The nutrients in the water cause algae to become abundant.)* **Why might other organisms benefit from abundant algae?** *(Algae are food for many fish, people, and other animals that feed on fish.)* **How would ocean life in this area be affected if upwelling stopped and warm water flowed in?** *(Algae and other organisms would be less abundant.)* **How would this affect the fishing industry?** *(It would hurt it; fewer fish could be caught.)*

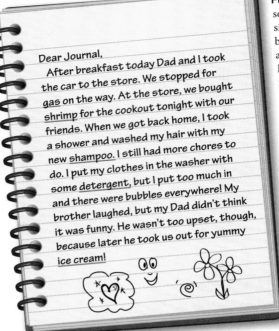

Dear Journal,
After breakfast today Dad and I took the car to the store. We stopped for gas on the way. At the store, we bought shrimp for the cookout tonight with our friends. When we got back home, I took a shower and washed my hair with my new shampoo. I still had more chores to do. I put my clothes in the washer with some detergent, but I put too much in and there were bubbles everywhere! My brother laughed, but my Dad didn't think it was funny. He wasn't too upset, though, because later he took us out for yummy ice cream!

FIGURE 3 ·······································
Ocean Resource Journal
The ocean provides materials for many products that you might not realize are used in everyday life.
✎ **Apply Concepts** In this journal entry, underline every use of an ocean product.

Fuels The remains of dead marine organisms are the source of another nonliving resource. The remains sink to the bottom of the ocean, where they are buried by sediments. As more sediments accumulate, the buried remains decompose. Over hundreds of millions of years, the heat and pressure from the overlying layers gradually transform the organisms' remains into oil and natural gas. Scientists have also discovered methane hydrates, or methane trapped on ice, on the ocean bottom. Since methane is the main component of natural gas, methane hydrates could be an energy source in the future. However, techniques need to be developed to extract the methane from methane hydrates.

Minerals Minerals are solid substances that are obtained from the ground and the water. When fresh water is removed from ocean water, the salts that are left behind are a valuable mineral resource. More than half of the world's supply of magnesium, a strong, light metal, is obtained from seawater in this way.

The ocean floor is another source of mineral resources. From the sediments covering the ocean floor, gravel and sand are mined for use in building construction. In some areas of the world, diamonds and gold are mined from sand deposits. Manganese and other metals accumulate on the ocean floor. The metals concentrate around pieces of shell, forming black lumps called **nodules** (NAJH oolz). Nodules sometimes occur in waters as deep as 5,000 meters. Recovering the nodules is a difficult process. The technology for gathering the nodules is still being developed.

Ocean Resources and Upwelling In most of the ocean, surface waters do not mix with deep ocean waters. Mixing sometimes occurs when winds cause upwelling. **Upwelling** is the movement of cold water upward from the deep ocean. As winds blow away the warm surface water, cold water rises to replace it.

Upwelling, as show in **Figure 4,** brings up tiny ocean organisms, minerals, and other nutrients from deeper waters. Without this motion, the surface waters of the open ocean would be scarce in nutrients. Because nutrients are plentiful, areas of upwelling are usually home to huge schools of fish. These fish are an important resource to the people and animals that feed on them.

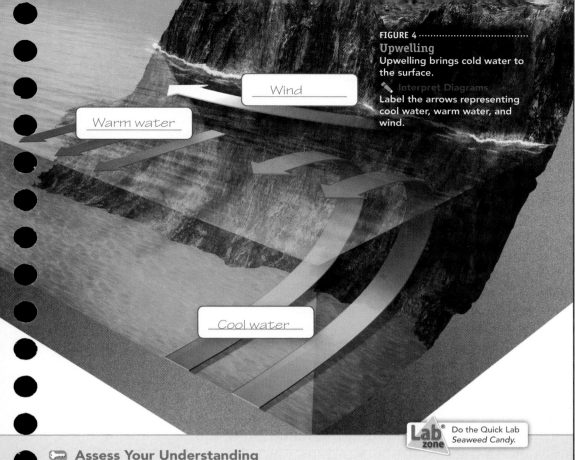

FIGURE 4 ....
Upwelling
Upwelling brings cold water to the surface.

✏ Interpret Diagrams
Label the arrows representing cool water, warm water, and wind.

Wind

Warm water

Cool water

 Do the Quick Lab
Seaweed Candy.

🗝 Assess Your Understanding

1a. Review The practice of (aquaculture/upwelling) can provide fish in areas not near an ocean.

b. Describe Where do the fuel deposits in the ocean come from? <u>Dead marine organisms break down over time under pressure and heat and become fuel.</u>

c. Relate Cause and Effect Explain how upwelling supports organisms in open ocean. <u>Upwelling brings cold, nutrient-rich waters to the surface. These nutrients can support schools of fish.</u>

got it? ....

○ **I get it!** Now I know the living and nonliving resources in the ocean include <u>fish and other edible organisms, algae, water, fuels, and minerals.</u>

○ **I need extra help with** <u>See TE note.</u>

Go to MY SCIENCE 🌐 COACH *online for help with this subject.*

165

Explain

Teach With Visuals

Figure 4 is only accurate for the Southern Hemisphere. Students may wonder why the arrow for the wind is pointing perpendicular to the water flow arrows. As the wind blows north, it causes a northward current of water. However, due to the rotation of the Earth, the Coriolis force causes it to turn counterclockwise. This moves water away from the coast and causes upwelling into the low-pressure near shore areas.

Elaborate

Lab Resource: Quick Lab 🔬

L2 SEAWEED CANDY Students will explore making an Asian dessert out of ingredients including algae.

Evaluate

Assess Your Understanding

After students answer the questions, have them evaluate their understanding by completing the appropriate sentence.

R T I Response to Intervention

1a. If students have trouble defining *aquaculture*, **then** have them locate the highlighted terms in the question and read their definitions.

b. If students cannot identify the source of ocean fuel deposits, **then** have them reread the paragraph about "Fuels."

c. If students need help with explaining effects of upwelling, **then** have them review **Figure 4** and the material under the red head *Ocean Resources and Upwelling*.

MY SCIENCE 🌐 COACH Have students go online for help in understanding the range of living and nonliving resources in the ocean.

Differentiated Instruction

L1 Explaining Upwelling Call on a succession of students to give a concise explanation of differing water temperatures near the surface and deep down in the ocean. Also ask about the principle of upwelling, and the effect of upwelling on ocean organisms, minerals and other nutrients, and schools of fish.

L3 Exploring the Ocean Floor Invite students to use reference books and reliable Web sites to learn more about the ocean floor. Students might focus research on mineral resources, oil and natural gas deposits, or the technology that allows people to study these remote regions.

Explain

Teach Key Concepts 🔑

Explain to students that ocean pollution is the result primarily of human activities, along with some natural occurrences. Review with students the definition of *pollution*—contamination of an environment with harmful substances. Ask: **How can humans cause pollution of the ocean?** *(Allowing runoff of chemicals from farm fields and industrial plants, releasing sewage, spilling oil)* **Can pollution also occur naturally?** *(Yes. Examples include excess fresh water runoff and toxins released by some algae.)* Point out that the Gulf of Mexico dead zone is an example of how human activities have affected the oceans. A dead zone is an area of water that has very low amounts of oxygen. Low oxygen levels make it difficult for most organisms to survive in these areas. The Gulf of Mexico dead zone is one of the largest dead zones in the world and is caused primarily by nutrient runoff from farms into the Mississippi River, which runs into the gulf waters. The nutrients allow algae to flourish and consume most of the oxygen supply in the water. Without enough oxygen, fish, shrimp, oysters, and other organisms cannot survive. This threatens the seafood industry in the Gulf of Mexico.

Support the Big Q ❓ UbD

PROTECT THE OCEAN Tell students that much of the ocean does not belong to any country and that many countries border the ocean. Discuss with them why controlling ocean pollution is so difficult and why cooperation between nations is important. Ask: **How much of the ocean does a country control?** *(The first 22 kilometers off its coasts)* **What does the term *high seas* mean?** *(Surface waters of the ocean that are not owned by any country)*

Elaborate

Do the Math!

The graph shows the predominance of human over natural causes of ocean pollution. The source *natural seeps* refers to the natural process by which oil leaks out of oil deposits in the oceans.

🔺 Interpret Data

Remind students to read the labels for the bars and to use the white horizontal lines to help them follow across to determine the quantity that each bar represents. Ask: **What is shown along the bottom of the graph?** *(Sources of ocean oil pollution)* **What is labeled along the left side of the graph?** *(Oil pollution measured in millions of liters)*

See *Math Skill and Problem-Solving Activities* for support.

What Are the Sources of Ocean Pollution?

The ocean is a self-cleaning system. It can absorb some wastes without permanent damage. Dumping large amounts of wastes into the ocean threatens many marine organisms. Most ocean pollution, however, comes from the land. 🔑 **Although some ocean pollution is the result of natural occurrences, most pollution is related to human activities.**

Natural Occurrences Some pollution is the result of weather. Heavy rains put fresh water into saltwater environments like marshes and swamps. This fresh water pollutes the ocean by lowering its salinity. It may kill organisms that cannot adjust.

Human Activities Sewage, chemicals, and trash dumped into coastal waters all come from human sources. Substances that run off fields and roads often end up in the ocean and can cause dead zones. A dead zone is an area that lacks enough oxygen for organisms to live. Pollutants can also build up in the organisms' bodies and poison the people and animals that feed on them. Trash can cause serious problems too. Air-breathing marine mammals can drown if they get tangled in fishing lines or nets. Other animals are harmed when they swallow plastic that blocks their stomachs.

Another major threat to ocean life is oil pollution. When an oil tanker or drilling platform is damaged, oil leaks into the ocean. Oil destroys the natural insulation of animals such as sea birds and otters. This affects their ability to float. Oil also harms animals when they swallow it.

do the math!

The graph shows some sources of oil pollution in the ocean. Give the graph a title and answer the questions.

❶ Interpret Data Which source causes the most oil pollution?

Land runoff

❷ Of the five sources on the graph, how many are the result of human activity?

Four

❸ Solve Problems What is one thing a coastal city could do to reduce oil pollution?

Sample: Repair ships on land so oil leaks do not enter the ocean.

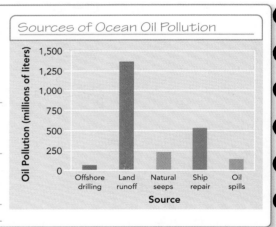

Sources of Ocean Oil Pollution

Digital Lesson: Assign the *Do the Math* activity online and have students submit their work to you.

MY SCIENCE ONLINE.com | Ocean Pollution

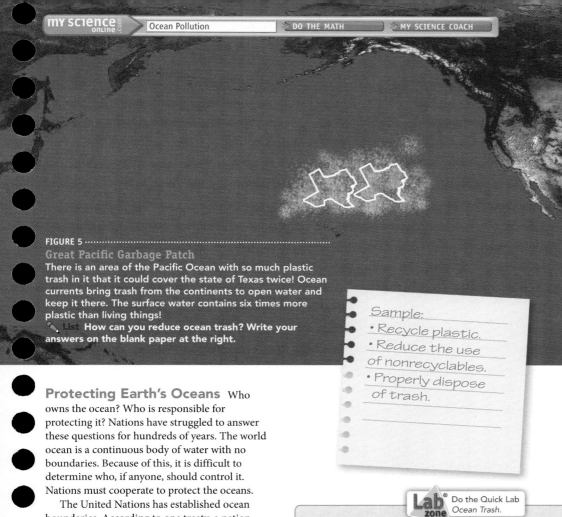

FIGURE 5 ······································

Great Pacific Garbage Patch

There is an area of the Pacific Ocean with so much plastic trash in it that it could cover the state of Texas twice! Ocean currents bring trash from the continents to open water and keep it there. The surface water contains six times more plastic than living things!

✎ **List** How can you reduce ocean trash? Write your answers on the blank paper at the right.

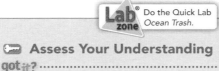

Sample:
• Recycle plastic.
• Reduce the use of nonrecyclables.
• Properly dispose of trash.

Protecting Earth's Oceans Who owns the ocean? Who is responsible for protecting it? Nations have struggled to answer these questions for hundreds of years. The world ocean is a continuous body of water with no boundaries. Because of this, it is difficult to determine who, if anyone, should control it. Nations must cooperate to protect the oceans.

The United Nations has established ocean boundaries. According to one treaty, a nation controls the first 22 kilometers off its coasts. The nation also controls the resources in the waters or on the ocean floor within 370 kilometers of its shore. This leaves approximately half of the ocean's surface waters as "high seas" owned by no nation. Ownership of the ocean floor beneath the high seas is still under debate.

Other international efforts have resulted in reducing ocean pollution. Examples include the creation of marine refuges and regulations for building safer oil tankers.

Lab zone® Do the Quick Lab *Ocean Trash.*

🔑 **Assess Your Understanding**

got it? ·······························

○ **I get it!** Now I know most ocean pollution is caused by _human activities._

_____

○ **I need extra help with** _See TE note._

_____

Go to **my science** COACH *online for help with this subject.*

167

Lab Resource: Quick Lab

L1 OCEAN TRASH Students will examine objects that often pollute the ocean and analyze their negative effects.

Evaluate ─────────

Assess Your Understanding

Have students evaluate their understanding by completing the appropriate sentence.

RTI Response to Intervention

If students cannot identify sources of ocean pollution, **then** have them reread the material under the red heads *Natural Occurrences* and *Human Activities.*

my science COACH Have students go online for help in understanding the causes of ocean pollution.

Differentiated Instruction

L1 Damage Caused by Pollutants
Ask pairs of students to reread the material under the red head *Human Activities.* Have them make a cause-and-effect chart and list the seven pollutants mentioned—sewage, chemicals, trash, run-off from fields and roads, fishing lines and nets, plastic, and oil. Encourage students to write the effect of each type of pollutant in the chart's right column.

L3 Debating Ocean Mineral Rights Have students imagine that they are delegates to the United Nations to discuss a major mineral deposit that has been discovered in the mid-Atlantic Ocean. Have student teams represent the nation that discovered the deposit, the nation with the technology to mine it, and the closest nations to the deposit. Monitor as students debate which country owns the deposit and which has the right to mine it.

Lab zone **After the Inquiry Warm-Up**

Ocean Resources

Inquiry Warm-Up, *Is It From the Ocean?*

In the Inquiry Warm-Up, you investigated food and product ingredients that come from the ocean. Using what you learned from that activity, answer the questions below.

1. **GRAPH** Draw a simple graph showing the number of products that contain ingredients from the ocean versus the number of foods that do not.

2. **MAKE JUDGMENTS** Based on your graph, how important are food and product ingredients from the ocean? Explain.

_____

_____

3. **DRAW CONCLUSIONS** Explain how pollution in the ocean might affect your health.

_____

_____

_____

4. **DRAW CONCLUSIONS** Explain how pollution in the ocean might affect the availability of or price of products that include ingredients from the ocean.

_____

_____

_____

Name _____ Date _____ Class _____

Ocean Resources

> **What Are the Ocean's Living and Nonliving Resources?**

1a. REVIEW The practice of (aquaculture/upwelling) can provide fish in areas not near an ocean.

b. DESCRIBE Where do the fuel deposits in the ocean come from?

_____

_____

c. RELATE CAUSE AND EFFECT Explain how upwelling supports organisms

in open ocean. _____

_____

_____

_____

gotit? ···

○ **I get it!** Now I know the living and nonliving resources in the ocean include _____

_____

○ **I need extra help with** _____

_____

> **What Are the Sources of Ocean Pollution?**

gotit? ···

○ **I get it!** Now I know most ocean pollution is caused by _____

_____

○ **I need extra help with** _____

_____

Ocean Resources

What Are the Ocean's Living and Nonliving Resources?

People use products made from living and nonliving resources in the ocean. **People depend on ocean organisms for food. Ocean organisms also provide materials that are used in products such as detergents and paints.** Fisheries renew themselves naturally each year, but overfishing has caused a shortage of fish in some areas. Aquaculture, the farming of salt- and freshwater organisms, is increasingly common. Algae is harvested for use in many products. **Some nonliving ocean resources include water, fuels, and minerals.** Water can be extracted from the ocean and, in a process called desalination, treated to remove salt. Fuels such as oil and natural gas have been created naturally over the course of hundreds of millions of years out of the remains of dead marine organisms. Minerals and metals accumulate on the ocean floor. The metals concentrate around pieces of shell, forming black lumps called **nodules.** Minerals and nutrients are brought to the surface of the ocean as a result of **upwelling,** the movement of cold water upward from the deep ocean.

What Are the Sources of Ocean Pollution?

The ocean cleans itself naturally. However, the ocean cannot absorb large amounts of wastes, and so many marine organisms are threatened by the dumping of such wastes. **Although some ocean pollution is the result of natural occurrences, most pollution is related to human activities.** Some pollution is caused by weather such as heavy rains. Yet sewage, chemicals, and trash are dumped into coastal waters by humans. Other substances run off fields and roads can end up in the ocean. Oil pollution from damaged tankers or drilling platforms can cause wide destruction to living things in the ocean. Because the world ocean is a continuous body of water with no boundaries, nations must cooperate to protect it.

On a separate sheet of paper, explain why it is vital for people to control ocean pollution.

Review and Reinforce

Ocean Resources

Understanding Main Ideas

Use the table below to answer Questions 1–3.

Total Catch (in metric tons)		
Fish Species	**1970**	**1993**
Haddock	829,300	226,500
Atlantic cod	2,817,500	1,028,700
Peruvian anchovy	11,845,300	7,464,600

1. How did the catches of these three fish change in the period shown?

_____

2. Why do you think these changes might have occurred?

_____

3. What can be done to protect fish populations?

_____

Answer the following questions in the space provided.

4. What happens to the remains of dead marine organisms to transform them into oil and gas?

_____

_____

5. Why must nations cooperate to reduce ocean pollution?

_____

_____

Building Vocabulary

On a separate sheet of paper, write a definition for each of these terms.

6. upwelling

7. nodules

Enrich

Ocean Resources

The graph below shows the amount of groundfish (cod, haddock, and flounder) caught in the Georges Bank area each year from 1960 to 1995. Use the graph to answer the questions that follow.

Fishing on Georges Bank

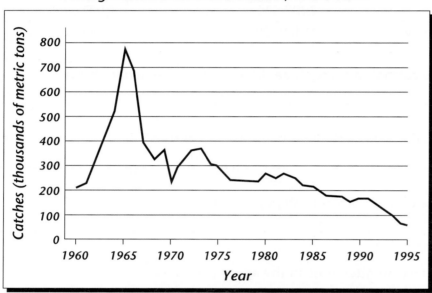

Georges Bank Groundfish Catches, 1960–1995

1. What do the numbers on the graph's vertical axis represent? _____

2. How many tons of groundfish were caught in 1960? _____

3. How many tons were caught in 1995? _____

4. How many fewer tons were caught in 1995 than in 1960? _____

5. When did the catch first fall below the 1960 level? _____

6. In late 1994, the U.S. National Marine Fisheries Service closed Georges Bank to commercial fishing. Why do you think this was done?

_____

_____

_____

_____

Lesson Quiz

Ocean Resources

If the statement is true, write *true*. If the statement is false, change the underlined word or words to make the statement true.

1. _____ People depend on ocean organisms for <u>food</u>.

2. _____ Nonliving ocean resources include water, <u>algae</u>, and minerals.

3. _____ Minerals and nutrients from deep in the ocean are brought to the surface in cold water as a result of <u>thermal pollution</u>.

4. _____ Fisheries renew themselves naturally each year, but <u>overfishing</u> has caused a shortage of fish in some areas.

5. _____ Fuels such as <u>coal</u> are created naturally over the course of hundreds of millions of years from the remains of dead marine organisms.

Fill in the blank to complete each statement.

6. _____, the farming of salt- and freshwater organisms, is increasingly common.

7. Although some ocean pollution is the result of natural occurrences, most pollution is related to _____.

8. Metals on the ocean floor concentrate around pieces of shell, forming black lumps called _____.

9. Fresh water can be produced by removing the salt from ocean water using a process called _____.

10. _____ from damaged tankers or drilling platforms can cause wide destruction to living things in the ocean.

Ocean Resources

Answer Key

After the Inquiry Warm-Up

1. Students should draw a simple bar graph contrasting the number of products that include ocean-derived ingredients versus the number of products that do not.

2. Accept all reasonable responses. Students will likely say: Ocean-derived ingredients are very important because they are used in many products.

3. Accept all reasonable responses. Students may say: Ocean pollution could harm people because it might end up in ocean-derived ingredients that are eventually used in food.

4. Accept all reasonable responses. Students may say: Ocean pollution may harm or kills plants, animals, and other organisms in the seas, making ingredients made from sea life scarcer and more expensive.

Key Concept Summaries

It is vital for people to control ocean pollution because people rely on the world's oceans for food and for many other living and nonliving resources.

Review and Reinforce

1. The catches of all three fish declined from 1970 to 1993.

2. The declines are probably caused by overfishing.

3. Limit catches so fish that are caught can be replaced by new fish that are born.

4. They sink to the ocean floor, are buried by sediments, and decompose. As sediments build up, heat and pressure from the overlying layers transform the remains into oil and gas.

5. The world's oceans are continuous, and no nation owns the high seas. Pollution in one nation's waters can reach the open ocean and spread to other nations' waters.

6. the movement of cold water upward from the deep ocean

7. black lumps that form around pieces of shell and are made of metals that accumulate on the ocean floor

Enrich

1. thousands of metrics tons of fish caught

2. a little more than 200,000 metric tons

3. about 60,000 metric tons

4. about 140,000 metric tons

5. 1986

6. to allow the fish population to renew itself naturally

Lesson Quiz

1. true
2. fuels
3. upwelling
4. true
5. oil and natural gas
6. Aquaculture
7. human activities
8. nodules
9. desalination
10. Oil pollution

Place the outside corner, the corner away from the dotted line, in the corner of your copy machine to copy onto letter-size paper.

Study Guide

Review the Big Q UbD

Have students fill in their answers in the statement at the top of the page. These Key Concepts support their understanding of the chapter's Big Question. Have them return to the chapter opener pages. What is different about how students view the image of shipping containers now that they have completed the chapter? Thinking about this will help them prepare for the *Apply the Big Q* activity in the Review and Assessment.

Partner Review

Have partners review definitions of vocabulary terms by using the Study Guide to quiz each other. Students could read the Key Concept statements and leave out words for their partner to fill in, or change a statement so that it is false and then ask their partner to correct it.

Class Activity: Mural

Have students create a mural that shows four aspects of Land, Air, and Water Resources. For each of the chapter's first four lessons, students should include an illustration or diagram, an explanation of how the lesson's title relates to the Big Idea, and a list of key terms and concepts. Ask students to use the following questions to help them organize their ideas:

- How do people use land?
- Why is soil management important?
- What are three solid waste disposal methods?
- What causes outdoor and indoor air pollution?
- How can air pollution be reduced?
- What are the major sources of water pollution?
- How can water pollution be reduced?

My Science Coach allows students to complete the *Practice Test* online.

The Big Question allows students to complete the *Apply the Big Q* activity about what people can do to use resources wisely.

Vocab Flash Cards offer a way to review the chapter vocabulary terms.

my science online.com — Land, Air, and Water Resources

CHAPTER 4 Study Guide

REVIEW THE BIG ? — To use resources wisely, people can reuse or <u>recycle</u> materials and they can properly dispose of hazardous wastes and other <u>pollutants</u>.

LESSON 1 Conserving Land and Soil

🔑 Three uses that change the land are agriculture, mining, and development.

🔑 Without soil, most life on land could not exist. Poor soil management results in three problems: erosion, nutrient depletion, and desertification.

Vocabulary
- litter • topsoil • subsoil • bedrock
- erosion • nutrient depletion • fertilizer
- desertification • drought • land reclamation

LESSON 2 Waste Disposal and Recycling

🔑 Solid waste is burned, buried, or recycled.

🔑 Recycling categories include metal, glass, paper, and plastic.

🔑 Hazardous wastes are stored depending on the type and potential danger.

Vocabulary
- municipal solid waste • incineration
- pollutant • leachate • sanitary landfill
- recycling • biodegradeable • hazardous waste

LESSON 3 Air Pollution and Solutions

🔑 A major source of outdoor air pollution is vehicle emissions. Indoor air pollution has a variety of causes.

🔑 The major cause of the ozone hole is CFCs.

🔑 Reducing air pollution requires reducing emissions.

Vocabulary
- emissions • photochemical smog • ozone
- temperature inversion • acid rain
- radon • ozone layer • chlorofluorocarbon

LESSON 4 Water Pollution and Solutions

🔑 Earth's water is about 97 percent salt water.

🔑 Most water pollution is caused by human activities.

🔑 The keys to keeping water clean include cleaning oil spills, proper sewage treatment, and the reduction of pollutants.

Vocabulary
- groundwater • pesticide • sewage • sediment

LESSON 5 Ocean Resources

🔑 Resources in the ocean include organisms such as fish and nonliving things such as oil.

🔑 Most ocean pollution is related to human activities.

Vocabulary
- nodule
- upwelling

(E L L) Support

4 Language Production

Arrange the class in small-group circles. Introduce one of the section head questions from the chapter. Then have one member of each circle give a fact or detail that helps answer the question. The students to their right should then provide a different fact or detail. The cycle continues until there is no new information to share and all questions have been discussed.

Beginning

LOW/HIGH Permit students to refer to their books or notes during the discussion.

Intermediate

LOW/HIGH Allow students extra time to share their facts and details.

Advanced

LOW/HIGH Challenge students to use vocabulary terms during the discussion.

Review and Assessment

LESSON 1 Conserving Land and Soil

1. What is an agricultural use of land?

- **a.** growing crops on land
- **b.** collecting water from land
- **c.** building structures on land
- **d.** removing minerals from land

2. Plant roots absorb nutrients and water from the layer of soil called _topsoil_ .

3. Relate Cause and Effect What type of land use can result in nutrient depletion? Explain.

Agriculture; if the same crop is planted each year, it will use most of the nutrients.

LESSON 2 Waste Disposal and Recycling

4. What is one benefit of recycling?

- **a.** It increases the volume of solid waste.
- **b.** If it is recycled, a material won't biodegrade.
- **c.** It conserves resources and energy.
- **d.** It uses more raw materials that need to be mined.

5. A _hazardous waste_ is a waste that can be harmful to human health or the environment.

6. Write About It How could your school reduce the amount of municipal solid waste it produces? Include where you think the most waste is produced in your school and propose at least two ways to reduce it.

See TE rubric.

LESSON 3 Air Pollution and Solutions

7. Which of the following describes a pollutant that has been released into the air?

- **a.** sewage
- **b.** leachate
- **c.** sediment
- **d.** emissions

8. The _ozone layer_ in the upper atmosphere prevents some of the sun's ultraviolet radiation from reaching Earth.

9. Predict Do you think the hole in the ozone layer will increase or decrease in size? Why?

Sample: Decrease, because of the ban on damaging CFCs

10. Solve Problems Describe two ways a large city can reduce air pollution.

Sample: Encourage people to use public transportation; require factories to clean hazardous emissions.

169

Review and Assessment

Assess Understanding

Have students complete the answers to the Review and Assessment questions. Have a class discussion about what students find confusing. Write Key Concepts on the board to reinforce knowledge.

RTI Response to Intervention

2. If students have trouble identifying topsoil, **then** have them review **Figure 2** in Lesson 1.
4. If students cannot name a benefit of recycling, **then** have them reread the benefits of different types of recycling.
7. If students need help with defining *emissions*, **then** have them scan Lesson 3 to find the term and its definition.

Alternate Assessment

L3 CONCEPT MAP Remind students that Earth's land, water, and air resources must be protected from pollution and conserved through recycling, proper disposal and cleanup, and reducing pollutants. Have students brainstorm to identify the key concepts, key terms, details, and examples of the chapter. Then challenge them to write each item on a sticky note and attach it at random to chart paper or to the board. Tell students that this concept map should be organized in hierarchical order, and have them begin at the top with key concepts. Asking questions such as *What are ways to conserve land and manage solid waste? What causes pollution of land, air, and water resources?* and *How can air and water pollution be reduced?* will help guide students in categorizing the information on the sticky notes.

CHAPTER 4

Write About It Assess student's writing using this rubric.

SCORING RUBRIC	SCORE 4	SCORE 3	SCORE 2	SCORE 1
waste reduction solution	Explains how school can reduce municipal solid waste	Identifies where school could reduce waste	Does not identify where school could reduce waste	No understanding of solid waste issues
identify school's waste and offer two ways to reduce it	Identifies waste source & gives two ways to reduce it	Identifies source of some waste and gives one way to reduce it	Misidentifies source of most waste and gives general way to reduce it	Does not identify source of waste and does not give any ways to reduce it

Review and Assessment, Cont.

RTI Response to Intervention

13. If students cannot explain the effects of fertilizer on a pond, **then** have them reread the section on the effects of pesticides and fertilizers on sources of fresh water.

14. If students cannot identify living and nonliving resources, **then** have them review the information under the red heads "Living Resources" and "Nonliving Resources."

Apply the Big Q ? UbD

TRANSFER Students should be able to demonstrate conservation of land, air, and water resources by answering this question. See the scoring rubric below.

Connect to the Big Idea ? UbD

BIG IDEA Living things interact with their environment.

Send students back to the Big Ideas of Science at the beginning of their student edition. Have them read what they wrote about interactions of living things and their environment before they started the chapter. Lead a class discussion about how their thoughts have changed. If all chapters have been completed, have students fill in the bottom section for the Big Idea.

L3 WRITING IN SCIENCE Ask students to write a summary of what they have learned about the importance of land, air, and water resources.

LESSON 4 Water Pollution and Solutions

11. Why is fresh water a limited resource?

a. because most water on Earth is in lakes

b. because most water on Earth is in clouds

c. because most water on Earth is in the ground

(d.) because most water on Earth is salt water

12. A <u>pesticide</u> is a chemical that kills crop-destroying organisms.

13. Draw Conclusions Rain may wash fertilizers into bodies of water, such as ponds. How might fertilizer affect a pond?

<u>Sample: Fertilizer can cause algae to grow, preventing other pond life from surviving.</u>

LESSON 5 Ocean Resources

14. The ocean contains living resources such as _____ and nonliving resources such as _____.

a. fuel; water

(b.) fish; minerals

c. seaweed; shrimp

d. organisms; pollution

15. <u>Upwelling</u> is the movement of cold water from the deep ocean to the surface.

16. Relate Cause and Effect How might oil used as fuel result in ocean pollution?

<u>Oil can get washed into streams and rivers and then washed into the ocean, destroying ocean life and damaging ecosystems.</u>

 What can people do to use resources wisely?

17. Every individual, including young people, can make decisions to use resources wisely. **Use the terms** *reduce, reuse,* **and** *recycle* **to explain how the students in the picture below can help minimize solid waste.**

<u>Sample: Students could reduce the number of napkins and disposable bags they use. They could use reusable lunch bags. They could recycle the bottles and cans on the table.</u>

 What can people do to use resources wisely?
Assess student's responses using this rubric.

SCORING RUBRIC	SCORE 4	SCORE 3	SCORE 2	SCORE 1
Identify sources of pollution and describe at least one thing to reduce each type	Identifies all six sources of pollution describes in detail ways to reduce each type of pollution	Identifies five sources of pollution describes in detail one way to reduce each type of pollution	Identifies two or more sources of pollution and describes general way to reduce each type of pollution	Does not identify any sources of pollution and does not describe any way to reduce each type

Standardized Test Prep

Multiple Choice

Circle the letter of the best answer.

1. According to the circle graph, what is the most common method of waste disposal in the United States?

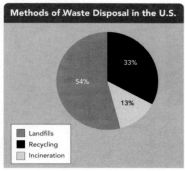

Methods of Waste Disposal in the U.S.

- 33%
- 54%
- 13%

Legend:
- Landfills
- Recycling
- Incineration

- A composting
- B recycling
- C incineration
- Ⓓ landfills

2. In which layer of soil would you expect to find rock fragments, nutrients, and decaying plant and animal matter?

- A litter
- Ⓑ topsoil
- C subsoil
- D bedrock

3. What types of materials could be broken down in a compost pile?

- A all recyclable materials
- Ⓑ biodegradable materials
- C all materials that can be incinerated
- D glass, metal, and other raw materials

4. How can sediments negatively affect an aquatic ecosystem?

- Ⓐ by blocking sunlight
- B by causing algae to grow
- C by causing plants to grow
- D by changing the water temperature

5. What are the main sources of ocean pollution?

- A upwellings
- B natural causes
- Ⓒ human activities
- D waves of sunlight reacting with water

Constructed Response

Use the diagram below and your knowledge of science to help you answer Question 6. Write your answer on a separate sheet of paper.

6. Compare and contrast the role of ozone in each of the images shown above.

See TE note.

171

Test-Taking Skills

INTERPRETING GRAPHS Tell students that when they answer questions like Question 1, which include a graph, they should read all parts of the graph carefully, including title, labels and other information in a key, and numbers. Students should make sure that they understand the meaning of colors, shapes, and other elements of the graph. One way to approach the answer is to eliminate those answer choices that are not supported by the graph.

Constructed Response

6. Ozone is involved in both situations, but the effects are different. Close to Earth, ozone is a pollutant. It is one of the main components of smog. High in the atmosphere, ozone occurs naturally. It protects Earth from the sun's ultraviolet rays. These rays can cause sunburns and lead to skin cancer.

Additional Assessment Resources

Chapter Test
EXAMVIEW® Assessment Suite
Performance Assessment
Progress Monitoring Assessments
SuccessTracker™

ⒺⓁⓁ Support

5 Assess Understanding

Have ELLs complete the Alternate Assessment. Provide guidelines on the information it must cover, and a rubric for assessment.

Beginning

LOW/HIGH Provide students with extra time to complete their concept maps.

Intermediate

LOW/HIGH Allow students to refer to their books or notes when completing their concept maps.

Advanced

LOW/HIGH Pair students with high language skills to those with less proficient language skills to complete the concept map.

Remediate If students have trouble with...

QUESTION	SEE LESSON	STANDARDS
1	2	
2	1	
3	2	
4	4	
5	4	
6	3	

Science Matters

Technology and Society

Have students read *Old MacDonald Had a Satellite.* Explain that the Global Positioning System (GPS) is a network of satellites that broadcast signals from space and can pinpoint an exact location. Farmers can efficiently water and apply additives to their fields where it is indicated by satellite pinpointed locations.

Tell students that farmers check their soil for many factors when trying to make the soil as fertile as possible. For example, the soil could have a high acidity level that could be harmful to the plants a farmer is trying to grow. Using precision farming allows farmers to assess the condition of the soil in all parts of their farms much more quickly and makes for more efficient farming.

Before students begin researching precision farming, have each form a hypothesis about one way precision farming might be helpful to farmers. When they complete their research, they should review and draw conclusions about their hypotheses. This will give them a basis for their poster display or multimedia presentation.

Ask: **Why is being able to view satellite images of their farms more helpful to farmers than previous methods?** *(Farmers can gather information about their farms faster and can get a more accurate picture of the soil conditions on each part of the whole farm.)* **What is another application GPS could have in helping the environment?** *(Sample: using satellite photos to determine the best places to plant more trees)*

SCIENCE MATTERS

Old MacDonald Had a Satellite

When listing the equipment needed for a farm, you might think of a tractor and irrigation equipment, but would you include a satellite on your list? Farming has come a long way since Old MacDonald's days! Precision farming uses high-tech tools, such as remote sensing and the Global Positioning System (GPS), to conserve resources and increase crop yields.

On large farms, soil fertility can vary in different areas. Before learning about precision farming, farmers usually averaged the amount of water and fertilizer that they needed for the whole farm. Then, they applied that amount evenly throughout their fields. Some areas might get too much fertilizer and water, while others might not get enough.

In precision farming, farmers can use data from GPS satellites to learn about what the soil on their farm needs. Satellite images of their farms can give farmers information about the fertility of specific fields, and whether these fields have enough nutrients and water. Because the farm machinery is equipped with a GPS receiver, the farmer can precisely adjust the amount of water, pesticides, or fertilizer applied to specific areas of a field, to make sure that each area gets exactly what it needs. This method reduces costs and increases crop yields. It also reduces the overuse of agricultural chemicals. Old MacDonald never had it this good!

Research It Find out more about how precision farming may protect water supplies from contamination or how these techniques can save farmers money. Create a poster display or multimedia presentation that explains your findings.

▲ Inside a crop-sprayer, a farmer uses a GPS receiver to read information from a GPS satellite about the soil in the field.

Quick Facts

Precision farming is just one of many interesting techniques in use by farmers today. For example, many farmers grow foods organically, meaning without using any chemicals or pesticides. Some farmers practice sustainable agriculture. They operate their farms in a way that helps the environment and minimize their use of nonrenewable resources. Other farms raise alternative livestock, or breeds of animals that are exotic, nontraditional, or rare. These include emus, game birds, bison, deer, elk, and turkeys. Other alternative farming methods include beekeeping and community farming. Have students research what alternative farming methods are used in your state and give reasons why these methods are preferred over traditional farming.

BEWARE of Greenwashing!

Many businesses claim to produce environmentally friendly products. But how can you know the truth? *Greenwashing* is a term that combines the words *green* and *whitewashing*. It refers to the practice of making a product, service, or company appear to be more environmentally friendly than it really is.

Sometimes, identifying greenwashing is difficult because advertisements can be very persuasive. Fortunately, thinking like a scientist can help. As you evaluate a company's environmental claims, consider the following questions.

✓ **Is there proof?** Is there a scientific basis for the claims made by the company?

✓ **Is there a trade-off?** Does creating or delivering the product or service have negative environmental effects that are greater than the benefits of the product or service?

✓ **Are the claims meaningless?** Some labels, such as "100% natural," have no scientific or regulatory meaning.

✓ **Who says so?** Has a reliable source tested the company's claims?

Apply It Find advertisements for products that claim to have environmental benefits. Use the questions above to evaluate the claims. Then, create a brochure to educate the public about greenwashing.

Now Safe for the Environment!

CFC free

With **Eco-sensitive** ingredients

173

Think Like a Scientist

Have students read *Beware of Greenwashing!* Explain that companies that use greenwashing make these claims to try to sell more of their product. Ask students to name some greenwashing claims they have seen on products at home.

Companies may use various methods of greenwashing. A company may advertise one environmentally friendly product and not reveal that the rest of the company's product line is not environmentally friendly. Some companies spend money advertising about being "green" instead of spending money making their products green. Sometimes a company will take credit for participating in cleanups or creating more green products, when in fact, these companies must comply with government standards to avoid penalties.

As students create greenwashing brochures, have them include ways people can take action against companies that participate in greenwashing. For example, students could boycott products by companies that make meaningless and unproven "green" claims or write letters to government representatives about greenwashing offenders.

Ask: **What are some examples of greenwashing claims?** *(Sample: eco-safe, eco-friendly, 100% natural)* **What could you do to support a company that does have genuinely green products?** *(Sample: buy only that brand, write to the company to tell them I appreciate their efforts)* **What is a similar example of a type of company that might make meaningless claims?** *(Sample: companies that make foods that claim to be healthy)*

Energy Resources

Introduce the Big Q ❓ UbD

Have students look at the image and read the Engaging Question and description. Have students make hypotheses about the sources of energy in their lives. Point out that wind turbines like the ones shown on these pages have become dramatically more common in the United States in recent years. Ask: **What is the source of the energy you used to get to school today?** *(Fossil fuels for gasoline, food for walking)* **What source of energy keeps your home warm?** *(Students may indicate oil, gas, wood, or electricity; accept all answers at this time.)* **What source of energy keeps you warm on a bright, clear summer afternoon?** *(The sun)*

Untamed Science Video

FARMING THE WIND Before viewing, invite students to suggest alternative energy resources to fossil fuels. Then play the video. Lead a class discussion and make a list of questions that the video raises. You may wish to have students view the video again after they have completed the chapter to see if their questions have been answered.

> To access the online resources for this chapter, search on or navigate to *Energy Resources*.
>
> **Untamed Science Video** compare wind energy to coal energy.
>
> **The Big Question** allows students to answer the Engaging Question about energy resources.

MY SCIENCE online.com ❯ **Energy Resources**

HOW CAN WIND KEEP YOUR LIGHTS ON?

THE BIG ❓

What are some of Earth's energy sources?

This man is repairing a wind turbine at a wind farm in Texas. Most wind turbines are at least 30 meters off the ground where the winds are fast. Wind speed and blade length help determine the best way to capture the wind and turn it into power. **Develop Hypotheses** Why do you think people are working to increase the amount of power we get from wind?

Sample: Wind energy captured by the turbine does not cause air pollution.

> ❯ UNTAMED SCIENCE Watch the **Untamed Science** video to learn more about energy resources.

174 Energy Resources

Professional Development Note ❯ From the Author

Humans are dependent on oil. The world uses energy at the rate of approximately 18 terawatts per second, most coming from dwindling reserves of fossil fuels. (For scale, one watt is about equal to lifting an apple up one meter each second. So human energy use equals 18 trillion apples going up and down each second.) What happens when fossil fuels run out? Well, potentially good news is around the corner: Earth receives about 7,000 times the total human energy use from the sun. This energy is unlimited and clean, and everybody has access to it. In the long term, our future could be very "bright."

✏ *Michael Wysession*

Energy Resources

Chapter at a Glance

CHAPTER PACING: 5–8 periods or $2\frac{1}{2}$–4 blocks

INTRODUCE THE CHAPTER: Engage students with the Engaging Question and the opening image. Activate prior knowledge and preteach vocabulary using the Getting Started pages.

Lesson 1: Fossil Fuels

Lesson 2: Alternative Sources of Energy

Lesson 3: Energy Use and Conservation

ASSESSMENT OPTIONS: Chapter Test, **EXAM**VIEW® Assessment Suite, Performance Assessment, Progress Monitoring Assessments, SuccessTracker™

Preference Navigator, in the online Planning tools, allows you to customize *Interactive Science* to your own teaching style. You can also edit lesson plans by selecting the Lesson Planner option.

Digital Teacher's Edition allows you to access your Teacher's Edition and Resource materials online.

my science online.com

my science online.com | Energy Resources | ▷ UNTAMED SCIENCE | ▷ THE BIG QUESTION | 175

Differentiated Instruction

L1 Interpret Visuals Help students understand that the photograph is taken from approximately 30 meters up in the air. Urge students to look at the structures in the distance to see that the photographer and the man doing repairs are on top of the pole that holds the blades of the turbine. Ask students whether they believe this location is appropriate for wind turbines, and why. *(High, open areas such as this one are ideal for gathering wind with turbines.)*

L3 Wind Turbines Challenge students to do research on the history and function of wind turbines. Students might include information about companies that manufacture such devices, various sizes and types of turbines, guidelines for placement and use, safety and health concerns, and what turbines require in terms of maintenance and repairs.

Getting Started

Check Your Understanding

This activity assesses students' understanding of the natural resources. Ask students to explain the difference between renewable and nonrenewable resources. After students have shared their answers, point out that all renewable and nonrenewable resources are natural resources.

Preteach Vocabulary Skills

Draw students' attention to the vocabulary listed in the *Chapter Preview*. Invite them to think about which of these terms might be considered high-use academic words. *Efficiency* might be an example. Have students look over the words *scarce* and *emit* with their meanings and examples in the chart. Then have them choose one word from the *Chapter Preview* and explain why they think it might have the characteristics of a high-use academic word. *(Students may indicate that words like* fuel, petroleum, efficiency, insulation, *and* energy conservation *are general enough to be used often in classrooms.)* Ask students to use these words in a sentence as they might be used in a classroom.

Check Your Understanding

1. **Background** Read the paragraph below and then answer the question.

> Aisha loves visiting her grandmother at work. Her grandmother says that the building she works in was designed to help conserve **natural resources.** Most of the building's electricity comes from **renewable resources,** such as sunlight and wind, instead of from **nonrenewable resources,** such as oil or coal.

A **natural resource** is any material that occurs naturally in the environment and is used by people.

A **renewable resource** is either always available or is naturally replaced in a short time.

A **nonrenewable resource** is a resource that is not replaced within a useful time frame.

• What is one example of a natural resource?

  Sample: wood, coal, water, oil, wind

> **MY READING WEB** If you had trouble completing the question above, visit **My Reading Web** and type in *Energy Resources.*

Vocabulary Skill

High-Use Academic Words High-use academic words are words that are used frequently in classrooms. Look for the words below as you read this chapter.

Word	Definition	Example
scarce	*adj.* rare; in limited supply	Tickets for the concert are becoming *scarce* because of the demand.
emit	*v.* to give off	When the oven is on, it *emits* heat, making the whole apartment warmer.

2. **Quick Check** Choose the word from the table above that best completes each sentence.

• Motor vehicles _emit_ chemicals that contribute to air pollution.

• As people continue to use oil faster than it can be replaced, it will become _scarce_.

My Reading Web offers leveled readings that provide a foundation for the chapter content.

Vocab Flash Cards offer extra practice with the chapter vocabulary words.

Digital Lesson
• Assign the *Check Your Understanding* activity online and have students submit their work to you.
• Assign the *Vocabulary Skill* activity online and have students submit their work to you.

my science online.com ▷ **Energy Resources**

fossil fuel

solar energy

biomass fuel

energy conservation

Chapter Preview

LESSON 1
- fuel
- fossil fuel
- hydrocarbon
- petroleum
- refinery
- petrochemical

⟳ Summarize
△ Communicate

LESSON 2
- solar energy
- hydroelectric power
- biomass fuel
- gasohol
- geothermal energy
- nuclear fission
- reactor vessel
- fuel rod
- control rod

⟳ Relate Cause and Effect
△ Infer

LESSON 3
- efficiency
- insulation
- energy conservation

⟳ Identify the Main Idea
△ Observe

▷ **VOCAB FLASH CARDS** For extra help with vocabulary, visit **Vocab Flash Cards** and type in *Energy Resources.*

177

CHAPTER 5

Preview Vocabulary Terms

Have students work together to create a word wall to display the vocabulary terms for the chapter. Be sure to discuss and analyze each term before posting it on the wall. As the class progresses through the chapter, the words can be sorted and categorized in different ways. A list of Academic Vocabulary for each lesson can be found in the Support All Readers box at the start of the lesson.

L1 Have students look at the images on this page as you pronounce each vocabulary word. Have students repeat the word after you. Then read the definition. Use the sample sentence in italics to clarify the meaning of the term.

fossil fuel *(FAWS ul fyool)* An energy-rich substance formed from the remains of plants, animals, and other organisms. *Gasoline is a product made from a fossil fuel called oil.*

solar energy *(SOH lur EN ur jee)* Energy from the sun. *Scientists have designed many devices to capture and distribute solar energy.*

biomass fuel *(BY oh mas fyool)* A fuel made from living things. *Corn is one example of a biomass fuel that is used as a source of energy.*

energy conservation *(EN ur jee kahn sur VAY shun)* Reducing energy use. *Riding a bike instead of driving a car is an effective form of energy conservation.*

177

ⒺⓁⓁ Support

Provide students additional support when working with the word wall activity. You may wish to create more basic categories for the words, depending on students' language proficiencies.

Beginning
LOW Create a drawing or symbol to support the vocabulary term. If literate, develop a definition using the native language.

HIGH Write the word on the cards and introduce it to the class by pointing and saying it aloud.

Intermediate
LOW/HIGH Provide an example for each vocabulary term.

Advanced
LOW/HIGH Choose categories for the word wall based on grammar or etymology.

Fossil Fuels

1 What are some of Earth's energy sources?

Lesson Pacing: 1–2 periods or $\frac{1}{2}$–1 block

🕐 **SHORT ON TIME?** To do this lesson in approximately half the time, do the Activate Prior Knowledge activity on page 178. A discussion of the key concepts on pages 179 and 185 will familiarize students with the lesson content. Have students do the Quick Lab. The rest of the lesson can be completed by students independently.

> **Preference Navigator,** in the online Planning tools, allows you to customize *Interactive Science* to your own teaching style. You can also edit lesson plans by selecting the Lesson Planner option.
>
> **Digital Teacher's Edition** allows you to access your Teacher's Edition and Resource materials online.

MY SCIENCE online.com

Lesson Vocabulary

- fuel • fossil fuel • hydrocarbon • petroleum
- refinery • petrochemical

 Content Refresher
Professional Development Note

Fuel Supplies Fossil fuels take hundreds of millions of years to form, thus making their supplies limited. They form from the decomposing remains of plants and animals. Over time, the remains become buried under hundreds of meters of mud, rock, sand, and sometimes water. The type of fuel that forms—oil, coal, natural gas—is determined by the combination of the plant and animal matter that is present, how long the material is buried, and the temperature and pressure that exists while the remains decompose.

LESSON OBJECTIVES

🗝 Name the three major fossil fuels.

🗝 Explain why fossil fuels are considered nonrenewable resources.

ENGAGE AND EXPLORE

Teach this lesson using a variety of resources. Begin by reading **My Planet Diary** as a class. Have students share ideas about how an energy crisis could impact their lives. Then have students do the **Inquiry Warm-Up activity.** Students will investigate and identify organic remains in a chunk of coal. The **After the Inquiry Warm-Up worksheet** sets up a discussion about the characteristics of coal which are developed during the formation process. Have volunteers share their answers to number 4 about how the layers of coal were formed.

EXPLAIN AND ELABORATE

Teach Key Concepts by explaining how the three major fossil fuels are developed and what they are made of. Use the **Support the Big Q** to identify some common uses for fossil fuels. **Lead a Discussion** about how coal is mined and the pros and cons of coal use. Use **Figures 3** and **4** to help students understand and visualize how coal and oil are formed over millions of years. Then have students practice the inquiry skill in the **Apply It activity. Lead a Discussion** about methane hydrates.

Continue to **Teach Key Concepts** by asking students what is likely to happen to fossil fuels if they continue to be used faster than they are formed. Hand out the **Key Concept Summaries** as a review of each part of the lesson. Students can also use the online **Vocab Flash Cards** to review key terms.

EVALUATE

Have students take the **Lesson Quiz.** For an alternate assessment, see the **EXAM**VIEW® Assessment Suite, Progress Monitoring Assessments, or SuccessTracker™.

E L L Support

1 Content and Language
Explain that the Latin prefix *re-* means again and the Latin prefix *non-* means not. Write the words *renewable* and *nonrenewable* on the board. Using what they know about the prefixes ask students to define *renewable resource* and *nonrenewable resource*. A *renewable* resource is a resource that is replaced again and again. A *nonrenewable* resource is a resource that is not replaced after it has been used.

DIFFERENTIATED INSTRUCTION KEY
L1 Struggling Students or Special Needs
L2 On-Level Students **L3** Advanced Students

LESSON PLANNER 5.1

Lab Inquiry Path
Hands-on learning in the Lab zone

ENGAGE AND EXPLORE

To teach this lesson with an emphasis on inquiry, begin with the **Inquiry Warm-Up activity**. Students will examine a piece of coal. Discuss any evidence of organic remains found in the coal sample. Have students do the **After the Inquiry Warm-Up worksheet**. Talk about the various stages of coal formation that occur over the course of millions of years. Have volunteers share their answers to number 4 about the layers in the coal samples.

EXPLAIN AND ELABORATE

Focus on the **Inquiry Skill** for the lesson. Explain that when you communicate, you share information, with others, in an organized format. What information did you communicate about fossil fuels in the **Inquiry Warm-Up?** *(There is evidence of organic remains in coal.)* Use the **Support the Big Q** to explain how fossil fuels are important sources of energy. The **Build Inquiry activity** allows students to replicate coal formation using everyday materials. During the second **Build Inquiry activity** students classify coal samples from different stages of the formation process. Use **Figure 4** and **5** to review how oil is formed and mined before beginning the **Apply It activity**. Ask volunteers to share their letters to the editor. The third **Build Inquiry activity** helps students to calculate and ponder the magnitude of the gas pipelines in the United States. Give students the chance to observe the consistency of crude oil by doing the **Quick Lab**.

Do the **Lab Investigation** to reinforce understanding of fossil fuels as nonrenewable resources. Students can use the online **Vocab Flash Cards** to review key terms.

EVALUATE

Have students take the **Lesson Quiz.** For an alternate assessment, see the **EXAM**VIEW® Assessment Suite, Progress Monitoring Assessments, or SuccessTracker™.

Digital Path
Online learning at **my science online**.com

ENGAGE AND EXPLORE

Teach this lesson using digital resources. Begin by having students explore real-world connections to fossil fuels at **My Planet Diary** online. Have them access the Chapter Resources to find the **Unlock the Big Question activity.** There they can answer the questions and refine their responses as they continue through the lesson. You can re-assign the activity and have students submit their work so you can track their progress.

EXPLAIN AND ELABORATE

Students reading above, at, or below the lexile measure of this lesson can access basic content readings at their level at **My Reading Web.** Have students review the **Art in Motion** images to better understand how oil is formed below the ocean floor. Have students use the online **Vocab Flash Cards** to preview key terms. Use **Figure 4** to remind students how oil is formed under bodies of water before assigning the online **Apply It activity.** Ask volunteers to share their letters to the editor. Have students submit their work to you. Do the **Quick Lab** and then ask students to share their results.

Review *fossil fuels* before assigning the **Do the Math activity** online. Have students submit their work to you.

The **Key Concept Summary** online allows students to read a summary and see an image associated with each part of the lesson. Online remediation is available at **My Science Coach.**

EVALUATE

Have students take the **Lesson Quiz.** For an alternate assessment, see the **EXAM**VIEW® Assessment Suite, Progress Monitoring Assessments, or SuccessTracker™.

2 Frontload the Lesson
Preview the lesson visuals, labels, and captions. Ask students what they know about the term *fossil fuels*. Explain the specific meanings these words have in science.

3 Comprehensible Input
Have students study the visuals and their captions, as well as, the graphic organizers on pages 179–182 and 184 to support the key concepts of the lesson.

4 Language Production
Pair or group students with varied language abilities to complete labs collaboratively for language practice. Have each student copy the completed written lab for personal reference.

5 Assess Understanding
Make true or false statements using lesson content and have students indicate if they agree or disagree with a thumbs up or thumbs down gesture to check whole-class comprehension.

LESSON 5.1

Fossil Fuels

Establish Learning Objectives

After this lesson, students will be able to:

🔑 Name the three major fossil fuels.

🔑 Explain why fossil fuels are considered nonrenewable resources.

Engage

Activate Prior Knowledge

MY PLANET DIARY Read *Hurricane Energy Crisis* with the class. Invite students to think back and recall their own perceptions of Hurricane Katrina or other hurricanes. Ask: **How did Hurricane Katrina affect people directly?** *(It flooded cities and towns on the Gulf Coast. People lost their homes and left the area.)* **How did the storm affect people indirectly?** *(Factories and businesses were shut down. There were gas and oil shortages.)*

BIG IDEAS OF SCIENCE REFERENCE LIBRARY 📖
Have students look up the following topics: Coal, Energy Conservation.

Explore

Lab Resource: Inquiry Warm-Up

L1 WHAT'S IN A PIECE OF COAL? Students will make observations about a chunk of coal looking for evidence of organisms from which it was formed.

---

1 Fossil Fuels

UNLOCK THE BIG ?

🔑 **What Are the Three Major Fossil Fuels?**

🔑 **Why Are Fossil Fuels Nonrenewable Resources?**

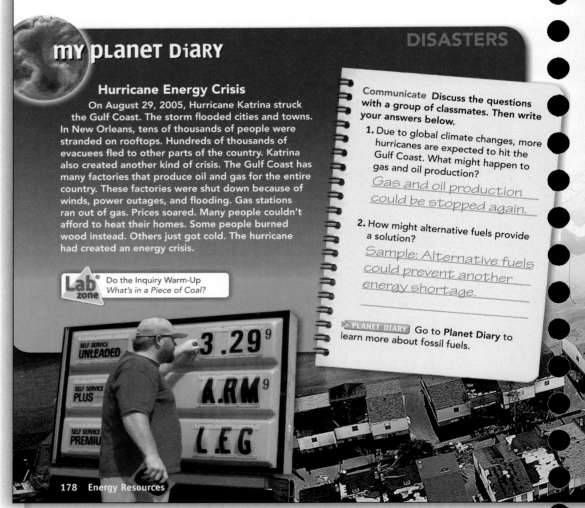

DISASTERS

MY PLANET DIARY

Hurricane Energy Crisis

On August 29, 2005, Hurricane Katrina struck the Gulf Coast. The storm flooded cities and towns. In New Orleans, tens of thousands of people were stranded on rooftops. Hundreds of thousands of evacuees fled to other parts of the country. Katrina also created another kind of crisis. The Gulf Coast has many factories that produce oil and gas for the entire country. These factories were shut down because of winds, power outages, and flooding. Gas stations ran out of gas. Prices soared. Many people couldn't afford to heat their homes. Some people burned wood instead. Others just got cold. The hurricane had created an energy crisis.

Lab zone Do the Inquiry Warm-Up *What's in a Piece of Coal?*

Communicate Discuss the questions with a group of classmates. Then write your answers below.

1. Due to global climate changes, more hurricanes are expected to hit the Gulf Coast. What might happen to gas and oil production?

    Gas and oil production could be stopped again.

2. How might alternative fuels provide a solution?

    Sample: Alternative fuels could prevent another energy shortage.

▶ PLANET DIARY Go to **Planet Diary** to learn more about fossil fuels.

178 Energy Resources

SUPPORT ALL READERS
Lexile Measure = 910L   Lexile Word Count = 1567

Prior Exposure to Content: Most students have encountered this topic in earlier grades

Academic Vocabulary: *communicate, summarize*

Science Vocabulary: *fossil fuel, hydrocarbon, petroleum, petrochemical*

Concept Level: Generally appropriate for most students in this grade

Preteach With: My Planet Diary "Hurricane Energy Crisis" and Figure 1 activity

Go to **My Reading Web** to access leveled readings that provide a foundation for the content.

MY SCIENCE ONLINE

Vocabulary
• fuel • fossil fuel • hydrocarbon
• petroleum • refinery
• petrochemical

Skills
🔊 Reading: Summarize
△ Inquiry: Communicate

What Are the Three Major Fossil Fuels?

Whether you travel in a car or a bus, walk, or ride your bike, you use some form of energy. The source of that energy is fuel. A **fuel** is a substance that provides energy, such as heat, light, motion, or electricity. This energy is the result of a chemical change.

Most of the energy used today comes from organisms that lived hundreds of millions of years ago. As these plants, animals, and other organisms died, their remains piled up. Layers of sand, rock, and mud buried the remains. Over time, heat and the pressure of the layers changed the remains into other substances. **Fossil fuels** are the energy-rich substances formed from the remains. 🔑 The three major fossil fuels are coal, oil, and natural gas.

Fossil fuels are made of hydrocarbons. **Hydrocarbons** are chemical compounds that contain carbon and hydrogen atoms. When the fossil fuels are burned, the atoms react. They combine with oxygen to form new molecules. These reactions release energy in the forms of heat and light.

Burning fossil fuels provides more energy per kilogram than burning other fuels. One kilogram of coal, for example, can provide twice as much energy as one kilogram of wood. Oil and natural gas can provide three times as much energy as an equal mass of wood.

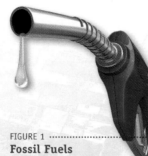

FIGURE 1 ·····················

Fossil Fuels in Everyday Life
Fossil fuels have many common uses.
✎ **Identify** Fill in the chart with ways that you or other people use the three fossil fuels in daily life.

Fossil Fuel	Common Uses	Uses in Your Life
Coal	• Used to generate half of all U.S. electricity • Used to make products like fertilizer and medicine • When heated, used to make steel	Sample: electricity
Oil	• As gasoline and diesel fuels, used to power vehicles • Used to heat homes • Used to make plastics and other petroleum products	Sample: cars, school bus, heat in home
Natural gas	• Used to generate electricity • Used to cook food • Used to heat homes	Sample: gas stove, heat in home

179

Explain

Introduce Vocabulary
Tell students that a *fuel* can be electricity, heat, motion, or light, as well as gasoline or oil. Point out that a fuel is a substance that provides energy.

Teach Key Concepts 🔑
Explain to students that the remains of dead organisms pile up and are buried under layers of sand, rock, and mud. Over hundreds of millions of years, the pressure of the layers change the remains into other substances that still contain the stored energy from the bodies of the dead organisms. Ask: **What three major fuels are formed from the remains of long-dead organisms?** *(Coal, oil, natural gas)* **What are these fuels made of?** *(Hydrocarbons)* **What are hydrocarbons?** *(Compounds that contain carbon and hydrogen atoms)*

Support the Big Q ❓ UbD
ENERGY FROM FUELS Remind students that burning fossil fuels releases energy. Ask: **How do fossil fuels compare to other fuels, such as wood?** *(Fossil fuels provide more energy per kilogram than wood does.)* **What are some ways hydrocarbons are used as an energy source?** *(They are burned to generate electricity, power vehicles, heat homes, and cook foods.)*

My Planet Diary provides an opportunity for students to explore real-world connections to fossil fuels.

my science online | Fossil Fuels

Explain

Lead a Discussion

COAL Most coal used in the United States is used to fuel electrical power plants. Point out that before natural gas and oil were used to heat homes, coal was the main fuel for heating homes. Ask: **How is coal removed from the ground?** *(It is chopped into pieces and lifted to the surface.)* **How is this done?** *(Miners use machines to lift coal from the ground)* **What makes working in a coal mine dangerous?** *(Miners can be killed in accidents or develop lung diseases because of the dust.)*

21st Century Learning

COMMUNICATION Have students read *Coal* in the **Big Ideas of Science Reference Library.** Students can demonstrate consumer literacy by researching causes of recent coal mining accidents. Then have them create a poster on safety precautions for coal miners. What equipment should they wear? What do they do in an emergency?

21st Century Learning

L3 CRITICAL THINKING Ask students to explain the sequence of events that must occur for coal to be used as a fuel. Students may wish to draw a diagram that shows the sequence of events from discovery of coal in a particular location, digging a mine, chopping chunks of coal, raising coal to the surface, and transportation of coal to places where it will be used as fuel.

Teach With Visuals

Tell students to look at **Figure 3.** Ask: **How would you describe the changes that happen on the land surface over time while plant matter below the surface is being transformed into peat and then into coal?** *(Sample response: A wet, swampy area changes gradually into a dry, wooded area.)*

Summarize Tell students that a summary is a short statement that presents the main ideas and most important details in a text. Summarizing can help students distinguish main ideas from the details that support those ideas.

FIGURE 2
Pros and Cons of Coal Use
Coal mining, shown above, is a dangerous job.
✎ **Compare and Contrast**
Fill in the chart below using information from the text.

Coal People have burned coal to produce heat for thousands of years. For much of that time, wood was more convenient and cheaper than coal for most people. But during the 1800s, the huge energy needs of growing industries made it worthwhile to find, mine, and transport coal. Today, coal makes up about 22 percent of the fuel used in the United States. Most of that coal fuels electrical power plants.

Before coal can be used to produce energy, it has to be removed from the ground. Miners use machines to chop the coal into chunks and lift it to the surface. Coal mining can be a dangerous job. Thousands of miners have been killed or injured in mining accidents. Many more suffer from lung diseases. Fortunately, modern safety procedures and better equipment have made coal mining safer, although it is still very dangerous.

Coal is the most plentiful fossil fuel in the United States. It is fairly easy to transport and provides a lot of energy when burned. But coal also has some disadvantages. Coal mining can increase erosion. Runoff from coal mines can cause water pollution. Burning most types of coal results in more air pollution than using other fossil fuels. See **Figure 2.**

Figure 3 shows how plant remains build up over time and form coal.

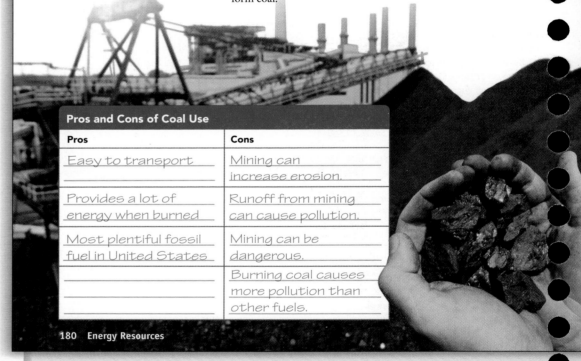

Pros and Cons of Coal Use	
Pros	**Cons**
Easy to transport	Mining can increase erosion.
Provides a lot of energy when burned	Runoff from mining can cause pollution.
Most plentiful fossil fuel in United States	Mining can be dangerous.
	Burning coal causes more pollution than other fuels.

180   Energy Resources

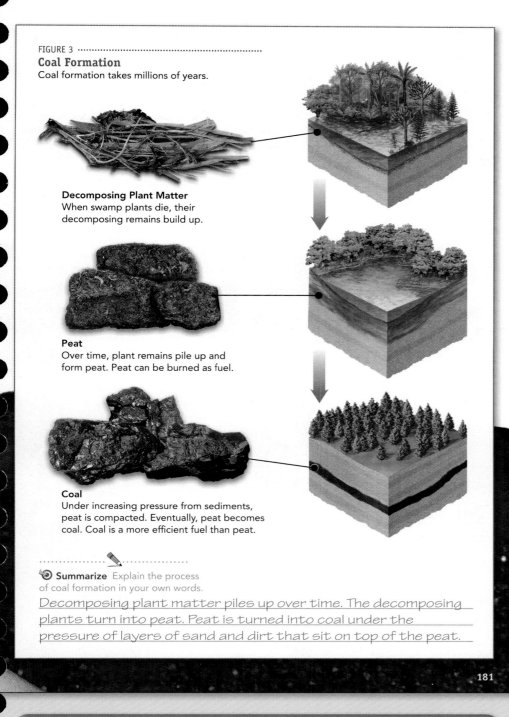

FIGURE 3

Coal Formation
Coal formation takes millions of years.

Decomposing Plant Matter
When swamp plants die, their decomposing remains build up.

Peat
Over time, plant remains pile up and form peat. Peat can be burned as fuel.

Coal
Under increasing pressure from sediments, peat is compacted. Eventually, peat becomes coal. Coal is a more efficient fuel than peat.

Summarize Explain the process of coal formation in your own words.

Decomposing plant matter piles up over time. The decomposing plants turn into peat. Peat is turned into coal under the pressure of layers of sand and dirt that sit on top of the peat.

181

Elaborate

Build Inquiry

L2 MODEL FOSSIL FUEL FORMATION

Materials clay, soil, sand, pebbles, leaves, colored paper, and books or heavy weights

Time 15 minutes

Challenge students to create a model showing how fossil fuels form over time. Models might include trapping materials such as leaves or colored paper between layers of soft material such as clay or soil, and then compressing these materials under heavy weights.

Ask: **What happens to buried materials that turns them into fossil fuels?** *(Over time, heat and pressure change the materials into hydrocarbons.)*

Build Inquiry

L3 CLASSIFY PEAT AND COAL

Materials samples of peat moss, lignite, bituminous coal, and anthracite; 2 small plastic bags; hand lenses

Time 10 minutes

Explain to students that peat is the decayed remains of plants—the early stage of coal formation. Give each group hand lenses, a plastic bag containing a sample of peat moss, and a second bag containing the three types of coal. **CAUTION:** *Rinse the coal thoroughly to remove any dust. Make sure students wash their hands after handling the samples.* Let students examine the samples, noting the similarities and differences between them. Then list the following names and characteristics on the board, and challenge students to identify each coal sample:
* *Lignite:* dark brown; layered; may contain recognizable fragments of plant remains
* *Bituminous coal:* denser than lignite; black; may have bands
* *Anthracite:* hardest type of coal; black; shiny

Ask: **Why are the coal samples darker and harder than the peat?** *(Coal has been buried longer than peat and therefore subjected to much greater pressure.)*

Differentiated Instruction

L1 The Use of Coal To solidify students' understanding of the extent to which coal is used as a fuel in the United States today, have students write a fraction that approximates how much of the fuel used in the United States today is coal.

L3 19th Century Uses of Coal
Challenge students to research what caused the huge energy needs that led to the mining and transportation of enormous amounts of coal during the 1800s. Students can write a short report or make an oral presentation of their findings.

L3 Illustrate Burning Fossil Fuels
Invite students to make a detailed illustration of the process of burning fossil fuels. Their illustrations should convey the composition of fossil fuels and of hydrocarbons, as well as the chain of causes and effects that create heat and light.

Explain

Teach With Visuals

Tell students to look at **Figure 4.** Ask: **What organisms shown in the first illustration will decompose on the ocean floor?** *(Fish, shellfish, plants)* **What processes are shown on the ocean floor and under the ocean floor in the second illustration?** *(More plants and shellfish will die and decompose on the ocean floor. Decomposition of earlier organisms proceeds below the ocean floor.)*

Make Analogies

L1 VARIETIES OF REFINING Explain that the process of refining crude oil is similar to the refining of other physical products, such as gold or sugar. Point out that the terms *crude* and *refined* are also used to describe aspects of human behavior. Ask: **What are examples of crude behavior at a dining table during a meal?** *(Talking with your mouth full, taking enormous portions of food, talking loudly and impolitely)* **What are examples of refined behavior at the table?** *(Eating quietly, offering food to others first and serving yourself afterwards, listening and speaking politely)*

FIGURE 4 ··

> ART IN MOTION Oil Formation
Oil is formed in a process similar to coal.

Interpret Diagrams Use what you know to fill in the steps of oil formation in the diagrams below.

300–400 million years ago

Sample: The remains of organisms pile up on the sea floor.

50–100 million years ago

Sample: Over time, layers of sand and dirt form over the remains.

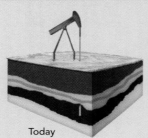

Today

Sample: Pressure and heat from the layers turn the remains into oil deposits.

182 Energy Resources

Oil Oil is a thick, black, liquid fossil fuel. It formed from the remains of small animals, algae, and other organisms that lived in oceans and shallow inland seas hundreds of millions of years ago. **Petroleum** is another name for oil. Petroleum comes from the Latin words *petra* (rock) and *oleum* (oil). Petroleum accounts for more than one third of the energy produced in the world. Fuel for most cars, airplanes, trains, and ships comes from petroleum. Many homes are heated by oil as well.

Most oil deposits are located underground in tiny holes in sandstone or limestone. **Figure 4** shows how oil is formed. The oil fills the holes somewhat like the way water fills the holes of a sponge. Because oil deposits are usually located deep below the surface, finding oil is difficult. Scientists can use sound waves to test an area for oil. Even using this technique, scientists may not always locate wells that will produce a usable amount of oil.

FIGURE 5 ·····················
Oil Pipeline
Workers build an oil pipeline in Russia.

Art in Motion shows the gradual formation of oil deposits beneath the ocean floor.

Digital Lesson: Assign the *Apply It* activity online and have students submit their work to you.

MY SCIENCE online **Fossil Fuels**

When oil is first pumped out of the ground, it is called crude oil. To be made into useful products, crude oil must undergo a process called refining. A factory in which crude oil is heated and separated into fuels and other products is called a **refinery**. Many of the products that you use every day are made from crude oil. **Petrochemicals** are compounds that are made from oil. Petrochemicals are used to make plastics, paints, medicines, and cosmetics.

Over 2,500 species of plants and animals live in Lake Baikal, in Russia. Eighty percent of these species live nowhere else on Earth. One of those species is the Baikal seal—one of only three freshwater seal species on Earth. The seal and other species were threatened when oil companies planned to build the world's longest oil pipeline within 800 meters of the lake's shore. The pipeline would bring oil from Russia's interior to China and ports along the Pacific Ocean. Citizens were concerned that oil leaks and spills would damage the lake. They worked together to convince the oil companies to move the pipeline 40 kilometers to the north. The design of the new pipeline protects the lake and also delivers oil to places that need it.

▲ **Communicate** An oil pipeline is proposed in your area near a body of water you think is important. Using Lake Baikal as an example, write a letter to the editor of your local paper explaining what you think should be done about the pipeline and why. Give your letter a headline.

Sample headline: Pipeline Problem
Sample letter: Dear Editor, The proposed pipeline in our area threatens our local ecosystem. I think we can work together to have both the oil pipeline and the nature we enjoy. A similar problem happened near Lake Baikal, in Russia, when an oil company wanted to build a pipeline near the water. Because the company moved the pipeline away from the lake, many species are now better protected against oil spills. I think we can better design this pipeline to avoid harming nature in our area. That way, we can still transport oil and protect our ecosystem.

183

Differentiated Instruction

L1 Compare Formation of Coal and Oil Have students use a compare-and-contrast chart or a Venn diagram to show the similarities and differences between the formation of coal and the formation of oil under the surface of Earth.

L3 Research Crude Oil Refining Have students use reference materials to learn the basic processes involved in refining oil. Students should gather information about several products made by heating crude oil to greater temperatures (gasoline, jet fuel, heating oil, diesel fuel, grease and wax, asphalt).

Elaborate

Apply It!

L1 Before students begin the *Apply It* activity, have them look carefully at the photograph of the lake. Invite them to name living things that live in and around the lake. Have them look again at **Figure 4** as a reminder of the process that leads to the formation of oil deposits under bodies of water. Encourage them to discuss how valuable resources lie beneath the lake as well as in and around the lake. Tell students that Lake Baikal, in Russia, holds 20 percent of the Earth's fresh water.

▲ **Communicate** Remind students that their letter to the editor will be more effective if it contains a strong, clear main idea and supporting details.

21st Century Learning

INFORMATION LITERACY Have students research the Alaskan pipeline that reaches from Prudhoe Bay to Valdez and the environmental questions that were raised by its construction.

Explain

Lead a Discussion

METHANE HYDRATES Methane hydrates are located in ocean sediments and polar permafrost. Blake Ridge, located off of the coast of the southeastern United States, contains a volume of methane hydrate that is equal to 30 times the United States consumption of gas. As of 2009, there is no economically profitable technique by which to extract methane from methane hydrate deposits. Also, it is a greenhouse gas that is 10 times more effective than carbon dioxide in causing climate change. Ask: **Do you think it is worthwhile to investigate methods of extracting methane?** *(Students may say that it is worthwhile because it would provide a lot of energy. Other students may say that it is not worthwhile because it could harm the environment.)*

Elaborate

Build Inquiry

L2 CALCULATE LENGTHS OF GAS PIPELINE

Materials calculator

Time 5 minutes

Point out the text statement "If all the gas pipelines in the United States were connected, they would reach to the moon and back—three times!" Have students use the moon's average distance from Earth *(384,392 km)* to calculate the total length of U.S. gas pipelines *(384,392 km × 6 = 2,306,352 km)*.

Ask: **How does this distance compare to the width of your state?** *(Have that value ready.)*

Lab Resources: Quick Lab

L1 OBSERVING OIL'S CONSISTENCY Students will model the consistency of crude oil using molasses.

Evaluate

Assess Your Understanding

After students answer the questions, have them evaluate their understanding by completing the appropriate sentence.

RTI Response to Intervention

1a. If students cannot define *petrochemicals*, **then** have them skim the section to locate the boldfaced term and read the definition.

b. If students have trouble making judgments about pipelines, **then** have them review the *Apply It!* feature and the information they provided about the costs and benefits of natural gas.

my science COACH Have students go online for help in understanding the three major fossil fuels.

Natural Gas Natural gas is a mixture of methane and other gases. Natural gas forms from some of the same organisms as oil. Because it is less dense than oil, natural gas often rises above an oil deposit, forming a pocket of gas in the rock.

Pipelines transport natural gas from its source to the places where it is used. If all the gas pipelines in the United States were connected, they would reach to the moon and back—three times! Natural gas can also be compressed into a liquid and stored in tanks as fuel for trucks and buses.

Natural gas has several benefits. It produces large amounts of energy, but has lower levels of many air pollutants compared to coal or oil. It is also easy to transport once pipelines are built. One cost of natural gas is that it is highly flammable. A gas leak can cause explosions and fires. If you use natural gas in your home, you probably are familiar with the "gas" smell alerting you when there is unburned gas in the air. You may be surprised to learn that natural gas actually has no odor. What causes the strong smell? Gas companies add a chemical with a distinct smell to the gas so that people can detect a gas leak.

FIGURE 6 ·······························
Natural Gas
A gas-top burner uses natural gas to cook food.
✎ **Analyze Costs and Benefits** Fill in the boxes with some costs and benefits of natural gas.

Costs of Natural Gas	Benefits of Natural Gas
Sample: highly flammable, still releases some air pollutants, could be expensive to find and extract through rock	Sample: produces fewer air pollutants than coal or oil, easy to transport if pipelines built

Lab zone Do the Quick Lab *Observing Oil's Consistency.*

🔑 **Assess Your Understanding**

1a. Define What are petrochemicals?
Compounds made from oil that are used to make plastics, paints, medicines, and cosmetics

b. Make Judgments Should the federal government decide where to build oil or natural gas pipelines? Explain.
Sample: No; they might not know people's needs in the local area.

got it? ································

○ I get it! Now I know that the three major fossil fuels are coal, oil, and natural gas.

○ I need extra help with See TE note.

Go to **my science COACH** online for help with this subject.

Why Are Fossil Fuels Nonrenewable Resources?

The many advantages of using fossil fuels as an energy source have made them essential to modern life. 🔑 **Since fossil fuels take hundreds of millions of years to form, they are considered nonrenewable resources.** Earth's known oil reserves, or the amount of oil that can currently be used, took 500 million years to form. Fossil fuels will run out if they are used faster than they are formed.

Many nations that consume large amounts of fossil fuels have very small reserves or supplies. They have to buy oil, natural gas, and coal from nations with large supplies to make up the difference. The United States, for example, uses about one quarter of all the oil produced in the world. But only two percent of the world's oil supply is located in this country. The uneven distribution of fossil fuel reserves has often been a cause of political problems in the world.

Use the graph to answer the questions below.

1 **Read Graphs** Which energy source generates the most electricity in the United States? <u>Coal</u>

2 **Calculate** What percentage of the fuels in the graph are fossil fuels? <u>71.4%</u>

3 [CHALLENGE] How might this graph look in 50 years? Give reasons to support your answer. <u>Sample: Fossil fuel use will decrease as supplies become limited, and use of other fuels will increase.</u>

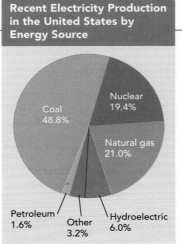

Recent Electricity Production in the United States by Energy Source

- Coal 48.8%
- Nuclear 19.4%
- Natural gas 21.0%
- Hydroelectric 6.0%
- Other 3.2%
- Petroleum 1.6%

Lab zone® Do the Quick Lab *Fossil Fuels*.

🔑 Assess Your Understanding

got it? ....

○ I get it! Now I know that fossil fuels are nonrenewable because <u>they take a very long time to form and are used up more rapidly than they are formed.</u>

○ I need extra help with <u>See TE note.</u>

Go to my science COACH *online for help with this subject.*

185

Differentiated Instruction

L1 **Observe States of Matter** Have students compare samples that represent the states of matter most commonly associated with the three fossil fuels: solid (chunks of coal), liquid (molasses to represent oil), and gas (closed, empty jar to represent natural gas). Make sure that students understand that the three fossil fuels are not the same substance in three different states. While they all are

hydrocarbons, each fuel is made up of different hydrocarbon compounds.

L3 **Research Pipelines** Challenge students to use reference books or online sources to find out where most natural gas pipelines are located in the United States. Have students learn how much natural gas moves through U.S. pipelines each day.

Explain

Teach Key Concepts 🔑

Explain to students that fossil fuels are unevenly distributed around the world. They are also nonrenewable resources. Ask: **What evidence do we have that our demand for fossil fuels might use up our supply of them?** *(Oil reserves take 500 million years to form. New reserves can't form quickly enough to replace those used up.)* **How might uneven distribution of fossil fuels contribute to global problems?** *(Students might indicate that fuel-rich and fuel-dependent nations may come into conflict.)*

Elaborate

Do the Math!

Point out that a circle graph can be used to show parts of a whole.
Ask: **If the entire circle represents 100 percent, what does one fourth of the circle represent?** *(Twenty-five percent)* **Why is a circle graph a good choice for this exercise?** *(Sample response: The graph emphasizes the differences between the proportions of the various energy sources.)*
See *Math Skill* and *Problem-Solving Activities* for support.

Lab Resource: Lab Investigation

L1 **FOSSIL FUELS** Students will make models comparing renewable and nonrenewable resources.

Evaluate

Assess Your Understanding

Have students evaluate their understanding by completing the appropriate sentence.

R T I Response to Intervention

If students have trouble classifying resources, **then** have them skim the section to find the Key Concept statement. Students should read the paragraph that includes this statement.

my science COACH Have students go online for help in understanding why fossil fuels are nonrenewable.

Digital Lesson: Assign the *Do the Math* activity online and have students submit their work to you.

my science online | Limited Fossil Fuels

After the Inquiry Warm-Up

Fossil Fuels

> **Inquiry Warm-Up, *What's In A Piece of Coal?***
> In the Inquiry Warm-Up, you investigated evidence of organic remains in coal. Using what you learned from that activity, answer the questions below.

1. **SEQUENCE** What is coal called before it becomes lignite?

   _____

2. **INFER** Do you think it is easier or more difficult to see fossils in coal older than lignite? Explain.

   _____
   _____
   _____
   _____

3. **INFER** Do you think it is easier or more difficult to see organic remains in the coal using a microscope compared to a hand lens? Explain why.

   _____
   _____
   _____
   _____

4. **RELATE CAUSE AND EFFECT** If your coal sample has layers, explain how they were formed.

   _____
   _____
   _____
   _____

Name _____ Date _____ Class _____

Energy Resources

What Are the Three Major Fossil Fuels?

1a. **DEFINE** What are petrochemicals? _____

_____

_____

b. **MAKE JUDGMENTS** Should the federal government decide
where to build oil or natural gas pipelines? Explain. _____

_____

_____

_____

_____

got it? ···

○ **I get it!** Now I know that the three major fossil fuels are _____

_____

○ **I need extra help with** _____

_____

Why Are Fossil Fuels Nonrenewable Resources?

got it? ···

○ **I get it!** Now I know that fossil fuels are nonrenewable because _____

_____

○ **I need extra help with** _____

_____

Key Concept Summaries

Energy Resources

What Are the Three Major Fossil Fuels?

A **fuel** is a substance that provides energy, such as heat, light, motion, or electricity. Most energy used today comes from organisms that lived hundreds of millions of years ago. **Fossil fuels** are the energy-rich substances formed from those remains. **The three major fossil fuels are coal, oil, and natural gas.** Fossil fuels are made of **hydrocarbons,** chemical compounds that contain carbon and hydrogen atoms. When the fossil fuels are burned, the atoms react and energy is released in the forms of heat and light. Burning fossil fuels provides more energy per kilogram than burning other fuels.

Coal is a solid fossil fuel that forms from plant remains. Before it can be used to produce energy, coal must be removed from the ground. Coal is the most plentiful fossil fuel in the United States. It is fairly easy to transport and provides a lot of energy when burned. However, mining coal causes erosion, and burning coal causes water and air pollution.

Petroleum is another name for oil, a thick, black, liquid fossil fuel. It accounts for more than one third of the energy used in the world. Most oil deposits lie underground in tiny holes in sandstone or limestone. A factory in which crude oil is heated and separated into fuels and other products is called a **refinery.** **Petrochemicals** are compounds that are made from oil. They are used to make many common products, including plastics, paints, medicines, and cosmetics. Natural gas, a mixture of methane and other gases, forms from some of the same organisms as oil. Pipelines transport natural gas from its source to the places where it is used. Burning natural gas produces large amounts of energy and releases lower levels of many air pollutants than coal or oil, but it is highly flammable.

Why Are Fossil Fuels Nonrenewable Resources?

Fossil fuels are essential to modern life. **Since fossil fuels take hundreds of millions of years to form, they are considered nonrenewable resources.** Fossil fuels will run out if they continue to be used faster than they are formed. Fossil fuels are not necessarily located in the places where they are used the most. The uneven distribution of fossil fuel reserves is a cause of international conflicts in the world.

On a separate sheet of paper, explain the importance of fossil fuels today, as well as the challenges and conflicts relating to their use.

Review and Reinforce

Energy Resources

Understanding Main Ideas
Answer the following questions on a separate sheet of paper.

1. What are the three major fossil fuels?
2. How do fossil fuels form?
3. How is energy produced from fossil fuels?
4. Why are fossil fuels considered nonrenewable?

Building Vocabulary
Write a definition for each of these terms on the lines below.

5. petroleum

_____

_____

6. hydrocarbons

_____

_____

7. refinery

_____

_____

8. petrochemicals

_____

_____

Enrich

Energy Resources

> The tables show the amount of fossil fuels produced and used in the United States from 1957 to 2007. The numbers represent quadrillions of BTUs, British thermal units, used for measuring energy. Calculate the total amount of fossil fuels produced and used each year. Enter your results in the tables. Then answer the questions on a separate sheet of paper.

Fossil Fuel Production and Use

U.S. Fossil Fuel Production (in quadrillions of BTUs)

Year	Coal	Oil	Natural Gas	Total Produced
1957	13.1	15.2	10.6	1.
1967	13.8	18.7	17.9	2.
1977	15.8	17.5	19.6	3.
1987	20.1	17.7	17.1	4.
1997	23.2	13.6	19.5	5.
2007	23.5	10.8	19.8	6.

U.S. Fossil Fuel Use (in quadrillions of BTUs)

Year	Coal	Oil	Natural Gas	Total Produced
1957	10.8	17.9	10.2	7.
1967	11.9	25.3	17.9	8.
1977	13.9	37.1	19.9	9.
1987	18.0	32.9	17.7	10.
1997	21.4	36.3	22.6	11.
2007	22.8	39.8	23.6	12.

13. Use your totals to make a bar graph. Plot years on the horizontal axis and amounts of fossil fuels on the vertical axis. Make two bars for each year—showing total fuel production and total fuel use. Use colors or shading for the bars. Give your graph a title and key.

14. Compare the two bars for every year shown. What pattern do you see? Which type of fossil fuel was most responsible for that pattern?

15. What happens when the country produces less fossil fuel than it needs?

Name _____ Date _____ Class _____

Lesson Quiz

Energy Resources

Fill in the blank(s) to complete each statement.

1. A fuel is a substance that provides _____.

2. _____ is a solid fossil fuel that forms from plant remains.

3. Petroleum is another name for the fossil fuel _____.

4. A factory in which crude oil is heated and separated into fuels and other products is called a _____.

If the statement is true, write *true*. If the statement is false, change the underlined word or words to make the statement true.

5. _____ Chemical compounds that contain carbon and hydrogen atoms are called <u>petrochemicals</u>.

6. _____ <u>Fossil fuels</u> are the energy-rich substances formed from the remains of long-dead organisms.

7. _____ The three major fossil fuels are coal, oil, and <u>petroleum</u>.

8. _____ <u>Oil</u> is the most plentiful fossil fuel in the United States.

9. _____ <u>Natural gas</u> forms from some of the same organisms as oil.

10. _____ Because fossil fuels are formed over hundreds of millions of years, they are considered <u>renewable</u> resources.

Energy Resources

Answer Key

After the Inquiry Warm-Up

1. peat

2. Sample: I think it should be more difficult because the fossils are altered and destroyed over time.

3. Sample: I think it is easier to see organic remains in coal using a microscope because a microscope has a higher resolution, so it can see finer and smaller details.

4. Students may say: Over many years, organic material is covered over by more organic material and compressed.

Key Concept Summaries

Answers will vary. Sample answer: Fossil fuels are important because they provide a majority of the energy used in the world for heating, electricity, and transportation today. However, the use of fossil fuels does present many problems. The mining of coal and pumping of oil and natural gas can lead to erosion and pollution of natural areas. The burning of fossil fuels also creates pollution. Because they are so heavily used and reserves are unevenly distributed throughout the world, fossil fuels can also be the source of international conflicts.

Review and Reinforce

1. coal, oil, natural gas

2. The remains of plants, animals, and other organisms become buried under layers of sand, rock, and mud. Over time, heat and the pressure of the layers turn the remains into other substances, such as fossil fuels.

3. Fossil fuels are made of hydrocarbons. When fossil fuels are burned, the atoms of hydrogen and carbon react and release energy in the form of heat and light.

4. Fossil fuels are considered nonrenewable because they take millions of years to form.

5. another name for oil

6. chemical compounds that contain carbon and hydrogen atoms

7. a factory in which crude oil is heated and separated into fuels and other products

8. compounds that are made from oil

Enrich

1. 38.9
2. 50.4
3. 52.9
4. 54.9
5. 56.3
6. 54.1
7. 38.9
8. 55.1
9. 70.9
10. 68.6
11. 80.3
12. 86.2

13. The graph should show that production and use were the same for 1957. After that, the bars for use are higher than the bars for production, with the difference increasing over time.

14. After 1957, the United States produced less fossil fuel than it needed. The difference between production and use generally increased over that period. Oil was most responsible for this pattern.

15. The country has to import fuels from other countries. Also, shortages may occur.

Lesson Quiz

1. energy
2. Coal
3. oil
4. refinery
5. hydrocarbons
6. true
7. natural gas
8. Coal
9. true
10. nonrenewable

Place the outside corner, the corner away from the dotted line, in the corner of your copy machine to copy onto letter-size paper.

Alternative Sources of Energy

 What are some of Earth's energy sources?

Lesson Pacing: 2–3 periods or 1–1½ blocks

🕐 **SHORT ON TIME?** To do this lesson in approximately half the time, do the Activate Prior Knowledge activity on page 186. A discussion of the key concepts on pages 186 and 194 will familiarize students with the lesson content. Use the Explore the Big Q to help students identify pros and cons of Earth's energy sources. Do the Quick Labs and have students do the Interactive Art online. The rest of the lesson can be completed by students independently.

Preference Navigator, in the online Planning tools, allows you to customize *Interactive Science* to your own teaching style. You can also edit lesson plans by selecting the Lesson Planner option.

Digital Teacher's Edition allows you to access your Teacher's Edition and Resource materials online.

MY SCIENCE online.com

Lesson Vocabulary

- solar energy
- hydroelectric power
- biomass fuel
- gasohol
- geothermal energy
- nuclear fission
- reactor vessel
- fuel rod
- control rod

 Content Refresher

Use of Renewable Energy Sources Renewable sources of energy exist in an inexhaustible or replaceable supply. They are generally considered less polluting than fossil fuels. In spite of these advantages, renewable energy sources are not widely used in the United States. Only 6 percent of the total U.S. energy consumed in 2007 was produced through renewable energy. In contrast, 40 percent of U.S. energy was produced with petroleum, 23 percent with natural gas, and 22 percent with coal.

Biomass Fuels Using biomass fuels helps reduce dependence on fossil fuels and waste-disposal problems. At the Mesquite Lake Resource Recovery Project in California, an electric power plant burns cow manure to produce enough electricity for thousands of homes. The manure would otherwise pose a disposal problem because of its high salt content and the presence of seeds that make it unsuitable for use as a fertilizer.

LESSON OBJECTIVES

- Identify and describe renewable sources of energy.
- Explain how a nuclear power plant produces electricity.

Blended Path Active learning using Student Edition, Inquiry Path, and Digital Path

ENGAGE AND EXPLORE

Teach this lesson using a variety of resources. Begin by reading **My Planet Diary** as a class. Have students share ideas about fossil fuels as sources of energy and identify alternative sources of energy. Then have students do the **Inquiry Warm-Up activity.** Students will use water to capture energy from sunlight and monitor temperature changes. The **After the Inquiry Warm-Up worksheet** sets up a discussion about why certain areas are better than others for capturing solar energy. Have volunteers share their answers to number 4 about the temperature changes that occur when the water is exposed to sunlight for longer lengths of time.

EXPLAIN AND ELABORATE

Teach Key Concepts by identifying a variety of sources of energy used by people. **Lead a Discussion** about how solar energy is captured and converted using different devices. Use **Figure 2** to illustrate how passive and active solar heating can be used to power a building or home. Next, **Lead a Discussion** about hydroelectric power and wind energy. Discuss the benefits and downfalls of these two alternative sources of energy. Then **Lead a Discussion** about how biomass fuels are made from natural sources, used to produce electricity, and converted into other fuels. Then have students do the **Apply It activity.** Use **Figure 5** to show students how electricity is generated using geothermal power plants. **Lead a Discussion** about geothermal heat pumps. **Lead a Discussion** about why scientists are working to develop hydrogen power. Use the **Explore the Big Q** to scrutinize various sources of energy from the Earth. Discuss responses to the **Answer the Big Q** about Earth's energy sources.

Continue to **Teach Key Concepts** by explaining how nuclear power plants turn nuclear fission reactions into electricity. **Lead a Discussion** about the general process and specific components used to generate electricity in a nuclear power plant. Hand out the **Key Concept Summaries** as a review of each part of the lesson. Students can also use the online **Vocab Flash Cards** to review key terms.

EVALUATE

Have students take the **Lesson Quiz.** For an alternate assessment, see the **EXAM**VIEW® Assessment Suite, Progress Monitoring Assessments, or SuccessTracker™.

ⓔⓛⓛ Support

1 Content and Language

Define the term *solar*. *Solar* means related to the sun. Identify terms that include *solar*: solar energy, solar power, solar eclipse, solar cars, solar system, solar panels. Discuss how each term is related to the sun.

Lab Inquiry Path
Hands-on learning in the Lab zone

ENGAGE AND EXPLORE

To teach this lesson with an emphasis on inquiry, begin with the **Inquiry Warm-Up activity.** Students will learn how solar energy is captured using a water-filled bag. Discuss how the location of the bag impacts the temperature of the water. Have students do the **After the Inquiry Warm-Up worksheet.** Talk about the temperature changes they recorded and where they captured the most solar energy. Have volunteers share their answers to number 4 about the impact of leaving the water in direct sunlight for a long duration of time.

EXPLAIN AND ELABORATE

Focus on the **Inquiry Skill** for the lesson. Point out that when you infer, you use evidence or logical thinking to draw a conclusion. **Build Inquiry** with students to observe how heat is trapped inside a passive solar object. Review the term *biomass* and how to read a line graph before beginning the **Apply It activity.** Ask volunteers to share their answers. **Explore the Big Q** by identifying energy sources represented in the illustrations. Have students work on the **Quick Lab** to reinforce understanding of how solar energy can warm food. Have students identify Earth's energy sources to **Answer the Big Q.**

Build Inquiry to help students understand the potential disadvantages of nuclear power. Have students complete the **Quick Lab** to understand how electricity is produced. Students can use the online **Vocab Flash Cards** to review key terms.

EVALUATE

Have students take the **Lesson Quiz.** For an alternate assessment, see the **EXAM**VIEW® Assessment Suite, Progress Monitoring Assessments, or SuccessTracker™.

Digital Path
Online learning at my science online.com

ENGAGE AND EXPLORE

Teach this lesson using digital resources. Begin by having students explore real-world connections to alternative energy sources at **My Planet Diary** online. Have them access the Chapter Resources to find the **Unlock the Big Question activity.** There they can answer the questions and refine their responses as they continue through the lesson. You can re-assign the activity and have students submit their work so you can track their progress.

EXPLAIN AND ELABORATE

Students reading above, at, or below the lexile measure of this lesson can access basic content readings at their level at **My Reading Web.** Have students use the online **Vocab Flash Cards** to preview key terms. Review the term biomass and how to interpret a line graph before assigning the online **Apply It activity.** Ask volunteers to share their interpretations of the graph. Have students submit their work to you. Use the **Interactive Art** to explore alternative energy sources. **Explore the Big Q** by identifying pros and cons of Earth's energy sources illustrated in **Figure 6.** Complete the **Quick Lab** to better understand how food can be cooked using solar energy. Discuss various sources of energy to **Answer the Big Q. My Science Coach** provides online support for students.

Have students do the online **Interactive Art activity** which illustrates how electricity is generated in nuclear power plants. Have students do the **Quick Lab** to explore how electricity is produced. The **Key Concept Summaries** online allow students to read a summary and see an image associated with each part of the lesson. Online remediation is available at **My Science Coach.**

EVALUATE

Have students take the **Lesson Quiz.** For an alternate assessment, see the **EXAM**VIEW® Assessment Suite, Progress Monitoring Assessments, or SuccessTracker™.

2 Frontload the Lesson
Preview the lesson visuals, labels, and captions. Ask students what they know about the terms *solar energy, hydroelectric power, biomass fuels, geothermal energy, nuclear fission, reactor vessel, fuel rod,* and *control rod.* Explain the specific meanings these words have in science.

3 Comprehensible Input
Have students study the visuals and their captions and diagrams on pages 187–194 to support the key concepts of the lesson.

4 Language Production
Encourage language practice by grouping students with diverse language abilities to collaboratively complete the labs. Have each student copy the completed written lab for personal reference.

5 Assess Understanding
Have students keep a content area log. Use a two-column format with the headings "What I Understand" and "What I Don't Understand." Follow up so that students can move items form the "Don't Understand" to the "Understand" column.

LESSON 5.2
Renewable Sources of Energy

Establish Learning Objectives

After this lesson, students will be able to:

🔑 Identify and describe various renewable sources of energy.

🔑 Explain how a nuclear power plant produces electricity.

Engage

Activate Prior Knowledge

MY PLANET DIARY Read *An Unlikely Decision* with the class. Point out that gas and oil deposits located beneath land in the United States have allowed American gas and oil companies to thrive for decades. Ask: **Why might someone who made their fortune in nonrenewable resources become involved in promoting renewable resources?** *(Students may say it is smart to look into renewable energy since nonrenewable sources won't be around forever.)*

BIG IDEAS OF SCIENCE REFERENCE LIBRARY 📖 Have students look up the following topics: Biofuels, Solar Power.

Explore

Lab Resource: Inquiry Warm-Up 🧪

L1 CAN YOU CAPTURE SOLAR ENERGY? Students will use water to capture energy from sunlight and monitor temperature increases.

LESSON **2**

Renewable Sources of Energy

UNLOCK THE BIG ❓

🔑 **What Are Some Renewable Sources of Energy?**

🔑 **How Does a Nuclear Power Plant Produce Electricity?**

my planeт DiaRY

BIOGRAPHY

An Unlikely Decision

T. Boone Pickens's family taught him the value of hard work during the Great Depression of the 1930s. At 11, he delivered newspapers. By 26, he founded his own oil and gas company and became rich. In 2007, T. Boone Pickens surprised everyone by announcing plans to build the world's largest wind farm. He insisted the country must replace oil with wind and solar power. Even though he still promotes oil, he was one of the first oil businessmen to admit a change was needed. "I've been an oil man all my life," Pickens said, "but this is one emergency we can't drill our way out of."

Communicate Discuss these questions with a group of classmates. Write your answers below.

1. Why do you think Pickens's decision was so surprising?
   <u>Sample: He made his</u>
   <u>fortune in oil and gas.</u>

2. Do you think more focus should be put on finding sources of energy other than oil? Why or why not?
   <u>Sample: Yes, because we</u>
   <u>might run out of oil.</u>

▶ PLANET DIARY Go to **Planet Diary** to learn more about renewable energy.

 Do the Inquiry Warm-Up *Can You Capture Solar Energy?*

What Are Some Renewable Sources of Energy?

Coal, oil, and natural gas are not the only energy options available on Earth. 🔑 **Renewable sources of energy include sunlight, water, wind, nuclear power, biomass fuels, geothermal energy, and hydrogen.** Scientists are trying to find ways to put these energy resources to work to meet people's energy needs.

186 Energy Resources

SUPPORT ALL READERS
Lexile Measure = 940L   Lexile Word Count = 2284

Prior Exposure to Context: Many students may have misconceptions on this topic

Academic Vocabulary: *cause, effect, infer*

Science Vocabulary: *biomass fuel, geothermal energy, nuclear fission*

Concept Level: Generally appropriate for most students in this grade

Preteach With: My Planet Diary "An Unlikely Decision" and Figure 2 activity

Go to **My Reading Web** to access leveled readings that provide a foundation for the content.

my science online

Vocabulary

- solar energy
- hydroelectric power
- biomass fuel
- gasohol
- geothermal energy
- nuclear fission
- reactor vessel
- fuel rod
- control rod

Skills

- 🔁 Reading: Relate Cause and Effect
- ◢ Inquiry: Infer

Solar Energy The warmth you feel on a sunny day is **solar energy,** or energy from the sun. The sun constantly gives off energy in the forms of light and heat. Solar energy is the source, directly or indirectly, of most other renewable energy resources. In one hour, Earth receives enough solar energy to meet the energy needs of the world for an entire year. Solar energy does not cause pollution. It will not run out for billions of years.

So why hasn't solar energy replaced energy from fossil fuels? One reason is that solar energy is only available when the sun is shining. Another problem is that the energy Earth receives from the sun is very spread out. To obtain a useful amount of power, it is necessary to collect solar energy from a large area.

Solar Power Plants One way to capture the sun's energy involves using giant mirrors. <u>In a solar power plant, rows of mirrors focus the sun's rays to heat a tank of water. The water boils. This creates steam.</u> The steam can then be used to generate electricity.

Solar Cells Solar energy can be converted directly into electricity in a solar cell. <u>When light hits the cell, an electric current is produced.</u> Solar cells power some calculators, lights, and other small devices.

🔁 **Relate Cause and Effect**
Underline one way solar energy is collected and circle the way it is used.

did you **know?**

Photovoltaic cells, or solar cells, are named for the Greek word for light, *photo*, and electricity pioneer Alessandro Volta.

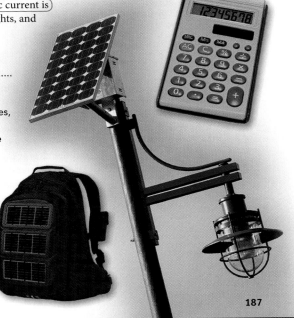

FIGURE 1
Everyday Solar Power
Many objects, including calculators, street lights, and even backpacks that charge electronic devices, can be powered by the sun.

✏️ **Describe** What object in your everyday life would you like to run on solar power? Would you want the sun to be its only power source? Why?

Sample: I would want a solar-powered digital music player. I would also want a battery backup so I could still use it on cloudy days.

187

Explain

Introduce Vocabulary
Point out that two of the vocabulary words, *hydroelectric* and *geothermal* combine a Greek root with an adjective to form a new word. Explain that *hydroelectric* means "producing electricity with water" and that *geothermal* means "having to do with the heat inside the earth."

Teach Key Concepts 🔑
Explain to students that fossil fuels are the most common, but not the only, sources of energy available to people. Ask: **What are two sources of energy that relate to weather?** *(Wind, sunlight)* **What renewable source of energy is made from living things?** *(Biomass fuels)* **What other renewable sources of energy are scientists trying to develop further?** *(Water, nuclear, geothermal, and hydrogen)*

Lead a Discussion
SOLAR TECHNOLOGIES It's energizing! Different technologies associated with capturing solar energy involve different energy conversions. Ask: **Which solar technology converts light energy directly to electricity?** *(Solar cells)* **Which solar technology converts light energy to heat?** *(Solar power plant)* Explain to students that there are many solutions being sought, and some that are already in use, for ways to store energy when the sun is not shining. Some of these solutions are molten or liquid salt, pumping water uphill, and pumping air underground.

🔁 **Relate Cause and Effect** Tell students that a cause makes something happen. An effect is what happens. When students recognize that one event causes another, they are relating cause and effect.

My Planet Diary provides an opportunity for students to explore real-world connections to renewable energy sources.

ⒺⓁⓁ Support

1 Content and Language
Write *bio-*, *mass*, *geo-*, and *thermal* on the board, defining each ("life," "physical quantity," "earth," and "heat"). Discuss how knowing these meanings can help students remember the meanings of the terms *biomass* and *geothermal*.

2 Frontload the Lesson
The key idea is full of new or unfamiliar terms, creating a very large language load for students. Write the key idea on the board, while providing a partially filled-in outline that uses the section headings. As students complete each section, have them return to the key idea to determine which of the sources listed belong in each category.

3 Comprehensible Input
Create a Venn diagram to compare and contrast biomass fuels and fossil fuels. Ask volunteers to provide similarities and differences.

Explain

Teach With Visuals

Tell students to look at **Figure 2.** Review the passive and active solar heating systems in the illustration. Call on students to describe the various features labeled in the solar house. Ask: **Which of these solar-powered systems do you have in your own home?** *(Most students will probably identify passive interior heating and window design.)* **Where else in the community do you see examples of passive or active solar-powered systems?** *(Allow a day or two for students to report examples.)* If any students say that their homes are equipped with active solar-powered systems, invite those students to describe the devices and their operation to the class. Remind students that office buildings and institutions might use solar-powered systems, as well.

△ **Infer** When students interpret an observation, they are inferring, or making an inference. Unlike a fact, an inference is one of many possible interpretations for an observation.

Elaborate

Build Inquiry

L1 OBSERVE PASSIVE SOLAR HEATING
Materials 2 thermometers, large glass jar

Time 10 minutes

Tell students that they can measure the difference in temperature inside and outside a passive solar object. Take students outdoors on a sunny day away from the pavement to a spot that receives direct sunlight. Have students note the temperatures of the two thermometers. Put one thermometer in a glass jar turned upside down on the ground and leave the other thermometer in open air. Have students compare the temperatures after several minutes.

Ask: **Why is the temperature higher inside the glass jar?** *(The glass allows light to pass into the jar but traps heat inside the jar.)*

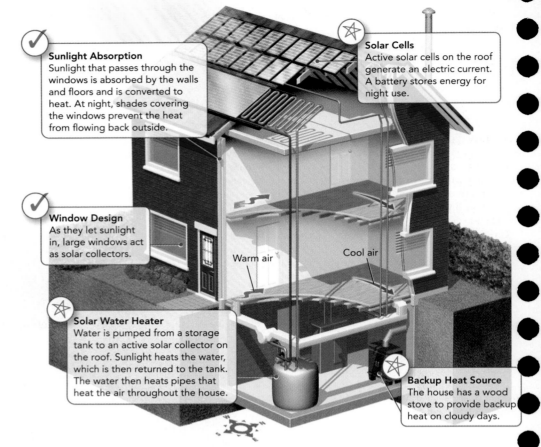

Sunlight Absorption
Sunlight that passes through the windows is absorbed by the walls and floors and is converted to heat. At night, shades covering the windows prevent the heat from flowing back outside.

Solar Cells
Active solar cells on the roof generate an electric current. A battery stores energy for night use.

Window Design
As they let sunlight in, large windows act as solar collectors.

Warm air

Cool air

Solar Water Heater
Water is pumped from a storage tank to an active solar collector on the roof. Sunlight heats the water, which is then returned to the tank. The water then heats pipes that heat the air throughout the house.

Backup Heat Source
The house has a wood stove to provide backup heat on cloudy days.

FIGURE 2 ....
Solar-Powered House
This house takes advantage of active and passive solar heating.
△ **Infer** Draw a checkmark in the blank circles on the passive sources of solar energy. Draw a star in the blank circles on the active sources.

Passive Solar Heating Solar energy can be used to heat buildings with passive solar systems. A passive solar system converts sunlight into heat, or thermal energy. The heat is then distributed without using pumps or fans. Passive solar heating is what occurs in a parked car on a sunny day. Solar energy passes through the car's windows and heats the seats and other car parts. These parts transfer heat to the air, warming the inside of the car. The same principle can be used to heat a home.

Active Solar Heating An active solar system captures the sun's energy, and then uses pumps and fans to distribute the heat. First, light strikes the dark metal surface of a solar collector. There, it is converted to thermal energy. Water is pumped through pipes in the solar collector to absorb the thermal energy. The heated water then flows to a storage tank. Finally, pumps and fans distribute the heat throughout the building. Refer to **Figure 2.**

188 Energy Resources

Hydroelectric Power

Solar energy is the indirect source of water power. In the water cycle, energy from the sun heats water on Earth's surface. The heat turns the water into water vapor. The vapor condenses and falls back to Earth as rain, sleet, hail, or snow. As the water flows over land, it provides another source of energy.

Hydroelectric power is electricity produced by flowing water. A dam across a river blocks the flow of water, creating a body of water called a reservoir. When a dam's gates are opened, water flows through tunnels at the bottom of the dam. As the water moves through the tunnels, it turns turbines (like a fan's blades). The turbines are connected to a generator. Once a dam is built, generating electricity is inexpensive. But dams can prevent some fish species from breeding. They can also damage aquatic habitats.

Capturing the Wind

Like water power, wind energy is also an indirect form of solar energy. The sun heats Earth's surface unevenly. As a result, different areas of the atmosphere have different temperatures and air pressures. The differences in pressure cause winds to form as air moves from one area to another.

Wind can be used to turn a turbine and generate electricity. Wind farms consist of many wind turbines. Together, the wind turbines generate large amounts of power. Wind is the fastest-growing energy source in the world. Wind energy does not cause pollution. In places where fuels are difficult to transport, wind energy is the major source of power if it is available.

Nuclear Power

Like water and wind power, nuclear power does not produce air pollution since no fuel is burned. Instead, the energy released from the splitting of atoms is used to create steam that turns turbines. This process can be dangerous and even cause explosions if too much energy is released. Wastes generated by nuclear plants can be dangerous if disposed of improperly.

FIGURE 3 ·····················

Hydroelectric and Wind Power
Hydroelectric and wind power do not rely on fossil fuels.

✎ **Compare and Contrast**
List similarities and differences between water and wind power in the Venn diagram.

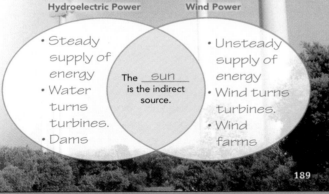

Hydroelectric Power
- Steady supply of energy
- Water turns turbines.
- Dams

The __sun__ is the indirect source.

Wind Power
- Unsteady supply of energy
- Wind turns turbines.
- Wind farms

189

Explain

Lead a Discussion

POWER FROM WATER Go with the flow. Explain that the water cycle plays a role in generating electricity from flowing water and that hydroelectric power depends on the controlled flow of water through tunnels (spillways or gates) in dams. Ask: **What energy conversion takes place as flowing water turns turbines connected to a generator?** *(Mechanical energy is converted to electrical energy.)* **What are some negative effects that dams might have on the environment?** *(Sample: Dams can change ecosystems when they are built.)*

Lead a Discussion

WIND ENERGY Sun can lead to wind. Solar energy produces convection currents in the atmosphere that create wind. The sun also provides energy for the water cycle, which is essential to hydroelectric power. Tell students that, like the way flowing water produces electricity in a hydroelectric dam, wind generates power by moving turbines that are connected to generators. Ask: **What weather conditions are disruptive to harnessing wind energy?** *(Irregular winds; no winds; winds too strong; stagnant weather—no winds generated)* **Name two reasons why wind farms are best placed in remote locations.** *(Wind farms are noisy; they require a lot of space; other fuels may be difficult to transport to remote sites.)* Tell students that there once was concern over wind turbines causing harm to flying birds. However, modern turbines are larger and can generate the same amount of energy by moving slowly. This improvement reduces the chances of birds being injured.

21st Century Learning

COMMUNICATION Divide the class into two groups; assign one group water power and the other group wind power. Ask groups to consider the advantages of the assigned source of power, and why their community should adopt it. *(Students should consider climate and geographic restrictions, cost, potential environmental damage, and so on.)* Have each group give a brief presentation on its position.

Differentiated Instruction

L1 **Illustrate a Solar Power Plant** To reinforce students' understanding of the causes and effects that underlie the operation of a solar power plant, have them create an illustration showing the functions of the sun, a row of mirrors, a tank of water, and steam in the generation of electricity.

L3 **Solar Power Timeline** Challenge students to do research in order to create an annotated, illustrated timeline showing the history of solar energy.

Point out that human beings have been using energy from the sun since prehistoric times. Urge students to note developments and setbacks in the movement to make solar energy more widespread.

L3 **Explain Solar Technologies** Invite pairs of students to take turns explaining the principles underlying examples of technology that capture solar energy for human use.

Explain

Lead a Discussion

FUELS FROM LIVING THINGS Wood is a common *biomass fuel*. Explain that biomass can be burned as fuel and converted into other fuels. Ask: **What are five biomass products that can be burned as fuel?** *(Samples: trees/wood, corn, sugar cane, landfill wastes, leaves, manure, food wastes)* **Why do you think biomass fuels are commonly used in less developed nations?** *(They are easy to obtain and do not require special technology.)* Tell students that there are negative environmental impacts when food crops are used to produce biomass fuels. Ecosystems can be affected when large amounts of land are used to grow a single biomass fuel crop. A genetically similar crop may become more susceptible to diseases and pests, which can lead to crop failure. Growing biomass fuel crops requires machinery that runs on fossil fuels and petroleum-based pesticides and fertilizers. Biomass fuel crops also compete with food production. As U.S. farmers started to use corn crops for ethanol in 2006 and 2007, the amount of corn available for food decreased. This caused corn prices to increase. Ask: **Do you think the positive uses of biomass fuels outweigh the negative impacts?** *(Sample: Yes, because it helps to reduce our dependence on fossil fuels.)*

Address Misconceptions

L1 NEW RENEWABLES? Many people believe that renewable energy sources have been developed only recently as environment-friendly alternatives to fossil fuels, but this is not the case. Explain to students that renewable energy has been around for a long time. Also point out that hydroelectric power is the most widely used renewable source in the world, accounting for 19 percent of total electricity production.

Ask: **What types of energy were used before electricity?** *(Burning wood, peat, other biomass fuels; wind, water)* **Why did renewable sources become less popular?** *(Energy from fossil fuels is easier to obtain and more convenient.)*

Elaborate

Apply It!

L1 Before students begin the *Apply It!* activity, have them reread the section on biomass fuels and study the elements of the graph, noting the title, the labels on the sides of the graph, and the key. Point out the two curves, labeled "Demand" and "Supply." Explain that by tracking the relationship between the red line and the blue line, students will be able to see how supply and demand affect each another.

FIGURE 4 ·······························

Corn Power
Biomass fuels come from living things, such as corn. It takes about 11.84 kilograms of corn to make one gallon of fuel!

Biomass Fuels Wood was probably the first fuel ever used for heat and light. Wood belongs to a group of fuels called **biomass fuels.** Biomass fuels are made from living things. Other biomass fuels include leaves, food wastes, and even manure. As fossil fuel supplies shrink, people are taking a closer look at biomass fuels. For example, when oil prices rose in the early 1970s, Hawaiian farmers began burning sugar cane wastes to generate electricity.

In addition to being burned as fuel, biomass materials can be converted into other fuels. For example, corn, sugar cane, and other crops can be used to make alcohol. Adding alcohol to gasoline forms **gasohol.** Gasohol can be used as fuel for cars. Bacteria can produce methane gas by decomposing biomass materials in landfills. That methane can be used to heat buildings. And some crops, such as soybeans, can produce oil. The oil can be used as fuel, which is called biodiesel fuel.

Biomass fuels are renewable resources. But it takes time for new trees to replace those that have been cut down. And it is expensive to produce alcohol and methane in large quantities. As a result, biomass fuels are not widely used today in the United States. But as fossil fuels become scarcer, biomass fuels may provide another source for meeting energy needs.

apply it!

What can happen when a food crop is used for fuel? The relationship is plotted with two curves on the graph.

❶ **Interpret Graphs** According to the graph, as demand for corn increases, what happens to the supply?

It decreases.

❷ **CHALLENGE** How would the price of corn change as demand for fuel increases? Why?

Sample: It would increase because there would be a smaller supply of corn to go around and people would be willing to pay more.

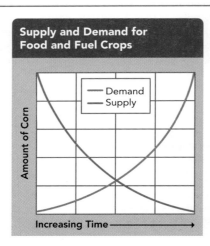

Supply and Demand for Food and Fuel Crops

— Demand
— Supply

Amount of Corn

Increasing Time ⟶

Digital Lesson: Assign the *Apply It* activity online and have students submit their work to you.

MY SCIENCE ONLINE.com Renewable Energy Sources

Tapping Earth's Energy Below Earth's surface are pockets of very hot liquid rock called magma. In some places, magma is very close to the surface. The intense heat from Earth's interior that warms the magma is called **geothermal energy.**

In certain regions, such as Iceland and New Zealand, magma heats underground water to the boiling point. In these places, the hot water and steam can be valuable sources of energy. For example, in Reykjavík, Iceland, 90 percent of the homes are heated by water warmed underground in this way. Geothermal energy can also be used to generate electricity, as shown in **Figure 5.**

Geothermal energy does have disadvantages. There are only a few places where Earth's crust is thin enough for magma to come close to the surface. Elsewhere, very deep wells would be needed to tap this energy. Drilling deep wells is very expensive. Even so, geothermal energy is likely to become a good method for meeting energy needs for some locations in the future.

FIGURE 5 ·······················

Geothermal Power in Iceland
Geothermal power plants like the one shown here use heat from Earth's interior to generate electricity.
✎ **Infer** On the diagram below, draw Earth's crust and show where magma might be located in relation to Iceland's surface.

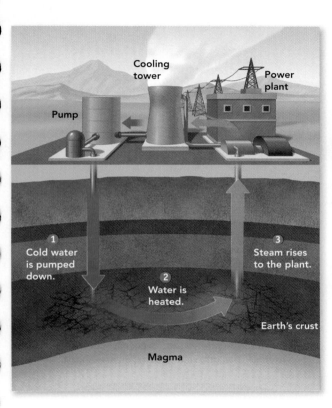

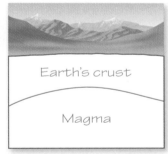

191

Explain

Teach With Visuals

Have students look at **Figure 5.** Remind students that geothermal energy is the intense heat from Earth's interior. Ask: **How is electricity generated in a geothermal power plant?** (*Cold water piped underground is heated by magma and turns into steam, which is used to generate electricity.*) **Why do you think geothermal energy isn't more commonly used?** (*Magma comes close to the surface only in a few areas; deep wells required in other places would be expensive.*)

Lead a Discussion

HEAT PUMPS Students may not think that they live in an area that can benefit from geothermal energy. However, geothermal heat pumps can be used in any location where pipes can be drilled into the ground. Because the ground beneath six feet stays at roughly the same temperature (14 degrees Celsius) year-round, it can be used to store energy. In the winter, cold water is pumped into the ground where it is heated to 14 degrees Celsius. In the summer, warm water is pumped into the ground to be cooled to 14 degrees Celsius. While geothermal heat pumps are more expensive to install than conventional heating and cooling systems, they are becoming more common throughout the United States. Many schools are beginning to install geothermal heat pumps to reduce heating and cooling costs. Ask: **Do you think your school should investigate the use of a heat pump to reduce costs?** (*Some students may think it is a good idea to help reduce costs in the long term. Other students may think it is a bad idea because of the cost in the short term.*)

21st Century Learning

CRITICAL THINKING Have students reread the last paragraph on this page. Encourage students to note the specific information about two disadvantages of geothermal energy. (*Limited number of places where Earth's crust is thin enough, expense of drilling deep wells*) **What can you conclude about Earth's crust in Iceland and New Zealand?** (*It must be thin.*) **What do you think could make geothermal energy a good method for meeting energy needs in the future?** (*Sample: Technological advances may make drilling less expensive.*)

Differentiated Instruction

L1 Describe Geothermal Energy Have students summarize in their own words the process for generating electricity with geothermal energy. Let students share their summaries with the class in a follow-up discussion. Guide students to agree on a "best sentence" for each step in the process.

L3 Five Powerful Plants Have students research the five plants in Iceland that produce electricity. Over one-fourth of the electricity used in Iceland is produced by these plants.

Explain

Lead a Discussion

ENERGY FOR THE FUTURE Tell students that scientists want to develop hydrogen power because of its potential to provide huge amounts of energy. Ask: **What are the advantages and disadvantages associated with hydrogen power?** *(Advantages—abundant, burns cleanly, doesn't pollute air; disadvantages—expensive to produce, almost all hydrogen is combined with oxygen in water)* **What examples do we have of hydrogen power being supplied by fuel cells?** *(Experimental cars, space shuttle)* Students may have heard about electric cars. Tell students that like cars powered by hydrogen, some electric cars do not create air pollution. When electric cars are recharged using electricity generated by a renewable energy source, they cause no air pollutants. If an electric car is recharged using electricity generated by a nonrenewable energy source, then pollutants can be emitted from the power plant. However, all electric cars are considered zero-emission vehicles because they do not release any tailpipe pollutants.

Make Analogies

BENEFIT VS. COST To help students understand the idea that obtaining pure hydrogen takes more energy than is produced by burning hydrogen, invite students to think about other situations where a particular course of action is judged "not worth it" because it will "take more energy than it's worth," such as driving a relatively long distance to purchase an item that is on sale.

Elaborate

Explore the Big Q ? UbD

Direct students' attention to the particular objects (corn stalks, gas tank, hydrogen tank, wind turbines), atmospheric details (steam), and structures (dam, nuclear plant, house with solar panels) included in the illustration to represent each energy source. Ask: **Which energy sources are limited because they can only be found or gathered in certain locations?** *(Hydroelectric, fossil fuels, wind, geothermal)* **Which energy sources do not damage the environment?** *(Solar, wind, biomass, geothermal, hydrogen)*

Lab Resource: Quick Lab

L3 DESIGN AND BUILD A SOLAR COOKER
Students will design and build something to cook food. The cooker will be powered only by the sun.

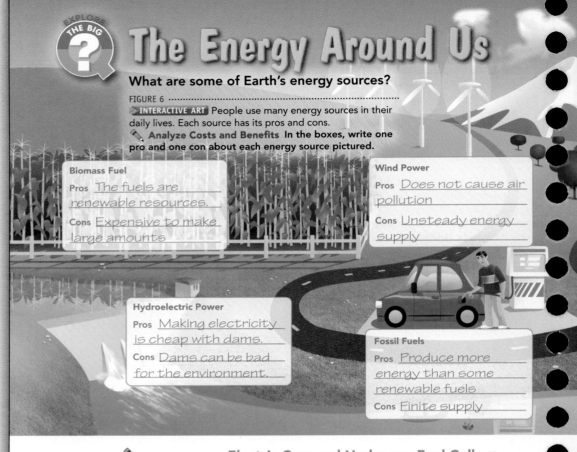

The Energy Around Us

What are some of Earth's energy sources?

FIGURE 6
INTERACTIVE ART People use many energy sources in their daily lives. Each source has its pros and cons.
Analyze Costs and Benefits In the boxes, write one pro and one con about each energy source pictured.

Biomass Fuel
Pros *The fuels are renewable resources.*
Cons *Expensive to make large amounts*

Wind Power
Pros *Does not cause air pollution*
Cons *Unsteady energy supply*

Hydroelectric Power
Pros *Making electricity is cheap with dams.*
Cons *Dams can be bad for the environment.*

Fossil Fuels
Pros *Produce more energy than some renewable fuels*
Cons *Finite supply*

Vocabulary High-Use Academic Words The word *emit* means "to give off." What do vehicles that run on hydrogen fuel cells emit?

Water vapor

Electric Cars and Hydrogen Fuel Cells
You may have heard about or even seen battery-powered electric cars. But what about cars that use hydrogen fuel cells? Both technologies, battery-powered electric cars and hydrogen fuel cells, have been developed to use renewable energy. See **Figure 6.**

Electric cars run entirely on batteries, and you plug them into an outlet to recharge them. The electricity used can be generated by power plants that use hydroelectric or solar energy. Some electric cars have adaptors that let you recharge them in minutes.

Some cars can run on hydrogen. They have tanks called hydrogen fuel cells that hold hydrogen instead of gasoline. Many power plants can use excess energy to break water molecules apart to make hydrogen. This hydrogen can then be pumped into cars. Cars that run on hydrogen fuel cells emit water vapor, not exhaust.

Interactive Art allows students to explore a hydroelectric power plant.

my science online.com
Renewable Energy Sources

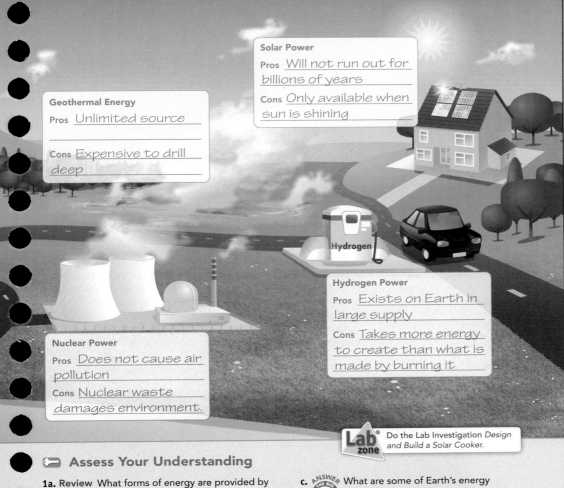

Geothermal Energy

Pros _Unlimited source_

Cons _Expensive to drill deep_

Solar Power

Pros _Will not run out for billions of years_

Cons _Only available when sun is shining_

Hydrogen Power

Pros _Exists on Earth in large supply_

Cons _Takes more energy to create than what is made by burning it_

Nuclear Power

Pros _Does not cause air pollution_

Cons _Nuclear waste damages environment._

Lab zone Do the Lab Investigation _Design and Build a Solar Cooker._

Assess Your Understanding

1a. Review What forms of energy are provided by the sun? _Light and heat_

b. Explain Are biomass fuels renewable? Why? _Yes; crops can be replanted, although this takes time._

**c. ANSWER THE BIG ? ** What are some of Earth's energy sources? _Fossil fuels, solar power, hydroelectric power, wind power, nuclear power, biomass fuels, geothermal energy, and hydrogen_

got it?

○ **I get it!** Now I know that alternative energy sources include _sunlight, water, wind, nuclear power, biomass fuels, geothermal energy, and hydrogen._

○ **I need extra help with** _See TE note._

_Go to_ **my science** 🗨ˢ **coach** _online for help with this subject._

193

Evaluate

Assess Your Understanding

After students answer the questions, have them evaluate their understanding by completing the appropriate sentence.

Answer the Big Q ❓ UbD

To help students focus on the Big Question, lead a class discussion about Earth's energy sources.

RTI Response to Intervention

1a. If students have trouble listing forms of energy provided by the sun, **then** have them reread the first paragraph under the red head _Solar Energy._

b. If students cannot explain what makes biomass renewable, **then** have them to review the last paragraph under the red head _Biomass Fuels._

c. If students need help identifying energy sources, **then** have them to skim the entire chapter to find examples of energy sources.

my science 🗨ˢ **coach** Have students go online for help in understanding renewable energy sources.

Differentiated Instruction

L1 Illustrate Local Energy Use Invite students to create drawings, paintings, or murals that show local buildings, landforms, and other sites where energy use is evident. Students might include a gas station, a private home with solar panels, a wind turbine, a dam, and so on. Have students share their drawings with the rest of the class and call on other students to name the energy use that is illustrated.

L3 Hydrogen Power Plants Hydrogen is the simplest of the elements and the most plentiful gas in the universe. Have students research the planned use of hydrogen to power electrical plants. Have them prepare diagrams to support their findings.

Explain

Teach Key Concepts 🗝

Nuclear fission, the splitting of an atom's nucleus into two nuclei, is the basis for nuclear power. Ask: **What form of energy given off by nuclear fission is used in a power plant?** *(Heat)* **In a nuclear power plant, how is heat used?** *(It turns water into steam.)* **What happens next?** *(The steam turns the blades of a turbine to create electricity.)*

Lead a Discussion

HOW FISSION GENERATES ELECTRICITY Compare a nuclear power plant to other power plants. A nuclear power plant functions like other power plants: a heat source—in this case, fission—changes water into steam that powers turbines. Have students review **Figure 7**. Ask: **What are the three main components of a nuclear power plant?** *(The generator, the reactor vessel and the heat exchanger)* **Name two other energy sources that can create steam to turn turbines that generate electricity at a power plant.** *(Fossil fuels, especially coal; geothermal energy)*

How Does a Nuclear Power Plant Produce Electricity?

Nuclear power plants generate much of the world's electricity. They generate about 20 percent of the electricity in the United States and more than 70 percent in France. Controlled nuclear fission reactions take place inside nuclear power plants. **Nuclear fission** is the splitting of an atom's nucleus into two nuclei. The splitting releases a lot of energy. 🗝 **In a nuclear power plant, the heat released from fission reactions is used to turn water into steam. The steam then turns the blades of a turbine to generate electricity.** Look at the diagram of a nuclear power plant in **Figure 7**. In addition to the generator, it has two main parts: the reactor vessel and the heat exchanger.

Reactor Vessel The **reactor vessel** is the part of the nuclear reactor in which nuclear fission occurs. The reactor contains rods of radioactive uranium called **fuel rods.** When several fuel rods are placed close together, a series of fission reactions occurs.

If the reactor vessel gets too hot, control rods are used to slow down the chain reactions. **Control rods,** made of the elements cadmium, boron or hafnium, are inserted near the fuel rods. The elements absorb particles released during fission and slow the speed of the chain reactions. The control rods can then be removed to speed up the chain reactions again.

FIGURE 7 ·······················

▶ INTERACTIVE ART Nuclear Power Plants
Nuclear power plants are designed to turn the energy from nuclear fission reactions into electricity.

✏ **Interpret Diagrams** Where does nuclear fission occur in the plant?

In the reactor vessel

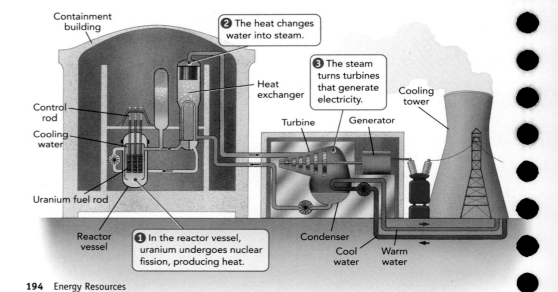

Containment building

❷ The heat changes water into steam.

Heat exchanger

❸ The steam turns turbines that generate electricity.

Cooling tower

Control rod

Cooling water

Turbine

Generator

Uranium fuel rod

Reactor vessel

❶ In the reactor vessel, uranium undergoes nuclear fission, producing heat.

Condenser

Cool water

Warm water

Interactive Art allows students to understand the process that leads to the generation of electricity in nuclear power plants.

my science online.com ▸ **Nuclear Power**

Heat Exchanger

Heat is removed from the reactor vessel by water or another fluid that is pumped through the reactor. This fluid passes through a heat exchanger. There, the fluid boils water to produce steam. The steam runs the electrical generator. The steam is condensed again and pumped back to the heat exchanger.

The Risks of Nuclear Power

At first, people thought that nuclear fission would provide an almost unlimited source of clean, safe energy. But accidents at nuclear power plants have led to safety concerns. In 1986, the reactor vessel in a nuclear power plant in Chernobyl, Ukraine, overheated. The fuel rods generated so much heat that they started to melt. This condition is called a meltdown. The excess heat caused a series of explosions, which injured or killed dozens of people immediately. In addition, radioactive materials escaped into the environment and killed many more people.

Plant operators can avoid accidents at nuclear facilities through careful planning and by improving safety features. A more difficult problem is the disposal of radioactive wastes. Radioactive wastes remain dangerous for many thousands of years. Scientists must find ways to store these wastes safely for very long periods of time.

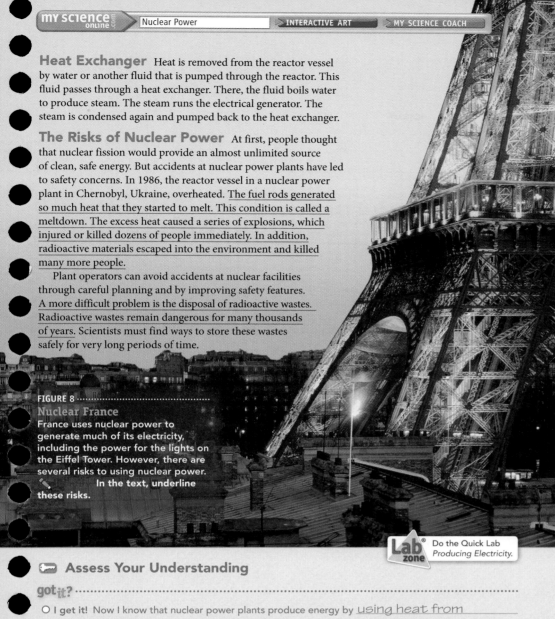

FIGURE 8
Nuclear France
France uses nuclear power to generate much of its electricity, including the power for the lights on the Eiffel Tower. However, there are several risks to using nuclear power.
✎ In the text, underline these risks.

 Lab zone Do the Quick Lab *Producing Electricity.*

🔑 Assess Your Understanding

got it? ....

○ I get it! Now I know that nuclear power plants produce energy by using heat from nuclear fission reactions to make steam that generates turbines.

○ I need extra help with See TE note.

Go to my science ⑤ coach *online for help with this subject.*

195

Elaborate

Build Inquiry 🔬Lab

L1 NUCLEAR POWER ACCIDENTS

Materials large world map

Time 15 minutes

Explain that radioactive fallout from the Chernobyl accident was spread by air currents. Display the map, and let volunteers locate Chernobyl (51° N, 30° about 130 km north of Kiev). Tell students that the force of the 1986 explosion carried radioactive materials high into the atmosphere, where they spread across the Northern Hemisphere and then settled back to Earth in what is called fallout. The heaviest fallout occurred in Ukraine, Belarus, Sweden, Norway, Denmark, France, and Switzerland. In addition, Finland, Lithuania, Germany, Poland, the Czech Republic, Slovakia, Austria, Hungary, Italy, and Great Britain suffered moderate fallout. Let students find all these countries on the map.

Ask: **Which affected country was farthest from Chernobyl?** *(Great Britain)* **What does this tell you about the dangers of nuclear power plants?** *(An accident can affect a huge area.)*

Lab Resource: Quick Lab 🔬Lab

L1 PRODUCING ELECTRICITY Students will draw a model of a nuclear power plant to learn how it generates electricity.

Evaluate

Assess Your Understanding

Have students evaluate their understanding by completing the appropriate sentence.

🄡🄣🄘 Response to Intervention

If students cannot explain how nuclear power plants work, **then** have them refer to **Figure 7** and read the numbered labels.

my science ⑤ coach Have students go online for help in understanding how nuclear power plants produce energy.

Differentiated Instruction

L1 Relate Cause and Effect Help students understand the process of producing power from nuclear fission by asking them to analyze the cause-and-effect relationships in the process. Have them create a flowchart beginning with nuclear fission and ending with electric current going to power lines.

L3 Identify Nuclear Accidents Challenge students to use reference books or online sources to learn the typical temperatures reached in a nuclear power plant's reactor vessel and then find the temperatures reached in the Chernobyl accident. Ask students to investigate and report on the occurrence of other nuclear accidents, such as Three Mile Island.

Name _____ Date _____ Class _____

Alternative Sources of Energy

> **Inquiry Warm-Up, *Can You Capture Solar Energy?***
> In the Inquiry Warm-Up, you investigated capturing solar energy with a water-filled bag. Using what you learned from that activity, answer the questions below.

1. **PREDICT** Assume you move a bag from a dark, shady area into an area with direct sunlight for 30 minutes and then back into the shade for 30 minutes. Draw a simple graph predicting the bag's temperature change over time.

2. **USE PRIOR KNOWLEDGE** Give at least one reason why solar energy cannot meet all of our energy needs.

   _____

   _____

3. **INFER** Explain your results for the temperature of the bag before and after you placed it in a dark area.

   _____

   _____

4. **PREDICT** Will the temperature of the water in the bag placed in direct sunlight be higher or lower if you leave it in direct sunlight for another 30 minutes?

   _____

   _____

Place the outside corner, the corner away from the dotted line, in the corner of your copy machine to copy onto letter-size paper.

Assess Your Understanding

Alternative Sources of Energy

What Are Some Alternative Sources of Energy?

1a. REVIEW What forms of energy are provided by the sun? _____

_____

b. EXPLAIN Are biomass fuels renewable? Why? _____

_____

c. ANSWER What are some of Earth's energy sources?

_____

_____

got it? ....

○ **I get it!** Now I know that alternative energy sources include _____

_____

○ **I need extra help with** _____

_____

How Does a Nuclear Power Plant Produce Electricity?

got it? ....

○ **I get it!** Now I know that nuclear power plants produce energy by _____

_____

_____

○ **I need extra help with** _____

_____

Key Concept Summaries

Alternative Sources of Energy

What Are Some Alternative Sources of Energy?

Alternative sources of energy include sunlight, water, wind, nuclear power, biomass fuels, geothermal energy, and hydrogen. Solar energy is energy from the sun. In solar power plants, mirrors focus the sun's rays on a water tank, creating steam to generate electricity. In solar cells, light falling on the cell is converted to electric current. **Hydroelectric power** is electricity produced by flowing water. Inside a dam, flowing water turns turbines (like a fan's blades) to generate electricity. Wind can also be used to turn turbines and generate electricity.

In nuclear power, the energy released by splitting atoms creates steam that turns turbines. **Biomass fuels** such as wood, leaves, food wastes, and manure are made from living things. Biomass materials can be burned as fuels themselves or converted into other fuels, such as **gasohol,** a mix of alcohol and gasoline. The intense heat from Earth's interior that warms magma below Earth's surface is called **geothermal energy.** Water pumped into deep wells is heated by the magma to generate electricity. Hydrogen power may someday be a source of clean energy, but first scientists must find an inexpensive way to release hydrogen atoms from water.

How Does a Nuclear Power Plant Produce Electricity?

Nuclear power plants generate electricity through controlled **nuclear fission,** the splitting of an atom's nucleus into two nuclei. **In a nuclear power plant, the heat released from fission reactions is used to turn water into steam. The steam then turns the blades of a turbine to generate electricity.** The **reactor vessel** is the part of the nuclear reactor in which fission occurs. When rods of uranium called **fuel rods** are placed close together, fission reactions occur. If the reactor gets too hot, **control rods,** made of the metal cadmium, are inserted between the fuel rods to absorb particles released during fission and slow the reactions. Water or another fluid pumped through the reactor is heated by the reactions. It passes through a heat exchanger, where the heat boils water to generate electricity. Nuclear energy has two main drawbacks. Accidents at nuclear plants have led to safety concerns, and scientists have yet to find safe ways to store dangerous radioactive wastes for thousands of years.

Choose five alternative sources of energy and, on a separate sheet of paper, list one drawback for each.

Review and Reinforce

Alternative Sources of Energy

Understanding Main Ideas
Answer the following questions on a separate sheet of paper.

1. Some sources of energy are called *alternative sources*. To what sources of energy are they an alternative?
2. Name five alternative sources of energy.
3. Explain how wind and flowing water can be used to produce electricity.
4. Describe how electricity is produced inside a nuclear plant.

Building Vocabulary
Match each term with its definition by writing the letter of the correct definition in the right column on the line beside the term in the left column.

5. ___ solar energy

6. ___ nucleaar fission

7. ___ hydroelectric power

8. ___ gasohol

9. ___ reactor vessel

10. ___ fuel rods

11. ___ biomass fuels

12. ___ geothermal energy

13. ___ control rods

a. a fuel made from a mix of alcohol and gasoline

b. the uranium rods inside a nuclear reactor that produce fission

c. a group of fuels made from living things

d. intense heat from Earth's interior that warms magma

e. the splitting of an atom's nucleus into two nuclei

f. energy from the sun

g. the cadmium rids inside a nuclear reactor that slow the reactions

h. the part of a nuclear reactor in which nuclear fission occurs

i. electricity produced by flowing water

Enrich

Alternative Sources of Energy

Wind generators are useful only in places where the wind blows steadily at 13 kilometers per hour or more. Could wind generators be used where you live? Try this activity to find out if the wind is strong enough to operate a wind generator.

Measuring Wind Speed

Materials

sewing needle

30 cm heavyweight thread

table-tennis ball

masking tape

protractor

Procedure 🔖 ✂️

1. Tie a knot in one end of the thread. Carefully use the needle to pull the thread all the way though the table-tennis ball.

2. Tape the other end of the thread to the center mark on a protractor.

3. Choose a windy place outdoors. With your back to the wind, hold the protractor with its straight edge up and parallel to the ground.

4. Prepare a data table to record the date, time, angle of the thread, and wind speed. Put in enough rows to record data twice a day for one week.

5. Read and record the angle where the thread crosses the protractor's curved edge. Use the table on this page to convert the angle to wind speed.

6. Repeat your measurements twice a day for one week. Calculate the average wind speed for the week. Is the wind in your area strong enough to operate a wind generator?

Angle	Wind Speed (km/h)
90°	0
85°	6
80°	8
75°	10
70°	12
65°	13
60°	15
55°	16
50°	18
45°	20
40°	21
35°	23
30°	26
25°	29
20°	33

Tape
Protractor
Thread
Table-tennis ball
Knot

Name _____ Date _____ Class _____

Alternative Sources of Energy

If the statement is true, write _true_. If the statement is false, change the underlined word or words to make the statement true.

1. _____ Sunlight, water, wind, nuclear power, biomass fuels, geothermal energy, and hydrogen are all <u>nonrenewable</u> energy sources.

2. _____ The fastest-growing energy source in the world is <u>wind energy</u>.

3. _____ In order to harness <u>geothermal</u> energy, cool water is pumped down into deep wells.

4. _____ Inside a nuclear power plant, nuclear fission takes place within the <u>heat exchanger</u>.

5. _____ The radioactive wastes produced by nuclear fission remain dangerous for <u>dozens</u> of years.

Fill in the blank to complete each statement.

6. Energy from the sun is called _____.

7. _____ is electricity produced by flowing water.

8. _____ can also be converted into other fuels, such as gasohol, which is formed by adding alcohol to gasoline.

9. The intense heat from Earth's interior that warms the magma is called _____.

10. _____ is the splitting of an atom's nucleus into two nuclei.

Alternative Sources of Energy

Answer Key

After the Inquiry Warm-Up

1. Description: The graph should look like a bell—a curve moving from low temperature to a higher temperature and back to a low temperature again.

2. Accept all reasonable responses. Students may say: The sun doesn't always shine; i.e., at night, or during cloudy weather.

3. Sample: The temperature did not change because it absorbed little or no solar energy.

4. Sample: The temperature of the water should be higher after an additional 30 minutes in the sun.

Key Concept Summaries

Accept any five of the following: Solar energy is spread out across the face of Earth and is only available when and where the sun is shining. Hydroelectric power can damage ecosystems when rivers are dammed. Wind power is only available when and where there is wind blowing. Producing nuclear power includes some risk of releasing radioactivity and leaves radioactive wastes that are difficult to store safely. In most places on Earth, releasing geothermal energy would require digging very deep wells. Until scientists find a cheap method for producing hydrogen, producing it takes more energy than is released by burning it.

Review and Reinforce

1. fossil fuels, such as coal, oil, and natural gas

2. Accept any five of the following: sunlight, water, wind, nuclear power, biomass fuels, geothermal energy, and hydrogen

3. Wind energy can be used to turn turbines and generate electricity. Water flowing through tunnels inside a dam turns turbines that generate electricity.

4. Sample: Inside the reactor vessel of a nuclear reactor, uranium fuel rods are placed close together. Particles given off by the uranium cause nuclear fission, splitting the nuclei of the atoms and releasing energy in the form of heat. The heat is absorbed by water in the reactor vessel, which is pumped outside to a heat exchanger. Inside the heat exchanger, pipes containing the hot water from the reactor vessel heat more water, which is turned to steam. The steam turns turbines to produce electricity.

5. f
6. e
7. i
8. a
9. h
10. b
11. c
12. d
13. g

Enrich

6. Wind speeds will vary. Students should answer Yes to the question if the wind is fairly steady and the average wind speed for the week is at least 13 km/h.

Lesson Quiz

1. alternative
2. true
3. true
4. reactor vessel
5. thousands
6. solar energy
7. Hydroelectric power
8. Biomass fuels
9. geothermal energy
10. Nuclear fission

Place the outside corner, the corner away from the dotted line, in the corner of your copy machine to copy onto letter-size paper.

Energy Use and Conservation

3 What are some of Earth's energy sources?

Blended Path Active learning using Student Edition, Inquiry Path, and Digital Path

Lesson Pacing: 1–2 periods or $\frac{1}{2}$–1 block

🕐 **SHORT ON TIME?** To do this lesson in approximately half the time, do the Activate Prior Knowledge activity on page 196. A discussion of the key concepts on pages 197 and 198 will familiarize students with the lesson content. Have students do the Quick Labs. The rest of the lesson can be completed by students independently.

> **Preference Navigator,** in the online Planning tools, allows you to customize *Interactive Science* to your own teaching style. You can also edit lesson plans by selecting the Lesson Planner option.
>
> **Digital Teacher's Edition** allows you to access your Teacher's Edition and Resource materials online.

my science online.com

Lesson Vocabulary

- efficiency
- insulation
- energy conservation

Professional Development Note — Content Refresher

Making Informed Decisions The federal government offers consumers a chance to make informed decisions when purchasing household appliances or homes. Appliances for homes earn the distinction of an "Energy Star" label when they meet energy efficiency standards established jointly by the Department of Energy and the U.S. Environmental Protection Agency (EPA). The Energy Star program estimates that a family can reduce its energy consumption by one third by choosing designated energy-efficient appliances.

According to the EPA, in 2008, Americans prevented 43 million metric tons of greenhouse gas emissions. That is equivalent to annual emissions by 29 million cars. Additionally, Americans saved over $19 billion dollars on utility bills by using Energy Star products and services.

LESSON OBJECTIVES

🔑 Explain how human energy use has changed over time.

🔑 Name ways to ensure that there will be enough energy for the future.

ENGAGE AND EXPLORE

Teach this lesson using a variety of resources. Begin by reading **My Planet Diary** as a class. Have students share what they know about various forms of insulation. Then have students do the **Inquiry Warm-Up activity.** Students will compare the efficiency of incandescent and fluorescent light bulbs. Discuss the characteristics of each type of light bulb. The **After the Inquiry Warm-Up worksheet** sets up a discussion about the benefits of using fluorescent light bulbs. Have volunteers share their answers to number 4 about the brightness of fluorescent and incandescent light bulbs.

EXPLAIN AND ELABORATE

Teach Key Concepts by explaining various ways that people created energy before using fossil fuels. Compare the energy sources shown on the timeline to **Support the Big Q.**

Continue to **Teach Key Concepts** by explaining the importance of conserving energy. Also discuss the importance of using energy efficiently. Use **Figures 1 and 2** to identify ways that human beings could conserve energy. **Lead a Discussion** about ways to increase the efficiency of our energy use in relation to heating and cooling systems, lighting, and transportation. Then have students complete the **Apply It activity.** Hand out the **Key Concept Summaries** as a review of each part of the lesson. Students can also use the online **Vocab Flash Cards** to review key terms.

EVALUATE

Have students take the **Lesson Quiz.** For an alternate assessment, see the **EXAM**VIEW® Assessment Suite, Progress Monitoring Assessments, or SuccessTracker™.

ⒺⓁⓁ Support

1 Content and Language

Identify the suffix in the terms *conservation* and *insulation*. When the Latin suffix *–ation* is added to a word it changes it from a verb to a noun. Determine the verb forms of *conservation* (to conserve) and *insulation* (to insulate). Identify similar nouns and their verb counterparts in this lesson: communication (to communicate); transportation (to transport); pollution (to pollute); suggestion (to suggest).

 **Inquiry Path** Hands-on learning in the Lab zone

Digital Path Online learning at my science online.com

ENGAGE AND EXPLORE

To teach this lesson with an emphasis on inquiry, begin with the **Inquiry Warm-Up activity.** Students will investigate incandescent and fluorescent light bulbs. Discuss the differences in efficiency between the two bulbs. Have students do the **After the Inquiry Warm-Up worksheet.** Talk about why it is more efficient to use a fluorescent light bulb. Have volunteers share their answers to number 4 comparing the brightness of the two types of light bulbs.

EXPLAIN AND ELABORATE

Focus on the **Inquiry Skill** for the lesson. Point out that when you observe, you carefully watch something. **Support the Big Q** by using the timeline to identify various sources of energy used over the course of time. Have students do the **Quick Lab** to understand human energy use in the 20th century and then share their results.

Use the **Real World Inquiry** to identify ways that energy can be conserved in a home. **Build Inquiry** by discussing energy conservation and efficiency in relation to the real world. Review transportation and energy conservation before beginning the **Apply It activity.** Ask volunteers to share their posters and responses. Have students do the **Quick Lab** to learn how to increase efficiency of energy use and conserve energy. Students can use the online **Vocab Flash Cards** to review key terms.

EVALUATE

Have students take the **Lesson Quiz.** For an alternate assessment, see the **EXAM**VIEW® Assessment Suite, Progress Monitoring Assessments, or SuccessTracker™.

ENGAGE AND EXPLORE

Teach this lesson using digital resources. Begin by having students explore different forms of insulation at **My Planet Diary** online. Have them access the Chapter Resources to find the **Unlock the Big Question activity.** There they can answer the questions and refine their responses as they continue through the lesson. You can re-assign the activity and have students submit their work so you can track their progress.

EXPLAIN AND ELABORATE

Students reading above, at, or below the lexile measure of this lesson can access basic content readings at their level at **My Reading Web. Support the Big Q** by discussing past, present, and future sources of energy. Do the **Quick Lab** to understand current human energy use and then ask students to share their results.

Assign the online **Real World Inquiry** to help students understand how they can conserve energy in their homes. Review *energy conservation* in relation to transportation before assigning the online **Apply It activity.** Ask volunteers to share their posters and have students submit their work to you. Have students do the **Quick Lab** about increasing efficiency of energy use and conserving energy. Then ask students to share their results. The **Key Concept Summaries** online allow students to read a summary and see an image associated with each part of the lesson. Online remediation is available at **My Science Coach.**

EVALUATE

Have students take the **Lesson Quiz.** For an alternate assessment, see the **EXAM**VIEW® Assessment Suite, Progress Monitoring Assessments, or SuccessTracker™.

2 Frontload the Lesson
Preview the lesson visuals, labels, and captions. Ask students what they know about the words *conservation* and *efficiency*. Explain the specific meanings these words have in science.

3 Comprehensible Input
Have students help make a chart about ways to conserve energy and to use energy more efficiently.

4 Language Production
Pair or group students with varied language abilities to complete labs collaboratively for language practice. Have each student copy the completed written lab for personal reference.

5 Assess Understanding
Divide the class into small groups. Have each student identify a key concept from the lesson to discuss in his or her group. After the discussions, have students talk about the key concepts as a group.

Energy Use and Conservation

Establish Learning Objectives

After this lesson, students will be able to:

🔑 Explain how human energy use has changed over time.

🔑 Name ways to ensure that there will be enough energy for the future.

Engage

Activate Prior Knowledge

MY PLANET DIARY Read *House of Straw* with the class. Invite students to think about whether they have ever seen bales of straw in fields or piled near a barn. Explain that straw is hollow stalks of wheat, rye, or other cereal plants, that are left after the grain has been threshed out. Ask: **What materials used for insulation are less natural and environmentally safe than straw?** *(Much insulation used in exterior walls is made of fiberglass.)*

BIG IDEAS OF SCIENCE REFERENCE LIBRARY 📖 Have students look up the following topics: Energy Conservation, Light Bulbs.

Explore

Lab Resource: Inquiry Warm-Up 🧪

L1 WHICH BULB IS MORE EFFICIENT? Students will compare the efficiency of incandescent and fluorescent light bulbs.

> **My Planet Diary** provides an opportunity for students to explore real-world connections to energy use and conservation.

my science ONLINE.com | Energy Use

---

3 Energy Use and Conservation

🔑 **How Has Energy Use Changed Over Time?**

🔑 **How Can We Ensure There Will Be Enough Energy for the Future?**

my planet diary

TECHNOLOGY

House of Straw

What was that first little pig thinking? Was he just lazy—building a house of straw as quickly as he could without much thought? Or was he helping the environment? It turns out that straw is one of the best materials for keeping warm air inside in cold weather and keeping hot air outside in hot weather. Builders place stacks of straw along the exterior walls of a building and then seal the straw with mud. Bales of straw are natural and cheap, since straw is left over after grain is harvested. It's no wonder that more and more people are using straw to insulate their homes!

Communicate Write your answers below.

1. How does using straw for insulation save energy?

Sample: People will use less energy to heat and cool their homes.

2. Why is using straw for insulation good for the environment?

Sample: Straw is cheap, and is a natural and renewable resource.

> **PLANET DIARY** Go to **Planet Diary** to learn more about energy use and conservation.

Lab zone Do the Inquiry Warm-Up *Which Bulb Is More Efficient?*

196 Energy Resources

SUPPORT ALL READERS

Lexile Measure = 910L   Lexile Word Count = 960

Prior Exposure to Content: May be the first time students have encountered this topic

Academic Vocabulary: *observe, identify*

Science Vocabulary: *efficiency, energy conservation, insulation*

Concept Level: Generally appropriate for most students in this grade

Preteach With: My Planet Diary "House of Straw" and Figure 1 activity

Go to **My Reading Web** to access leveled readings that provide a foundation for the content.

my science ONLINE.com

Vocabulary
- efficiency
- insulation
- energy conservation

Skills
- Reading: Identify the Main Idea
- Inquiry: Observe

How Has Energy Use Changed Over Time?

Energy, beyond using your own muscle power, is essential to the way most people live. The methods people use to obtain energy have changed, especially in the last 200 years. **For most of human history, people burned wood for energy. Only recently have fossil fuels become the main energy source.**

Eventually, people harnessed the power of other renewable resources. Ships used tall sails to capture wind energy. Flowing water turned wheels connected to stones that ground grain into flour.

Wood, wind, and water were also the main sources of energy in the United States until the nineteenth century. Coal gained in popularity as a fuel during the westward expansion of the railroads. Coal remained the dominant fuel until 1951, when it was replaced by oil and natural gas.

Today, scientists are continually looking for new and better fuels to meet the world's energy needs. As fossil fuel supplies continue to decrease, the interest in renewable energy sources has increased. With more focus on protecting the environment, scientists are working to meet our energy needs while reducing and eliminating many sources of pollution.

Identify the Main Idea
Energy use has changed over time. On the timeline, label and shade the periods in which coal and oil were the dominant fuel sources in the United States.

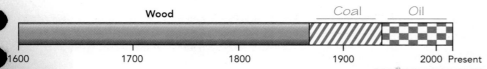

Wood | Coal | Oil

1600 — 1700 — 1800 — 1900 — 2000 — Present

Lab zone Do the Quick Lab *Human Energy Use.*

Assess Your Understanding

got it? ....

○ I get it! Now I know that human energy use has _changed over time from mostly wood burning to burning fossil fuels._

○ I need extra help with _See TE note._

Go to **MY SCIENCE COACH** online for help with this subject.

197

Explain

Introduce Vocabulary
Tell students that the word *efficient* means "bringing about a desired result with the least waste of time, effort, or materials." It is the adjective form of *efficiency.*

Teach Key Concepts
Explain to students that the last few centuries have brought dramatic changes to the way human beings create energy. Ask: **Until about 200 years ago, what did people do to create heat, light, and energy?** *(Burn wood, use energy from wind and water.)* **During the last two centuries, what has become the most common source of energy?** *(Fossil fuels)*

Support the Big Q (?) UbD
ENERGY SOURCES Have students look at the timeline. Ask: **What energy source do you think was used before 1600?** *(Wood)* Point out that wind and water were also used before 1600. Ask: **How will future energy sources likely be different from the sources shown on the timeline?** *(They will be renewable sources.)*

Identify the Main Idea Tell students that the main idea is the most important or biggest idea in a paragraph or section of text. The other information in the paragraph or section supports or further explains the main idea.

Elaborate

Lab Resource: Quick Lab
L2 HUMAN ENERGY USE Students will use a graph to analyze how energy and fuels were used during the second half of the 20th century.

Evaluate

Assess Your Understanding
Have students evaluate their understanding by completing the appropriate sentence.

RTI Response to Intervention
Provide additional exercises to reinforce this concept. **If** students have trouble describing changes in energy use, **then** have them locate and read the boldface Key Concept statement for this section.

L1 MY SCIENCE COACH Online remediation to assist students in understanding changes in human energy use.

Explain

Teach Key Concepts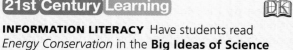

Explain to students that human beings will exhaust the supply of fossil fuels in the future. Ask: **What is the difference between *efficiency* and *conservation* as the terms relate to energy?** *(Sample: Energy conservation means cutting back on the amount of energy we use. Energy efficiency involves improving the percentage of energy used for work.)*

Teach With Visuals

Tell students to look at **Figure 2.** Ask: **What is wasteful about the use of energy in the bathroom, bedroom, and attic of the house?** *(Lights, television, and a computer are left on when not in use.)* **Where is energy being wasted in the kitchen?** *(The refrigerator door has been left open.)*

⚠ **Observe** When students use one or more of their five senses to gather information about the world, they are observing. Point out that an observation should be an accurate report of what the senses detect.

21st Century Learning

INFORMATION LITERACY Have students read *Energy Conservation* in the **Big Ideas of Science Reference Library.** Ask students to evaluate scientific claims by reading literature on compact fluorescent light bulbs and comparing a company's claim to information featured on either a government or academic website. Have them share their findings with a partner and submit a consumer alert report.

How Can We Ensure There Will Be Enough Energy for the Future?

What would happen if the world ran out of fossil fuels today? The heating and cooling systems in most buildings would stop functioning. Forests would disappear as people began to burn wood for heating and cooking. Cars, buses, and trains would be stranded wherever they ran out of fuel. About 70 percent of the world's electric power would disappear. Since televisions, computers, and telephones depend on electricity, communication would be greatly reduced. Lights and most home appliances would no longer work.

Although fossil fuels won't run out immediately, they also won't last forever. Most people think that it makes sense to use fuels more wisely now to avoid fuel shortages in the future. **One way to preserve our current energy resources is to increase the efficiency of our energy use. Another way is to conserve energy whenever possible.** Refer to **Figure 1.**

FIGURE 1 ·····················
▶ REAL-WORLD INQUIRY **Wasting Energy**
Many things, such as lights and appliances, use energy. If people do not use these things properly, energy can be wasted.
◗ **Observe** Circle everything in this scene that is wasting energy.

198 Energy Resources

Teacher to Teacher
Professional Development Note

Energy Resources To give historical context to human energy use, I have groups of students research the way(s) people have used energy resources. Early humans used wood to make fires for warmth. During the Renaissance, people learned to use windmills. Modern people use fossil fuels as well as solar, geothermal, tidal, nuclear, and biomass fuel sources. As we discuss natural, renewable, and nonrenewable resources, we further integrate our unit by having students identify civilizations that thrived because of their judicious use of energy resources.

✎ *Leslie Pohley*
Largo Middle School
Largo, Florida

Energy Efficiency One way to make energy resources last longer is to use fuels more efficiently. **Efficiency** is the percentage of energy that is actually used to perform work. The rest of the energy is "lost" to the surroundings, usually as heat. People have developed many ways to increase energy efficiency.

Heating and Cooling One method of increasing the efficiency of heating and cooling systems is insulation. **Insulation** is a layer of material that traps air. This helps block the transfer of heat between the air inside and outside a building. You have probably seen insulation made of fiberglass. It looks like pink cotton candy. A layer of fiberglass 15 centimeters thick insulates a room as well as a brick wall 2 meters thick!

Trapped air can act as insulation in windows too. Many windows consist of two panes of glass with space in between them. The air between the panes of glass acts as insulation.

Lighting Much of the electricity used for home lighting is wasted. For example, less than 10 percent of the electricity that an incandescent light bulb uses is converted into light. The rest is given off as heat. In contrast, compact fluorescent bulbs use about one fourth as much energy to provide the same amount of light.

FIGURE 2 ....
Solutions to Wasting Energy
There are many ways to save energy in a home.
✎ **Explain** Pick at least three of the things you circled in the scene and explain what people could do to stop wasting energy.

Ways to Conserve Energy

Sample: Wear warmer clothes instead of turning up the heat, turn lights off when you leave the room, and don't leave cars running idle.

199

Lead a Discussion

EFFICIENT USE OF ENERGY Remind students that when we say we are increasing the energy efficiency of a device that consumes energy, we mean that we are increasing the percentage of consumed energy the device uses to do work and decreasing the percentage of consumed energy that is lost to the surroundings. Explain that energy efficiency can be improved in many areas of our lives. Draw a chart on the board that will show types of energy use and ways to increase efficiency. Fill it in as students discuss. Ask: **What is the most common way to improve efficiency of heating and cooling?** *(Adding fiberglass insulation or a layer of air)*

Elaborate

21st Century Learning

ACCOUNTABILITY Look over **Figure 2** with students, noting various details of energy loss in a group discussion. Then ask students to reflect on their own bedroom and their own home in order to make a generalization about how they and their families can better conserve energy. *(Sample: My family and I can better conserve energy by paying more attention to turning off lights and other electrical devices when they are not in use.)*

Real-World Inquiry allows students to explore energy conservation in and around a typical home.

my science online · Energy Conservation

Differentiated Instruction

L1 Identify Energy Efficiency Pair students having difficulty with those who have a clear concept of energy efficiency. Have each pair of students compile a list of ways to individually improve energy efficiency on a daily basis.

L3 The National Appliance Energy Conservation Act Challenge students to find out about the National Appliance Energy Conservation Act, which sets energy-efficiency standards for appliances. As a result of this law, refrigerators built today use at least 80 percent less energy than those built in the 1980s.

Explain

Lead a Discussion

EFFICIENT USE OF ENERGY Continue filling in your chart by discussing energy use for transportation. Ask: **What are some ways that energy efficiency can be improved in transportation?** *(Transportation—better engines and tires, public transportation, carpooling; lighting—using compact fluorescent bulbs)* **How can you personally improve energy efficiency?** *(Take the bus or carpool, check on lighting and heating/cooling at home)* Remind students that the efforts of any one person to conserve energy always make a difference. Invite volunteers to share ways their families save energy at home.

Point out to students what the differences are between the different types of energy efficient vehicles on the market. Electric Vehicles (EVs) operate using an electric motor and rechargeable batteries. Plugging the batteries into an electrical outlet or other electrical source, such as a solar panel, can recharge them. Hybrid-Electric Vehicles (HEVs) combine the small combustion engine of a traditional vehicle with the electric motor and battery of an EV. Plug-in Hybrid-Electric Vehicles (PHEVs) are similar to the HEV, but use much larger batteries. The batteries in a PHEV have a longer all-electric range and can also be recharged by plugging them into an external power source.

Elaborate

Build Inquiry

L2 INTERPRET ILLUSTRATIONS

Materials For each group of students, photocopies of four pictures of energy use taken from newspapers or magazines, markers

Time 15 minutes

Review with students the types of objects and activities that function because of the burning of fossil fuels. Then ask them to use markers to identify particular examples of dramatic energy use and of energy loss in the photographs. Then have the students classify these examples into categories, such as heating and transportation, heating and cooling, lighting, and recreation.

Ask: **Why is it important for each individual to conserve energy and to increase energy efficiency?** *(Sample: If each individual conserves energy and increases energy efficiency in his or her own life, it will dramatically improve the energy situation for the entire planet.)*

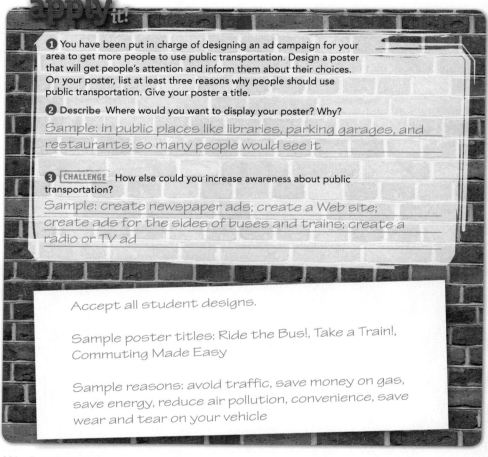

Transportation Engineers have improved the energy efficiency of cars by designing better engines and batteries. For instance, many new cars use high-efficiency hybrid engines that go twice as far on a tank of fuel than other cars. Buses in some cities are now entirely electric, running on high-power rechargeable batteries. New kinds of batteries allow some electric cars to drive hundreds of kilometers before recharging.

Another way to save energy is to reduce the number of cars on the road. In many communities, public transit systems provide an alternative to driving. Other cities encourage carpooling and bicycling. Many cities now set aside lanes for cars containing two or more people.

apply it!

❶ You have been put in charge of designing an ad campaign for your area to get more people to use public transportation. Design a poster that will get people's attention and inform them about their choices. On your poster, list at least three reasons why people should use public transportation. Give your poster a title.

❷ **Describe** Where would you want to display your poster? Why?

Sample: in public places like libraries, parking garages, and restaurants; so many people would see it

❸ **CHALLENGE** How else could you increase awareness about public transportation?

Sample: create newspaper ads; create a Web site; create ads for the sides of buses and trains; create a radio or TV ad

Accept all student designs.

Sample poster titles: Ride the Bus!, Take a Train!, Commuting Made Easy

Sample reasons: avoid traffic, save money on gas, save energy, reduce air pollution, convenience, save wear and tear on your vehicle

Digital Lesson: Assign the *Apply It* activity online and have students submit their work to you.

MY SCIENCE ONLINE.com   **Energy Conservation**

Energy Conservation Another approach to making energy resources last longer is conservation. **Energy conservation** means reducing energy use.

You can reduce your personal energy use by changing your behavior in some simple ways. For example, if you walk to the store instead of getting a ride, you are conserving the gasoline it would take to drive to the store.

While these suggestions seem like small things, multiplied by millions of people they add up to a lot of energy saved for the future.

> Sample: I could walk or ride my bike on short trips, recycle, use fans instead of air conditioners, and turn off lights and the television when I leave a room.

FIGURE 3 ....

Energy Conservation in Your Everyday Life
Even students like you can conserve energy.
✏️ **Communicate** With a partner, think of ways you can conserve energy in your daily life. Write your answers in the notebook.

 Do the Quick Lab
Future Energy Use.

🔑 **Assess Your Understanding**

1a. Define What does it mean to say that something is "energy efficient"?

Sample: It means that when compared to other products, more energy is used to perform work and is not lost to heat.

b. Solve Problems What are some strategies a city could use to increase energy conservation?

Sample: Invest in good public transportation and encourage energy-efficient building development.

got it? ....

○ **I get it!** Now I know that ensuring that the future has enough energy requires *increasing energy efficiency and conserving energy whenever possible.*

○ **I need extra help with** *See TE note.*

Go to MY SCIENCE 💬 **COACH** *online for help with this subject.*

201

Apply It!
L1 Review the sections of text that discuss transportation and energy conservation before beginning the activity. Ask students to think about who the audience is for a poster like this one.

Lab Resource: Quick Lab 🔬
L2 **FUTURE ENERGY USE** Students will investigate the efficiency of their school's use of energy to heat and cool the classroom.

Evaluate ————————
Assess Your Understanding
After students answer the question, have them evaluate their understanding by completing the appropriate sentence.

🟥🟥🟥 Response to Intervention
1a. If students need help defining *energy efficient*, **then** have them reread the first paragraph under the red head *Energy Efficiency*.

b. If students have trouble identifying ways to increase energy conservation, **then** have them review the information about energy conservation on this page.

MY SCIENCE 💬 **COACH** Have students go online for help in understanding what is needed to ensure that the future has enough energy.

Differentiated Instruction

L1 **Illustrate How Insulation Works** Have each student draw and label a diagram to explain how insulation conserves energy. Encourage students to indicate a context for the insulation, such as the walls of a house or a layer in a winter jacket.

L3 **Timeline of Automotive Efficiency** Challenge students to do research to create a timeline showing changes in gas mileage in motor vehicles from 1970 until the present. Encourage students to annotate their timelines with historical context, such as the OPEC oil embargo of the mid 1970s.

Name _____ Date _____ Class _____

Energy Use and Conservation

> **Inquiry Warm-Up, *Which Bulb Is More Efficient?***
> In the Inquiry Warm-Up, you investigated differences in efficiency between incandescent and fluorescent light bulbs. Using what you learned from that activity, answer the questions below.

1. **CALCULATE** You use only incandescent bulbs in your home, and your electric bill is $200. About how much will your bill be if you switch and use only fluorescent light bulbs? Base your answer on your response to question 2 in the Inquiry Warm-Up. Use the space below for your work if necessary.

   _____

2. **INFER** Which type of light bulb is best to use in an aquarium with fish that are very sensitive to high temperatures? Explain.

   _____

   _____

3. **DRAW CONCLUSIONS** Which light bulb, a 40-watt fluorescent or a 40-watt incandescent, uses less energy? Which uses more energy? Explain.

   _____

   _____

   _____

4. **PREDICT** Of the two 40-watt light bulbs in question 3 above, which would be brighter? Explain.

   _____

   _____

   _____

Place the outside corner, the corner away from the dotted line, in the corner of your copy machine to copy onto letter-size paper.

Name _____ Date _____ Class _____

Energy Use and Conservation

> **How Has Energy Use Changed Over Time?**

got₁ₜ?··

○ **I get it!** Now I know that human energy use has _____

_____

○ **I need extra help with** _____

_____

> **How Can We Ensure There Will Be Enough Energy for the Future?**

1a. **DEFINE** What does it mean to say that something is "energy efficient"? _____

_____

_____

b. **SOLVE PROBLEMS** What are some strategies a city could use to increase energy conservation? _____

_____

_____

got₁ₜ?··

○ **I get it!** Now I know that ensuring that the future has enough energy requires _____

_____

○ **I need extra help with** _____

_____

Energy Use and Conservation

How Has Energy Use Changed Over Time?

For most of human history, people burned wood for light, heat, and energy. Only recently have fossil fuels become the main energy source. For 200 years, wood, wind, and water were the main sources of energy in the American colonies that became the United States. Ships used sails to capture wind energy, and mills used flowing water to turn wheels and grind grain into flour. Then, in the nineteenth century, coal gained in popularity with the westward expansion of the railroads. Coal remained the dominant fuel until 1951, when it was replaced by oil and natural gas. As fossil fuel supplies decrease, interest in renewable energy sources has increased.

How Can We Ensure There Will Be Enough Energy for the Future?

If the world ran out of fossil fuels suddenly, most heating and cooling systems would stop functioning. Cars, buses, and trains would be useless. And because about 70 percent of the world's electric power would disappear, lights and most home appliances would no longer work. Communications—through televisions, computers, and telephones—would also be greatly reduced.

People have begun to take steps to try to use fuels more wisely as scientists seek new and better fuels. **One way to preserve our current energy resources is to increase the efficiency of our energy use. Another way is to conserve energy whenever possible.** One way to make energy resources last longer is to use fuels more efficiently. **Efficiency** is the percentage of energy that is actually used to perform work. The rest of the energy is "lost" to the surroundings, usually as heat. **Insulation,** a layer of material that traps air, is used to increase the efficiency of heating and cooling systems. Compact fluorescent light bulbs provide the same amount of light as incandescent bulbs but use about one fourth as much energy. Energy can be saved by reducing the number of motor vehicles on the road and the number of miles people drive, and by designing better engines and tires. Another way to make energy resources last longer is conservation. **Energy conservation** means reducing energy use.

Is interest in renewable resources new to the United States? Write and explain your answer on a separate sheet of paper.

Energy Use and Conservation

Understanding Main Ideas

Answer the following questions in the spaces provided.

1. Until the nineteenth century, what were the three main sources of energy in the United States?

   _____

2. In the last two hundred years, what fuels have people used most?

   _____

3. Why are scientists looking for new fuels to replace fossil fuels?

   _____

   _____

4. What is energy efficiency, and why is increasing it important?

   _____

   _____

5. Why is a compact fluorescent light bulb more efficient than an incandescent bulb?

   _____

   _____

6. How can insulation in a building save energy?

   _____

   _____

Building Vocabulary

Fill in the blank to complete each statement.

7. _____ is the percentage of energy used to perform work.

8. A layer of material that traps air is _____.

9. Energy _____ means reducing energy use.

Enrich

Energy Use and Conservation

For a school project, Arturo Diaz wants to find out how much energy his family's home uses in a month. Their furnace uses oil. Their water heater and stove use natural gas. The table shows the data that Arturo collected for the month. Complete the table. On a separate sheet of paper, answer the questions that follow the table.

One Family's Household Energy Use

Energy Use Data

Energy Source	Meter/Gauge Readings		Difference in Readings
	Sept. 15	Oct. 15	
Electricity	76, 854 kWh	77,638 kWh	1.
Natural Gas	14, 786 ft³	15,073 ft³	2.
Fuel Oil	full tank (200 gal.)	3/4 tank (150 gal.)	3.

4. How many BTUs of electricity did the Diaz family use? (1 kWh = 3,413 BTUs)

5. How many BTUs of natural gas did the Diaz family use? (1 ft³ of gas produces 100 BTUs)

6. How many BTUs of fuel oil did the Diaz family use? (1 gallon of oil produces 144,000 BTUs)

7. What was the Diaz family's total energy use for the month from these three sources?

8. Calculate the percentage of each energy use.

9. Draw and label a circle graph to show the percentage of each energy use. (*Hint:* Divide the BTUs for each use by the total BTUs. Multiply each percentage by 360° to determine the arc of each wedge.)

Lesson Quiz

Energy Use and Conservation

Fill in the blank(s) to complete each statement.

1. Only recently have _____ become the main energy source in the U.S.

2. In the nineteenth century, with the westward expansion of railroads, _____ gained in popularity as a fuel.

3. One way to preserve our current energy resources is to increase the _____ of our energy use.

4. Another way to preserve those resources is to _____ energy whenever possible.

If the statement is true, write *true*. If the statement is false, change the underlined word or words to make the statement true.

5. _____ For most of human history, people <u>burned wood</u> for light, heat, and energy.

6. _____ In addition, people harnessed the power of renewable resources such as <u>wind and water</u>.

7. _____ In the mid-twentieth century, <u>wood and water</u> joined coal as the dominant fuels.

8. _____ As fossil fuel supplies decrease, interest has increased in looking for <u>nonrenewable</u> energy sources.

9. _____ <u>Insulation</u> is the percentage of energy that is actually used to perform work.

10. _____ <u>Energy conservation</u> means reducing energy use.

Energy Use and Conservation

Answer Key

After the Inquiry Warm-Up

1. about $50

2. A fluorescent light bulb is better to use because it gives off less heat for about the same amount of light.

3. Sample: They use the same amount of energy. The amount of energy used by a light bulb is expressed by its wattage. Since both bulbs have the same wattage, they use the same amount of energy.

4. The fluorescent bulb will be brighter because it is more efficient, giving off less energy as heat, than the incandescent light bulb.

Key Concept Summaries

For most of human history, people used renewable resources—wood, water, and wind—for light, heat, and energy. The use of fossil fuels has dominated people's energy use for the last two centuries. Today, people are growing interested again in renewable resources, since fossil fuel supplies are decreasing.

Review and Reinforce

1. wood, wind, and water

2. coal, oil, and natural gas

3. Fossil fuels are not renewable. Supplies are decreasing and will run out some day. Fossil fuels are also a major cause of pollution.

4. Energy efficiency is the percentage of energy that is used to perform work. Increasing energy efficiency is important because people and devices can use less energy to perform the same amount of work.

5. Compact fluorescent light bulbs use about one fourth as much energy to produce the same amount of light as an incandescent bulb.

6. Insulation helps block the transfer of heat between the air inside and outside a building. It saves energy by keeping the building cool in summer and warm in the winter.

7. Efficiency

8. insulation

9. conservation

Enrich

1. 784 kWh

2. 28,700 ft³

3. 50 gal

4. 2,675,792

5. 28,700,000

6. 7,200,000

7. 38,575,792

8. Natural gas, 74%; fuel oil, 19%; electricity, 7%.

9. Based on the percentages, wedge sizes are 266° for natural gas, 86° for fuel oil, and 25° for electricity—for a total of 359°. Sizes must be adjusted to total 360°.

Lesson Quiz

1. fossil fuels

2. coal

3. efficiency

4. conserve

5. true

6. true

7. oil and natural gas

8. renewable

9. Efficiency

10. true

Place the outside corner, the corner away from the dotted line, in the corner of your copy machine to copy onto letter-size paper.

Study Guide

Review the Big Q UbD

Have students complete the statement at the top of the page. These Key Concepts support their understanding of the chapter's Big Question. Have them return to the chapter opener pages. What is different about how students view the image of the wind turbine now that they have completed the chapter? Thinking about this will help them prepare for the *Apply the Big Q* activity in the Review and Assessment.

Partner Review

Have students review definitions of vocabulary terms by using the Study Guide to quiz each other. Students can read the Key Concept statements and leave out words for their partner to fill in, or change a statement so that it is false and then ask their partner to correct it.

Class Activity: Concept Map

Have students work in three groups to develop concept maps to show how the information in this chapter is related. Each group can focus on one lesson, brainstorming to identify Key Concepts, vocabulary, and examples and other details. Encourage each group to create its map on chart or poster paper using sticky notes. Explain that each concept map should begin at the top with Key Concepts. After each group has finished its work, bring the groups together to analyze how the maps relate to one another. Ask students to use the following questions to help them organize the information on their sticky notes:

- What are the three major fossil fuels?
- What is a nonrenewable resource?
- What are some renewable sources of energy?
- What have human beings used as fuel sources during the course of history?
- What steps can human beings take to preserve current energy resources?

My Science Coach allows students to complete the *Practice Test* online.

The Big Question allows students to complete the *Apply the Big Q* activity about what some of Earth's energy sources are.

Vocab Flash Cards offer a way to review the chapter vocabulary words.

my science online.com Energy Resources

CHAPTER
5 Study Guide

REVIEW THE BIG ?

Earth has many energy sources, including <u>fossil fuels</u> such as coal; the sun, which can be used for <u>solar energy</u>; and flowing water, which can be used for hydroelectric power.

LESSON 1 Fossil Fuels

🔑 The three major fossil fuels are coal, oil, and natural gas.

🔑 Since fossil fuels take hundreds of millions of years to form, they are considered nonrenewable resources.

Vocabulary
- fuel • fossil fuel
- hydrocarbon
- petroleum • refinery
- petrochemical

LESSON 2 Renewable Sources of Energy

🔑 Renewable sources of energy include sunlight, water, wind, nuclear power, biomass fuels, geothermal energy, and hydrogen.

🔑 In a nuclear power plant, the heat released from fission reactions is used to change water into steam. The steam then turns the blades of a turbine to generate electricity.

Vocabulary
- solar energy • hydroelectric power • biomass fuel • gasohol
- geothermal energy • nuclear fission
- reactor vessel • fuel rod • control rod

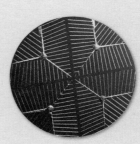

LESSON 3 Energy Use and Conservation

🔑 For most of human history, the main fuel source was wood. Only recently have fossil fuels become the main energy source.

🔑 One way to preserve our current energy resources is to increase the efficiency of our energy use. Another way is to conserve energy whenever possible.

Vocabulary
- efficiency • insulation • energy conservation

(E L L) Support

4 Language Production

Divide the class into small groups to create a poster or flyer promoting energy conservation at home and in school. Students should work together to create visually-engaging posters that persuade students to take a more active role in conserving energy.

Beginning

LOW/HIGH Allow students to work on the visuals for the posters.

Intermediate

LOW/HIGH Permit students to refer to their books or notes during the discussion.

Advanced

LOW/HIGH Have students write the text and captions for the poster.

Review and Assessment

LESSON 1 Fossil Fuels

1. What is one similarity among oil, coal, and natural gas?

a. They are all petrochemicals.

b. They all must be processed in a refinery.

c. They are all gases at room temperature.

d. They are all formed from the remains of dead organisms.

2. Fossil fuels take hundreds of millions of years to form, and therefore are considered _nonrenewable_ energy sources.

3. Compare and Contrast Describe one main use for each fuel: coal, oil, and natural gas.

Sample: Coal can be used to produce electricity, oil can power vehicles, natural gas can be used in stoves.

4. Sequence How does coal form?

Sample: Coal forms from decomposing plant matter. Over time, the plant matter turns into peat under pressure. With more time and pressure, the peat becomes coal.

5. Write About It Imagine a day without fossil fuels. Describe your day, from when you wake up until when you eat lunch. Identify each time you would have used energy from fossil fuels.

See TE rubric.

LESSON 2 Renewable Sources of Energy

6. Which of the following is not a biomass fuel?

a. gasohol

b. methane from landfills

c. hydrogen

d. sugar cane wastes

7. Running water can be used as an energy source to produce _hydroelectric_ power.

8. Apply Concepts Fill in the boxes with two benefits and two costs of hydrogen power.

Benefits	Costs
Sample: exists in large supply; does not cause smog	_Sample: requires a lot of energy; expensive to produce_

9. Interpret Photos Explain how a nuclear power plant, like the one pictured below, produces energy.

Sample: Nuclear fission reactions generate heat. The heat turns water into steam. The steam turns turbines that generate electricity.

203

Review and Assessment

Assess Understanding

Have students complete the answers to the Review and Assessment questions. Have a class discussion about what students find confusing. Write Key Concepts on the board to reinforce knowledge.

RTI Response to Intervention

1. If students need help explaining fossil fuels, **then** have them use their knowledge of the word *fossil* to remember that fossil fuels are formed from the decomposing matter of once-living organisms.

9. If students cannot explain how a power plant produces energy, **then** have them review **Figure 7.**

Alternate Assessment

L1 DESIGN FOR THE FUTURE Have students use a pencil, drawing paper, and a ruler as they design a home or a car of the future that operates entirely on renewable energy sources. Students should apply the concepts they have learned about the types of renewable energy sources that exist, the technology required to make practical use of those sources, and the sources' advantages over fossil fuels.

CHAPTER 5

Write About It	Assess student's writing using this rubric.			
SCORING RUBRIC	**SCORE 4**	**SCORE 3**	**SCORE 2**	**SCORE 1**
Describe day from waking to lunch	Student describes day from waking to lunch in vivid detail.	Student describes day from waking to lunch without much detail.	Student describes part of time between waking to lunch.	Student does not describe a day from waking to lunch.
Identify each time writer would have used fossil fuels	Student identifies every time he or she would have used fossil fuels.	Student identifies many times he or she would have used fossil fuels.	Student identifies a few times he or she would have used fossil fuels.	Student does not identify times he or she would have used fossil fuels.

RTI Response to Intervention

12. If students have trouble drawing a conclusion, **then** have them review the timeline.

Apply the Big Q UbD

TRANSFER Students should be able to demonstrate understanding of Earth's energy sources by answering this question. See the scoring rubric below.

Connect to the Big Idea ⑦ UbD

BIG IDEA Living things interact with their environment.

Send students back to the Big Ideas of Science at the beginning of their student edition. Have them read what they wrote about interactions of living things and their environment before they started the chapter. Lead a class discussion about how their thoughts have changed. If all chapters have been completed, have students fill in the bottom section for the Big Idea.

L3 **WRITING IN SCIENCE** Ask students to write a blog entry about how this chapter's Big Question relates to the Big idea.

CHAPTER
5 Review and Assessment

LESSON 3 Energy Use and Conservation

10. What is efficiency?

- **a.** the percentage of energy that is lost to the environment as heat
- **(b.)** the percentage of energy that is used to perform work
- **c.** the percentage of energy that is conserved when work is done
- **d.** the percentage of energy that is wasted when electronics are left on

11. <u>Energy conservation</u>

involves using less energy, helping energy resources last longer.

12. Draw Conclusions How is energy use today different from energy use 200 years ago?
<u>Sample: Two hundred years ago, people mainly used wood to power their lives. Today, most energy comes from burning fossil fuels.</u>

13. Solve Problems Describe three actions a person can take to conserve energy.
<u>Sample: walk or bike instead of using a car, wear warmer clothing instead of turning up the heat, turn lights off when leaving a room</u>

 What are some of Earth's energy sources?

14. Earth's energy sources include both renewable and nonrenewable resources. Name at least three sources of energy that could be used in a classroom like the one below. Then describe the ideal energy source for generating most of your school's electricity and explain why you chose this source.

<u>Sample: Solar energy could be used to power the calculators. Natural gas or oil could be used to heat the building. Some of the electricity could be generated by wind power. I think wind power is an ideal source of energy for my school because it does not cause air pollution and I live in a windy area. See TE rubric.</u>

---

⑦ What are some of Earth's energy sources?
Assess student's response using this rubric.

SCORING RUBRIC	SCORE 4	SCORE 3	SCORE 2	SCORE 1
Name three sources of energy	Student names more than three sources of energy.	Student names three sources of energy.	Student names one or two sources of energy.	Student does not name sources of energy.
Describe ideal energy source and explain choice	Describes ideal energy source in detail with thorough explanation	Describes ideal energy source in some detail with brief explanation	Describes ideal energy source with incomplete explanation	Does not describe source and gives no explanation

Standardized Test Prep

Multiple Choice

Circle the letter of the best answer.

1. Which statement is best supported by the table below?

2007 Global Oil Production and Use		
Country	Oil production global rank	Oil use global rank
United States	3	1
Russia	1	6
China	5	3
Brazil	15	8

  A   Brazil produces more oil than China.
  Ⓑ   Saudi Arabia produces the most oil.
  C   China consumes the most oil.
  D   The United States consumes and produces the most oil in the world.

2. Which of the following is not a fossil fuel?

  A   oil
  B   coal
  C   natural gas
  Ⓓ   wood

3. The interior of a car heats up on a sunny day because of

  A   solar cells.
  B   active solar heating.
  Ⓒ   passive solar heating.
  D   direct solar heating.

4. How does increasing the efficiency of energy use help preserve energy resources?

  A   by increasing the energy resources available
  B   by doing less work while giving off more heat
  Ⓒ   by using less energy to do the same amount of work
  D   by increasing the amount of energy needed to generate electricity

5. How does a nuclear power plant produce energy?

  A   with solar panels
  Ⓑ   through nuclear fission reactions
  C   with geothermal heat
  D   through nuclear meltdown reactions

Constructed Response

Use the diagram below and your knowledge of science to help you answer Question 6. Write your answer on a separate sheet of paper.

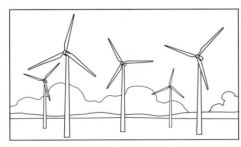

6. Describe how energy is produced in the diagram above. Then, describe one advantage and one disadvantage of this source.
   See TE note.

Standardized Test Prep

Test-Taking Skills

INTERPRETING TABLES Tell students that when they answer questions like Question 1, which include tables, they should read all parts of the table carefully, including the title, the labels of vertical columns and horizontal rows, and the numbers. Point out that students should clarify the table's information in their own minds before reviewing how the table relates to the question as a whole.

Constructed Response

6. Wind turns the blades of the turbine. The turbine is connected to a generator. As the turbine turns, the generator creates electricity. Wind energy does not create air pollution like burning fossil fuels such as oil or coal. Wind turbines are loud, and some people may think they are unattractive on the landscape. They can also interrupt bird migrations.

Additional Assessment Resources

Chapter Test
EXAMVIEW® Assessment Suite
Performance Assessment
Progress Monitoring Assessments
SuccessTracker™

ⒺⓁⓁ Support

5 Assess Understanding
Have ELLs complete the Alternate Assessment. Provide guidelines on the information it must cover, and a rubric for assessment.

Beginning
LOW/HIGH Provide students with extra time to complete their designs.

Intermediate
LOW/HIGH Allow students to refer to their books or notes when completing their designs.

Advanced
LOW/HIGH Have students use vocabulary terms from the lesson to write captions for their designs.

Remediate If students have trouble with...		
QUESTION	SEE LESSON	STANDARDS
1	3	
2	1	
3	2	
4	3	
5	2	
6	2	

Science Matters

Think Like a Scientist

Have students read *How Low Is Low-Impact?*
Point out that technologies that are genuinely
low-impact generally collect energy from natural
renewable resources. For example, hydroelectric
dams harness the power of running rivers and turn
it into electricity. There is some initial impact on the
environment associated with the dam's construction,
but this is usually quickly offset by the amount of
energy produced by the dam.

Hybrid cars are an example of a product that claims
to be low-impact. They run primarily on electricity,
which means they do not rely on fossil fuels to power
them and do not produce pollution by burning those
fossil fuels. However the electricity used to power
these cars is often generated by burning coal or oil.
A truly low-impact mode of transportation that can
be used by everyone has not been invented yet, so
hybrid cars are a good step in the right direction,
since they generally use less fossil fuels.

As students discuss the costs and benefits of low-
impact technologies, suggest they make a two-
column list to organize their arguments for and
against. Remind them that time and money could
be considered costs of these technologies. If a
technology takes a long time to invent or is too
expensive for most people to use, it makes it less
viable.

Ask: **What are some examples of truly low-
impact technologies?** *(Sample: solar power,
wind power, hydroelectric power)* **What makes
a technology truly low-impact?** *(It provides
energy without having a harmful impact on the
environment.)*

SCIENCE MATTERS

Think Like a Scientist

How Low Is Low-Impact?

▲ This electric car is charged
by attaching an electric
cord to an outlet. However,
the source of the electricity
may be a fossil fuel-based
power plant.

Hybrid engines, windmills, low-impact this,
alternative-energy that—everywhere you look,
people are trying to find ways to create energy by
using renewable resources. Sometimes, a technology
seems to conserve energy, but in reality it has hidden
costs. For example, electric cars do not release air
pollutants during use, but the method that is used
to generate the electricity for the car may cause
pollution. Is the electricity really "clean"?

Evaluating the costs and benefits of different
technologies is an important scientific skill. Use
the following questions to sharpen your decision-
making skills.

What is the source? What materials are used to
create or power the technology? How are they
obtained?

What are the products? What is produced when
the technology is created or used? How do these
products affect the environment? How are these
products stored, recycled, or disposed of?

How does it affect our lives? Does using a
technology encourage people to use more energy?
If it does, do the benefits of the technology
outweigh the environmental costs?

Every technology has costs and benefits. However, it
is important to be able to evaluate new technologies
to find out if the benefits outweigh the costs!

Write About It In a group, discuss the questions
listed above. Can you think of ways to add to them
or to change them? Then, create an Environmental
Decision-Making Guide and use it to evaluate two of
the energy technologies described in this chapter.

206 Energy Resources

Quick Facts

You've probably seen a farm where crops are grown. You've probably seen
a farm where animals are raised. But have you seen a farm where wind is
farmed and energy is the result? On the land of a wind farm there are tall
fan-like structures called wind turbines. The wind turns the blades of these
turbines and the energy collected is sent to a generator to be converted to
electricity. Wind is a completely clean source of energy that doesn't pollute.
Wind is also a renewable resource. However, winds are not always reliable,
wind energy cannot be stored, and often wind farms are in rural areas far from
the cities that require the electricity. Scientists are hard at work to improve the
efficiency and use of wind power. Have students research where the closest
wind farm is and how their area might benefit from its energy.

Life on an Oil Rig

OFFSHORE PETROLEUM ENGINEER

This professional's office is on a huge steel platform that is half the area of a football field, surrounded by water. With much of Earth's oil located under the ocean floor, petroleum engineers must go where the oil is. Many of them work on offshore oil rigs—large drilling platforms that extract oil from under the ocean floor.

Conditions far out in the the ocean can be harsh or dangerous. Large equipment, fires, and even hurricanes threaten workers' safety. However, far out in the ocean, workers on oil rigs can see sharks, manta rays, and other marine life.

Petroleum engineers study geology, physics, and chemistry to understand the properties of rock formations that contain oil. They use high-tech remote sensing equipment to find oil and computer modeling software to figure out how to get the oil out of the ocean's floor.

Write About It Find out more about life on an offshore oil rig. Then, write a diary or blog entry that describes a week in the life of an offshore petroleum engineer.

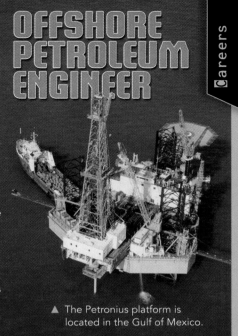

▲ The Petronius platform is located in the Gulf of Mexico.

Hydrokinetic Energy

Whirlpool! Maelstrom! Vortex! Do these words make you think of a rushing spiral of water, sucking fish and boats into its center? Not all vortexes sink ships. Fish and whales cause little vortexes when they swim. As the animals move, they create turbulence in the water. Turbulent water moves away from the animal and gives it a little push.

An engineer named Michael Bernitsas has developed a device that uses this effect to generate electricity. As currents push water around a cylindrical device, a vortex forms. As the vortex moves away from the device, the cylinder moves up and down. The device then converts that mechanical energy into electrical energy. Bernitsas has even improved the device by adding mechanical "fish tails" to the generators! Bernitsas is still testing his system, but he hopes that it can someday be used to help meet society's needs for a renewable source of energy.

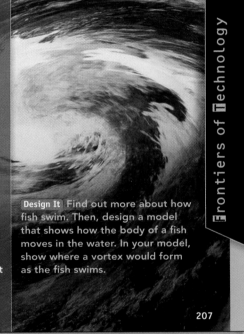

Design It Find out more about how fish swim. Then, design a model that shows how the body of a fish moves in the water. In your model, show where a vortex would form as the fish swims.

207

Careers

Have students read *Offshore Petroleum Engineer.* Point out that because most of Earth's surface is covered by water, it makes sense that a lot of its oil would be beneath the ocean floor. Oil rig workers work out at sea for months.

Petroleum engineers are responsible for finding safe and environmentally responsible ways to extract the oil from the sea floor. As students work on their diary or blog entries, have them think about what fields of science they might need to think about.

Ask: **What are some factors that might make drilling for oil at sea different than on land?** *(Sample: the movement of the ocean, the water pressure)* **Why do petroleum engineers use remote equipment to study the sea floor?** *(The sea floor is a great distance below the surface in some places and they cannot study it in person.)*

Frontiers of Technology

Have students read *Hydrokinetic Energy.* Explain that turbulence in the water is much like turbulence in the air. Turbulent air pushes on the object moving through it. Ask students if they have ever been on an airplane that experienced turbulence.

When an object sinks into the water, a vortex is created around it. The power of this vortex can draw other things down into the water. That is why rescue or salvage boats must be careful when working near a boat that is sinking.

Ask: **Aside from an object moving through the water, what is another cause of vortexes?** *(Sample: weather phenomenons can cause vortexes to form.)* **How do you think the addition of fish tails help the cylindrical device developed by Bernitsas?** *(Sample: There are more moving parts so there are more places for vortexes to form.)*

A

abiotic factor A nonliving part of an organism's habitat. (6)
factor abiótico La parte sin vida del hábitat de un organismo.

acid rain Rain or another form of precipitation that is more acidic than normal, caused by the release of molecules of sulfur dioxide and nitrogen oxide into the air. (145)
lluvia ácida Lluvia u otra forma de precipitación que es más ácida de lo normal, debido a la contaminación del aire con moléculas de dióxido de azufre y óxido de nitrógeno.

adaptation An inherited behavior or physical characteristic that helps an organism survive and reproduce in its environment. (19)
adaptación Comportamiento o característica física hereditaria que le permite a un organismo sobrevivir y reproducirse en su ambiente.

aquaculture The practice of raising fish and other water-dwelling organisms for food. (107)
acuicultura Técnica del cultivo de peces y otros organismos acuáticos para consumo humano.

B

bedrock Rock that makes up Earth's crust; also the solid rock layer beneath the soil. (130)
lecho rocoso Roca que forma la corteza terrestre; roca sólida debajo del suelo.

biodegradable Capable of being broken down by bacteria and other decomposers. (138)
biodegradable Sustancia que las bacterias y otros descomponedores pueden descomponer.

biodiversity The total number of different species on Earth, including those on land, in the water, and in the air. (108)
biodiversidad Número total de especies diferentes que habitan la Tierra, incluyendo especies terrestres, marinas y del aire.

biogeography The study of where organisms live and how they got there. (73)
biogeografía Estudio del hábitat de los organismos y de cómo han llegado a ese hábitat.

biomass fuel Fuel made from living things. (190)
combustible de biomasa Combustible creado a partir de seres vivos.

biome A group of ecosystems with similar climates and organisms. (58)
bioma Grupo de ecosistemas con organismos y climas parecidos.

biotic factor A living or once living part of an organism's habitat. (6)
factor biótico Parte viva, o que alguna vez tuvo vida, del hábitat de un organismo.

birth rate The number of births per 1,000 individuals for a certain time period. (11)
tasa de natalidad Número de nacimientos por 1.000 individuos durante un período de tiempo determinado.

boreal forest Dense forest of evergreens located in the upper regions of the Northern Hemisphere. (64)
bosque boreal Bosque denso donde abundan las plantas coníferas y que se encuentra en las regiones más al norte del Hemisferio Norte.

C

canopy A leafy roof formed by tall trees in a rain forest. (61)
dosel Techo de hojas que forman los árboles en la selva tropical.

captive breeding The mating of animals in zoos or wildlife preserves. (115)
reproducción en cautiverio Apareamiento de animales en zoológicos y reservas naturales.

carnivore A consumer that obtains energy by eating only animals. (44)
carnívoro Consumidor que adquiere su energía al alimentarse de animales solamente.

carrying capacity The largest population that a particular environment can support. (16)
capacidad de carga Población mayor que un ambiente en particular puede mantener.

chlorofluorocarbons Human-made gases containing chlorine and fluorine (also called CFCs) that are the main cause of ozone depletion. (148)
clorofluorocarbonos Gases generados por el hombre, que contienen cloro y fluor (también llamados CFC) y que son la causa principal del deterioro de la capa de ozono.

clear-cutting The process of cutting down all the trees in an area at once. (104)
tala total Proceso de cortar simultáneamente todos los árboles de un área.

climate The average annual conditions of temperature, precipitation, winds, and clouds in an area. (58)
clima Condiciones promedio anuales de temperatura, precipitación, viento y nubosidad de un área.

commensalism A type of symbiosis between two species in which one species benefits and the other species is neither helped nor harmed. (26)
comensalismo Tipo de relación simbiótica entre dos especies en la cual una especie se beneficia y la otra especie ni se beneficia ni sufre daño.

community All the different populations that live together in a particular area. (8)
comunidad Todas las poblaciones distintas que habitan en un área específica.

competition The struggle between organisms to survive as they attempt to use the same limited resources in the same place at the same time. (21)
competencia Lucha por la supervivencia entre organismos que se alimentan de los mismos recursos limitados en el mismo lugar y al mismo tiempo.

condensation The change in state from a gas to a liquid. (51)
condensación Cambio del estado gaseoso al estado líquido.

coniferous tree A tree that produces its seeds in cones and that has needle-shaped leaves coated in a waxy substance to reduce water loss. (64)
árbol conífero Árbol que produce sus semillas en piñones y que tiene hojas en forma de aguja y cubiertas por una sustancia cerosa que reduce la pérdida de agua.

conservation The practice of using less of a resource so that it can last longer. (97)
conservación Práctica que consiste en reducir el uso de un recurso para prolongar su duración.

consumer An organism that obtains energy by feeding on other organisms. (44)
consumidor Organismo que obtiene energía al alimentarse de otros organismos.

continental drift The hypothesis that the continents slowly move across Earth's surface. (73)
deriva continental Hipótesis según la cual los continentes se desplazan lentamente en la superficie de la Tierra.

control rod A cadmium rod used in a nuclear reactor to absorb neutrons from fission reactions. (194)
varilla de control Varilla de cadmio que se usa en un reactor nuclear para absorber los neutrones emitidos por reacciones de fisión.

D
---

death rate The number of deaths per 1,000 individuals for a certain time period. (11)
tasa de mortalidad Número de muertes per 1.000 individuos durante un período de tiempo determinado.

deciduous tree A tree that sheds its leaves during a particular season and grows new ones each year. (63)
árbol caducifolio Árbol que pierde las hojas durante una estación específica y al que le salen hojas nuevas cada año.

decomposer An organism that gets energy by breaking down biotic wastes and dead organisms, and returns raw materials to the soil and water. (45)
descomponedor Organismo que obtiene energía al descomponer desechos bióticos y organismos muertos, y que devuelve materia prima al suelo y al agua.

desert A dry region that on average receives less than 25 centimeters of precipitation per year. (59)
desierto Región seca en la que se registra un promedio menor de 25 centímetros de precipitación anual.

desertification The advance of desert-like conditions into areas that previously were fertile; caused by overfarming, overgrazing, drought, and climate change. (132)
desertificación Paso de condiciones desérticas a áreas que eran fértiles; resulta de la agricultura descontrolada, el uso exagerado de los pastos, las sequías y los cambios climáticos.

dispersal The movement of organisms from one place to another. (74)
dispersión Traslado de los organismos de un lugar a otro.

drought A long period of low precipitation. (132)
sequía Período prolongado de baja precipitación.

E
---

ecological footprint The amount of land and water that individuals use to meet their resource needs and to absorb the wastes that they produce. (96)
espacio ecológico Cantidad de tierra y agua que los individuos usan para cubrir sus necesidades y absorber sus desechos.

ecology The study of how organisms interact with each other and their environment. (9)
ecología Estudio de la forma en que los organismos interactúan entre sí y con su medio ambiente.

ecosystem The community of organisms that live in a particular area, along with their nonliving environment. (9)
ecosistema Comunidad de organismos que viven en un área específica, y el medio ambiente que los rodea.

efficiency The percentage of input work that is converted to output work. (199)
eficacia Porcentaje de trabajo aportado que se convierte en trabajo producido.

emergent layer The tallest layer of the rain forest that receives the most sunlight. (61)
capa emergente Capa superior de la selva tropical, que recibe la mayor cantidad de luz solar.

emigration Movement of individuals out of a population's area. (12)
emigración Traslado de individuos fuera del área de una población.

emissions Pollutants that are released into the air. (143)
gases contaminantes Contaminantes liberados al aire.

endangered species A species in danger of becoming extinct in the near future. (113)
especie en peligro de extinción Especie que corre el riesgo de desaparecer en el futuro próximo.

energy conservation The practice of reducing energy use. (201)
conservación de energía Práctica de reducción del uso de energía.

energy pyramid A diagram that shows the amount of energy that moves from one feeding level to another in a food web. (48)
pirámide de energía Diagrama que muestra la cantidad de energía que fluye de un nivel de alimentación a otro en una red alimentaria.

environmental science The study of the natural processes that occur in the environment and how humans can affect them. (90)
ciencias del medio ambiente Estudio de los procesos naturales que ocurren en el medio ambiente y de cómo los seres humanos pueden afectarlos.

erosion The process by which water, ice, wind, or gravity moves weathered particles of rock and soil. (131)
erosión Proceso mediante el cual el agua, el hielo, el viento o la gravedad mueven partículas de roca y suelo expuestas al ambiente.

estuary A kind of wetland formed where fresh water from rivers mixes with salty ocean water. (70)
estuario Tipo de pantanal que se forma donde el agua dulce de los ríos se junta con el agua salada del océano.

evaporation The process by which molecules at the surface of a liquid absorb enough energy to change to a gas. (51)
evaporación Proceso mediante el cual las moléculas en la superficie de un líquido absorben suficiente energía para pasar al estado gaseoso.

exotic species Species that are carried to a new location by people. (74)
especies exóticas Especies que las personas trasladan a un nuevo lugar.

exponential growth Growth pattern in which individuals in a population reproduce at a constant rate, so that the larger a population gets, the faster it grows. (99)
crecimiento exponencial Patrón de crecimiento en el cual los individuos de una población se reproducen a una tasa constante, de modo que mientras más aumenta la población, más rápido crece ésta.

extinction The disappearance of all members of a species from Earth. (113)
extinción Desaparición de la Tierra de todos los miembros de una especie.

F

fertilizer A substance that provides nutrients to help crops grow better. (131)
fertilizante Sustancia que proporciona nutrientes para ayudar a que crezcan mejor los cultivos.

fishery An area with a large population of valuable ocean organisms. (106)
pesquería Área con una gran población de organismos marinos aprovechables.

food chain A series of events in an ecosystem in which organisms transfer energy by eating and by being eaten. (46)
cadena alimentaria Serie de sucesos en un ecosistema por medio de los cuales los organismos transmiten energía al comer o al ser comidos por otros.

food web The pattern of overlapping feeding relationships or food chains among the various organisms in an ecosystem. (46)
red alimentaria Patrón de las relaciones de alimentación intercruzadas o de cadenas alimentarias entre los diferentes organismos de un ecosistema.

fossil fuel Coal, oil, or natural gas that forms over millions of years from the remains of ancient organisms; burned to release energy. (179)
combustible fósil Carbón, petróleo o gas natural que se forma a lo largo de millones de años a partir de los restos de organismos antiguos; se queman para liberar energía.

fuel A substance that provides energy as the result of a chemical change. (179)
combustible Sustancia que libera energía como resultado de un cambio químico.

fuel rod A uranium rod that undergoes fission in a nuclear reactor. (194)
varilla de combustible Varilla de uranio que se somete a la fisión en un reactor nuclear.

G

gasohol A mixture of gasoline and alcohol. (190)
gasohol Mezcla de gasolina y alcohol.

gene A sequence of DNA that determines a trait and is passed from parent to offspring. (112)
gen Secuencia de ADN que determina un rasgo y que se pasa de los progenitores a los hijos.

geothermal energy The intense heat energy that comes from Earth's interior. (191)
energía geotérmica Energía intensa que proviene del interior de la Tierra.

grassland An area populated mostly by grasses and other nonwoody plants that gets 25 to 75 centimeters of rain each year. (62)
pradera Área poblada principalmente por hierbas y otras plantas no leñosas, y donde caen entre 25 y 75 centímetros de lluvia cada año.

groundwater Water that fills the cracks and spaces in underground soil and rock layers. (153)
aguas freáticas Agua que llena las grietas y huecos de las capas subterráneas de tierra y roca.

H

habitat An environment that provides the things a specific organism needs to live, grow, and reproduce. (5)
hábitat Medio que provee lo que un organismo específico necesita para vivir, crecer y reproducirse.

habitat destruction The loss of a natural habitat. (114)
destrucción del habitat Pérdida de un hábitat natural.

habitat fragmentation The breaking of a habitat into smaller, isolated pieces. (114)
fragmentación del hábitat Desintegración de un hábitat en porciones aisladas más pequeñas.

hazardous waste A material that can be harmful if it is not properly disposed of. (140)
desecho peligroso Material que puede ser dañino si no se elimina adecuadamente.

herbivore A consumer that obtains energy by eating only plants. (44)
herbívoro Consumidor que obtiene su energía al alimentarse de plantas solamente.

host An organism that a parasite lives with, in, or on, and provides a source of energy or a suitable environment for the parasite to live. (26)
huésped Organismo en el cual vive un parásito y que le sirve de fuente de energía o de medio ambiente.

hydrocarbon An organic compound that contains only carbon and hydrogen atoms. (179)
hidrocarburo Compuesto orgánico que contiene átomos de carbón e hidrógeno solamente.

hydroelectric power Electricity produced by the kinetic energy of water moving over a waterfall or dam. (189)
energía hidroeléctrica Electricidad producida a partir de la energía cinética del agua que baja por una catarata o presa.

I

immigration Movement of individuals into a population's area. (12)
inmigración Movimiento de individuos al área de una población.

incineration The burning of solid waste. (135)
incineración Quema de desechos sólidos.

GLOSSARY

insulation Material that traps air to help block heat transfer between the air inside and outside of a building. (199)
aislante Material que atrapa el aire para ayudar a bloquear el paso del calor del aire adentro y afuera de un edificio.

intertidal zone An area between the highest high-tide line on land to the point on the continental shelf exposed by the lowest low-tide line. (70)
zona intermareal Área entre el punto más alto de la marea alta y el punto más bajo de la marea baja.

K

keystone species A species that influences the survival of many other species in an ecosystem. (109)
especie clave Especie que tiene un impacto en la supervivencia de muchas otras especies de un ecosistema.

L

land reclamation The process of restoring land to a more natural, productive state. (133)
recuperación de la tierra Proceso que consiste en restaurar la tierra y llevarla a un estado productivo más natural.

leachate Polluted liquid produced by water passing through and dissolving chemicals from buried wastes in a landfill. (136)
lixiviado Líquido contaminado producido por el agua que pasa por y disuelve químicos provenientes de desechos bajo la tierra y en rellenos sanitarios.

limiting factor An environmental factor that causes a population to decrease in size. (15)
factor limitante Factor ambiental que causa la disminución del tamaño de una población.

litter The very top layer of fertile soil made of dead leaves and grass. (130)
mantillo Capa superior del suelo fértil, que está formada por hojas y pasto muertos.

M

municipal solid waste Waste produced in homes, businesses, schools and in a community. (135)
desechos sólidos urbanos Desechos generados en los hogares, los negocios, las escuelas y las comunidades.

mutualism A type of symbiosis in which both species benefit from living together. (25)
mutualismo Tipo de relación simbiótica entre dos especies en la cual ambas especies se benefician de su convivencia.

N

natural resource Anything naturally occuring in the environment that humans use. (88)
recurso natural Cualquier elemento natural ambiental que el ser humano usa.

natural selection The process by which organisms that are best adapted to their environment are most likely to survive and reproduce. (19)
selección natural Proceso mediante el cual los organismos que se adaptan mejor a su ambiente tienen mayor probabilidad de sobrevivir y reproducirse.

neritic zone The area of the ocean that extends from the low-tide line out to the edge of the continental shelf. (70)
zona nerítica Área del océano que se extiende desde la línea de bajamar hasta el borde de la plataforma continental.

niche How an organism makes its living and interacts with the biotic and abiotic factors in its habitat. (20)
nicho Forma en que un organismo vive e interactúa con los factores bióticos y abióticos de su hábitat.

nitrogen fixation The process of changing free nitrogen gas into nitrogen compounds that plants can absorb and use. (54)
fijación del nitrógeno Proceso que consiste en transformar el gas de nitrógeno libre en compuestos de nitrógeno que las plantas pueden absorber y usar.

nodule A lump on the ocean floor that forms when metals such as manganese build up around pieces of shell. (164)
nódulo Protuberancia formada en el suelo oceánico cuando metales, como el manganeso, se depositan sobre pedazos de concha.

nonpoint source A widely spread source of pollution that is difficult to link to a specific point of origin. (89)
fuente dispersa Fuente muy extendida de contaminación que es difícil vincular a un punto de origen específico.

nonrenewable resource A natural resource that is not replaced in a useful time frame. (94)
recurso no renovable Recurso natural que no se restaura, en un período relativamente corto, una vez se utiliza.

nuclear fission The splitting of an atom's nucleus into two smaller nuclei and neutrons, releasing a large quantity of energy. (194)
fisión nuclear Separación del núcleo de un átomo en núcleos y neutrones más pequeños, en la cual se libera una gran cantidad de energía.

nutrient depletion The situation that arises when more soil nutrients are used than the decomposers can supply. (131)
agotamiento de nutrientes Situación que se produce cuando se usan más nutrientes del suelo de lo que los descomponedores pueden proporcionar.

O

omnivore A consumer that obtains energy by eating both plants and animals. (44)
omnívoro Consumidor que adquiere su energía al alimentarse de plantas y animales.

organism A living thing. (5)
organismo Ser vivo.

ozone A form of oxygen that has three oxygen atoms in each molecule instead of the usual two; toxic to organisms where it forms near Earth's surface. (144)
ozono Forma de oxígeno que tiene tres átomos de oxígeno en cada molécula, en vez de dos; donde se forma en la superficie terrestre, es tóxico para los organismos.

ozone layer The layer of the upper atmosphere that contains a higher concentration of ozone than the rest of the atmosphere. (147)
capa de ozono Capa superior de la atmósfera que contiene una concentración mayor de ozono que el resto de la atmósfera.

P

parasite The organism that benefits by living with, on, or in a host in a parasitism interaction. (26)
parásito Organismo que se beneficia al vivir con o en un huésped, en una relación parasítica.

parasitism A type of symbiosis in which one organism lives with, on, or in a host and harms it. (26)
parasitismo Tipo de relación simbiótica en la cual un organismo vive con o en un huésped y le hace daño.

permafrost Permanently frozen soil found in the tundra biome climate region. (65)
permagélido Suelo que está permanentemente congelado y que se encuentra en el bioma climático de la tundra.

pesticide A chemical that kills insects and other crop-destroying organisms. (154)
pesticida Químico usado para matar insectos y otros organismos que destruyen los cultivos.

petrochemical A compound made from oil. (183)
petroquímico Compuesto que se obtiene del petróleo.

petroleum Liquid fossil fuel; oil. (182)
petróleo Combustible fósil líquido.

photochemical smog A brownish thick haze that is a mixture of ozone and other chemicals formed when pollutants react with sunlight. (144)
neblina tóxica fotoquímica Nubosidad gruesa de color marrón, resultado de la mezcla del ozono y otras sustancias químicas que se forman cuando los contaminantes reaccionan a la luz del sol.

pioneer species The first species to populate an area during succession. (29)
especies pioneras La primera especie que puebla un área durante la sucesión.

poaching Illegal killing or removal of wildlife from their habitats. (114)
caza ilegal Matanza o eliminación de la fauna silvestre de su hábitat.

point source A specific source of pollution that can be identified. (89)
fuente localizada Fuente específica de contaminación que puede identificarse.

pollutant A substance that causes pollution. (136)
contaminante Sustancia que provoca contaminación.

pollution Contamination of Earth's land, water, or air. (89)
polución Contaminación del suelo, el agua o el aire de la Tierra.

population All the members of one species living in the same area. (8)
población Todos los miembros de una especie que viven en el mismo lugar.

population density The number of individuals in an area of a specific size. (14)
densidad de población Número de individuos en un área de un tamaño específico.

precipitation Any form of water that falls from clouds and reaches Earth's surface as rain, snow, sleet, or hail. (51)
precipitación Cualquier forma del agua que cae de las nubes y llega a la superficie de la tierra como lluvia, nieve, aguanieve o granizo.

predation An interaction in which one organism kills another for food or nutrients. (22)
depredación Interacción en la cual un organismo mata a otro para alimentarse u obtener nutrientes de él.

predator The organism that does the killing in a predation interaction. (22)
depredador Organismo que mata durante la depredación.

prey An organism that is killed and eaten by another organism in a predation interaction. (22)
presa Organismo que es consumido por otro organismo en el proceso de depredación.

primary succession The series of changes that occur in an area where no soil or organisms exist. (29)
sucesión primaria Serie de cambios que ocurren en un área donde no existe suelo ni organismos.

producer An organism that can make its own food. (43)
productor Organismo que puede generar su propio alimento.

---------------- **R** ----------------

radon A colorless, odorless, radioactive gas. (146)
radón Gas radioactivo que no tiene color ni olor.

rain forest A forest that receives at least 2 meters of rain per year, mostly occurring in the tropical wet climate zone. (60)
selva tropical Bosque donde caen al menos 2 metros de lluvia al año, principalmente en la zona

reactor vessel The part of a nuclear reactor in which nuclear fission occurs. (194)
cuba de reactor Parte de un reactor nuclear donde ocurre la fisión.

recycling The process of reclaiming and reusing raw materials. (137)
reciclaje Proceso de recuperar y volver a usar materias primas.

refinery A factory in which crude oil is heated and separated into fuels and other products. (183)
refinería Planta en la que el petróleo crudo se calienta y fracciona en combustibles y otros productos.

renewable resource A resource that is either always available or is naturally replaced in a relatively short time. (93)
recurso renovable Recurso que está siempre disponible o que es restituido de manera natural en un período relativamente corto.

---------------- **S** ----------------

sanitary landfill A landfill that holds nonhazardous waste such as municipal solid waste, construction debris, and some agricultural and industrial wastes. (136)
relleno sanitario Vertedero que contiene desechos que no son peligrosos, como desechos sólidos municipales, de construcción y algunos tipos de desechos industriales y resultantes de la agricultura.

savanna A grassland located close to the equator that may include shrubs and small trees and receives as much as 120 centimeters of rain per year. (62)
sabana Pradera que puede tener arbustos y árboles pequeños, ubicada cerca del ecuador y donde pueden caer hasta 120 centímetros de lluvia al año.

scavenger A carnivore that feeds on the bodies of dead or decaying organisms. (44)
carroñero Carnívoro que se alimenta de los restos de organismos muertos o en descomposición.

secondary succession The series of changes that occur in an area where the ecosystem has been disturbed, but where soil and organisms still exist. (30)
sucesión secundaria Serie de cambios que ocurren en un área después de la perturbación de un ecosistema, pero donde todavía hay suelo y organismos.

sediment Small, solid pieces of material that come from rocks or the remains of organisms; earth materials deposited by erosion. (155)
sedimento Trozos pequeños y sólidos de materiales que provienen de las rocas o de los restos de organismos; materiales terrestres depositados por la erosión.

selective cutting The process of cutting down only some tree species in an area. (104)
tala selectiva Proceso que consiste en cortar solo algunas especies de árboles de un área.

sewage The water and human wastes that are washed down sinks, toilets, and showers. (154)
aguas residuales Agua y desechos humanos que son desechados por lavamanos, servicios sanitarios y duchas.

solar energy Energy from the sun. (187)
energía solar Energía del Sol.

species A group of similar organisms that can mate with each other and produce offspring that can also mate and reproduce. (8)
especie Grupo de organismos semejantes que pueden aparearse y producir descendencia fértil.

subsoil The layer of soil below topsoil that has less plant and animal matter than topsoil and contains mostly clay and other minerals. (130)
subsuelo Capa de suelo debajo del suelo superior que tiene menos materia de plantas y animales que el suelo superior, y que principalmente contiene arcilla y otros minerales.

succession The series of predictable changes that occur in a community over time. (28)
sucesión Serie de cambios predecibles que ocurren en una comunidad a través del tiempo.

sustainable use The use of a resource in ways that maintain the resource at a certain quality for a certain period of time. (96)
uso sostenible Uso de un recurso que permite que ese recurso mantenga cierta calidad por un período de tiempo determinado.

sustainable yield An amount of a renewable resource that can be harvested regularly without reducing the future supply. (105)
rendimiento sostenible Cantidad de un recurso renovable que puede ser recolectado constantemente sin reducir el abastecimiento futuro.

symbiosis Any relationship in which two species live closely together and that benefits at least one of the species. (25)
simbiosis Cualquier relación en la cual dos especies viven muy cerca y al menos una de ellas se beneficia.

T

temperature inversion A condition in which a layer of warm air traps polluted air close to Earth's surface. (144)
inversión térmica Condición en la que una capa de aire caliente atrapa aire contaminado cerca de la superficie de la Tierra.

threatened species A species that could become endangered in the near future. (113)
especie amenazada Especie que puede llegar a estar en peligro de extinción en el futuro próximo.

topsoil The crumbly, topmost layer of soil made up of clay and other minerals and humus (nutrients and decaying plant and animal matter). (130)
suelo superior Capa superior arenosa del suelo formada por arcilla, otros minerales y humus (nutrientes y materia orgánica de origen vegetal y animal).

tundra An extremely cold, dry biome climate region characterized by short, cool summers and bitterly cold winters. (65)
tundra Bioma de la región climática extremadamente fría y seca, que se caracteriza por veranos cortos y frescos e inviernos sumamente fríos.

U

understory A layer of shorter trees and vines that grows in the shade of a forest canopy. (61)
sotobosque Capa de árboles de poca altura y plantas trepadoras que crecen bajo la sombra del dosel de un bosque.

upwelling The movement of cold water upward from the deep ocean that is caused by wind. (164)
corriente de ascenso Movimiento ascendente de aguas frías desde las profundidades del mar, causado por los vientos.

INDEX

Page numbers for key terms are printed in **boldface type**. Red indicates Teacher's Edition entries.

INDEX

Page numbers for key terms are printed in **boldface** type. Red indicates Teacher's Edition entries.

INDEX

Page numbers for key terms are printed in **boldface** type. Red indicates Teacher's Edition entries.

ACKNOWLEDGMENTS

Staff Credits

The people who made up the *Interactive Science* team—representing composition services, core design digital and multimedia production services, digital product development, editorial, editorial services, manufacturing, and production—are listed below.

Jan Van Aarsen, Samah Abadir, Ernie Albanese, Bridget Binstock, Suzanne Biron, MJ Black, Nancy Bolsover, Stacy Boyd, Jim Brady, Katherine Bryant, Michael Burstein, Pradeep Byram, Jessica Chase, Jonathan Cheney, Arthur Ciccone, Allison Cook-Bellistri, Rebecca Cottingham, AnnMarie Coyne, Bob Craton, Chris Deliee, Paul Delsignore, Michael Di Maria, Diane Dougherty, Kristen Ellis, Theresa Eugenio, Amanda Ferguson, Jorgensen Fernandez, Kathryn Fobert, Julia Gecha, Mark Geyer, Steve Gobbell, Paula Gogan-Porter, Jeffrey Gong, Sandra Graff, Adam Groffman, Lynette Haggard, Christian Henry, Karen Holtzman, Susan Hutchinson, Sharon Inglis, Marian Jones, Sumy Joy, Sheila Kanitsch, Courtenay Kelley, Chris Kennedy, Toby Klang, Greg Lam, Russ Lappa, Margaret LaRaia, Ben Leveillee, Thea Limpus, Dotti Marshall, Kathy Martin, Robyn Matzke, John McClure, Mary Beth McDaniel, Krista McDonald, Tim McDonald, Rich McMahon, Cara McNally, Melinda Medina, Angelina Mendez, Maria Milczarek, Claudi Mimo, Mike Napieralski, Deborah Nicholls, Dave Nichols, William Oppenheimer, Jodi O'Rourke, Ameer Padshah, Lorie Park, Celio Pedrosa, Jonathan Penyack, Linda Zust Reddy, Jennifer Reichlin, Stephen Rider, Charlene Rimsa, Stephanie Rogers, Marcy Rose, Rashid Ross, Anne Rowsey, Logan Schmidt, Amanda Seldera, Laurel Smith, Nancy Smith, Ted Smykal, Emily Soltanoff, Cindy Strowman, Dee Sunday, Barry Tomack, Patricia Valencia, Ana Sofia Villaveces, Stephanie Wallace, Christine Whitney, Brad Wiatr, Heidi Wilson, Heather Wright, Rachel Youdelman

Photography

All uncredited photos copyright © 2011 Pearson Education.

Cover, Front and Back

tr Raymond Kasprzak/Shutterstock; **m** David Aubrey/Photolibrary New York; **b** Tamara Kulikova/Shutterstock.

Front Matter

Page vi, Gary Bell/Zefa/Corbis; **vii,** Rolf Nussbaumer/Minden Pictures; **viii,** Shin Yoshino/Minden Pictures; **ix,** Benedict Luxmoore/Arcaid/Corbis; **x,** Greg Smith/Corbis; **xi laptop, TV screens, touch-screen phone,** iStockphoto.com; **xiii tr,** iStockphoto.com; **xv br,** JupiterImages/Getty Images; **xviii t,** iStockphoto.com; **xx–xxi,** Shin Yoshino/Minden Pictures.

Chapter 1

Pages xxii–1, Gary Bell/Zefa/Corbis; **3 t,** Photodisc/Getty Images; **3 m,** age Fotostock/SuperStock; **3 b,** Imagebroker/Alamy; **4 bkgrnd,** Nick Garbutt/Nature Picture Library; **4 tr,** Frans Lanting/Corbis; **4 bl,** Jörn Köhler; **4 br,** Wildlife/A. Visage/Peter Arnold Inc.; **5 bkgrnd,** Bruno Morandi/Robert Harding World; **5 inset,** Jim Brandenburg/Minden Pictures; **8–9,** S.J. Krasemann/Peter Arnold Inc.; **10,** Shattil & Rozinski/Nature Picture Library; **11,** Chris Johns/National Geographic Stock; **12,** Photodisc/Getty Images; **13,** Kim Taylor/Nature Picture Library; **15,** Weatherstock/Peter Arnold; **16–17,** Matt Brown/Corbis; **16 inset,** Tim Mannakee/Grand Tour/Corbis;

17 tr, Taylor S. Kennedy/National Geographic Society; **18,** Alex Wild; **21 tr,** Tom Vezo/Minden Pictures; **21 mr and mb,** Jim Zipp/Photo Researchers, Inc.; **21 bl,** Michael P. Gadomski/Photo Researchers, Inc.; **22 tr,** Bill Curtsinger/National Geographic Stock; **22 r,** Sándor F. Szabó/iStockphoto.com; **22 bl,** Hiroya Minakuchi/Minden Pictures; **22 bc,** Imagebroker/Alamy; **23 tl,** Jeff Hunter/Getty Images; **23 tr,** Michael D. Kern/Nature Picture Library; **23 cl,** Ethan Daniels/Alamy; **23 cr,** age Fotostock/SuperStock; **23 bl,** Fabrice Bettex/Alamy; **23 br,** Nature's Images/Photo Researchers, Inc.; **25 l,** Manoj Shah/Animals Animals/Earth Scenes; **25 r,** Michael Fogden/Animals Animals/Earth Scenes; **26 l,** Jeff Foott/Getty Images; **26 tr,** Anthony Bannister/Animals Animals/Earth Scenes; **26 br,** USGA; **27 t,** Norbert Wu/Minden Pictures; **27 c,** Jim Clare/NPL/Minden Pictures; **27 b,** Dietmar Nill/Nature Picture Library; **28,** Ilene MacDonald/Alamy; **32,** Anthony Bannister/Animals Animals/Earth Scenes.

Interchapter Feature

Page 36, Photo courtesy of Roger del Moral; **37 t,** Dave & Les Jacobs/Blend Images/Getty Images; **37 b,** Chris Gomersall/Alamy.

Chapter 2

Pages 38–39, Rolf Nussbaumer/Minden Pictures; **41 t,** Dorling Kindersley; **41 b,** Karen Huntt/Getty Images; **42,** Ian McAllister/Photolibrary New York; **43 inset,** Edward Kinsman/Photo Researchers, Inc.; **43 b,** Jerome Wexler/Photo Researchers, Inc.; **46 t,** Dorling Kindersley; **46 m,** Jerry Young/Dorling Kindersley; **46 b,** Peter Blottman/iStockphoto.com; **47 snail,** Nicholas Homrich/iStockphoto.com; **47 heron,** Judy Foldetta/iStockphoto.com; **47 frog,** Geoff Brightling/Dorling Kindersley; **47 shrew,** Rollin Verlinde/Dorling Kindersley; **47 garter snake,** Jerry Young/Dorling Kindersley; **47 mushrooms,** Neil Fletcher/Dorling Kindersley; **47 crayfish,** Frank Greenaway/Dorling Kindersley/Courtesy of the Natural History Museum, London; **47 fox,** Dorling Kindersley; **47 grasshopper,** Jerry Young/Dorling Kindersley; **47 plants,** Peter Blottman/iStockphoto.com; **48 t,** Eric Isselée/iStockphoto.com; **48 tm,** Dave King/Dorling Kindersley; **48 bm,** Frank Greenaway/Dorling Kindersley; **48 b,** Kim Taylor and Jane Burton/Dorling Kindersley; **50,** Juniors Bildarchiv/Alamy; **52,** Emma Firth/Dorling Kindersley; **54,** Dr. Paul A. Zahl/Photo Researchers, Inc.; **58,** Imagebroker/Alamy; **59 bkgrnd,** Karen Huntt/Getty Images; **59 inset,** Graham Hatherley/NPL/Minden Pictures; **60–61,** Peter Chadwick/Dorling Kindersley; **61 c,** Pete Oxford/Minden Pictures; **62 l,** Juan Carlos Munoz/Peter Arnold Inc.; **62 c,** Arco Images GmbH/Alamy; **62 r,** Peter Lillie/Photolibrary New York; **63 tr,** Joe McDonald/Visuals Unlimited/Getty Images; **63 br,** Tim Shepard, Oxford Scientific Films/Dorling Kindersley; **64 t,** Randy Green/Getty Images; **64 b,** Tom Brakefield/Corbis; **65,** Momatiuk–Eastcott/Corbis; **66,** Mitsuaki Iwago/Minden Pictures; **68–69,** PIER/Getty Images; **68 m,** Sandy Felsenthal/Corbis; **72,** Ken Findlay/Dorling Kindersley; **74 l,** Martin M. Bruce/SuperStock; **74 r,** Derek Middleton/Minden Pictures; **75,** Inge Johnsson/Alamy; **76,** Peter Blottman/iStockphoto.com; **77,** Cheerz/Dreamstime.com.

Interchapter Feature

Page 80, Westend 61 GmbH/Alamy; **81 bkgrnd,** Brent Waltermire/Alamy; **81 inset,** Jupiterimages/Creatas/Alamy.

take note

use this space for lesson planning ideas and notes

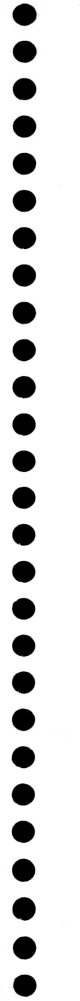